ION EXCHANGE

ION EXCHANGE

Friedrich Helfferich

SHELL DEVELOPMENT COMPANY, EMERYVILLE, CALIFORNIA
LECTURER AT THE UNIVERSITY OF CALIFORNIA, BERKELEY

1962

New York
San Francisco
Toronto
London

McGraw-Hill Book Company, Inc.

ION EXCHANGE

II

28070

First published in the German language under the title "IONENAUS-TAUSCHER" and copyright 1959 by Verlag Chemie GmbH, Weinheim/Bergstrasse, Germany.

Preface

Ion exchange is not a recent invention. For more than half a century ion exchangers have been used to an increasing extent both in the laboratory and in plant operations. The theory of ion exchange, however, is of a more recent origin. Only in the course of the last fifteen years have detailed theories been developed from which a sound and consistent framework covering the most important aspects of ion exchange can be built. Thus it seems that the time has come when a comprehensive treatise on ion exchange can be written. The main difficulty confronting such an endeavor is not that too little, but rather that too much is known about ion exchange. By now, the theories and experimental evidence are well in excess of what any author would dare to offer to his readers. Therefore I have consciously based this book on a limited selection of theoretical approaches and experimental results which appear to me to be suitable for giving a clear-cut picture of the phenomena and their physical causes. Rather than striving for completeness or emphasizing abstract theories, I have attempted to give tangible, but nevertheless quantitative, explanations of the "how" and "why." This book is intended to provide the reader with a sound understanding of the relevant factors in ion exchange and with the theoretical tools that might help him in solving his specific problems.

The German edition of this book appeared in 1959 as the first volume in a series of which later volumes will deal with practical applications. The English edition includes a more detailed discussion of the various types of ion-exchange column operations. However, the emphasis has remained on general principles. No detailed prescriptions for particular applications have been included. The reader looking for advice on such details is referred to the literature.

The German edition has, on occasion, been mildly criticized by exponents of the two extremes of the wide spectrum of users. A plant engineer and an organic chemist have complained that studying this book requires too much background in mathematics and theoretical physical chemistry. On the other hand, a scholar whose superior command of thermodynamics I greatly admire has expressed his concern with one or the other attempt to give too facile an explanation for a very complex phenomenon. These criticisms have prompted me to separate, where possible, the qualitative and the quantitative treatment even more sharply than in the German edition. The mathematically disinclined reader may now cheerfully skip all mathematical equations and deductions without loss in continuity. The theoretical perfectionist will, I hope, excuse the sacrifice of rigor for the sake of simplicity in qualitative explanations and interpretations which were written for the benefit of his more pedestrian colleagues.

In a book of this kind it is virtually impossible to mention all those who have contributed to the development and present knowledge of ion exchange. Quotations and literature references have been restricted to publications which are apt to illustrate the discussion in the text. The choice is, by necessity, a matter of the author's own views and preferences. May I be forgiven by those to whom I have not given due credit.

The American publisher has entrusted me with the task of translating my own book. As English is not my native tongue, I must beg the reader's forbearance regarding my style.

My sincerest thanks are due to the many experts who have contributed to this book with helpful suggestions and constructive criticism. It is a pleasure to acknowledge the valuable help of Dr. G. E. Boyd in revising the English manuscript. Furthermore, I am particularly indebted to Dr. R. Schlögl, Dr. G. Scatchard, Dr. K. S. Spiegler, Dr. T. Vermeulen, Dr. E. Glueckauf, Dr. R. M. Barrer, Dr. U. Schindewolf, and Dr. R. E. Meeker, and to A. K. Dunlop who struggled valiantly with my style.

Friedrich G. Helfferich

Contents

Introduction

"Corpora non agunt nisi fluida sive soluta"—substances do not react unless in a liquid or dissolved state. This ancient empirical rule is not universal. One of the noteworthy exceptions is ion exchange. Here, a solid reacts with a solution. Ions can be exchanged and electrolytes and even precipitates can be removed by treating the solution with a solid ion exchanger.

These reactions are by no means a recent discovery. Nature makes extensive use of them and has done so long before man attempted to elucidate and apply its principles and to copy and surpass its performance. Ion exchange occurs in inanimate soils, sands, and rocks, and in living organisms. At first, these processes remained unnoticed by chemists, geologists, and biologists. Later, when ion exchange in soils was discovered, it was considered as an exceptional phenomenon, a "miracle," in which other than purely natural causes were supposed to have their part. To show that here, too, the well-established rules of nature hold remained the task of scientists in the second half of the nineteenth century. Still later, about two decades ago, organic chemists succeeded in synthesizing ion exchangers which proved to be far superior to the natural materials. Ion exchange in living organisms is indispensable for most vital functions, but its significance remained obscure until recent times. Only in our day has progress been made in understanding this phenomenon.

Ion exchange has an interesting history. Thorough investigators have shunned no efforts to discover ancient references. The earliest of these, it seems, is found in the Holy Bible. In establishing Moses' priority it reads

They could not drink of the waters of Marah, for they were bitter. . . . And he cried unto Jehovah; and Jehovah showed him a tree, and he cast it into the waters, and the waters were made sweet.

Exodus 15: 23–25

1

Thus Moses succeeded in preparing drinking water from brackish water, undoubtedly by an ion-exchange technique which he developed on an industrial scale. About a thousand years later, Aristotle stated that sea water loses part of its salt content when percolating through certain sands [2]. Subsequent to this time, only scarce references are found until, in 1850, Thompson [8] and Way [9], two English chemists, rediscovered "base exchange" (cation exchange) in soils. The materials which are responsible for these phenomena were identified chiefly by Lemberg [7] and later by Wiegner [10] as clays, glauconites, zeolites, and humic acids. These discoveries led to attempts to use such materials in plant operations for water softening and other purposes and to synthesize products with similar properties. The first synthetic industrial ion exchanger was prepared in 1903 by Harm and Rümpler [4], two German chemists. Gans [3], also a German and perhaps the most colorful pioneer of ion exchange, had far-reaching applications in mind even at that time, for example, the recovery of gold from sea water. However, the "permutits" then available proved to be inadequate for such ambitious plans.

A spectacular evolution began in 1935 with the discovery by two English chemists, Adams and Holmes, that crushed phonograph records exhibit ion-exchange properties. The study of this remarkable effect led the inventors to the synthesis of organic ion-exchange resins which had much better properties than any of the previous products [1]. These new resins were developed and improved by the former I. G. Farbenindustrie in Germany, and after World War II chiefly by companies in the United States and England. Nearly all current industrial and laboratory applications of ion exchange are based on such resins. At the same time, the synthesis of organic resins made it possible to vary the properties of ion exchangers in a systematic manner. A large part of our present theoretical knowledge is due to this latter fact. It is an outstanding achievement of organic chemistry to have surpassed the performance of nature which, in this case, makes use of inorganic substances.

Today, ion exchange is firmly established as a unit operation and is an extremely valuable supplement to other procedures such as filtration, distillation, and adsorption. All over the world, numerous plants are in operation, accomplishing tasks that range from the recovery of metals from industrial wastes to the separation of rare earths, and from catalysis of organic reactions to decontamination of water in cooling systems of nuclear reactors. In the laboratory, ion exchangers are used as an aid in analytical and preparative chemistry. The aims of scientific research with ion-exchanger membranes extend far into physiological chemistry and biophysics. However, the most important application is still the purification and demineralization of water, a perennial challenge since Moses and Aristotle, and a task which the growth of population and industries has made more pressing than ever.

The development of ion-exchange resins and their applications progressed so rapidly that the theory lagged behind. For a considerable time ion exchangers were used on a purely empirical basis and without the possibility of predicting efficiency and optimum operating conditions. The only exception is the most recent product, the ion-exchanger membrane. When synthesized in 1950 [5,6] the ion-exchanger membrane fitted nicely into the essentially complete theoretical framework which had been worked out for physiological, collodion, and other membranes. Ion-exchanger membranes have not only opened up new technological possibilities but, in addition,

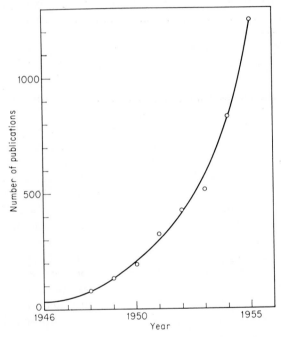

FIG. 1. Number of scientific publications on ion exchange as a function of time. *From R. Kunin and F. X. McGarvey, Ind. Eng. Chem.,* **47,** 565 (1955).

have contributed to a better understanding of the electrochemical and kinetic phenomena in ion exchange. This, in turn, proved to be of great value to the general theory of ion-exchange materials.

After a period characterized by predominantly empirical approaches, research efforts in the last fifteen years have led to a comprehensive and consistent picture of the relevant factors in ion exchange. This picture may be considered as qualitatively and quantitatively sound, though a few questions remain unanswered and the solution of certain equations poses mathematical difficulties. At the same time, the scientific literature on ion exchange has grown to such an extent that it has become virtually

impossible for a single individual to keep track of every detail.   The
constant increase in the number of publications (see Fig. 1) may be taken
as the best evidence for the spreading interest in ion exchange and for the
hopes and expectations that accompany its future development.

REFERENCES

1. Adams, B. A., and E. L. Holmes, *J. Soc. Chem. Ind. (London)*, **54,** 1T (1935).
2. Aristotle, Works, vol. 7, p. 933b, about 330 B.C. (Clarendon Press, London, 1927).
3. Gans, R., *Jahrb. preuss. geol. Landesanstalt (Berlin)*, **26,** 179 (1905), and **27,** 63 (1906); *Zentr. Mineral. Geol.*, **22,** 699, 728 (1913); Ger. Patent 174,097 and 197,111, 1906.
4. Harm, F., and A. Rümpler, *5th Intern. Congr. Pure Appl. Chem.*, **1903,** 59.
5. Juda, W., and W. A. McRae, *J. Am. Chem. Soc.*, **72,** 1044 (1950); U.S. Patent 2,636,851-52, 1953.
6. Kressman, T. R. E., *Nature*, **165,** 568 (1950).
7. Lemberg, J., *Z. deut. geol. Ges.*, **22,** 355 (1870); **28,** 519 (1876).
8. Thompson, H. S., *J. Roy. Agr. Soc. Engl.*, **11,** 68 (1850).
9. Way, J. T., *J. Roy. Agr. Soc. Engl.*, **11,** 313 (1850); **13,** 123 (1852).
10. Wiegner, G., *J. Landwirtsch.*, **60,** 111,197 (1912).

1

Elementary Principles

Ion exchangers, by common definition, are insoluble solid materials which carry exchangeable cations or anions. These ions can be exchanged for a stoichiometrically equivalent amount of other ions of the same sign when the ion exchanger is in contact with an electrolyte solution. Carriers of exchangeable cations are called *cation exchangers*, and carriers of exchangeable anions, *anion exchangers*. Certain materials are capable of both cation and anion exchange. These are called *amphoteric ion exchangers*.

A typical cation exchange is

$$2\underline{NaX} + CaCl_2(aq) \rightleftharpoons \underline{CaX_2} + 2NaCl(aq) \qquad (1\text{-}1)$$

and a typical anion exchange is

$$2\underline{XCl} + Na_2SO_4(aq) \rightleftharpoons \underline{X_2SO_4} + 2NaCl(aq) \qquad (1\text{-}2)$$

X represents a structural unit of the ion exchanger; solid phases are underlined; *aq* indicates that the electrolyte is in aqueous solution.

The process (1-1) occurs, for example, in water softening by ion exchange. A solution containing dissolved $CaCl_2$ (hard water) is treated with a solid ion exchanger $\underline{NaX}$ containing exchangeable Na^+ ions. The ion exchanger removes the Ca^{2+} ions from the solution and replaces them by Na^+ ions.

An ion exchanger containing, say, exchangeable Na^+ ions is said to be in Na^+ form. In the process (1-1) the cation exchanger, originally in Na^+ form, is "converted" to the Ca^{2+} form. Complete conversion to, say, Ca^{2+} form can be achieved by treating the ion exchanger with a sufficient excess of a solution of a calcium salt.

Ion exchange is, with very few exceptions, a reversible process. In water softening, for example, a cation exchanger which has lost all its Na^+ ions and thus has become "exhausted," can be "regenerated" with a solution of a sodium salt such as NaCl. In regeneration the process (1-1) is reversed, and the ion exchanger is reconverted to the Na^+ form.

Ion exchange resembles sorption in that, in both cases, a dissolved species is taken up by a solid. The characteristic difference between the two phenomena is that ion exchange, in contrast to sorption, is a *stoichiometric* process. Every ion which is removed from the solution is replaced by an equivalent amount of another ionic species of the same sign. In sorption, on the other hand, a solute (an electrolyte or non-electrolyte) is taken up without being replaced by another species. This

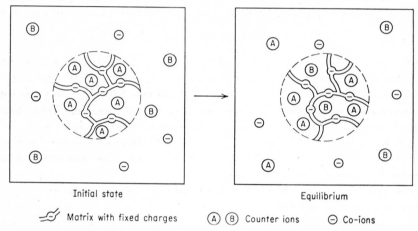

Initial state   Equilibrium

〜 Matrix with fixed charges   Ⓐ Ⓑ Counter ions   ⊖ Co-ions

FIG. 1-1. Ion exchange with a solution (*schematic*). A cation exchanger containing counter ions A is placed in a solution containing counter ions B (*left*). The counter ions are redistributed by diffusion until equilibrium is attained (*right*).

distinction seems clear-cut. However, it is sometimes difficult to apply it in practice since nearly every ion-exchange process is accompanied by electrolyte sorption or desorption, and most of the common sorbents such as alumina and activated carbon can act, in turn, as ion exchangers.

Ion exchangers owe their characteristic properties to a peculiar feature of their structure. They consist of a framework which is held together by chemical bonds or lattice energy. This framework carries a positive or negative electric surplus charge which is compensated by ions of opposite sign, the so-called *counter ions*. The counter ions are free to move within the framework and can be replaced by other ions of the same sign. The framework of a cation exchanger may be regarded as a macromolecular or crystalline polyanion, that of an anion exchanger as a polycation.

To give a very simple picture, the ion exchanger may be compared to a sponge with counter ions floating in the pores. When the sponge is immersed in a solution, the counter ions can leave the pores and float

out. However, electroneutrality must be preserved, i.e., the electric surplus charge of the sponge must be compensated at any time by a stoichiometrically equivalent number of counter ions within the pores. Hence a
counter ion can leave the sponge only when, simultaneously, another counter
ion enters and takes over the task of contributing its share to the compensation of the framework charge.

According to this simple model, the counter-ion content of the ion
exchanger—the so-called *ion-exchange capacity*—is a constant which is
given solely by the magnitude of the framework charge and is independent
of the nature of the counter ion. The actual situation is somewhat more
complex because electrolyte sorption may occur (see below and see Chap.
4).

When an ion exchanger in A form (where A is an arbitrary counter ion)
is placed in a solution of an electrolyte BY, counter ions A will migrate
from the exchanger into the solution and counter ions B* from the solution into the ion exchanger, i.e., an exchange of counter ions takes place.
After a certain time, *ion-exchange equilibrium* is attained. Now, both
the ion exchanger and the solution contain both counter-ion species A and
B. The concentration ratio of the two counter ions, however, is not
necessarily the same in both phases.

As a rule, the pores are occupied not only by counter ions but also by
solvent and solutes which can enter the pores when the ion exchanger is in
contact with a solution. Uptake of solvent may result in *swelling* of the ion
exchanger. Uptake of solutes is usually called *sorption*, though it is essentially a distribution of the solute between two liquid phases, namely, the
pore liquid and the solution outside.

Sorption of an electrolyte increases the counter-ion content of the ion
exchanger. The sorbed counter ions, which are present in addition to
those compensating the framework charge, are accompanied by an equivalent amount of so-called *co-ions*.* These are mobile ions with charges
of the same sign as the framework charge. The counter-ion content of an
ion exchanger thus depends not only on the magnitude of the framework
charge but also on its co-ion content. The common definitions of ion-
exchange capacities refer, for this reason, to ion exchangers which are
free of co-ions.

---

* Often the term "counter ion" is used exclusively for ions *within* the ion exchanger.
According to this definition an ion becomes a counter ion only when entering the exchanger. In this book, the notation will be used in a broader sense: whether in the
exchanger or in the external solution, all ionic species with charge sign opposite to that
of the exchanger framework will be called counter ions. Correspondingly, the notation
co-ions will be used for all ionic species with the same charge sign as the exchanger
framework.

In the discussion above and later in this book, the interstices in the framework are called "pores," regardless of their actual geometric form. Often the term pore is used specifically for channels or capillaries of uniform cross section. Channels of this kind are present in only a few mineral ion exchangers. Most ion exchangers have an irregular, three-dimensional framework which resembles, in some respects, the crisscrossing steel structure of a bridge or a television tower. Here, the "pores" are the void spaces between the girders.

The simple model outlined above represents the most important properties of ion exchangers correctly. It shows at first sight why ion exchange is a stoichiometric process and why the capacity does not depend on the nature of the counter ion. The physical cause for both facts is the electroneutrality condition. In addition, the model shows that ion exchange is essentially a statistical redistribution of counter ions between the pore liquid and the external solution, a process in which neither the framework nor the co-ions take part. Therefore Eqs. (1-1) and (1-2) should be rewritten:

$$2\overline{Na^+} + Ca^{2+} \rightleftharpoons \overline{Ca^{2+}} + 2Na^+ \tag{1-3}$$

$$2\overline{Cl^-} + SO_4^{2-} \rightleftharpoons \overline{SO_4^{2-}} + 2Cl^- \tag{1-4}$$

Quantities with bars refer to the inside of the ion exchanger.

The model also describes *ion-exchange kinetics* correctly. Ion exchange is a diffusion process. Its rate depends on the mobilities of the counter ions. Thus ion-exchange kinetics has no resemblance to chemical reaction kinetics in the usual sense. However, the simple, well-known rate laws of diffusion hold only in exceptional cases. As a rule, electric forces affect the fluxes of the ions and cause deviations (see Chap. 6).

Occasionally, ion exchange has been referred to as a "chemical" process, in contrast to adsorption as a "physical" process. This distinction, though plausible at first glance, is misleading. Usually, in ion exchange as a redistribution of ions by diffusion, chemical factors are less significant than in adsorption where the solute is held by the sorbent by forces which may not be purely electrostatic. The absence of an actual chemical reaction also explains why the heat evolved in the course of ion-exchange processes is usually rather small (often less than 2 kcal/mole, unless ion exchange is followed by reactions such as neutralization, etc.).

It has been mentioned above that, in ion-exchange equilibrium, the concentration ratios of the competing counter-ion species in the ion exchanger and in the solution are not the same. As a rule, the ion exchanger prefers one species to the other. This shows that the redistribution of the counter ions is not purely statistical. The preference for one species may have several causes. The most important of these are:

1. The electrostatic interactions between the charged framework and the counter ions depend on the size and, in particular, on the valence of the counter ion.

2. In addition to the electrostatic forces, other interactions between the ions and their environment are effective.

3. Large counter ions may be sterically excluded from the narrow pores of the ion exchanger.

All these effects depend on the nature of the counter ion and thus may lead to preferential uptake of a species by the ion exchanger (see Sec. 5-4). The ability of the ion exchanger to distinguish between various counter ion species is called *selectivity*. The selectivity is not adequately explained by the simple sponge model.

The *electrochemical properties* of ion exchangers are readily interpreted in terms of the sponge model. Swollen ion exchangers have a high electric conductivity which is due to their high content of mobile ions (see Chap. 7). The model also shows that the ion exchanger must contain many more counter ions than co-ions. Many electrochemical phenomena in systems with ion-exchanger membranes can be explained with this fact (see Chap. 8).

The model also gives an obvious explanation for the *catalytic activity* of ion exchangers. Reactions which are catalyzed by certain ions in solution can occur equally well in the pores of an ion exchanger which contains the catalytically active species as the counter ion (see Chap. 11).

For a quantitative treatment, a model as simple as the charged sponge is, of course, insufficient. Nevertheless, this model is often useful in explaining the mechanisms of the processes.

SUMMARY

Ion exchangers consist of a framework carrying a positive or negative electric surplus charge which is compensated by mobile counter ions of opposite sign. Cation exchangers contain cations, and anion exchangers anions, as counter ions. The counter ions can be exchanged for other ions of the same sign. The exchange is stoichiometric and, as a rule, reversible. Ion exchange is essentially a diffusion process and has little, if any, relation to chemical reaction kinetics in the usual sense. Usually the ion exchanger is selective, i.e., it takes up certain counter ions in preference to others. Ion exchangers can also sorb solvent and solutes. A simple model for the ion exchanger is a sponge carrying an electric charge which must be compensated by charged particles within its pores. Many phenomena can be qualitatively explained with this model.

2

Structure and Properties of Ion Exchangers

Many different natural and synthetic products show ion-exchange properties. The most important of these are ion-exchange resins, ion-exchange coals, mineral ion exchangers, and synthetic inorganic ion exchangers. Several other types of ion exchangers are historically interesting, but are now obsolete. Still others are used for special purposes.

The general structural principle—a framework with electric surplus charge and mobile counter ions—is common to all ion exchangers. Nevertheless, the various types of materials show marked differences in behavior. Characteristic features of the most important and interesting materials will be briefly discussed in this chapter.

2-1. MINERAL ION EXCHANGERS

Most natural ion-exchange minerals are crystalline alumosilicates with cation-exchange properties. Characteristic representatives of this group of materials are the *zeolites* which include, among others, the minerals *analcite*, $Na[Si_2AlO_6]_2 \cdot H_2O$, *chabazite*, $(Ca,Na)[Si_2AlO_6]_2 \cdot 6H_2O$, *harmotome*, $(K,Ba)[Si_5Al_2O_{14}] \cdot 5H_2O$, *heulandite*, $Ca[Si_3AlO_8] \cdot 5H_2O$, and *natrolite*, $Na_2[Si_3Al_2O_{10}] \cdot 2H_2O$. All these materials have a relatively open three-dimensional framework structure with channels and interconnecting cavities in the alumosilicate lattice. The lattice structure of a typical zeolite is shown in Fig. 2-1. The zeolite lattice consists of SiO_4 and AlO_4 tetrahedra which have their oxygen atoms in common. Since aluminum is trivalent, the lattice carries a negative electric charge (one elementary charge per aluminum atom). This charge is balanced by alkali or alkaline-earth cations which do not occupy fixed positions, but are free to move in the channels of the lattice framework. These ions act as counter ions and can be replaced by other cations [7,10,12,13,16,18,31,45,51,56,56a,75,100,107.128, 131].

Other alumosilicates with cation-exchange properties have a loose layer structure. They carry their counter ions in between the layers of the lattice. Characteristic minerals of this type are *montmorillonite* and *beidellite*, clays with the approximate compositions $Al_2[Si_4O_{10}(OH)_2]\cdot nH_2O$ and $Al_2[(OH)_2AlSi_3O_9OH]\cdot 4H_2O$, respectively [14,31,43,44,47,50,51,56,58,59,65, 80,83,85,91,92,112]. These materials can swell in one dimension by increasing their interlayer distance.

Glauconites are ferrous alumosilicates containing exchangeable potassium. Their crystal lattice is rather dense and rigid, so that cation exchange can occur only at the crystal surfaces. Nevertheless, these materials have a considerable cation-exchange capacity when in colloidal form [31,51,56,63, 80,98,130].

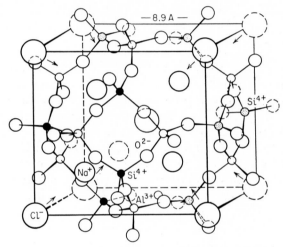

FIG. 2-1. Structure of sodalite, $Na_4[Si_3Al_3ClO_{12}]$. A unit cell of the crystal is shown. The arrows indicate channels which connect the cavities in the alumosilicate framework. Chabazite has a very similar, but slightly distorted structure. *From S. B. Hendricks* [56].

Certain alumosilicates can also act as anion exchangers. For example, exchange of OH^- for Cl^-, SO_4^{2-}, and PO_4^{3-} has been observed in montmorillonite [82], kaolinite [124], and in feldspars belonging to the sodalite and cancrinite groups [75]. However, the only mineral anion exchangers which have been used for practical purposes are *apatite*, $[Ca_5(PO_4)_3]F$, and *hydroxylapatite*, $[Ca_5(PO_4)_3]OH$ [3,20,115].

The zeolites are relatively soft minerals and thus not very abrasion resistant. Their frameworks are less open (pore widths about 3 to 9 A) and more rigid than those of most other ion exchangers. Therefore they swell very little, and the counter ions in their pores are not very mobile. Perhaps the most interesting property of the zeolites is their small and strictly uniform pore size which gives rise to a pronounced "sieve action" on a molecular scale. Large cations (such as quaternary ammonium ions with bulky substituents) [15,131] and large nonelectrolyte molecules [18,27,101] cannot be accommodated, whereas smaller species can be exchanged or sorbed (see also pages 123 and 186). Even inorganic cations such as Cs^+ are partially or completely excluded by several zeolites [7,16,18]. Mineral ion exchangers with layer structure can swell more. Interlayer distances up to, and in some cases exceeding, 20 A have been found [91,92]. However, these materials are less resistant to mechanical breakdown. Glauconites are harder than zeolites, but unfortunately they tend to peptize. This tendency can be overcome only by a special stabilization treatment, usually with alumina and silicate solutions (Neopermutit, Superneopermutit) [25,96,97,129]. All inorganic cation exchangers including the synthetic products suffer partial decomposition from attack of acids and bases. Hence their practical use is restricted to a rather narrow pH range, around pH 7. Furthermore, many of the ion exchangers mentioned are only moderately stable in solutions of very low silica or salt content.

2-2. SYNTHETIC INORGANIC ION EXCHANGERS

The first attempts to synthesize products resembling the natural zeolites were made more than 50 years ago. The first cation exchangers which became commercially available were prepared by fusion of mixtures of soda, potash, feldspar, and kaolin, or similar components. Except for their more irregular structure, these "fusion permutits" resemble the natural zeolites [31,39,51,81,93,102,103]. Later, cation exchangers with improved properties were prepared by precipitation with caustic from acidic solutions of aluminum sulfate and sodium silicate, followed by drying of the gelatinous precipitate. In their chemical composition, these "gel permutits" are similar to the zeolites. However, in contrast to the latter, they have an irregular gel structure which resembles that of silica gel and ion-exchange resins [31,34,41,46,48,51,94,116,123]. Today, both the fusion permutits and the gel permutits can claim but historical interest.

In recent years, various zeolites with completely regular crystal structure have been synthesized [7–9,11,15–19,27,42,53,56a,86], most of them by a so-called hydrothermal preparation method which involves crystallization at an elevated temperature from solutions containing silica, alumina, and alkali. These products are exact counterparts of the natural materials. As ion exchangers they are of little practical importance. However, they are very useful as highly specific sorbents. Because of their narrow, rigid, and strictly uniform pore structure they act as "molecular sieves" which can sorb small molecules, but completely exclude molecules which are larger than the openings in the crystal framework [18,27,29,56a,101]; see also page 123. To a certain degree the pore size can be adjusted by converting the materials to other ionic forms [6,42,86,110]. Several types of molecular sieves, prepared by the Linde Corporation, are commercially available.

Linde sieves type X (synthetic faujasite) and type A (no exact counterpart in nature) have pore diameters of about 10 to 13 and 3 to 5 A, respectively. The sieves are available both as microcrystalline powders and as pellets [57] which consist of microcrystals in a porous clay binder.

Various attempts have been made to synthesize inorganic cation exchangers with other frameworks than alumosilicate. Fusion permutits have been prepared in which silicon was partly or completely replaced by other

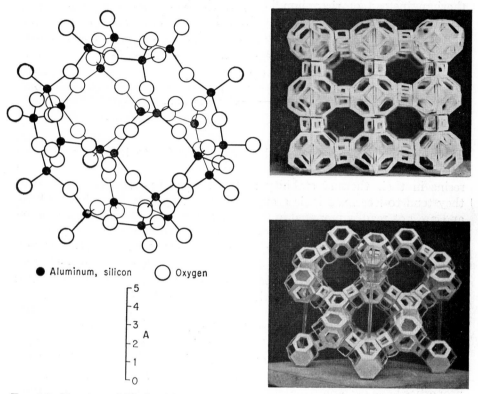

● Aluminum, silicon　　○ Oxygen

Fig. 2-2. Structure of Linde "Molecular Sieves." The structure of the cubooctahedral unit (*left*) and the packing of the cubooctahedra in the sieves type A (*top, right*) and type X (*bottom, right*) are shown. *From R. M. Barrer* [18].

tetravalent elements such as titanium and tin, and aluminum by other trivalent elements such as iron, manganese, vanadium, and phosphorus [33,95,111]. However, the properties of these products were unsatisfactory. Many hydrous oxide gels including Fe_2O_3, Al_2O_3, Cr_2O_3, Bi_2O_3, TiO_2, ZrO_2, ThO_2, SnO_2, MoO_3, and WO_3 are amphoteric and can act as cation exchangers at pH values above their isoelectric points (varying between 4.8 for SnO_2 and 9.8 for ThO_2) [4,67,70,84]. However, these materials are of little, if any, practical importance because they are dissolved by acids and bases. The oxides of zirconium and tin seem to be the most stable.

Recently, inorganic cation exchangers with much more satisfactory properties have been prepared by combining group IV oxides with the more acidic oxides of group V and VI. For example, zirconium phosphates with variable $ZrO_2:P_2O_5$ ratios have been obtained by precipitation with alkali phosphates or phosphoric acid from solutions of zirconyl chloride [4,5,69,70,84]. Similar materials can be prepared using arsenic, molybdic, and tungstic acids instead of phosphoric acid, and titanium, tin, and thorium instead of zirconium [5,68,70,84]. The products are extremely insoluble. Their chemical composition is nonstoichiometric and depends on the conditions under which they are precipitated. Structure determinations have not yet been attempted. A likely configuration is

$$
\begin{array}{ccc}
OPO_3^= & OPO_3^= \\
| & | \\
\ldots\,{-}Zr{-}O{-}Zr{-}O{-}\,\ldots \\
| & | \\
OPO_3^= & OPO_3^=
\end{array}
$$

These new ion exchangers have high capacities (up to 12 meq/g on a dry basis), give high rates of ion exchange, and are superior to the organic resins in their thermal stability and resistance to radiation. However, they tend to lose fixed ionic groups because of hydrolysis at high pH [70a] and are not readily prepared in the form of mechanically stable particles of convenient size. Ion exchangers of this type were developed chiefly at the Oak Ridge National Laboratory (Oak Ridge, Tenn.) and at the Atomic Energy Research Establishment (Harwell, England). The materials prepared at Oak Ridge are granular precipitates of very small particle size; those prepared at Harwell are dried gels of much larger particle size.

Only very few synthetic inorganic anion exchangers have been made. Gelatinous precipitates of aluminum and iron oxides were occasionally used before organic anion-exchange resins became available [51,60,97]. More recently, hydrous oxide gels of zirconium and tin with anion exchange properties have been prepared [67,84].

2-3. ION-EXCHANGE RESINS

The most important class of ion exchangers are the organic ion-exchange resins. They are typical gels. Their framework, the so-called *matrix*, consists of an irregular, macromolecular, three-dimensional network of hydrocarbon chains. The matrix carries ionic groups such as

$$-SO_3^- \qquad -COO^- \qquad -PO_3^{2-} \qquad -AsO_3^{2-}$$

in cation exchangers, and

$$-NH_3^+ \qquad {\diagdown}NH_2^+ \qquad {\diagdown}N^+{\diagup} \qquad {\diagdown}S^+$$

in anion exchangers.   Ion-exchange resins thus are crosslinked polyelectrolytes.

The matrix of the resins is hydrophobic.   However, hydrophilic components are introduced by the incorporation of ionic groups such as —$SO_3^-H^+$. Linear hydrocarbon macromolecules with such groups are soluble in water. The ion-exchange resins, in contrast, are made insoluble by introduction of crosslinks which interconnect the various hydrocarbon chains.   An ion-exchange resin particle is practically one single macromolecule.   Its dissolution would require rupture of carbon-carbon bonds.   Thus the resins are insoluble in all solvents by which they are not destroyed.   However, the matrix is elastic and can be expanded.   Hence the resins can swell by

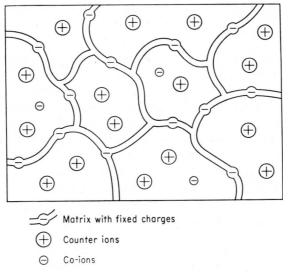

—⌇⌇⁄   Matrix with fixed charges

⊕   Counter ions

⊖   Co-ions

Fig. 2-3. Structure of an ion-exchange resin (*schematic*).

taking up solvent.   The framework of the resins, in contrast to that of the zeolites, is a flexible random network (see Fig. 2-3).   The mesh width is not uniform, a fact that is referred to as "heteroporosity" or "heterodictiality."

The chemical, thermal, and mechanical stability and the ion-exchange behavior of the resins depend chiefly on the structure and the degree of crosslinking of the matrix and on the nature and number of the fixed ionic groups.

The degree of crosslinking determines the mesh width of the matrix and thus the swelling ability of the resin and the mobilities of the counter ions in the resin.   The latter, in turn, determine the rates of ion exchange and other processes and the electric conductivity of the resin.   The (average) mesh width of very highly crosslinked resins is of the order of only a few angstrom units.   The mesh width of very weakly crosslinked and fully swollen resins may exceed 100 A.   Highly crosslinked resins are harder and more resistant to mechanical breakdown and attrition.

The chemical and thermal stability of the resins is not unlimited.   The most frequent causes for resin deterioration are chemical and thermal degradation of the matrix, for example, by oxidation, and loss of fixed ionic groups, for example, by thermal hydrolysis.   Most of the present commercial resins are stable in all common solvents, except in the presence of strong oxidizing or reducing agents, and withstand temperatures up to slightly more than 100°C.   Strong-base anion-exchange resins begin to deteriorate above 60°C.

The ion-exchange behavior of the resins is chiefly determined by the fixed ionic groups.   The number of the groups determines the ion-exchange capacity.   The chemical nature of the groups greatly affects ion-exchange equilibria.   An important factor is the acid or base strength of the groups.   Weak-acid groups such as $—COO^-$ are ionized only at high pH.   At low pH, they combine with H^+, forming undissociated $—COOH$, and thus no longer act as fixed charges.   In contrast, strong-acid groups such as $—SO_3^-$ remain ionized even at low pH.   Similarly, weak-base groups such as $—NH_3^+$ lose a proton, forming uncharged $—NH_2$, when the pH is high, and strong-base groups such as $—N^+(CH_3)_3$ remain ionized even at high pH.   Because of the progressive neutralization of fixed charges with decreasing or increasing pH, the operative capacity of weak-acid and weak-base resins is pH-dependent.   Also, the salt forms of these resins tend to hydrolyze in the same manner as salts of weak acids and weak bases.

The nature of the fixed ionic groups also affects the selectivity of the resins.   Counter ions which tend to associate with the fixed ionic groups by, say, forming ion pairs or complexes are preferred by the resin.   For example, resins with sulfonic acid groups prefer Ag^+, resins with carboxylic acid groups prefer alkaline-earth cations, and resins with chelating groups prefer certain heavy-metal cations.   Evidence pointing to interactions between the fixed ionic groups and the preferred counter ions in all these cases is the relatively low solubility or weak dissociation of the corresponding monomeric salts, i.e., the silver sulfonates, the alkaline-earth carboxylates, and the heavy-metal chelates.   The question whether actual bonds between the fixed ionic groups and the counter ions are formed and the latter are, so to speak, "precipitated" within the pores is, in some cases, still somewhat controversial.

Innumerable types of ion-exchange resins with different properties can be prepared.   Not only the nature and number of the fixed ionic groups, but also the composition and the degree of crosslinking of the matrix can be varied and be adapted to intended applications.   The preparation and composition of different types of ion-exchange resins is described in the next chapter.   The properties of the resins are discussed in more detail in the later chapters.

2-4. ION-EXCHANGE COALS

Many coals are natural ion exchangers. They contain carboxylic and possibly other weak-acid groups and can thus be used as cation exchangers. However, most of these materials swell excessively, are easily decomposed by alkali, and tend to peptize. Therefore they must be "stabilized" before

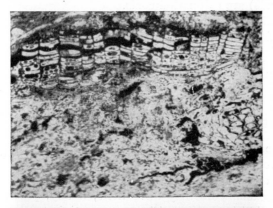

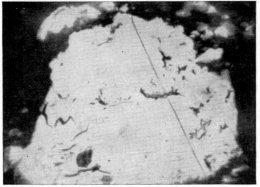

FIG. 2-4. Soft lignitic coal (Cologne, Germany) in the natural state (*top*) and after sulfonation (*bottom*). The natural coal has a coarse pore structure. In the course of the sulfonation the material is gelified and becomes more homogeneous. The light reflection is increased. *Linear magnification* 120:1; *from H. Stach* [122].

use. Soft and hard lignitic coals have been stabilized by treatment with solutions of copper, chromium, or aluminum salts [26,51,121,122,125]. Pitch and glance coals treated with sodium hydroxide or hydrochloric acid solutions are chemically more stable [120].

Most lignitic and bituminous coals and anthracites can be converted into strong-acid cation exchangers by sulfonation with fuming sulfuric acid. Sulfonic acid groups are introduced and additional carboxylic acid groups are formed by oxidation. At the same time, the sulfuric-acid treatment causes polycondensation reactions by which the coal is "gelified" (see

Fig. 2-4) and its chemical and mechanical stability is improved. In certain respects, sulfonated coals resemble organic ion-exchange resins. They have fixed ionic groups and a gel structure. However, their composition is less uniform and their mechanical and chemical stability, particularly their resistance to alkali, is inferior [1,49,51,78,104,105,113,122,127]. The earlier Zeo-Karb ion exchangers, Zeolite H-53 and S-53 and Dusarit S (Activit N.V., Netherlands) are sulfonated coals.

Other "activation" methods such as thermal activation [61] or treatment with oxygen and nitrous gases [119], nitric acid, or phosphoric acid [99] have been used. They result essentially in a gelification of the coal with or without simultaneous oxidative formation of carboxylic groups. All these methods lost much of their appeal when sulfonation was developed.

2-5. OTHER MATERIALS WITH ION-EXCHANGE PROPERTIES

In addition to the materials mentioned so far, a number of others show ion-exchange properties [38]. *Alumina* [108,109,126], *alginic acid* [88,118], *collodion* [117], and *keratin* [132] are a few typical representatives of this group. As ion exchangers they have little, if any, practical importance because their stabilities or capacities are unsatisfactory. However, their ion-exchange properties may deeply affect their behavior and should not be overlooked. For example, chromatography on alumina [126] and membrane potentials across collodion membranes [117] have been successfully explained in terms of the ion-exchange properties of these substances.

A still larger number of materials can be transformed into ion exchangers by chemical treatment [38]. From many soluble substances which carry ionogenic groups, insoluble ion-exchanger gels can be obtained simply by crosslinking with agents such as formaldehyde or epichlorohydrin. *Pectins* [35,36] and *carrageen* [37] are typical examples. From many insoluble substances ion exchangers can be made by incorporation of fixed ionic groups. The most common procedures are sulfonation and phosphorylation which are by no means restricted to synthetic resins and coals. In fact, cation exchangers can be made from almost any material which reacts with sulfuric acid without being dissolved. This is illustrated by an Israeli patent covering the sulfonation of *olive pits* [55] and Indian patents covering the sulfonation of *nut shells* and *spent ground coffee* [87]. Other materials which can be sulfonated or phosphorylated are *tar* [2,114], *wood* [2,49,77], *paper* [54,66,72–74,133], *cotton* [32,52,64], etc. Still other materials such as *lignin* [1,71] and *tannins* [22] must be crosslinked before or after sulfonation.

A description of the properties of all these ion exchangers is beyond the scope of this book, especially since they are of little practical importance. Only two special-purpose products shall be mentioned. *Ion-exchange papers* can be prepared by impregnating filter paper with dissolved polyelectrolytes [73,74] or liquid ion exchangers [30], by adding colloidal ion exchangers to

the pulp from which the paper is made [54,66a,75a,133], or by treating the paper with chloroacetic acid, butane sulfone, pyridine and p-toluylsulfo-chloride, or other agents by which ionic groups are introduced [3a,72]. Ion-exchange papers have been used for paper chromatography of electrolytes. Anion- and cation-exchange papers will soon be made available by Rohm & Haas Co. [133]. *Phosphorylated cotton* [32,52,64], a cation exchanger, is readily prepared in the form of infinite belts which have been suggested for continuous counter-current operations [90].

2-6. LIQUID ION EXCHANGERS

Conventional ion exchangers are insoluble solids. However, ion exchange can also occur between two immiscible liquid phases. In recent years, liquids with ion-exchange properties have attracted considerable attention. These *liquid ion exchangers* are prepared by dissolving compounds with iono-genic groups in organic solvents such as kerosene, trichloroethylene, chloroform, and xylene which are immiscible with water. The ionogenic compound must have hydrophobic groups in order to remain in the organic phase when the latter is contacted with aqueous solutions. Long-chain aliphatic amines have been used for making liquid anion exchangers [28,40,79, 89,106], and fatty acids [48a] and dialkylphosphates for cation exchangers [23,62,76]. Suitable amines have been made available by Rohm & Haas Co. (Amberlite LA-1 and LA-2). Liquid ion exchangers are used for ion exchange with aqueous electrolytes and for liquid-liquid extraction of electrolytes from aqueous solutions.

Liquid ion exchangers have several advantages. They are easily prepared, the concentration of the functional groups in the ion-exchanger phase is readily adjusted, high ion-exchange rates can be attained by efficient dispersion of the organic phase in the aqueous phase, and continuous countercurrent operation is much simpler with liquid than with solid ion exchangers. Disadvantages are that phase separation is somewhat more difficult and that losses of ion-exchange material can hardly be avoided, especially if the components of the organic phase are not completely insoluble in water.

Liquid ion exchangers differ from their solid counterparts in several respects. They absorb very little water from aqueous solutions, their dielectric constants are rather low, and the functional groups are not attached to a solid framework. Because of the low dielectric constant one must expect considerable association between the functional groups and the counter ions. The molecules carrying the functional groups are free to diffuse within the ion-exchanger phase, and when ionized, are subject to electric forces which may arise in the course of ion exchange.

Liquid ion exchangers are not a recent invention. About half a century ago, Beutner [21] studied "oil membranes" which were, in principle, liquid ion exchangers. The electrochemistry of such systems has recently been investigated in more detail [24].   Experimental evidence on equilibria and ion-exchange rates is still insufficient for serving as a basis for quantitative theories.   The theoretical considerations in later chapters are not necessarily applicable to liquid ion exchangers.

2-7. SURVEY AND COMPARISON

As far as practical applications are concerned, the organic resins are by far the most important ion exchangers.   Their main advantages are high chemical and mechanical stability, high ion-exchange capacity and high exchange rates.   An additional advantage is the possibility of selecting the fixed ionic groups and the degree of crosslinking of the matrix according to the intended applications.   In these respects the resins are superior to the other materials.   It is true that certain other materials can compete with the organic resins.   For example, high capacities and exchange rates can also be obtained with the new inorganic ion-exchanger gels.   However, in most applications such advantages are more than outweighed by the lack of chemical or mechanical stability or by other undesirable properties.

Inorganic ion exchangers are superior to the organic resins in their thermal stability and resistance to radiation.   For example, zeolites can be used as catalysts for gas reactions at temperatures well above the range in which the resins are stable.   The new inorganic ion-exchanger gels offer advantages in the decontamination of cooling water in nuclear reactors where both the temperature and the radiation level are high.   Furthermore, crystalline ion exchangers with regular framework structures often show higher selectivities than materials with irregular gel structures.

Certain other ion exchangers such as sulfonated coals or sulfonated waste products are relatively inexpensive.   Nevertheless, they have not been able to compete with the synthetic resins.   In spite of their lower price per pound, these materials are usually found to be less economical than the resins when factors such as effective ion-exchange capacity, useful life, and product purity are taken into account.

The basic laws of ion exchange are consequences of the general structural principle according to which the materials are built.   Thus they are common to all ion exchangers.   Of course, every material has its individual features and peculiarities.   As far as possible, the treatment of the theoretical principles in the later chapters is kept in general terms.   Beyond that, the behavior of ion-exchange resins as the most important materials will receive special attention.

SUMMARY

Various alumosilicate minerals with cation-exchange properties are known.   The zeolites have a rigid three-dimensional framework structure with cavities and channels in which the counter ions can move.   Clays such

as montmorillonite have a layer structure and carry their counter ions in between the layers. Glauconites have a dense three-dimensional framework structure and carry exchangeable counter ions only at the crystal surfaces. A few minerals such as apatite can act as anion exchangers.

Synthetic alumosilicate cation exchangers have been prepared by fusion and precipitation methods. These materials are now obsolete. In recent years, zeolites with regular crystal structures have been synthesized. They are used as "molecular sieves" which sorb small molecules, but exclude molecules which are larger than the channels in the crystal lattice. New inorganic cation and anion-exchanger gels with excellent properties have recently been prepared from zirconium and tin hydroxides. The cation exchangers contain phosphate or tungstate groups.

Organic ion-exchange resins consist of an elastic three-dimensional network of hydrocarbon chains which carry fixed ionic groups. The charge of the groups is balanced by mobile counter ions. The resins are crosslinked polyelectrolytes. They are insoluble, but can swell to a limited degree. The ion-exchange behavior of the resins depends chiefly on the nature of the fixed ionic groups. Important factors are the acid or base strength of the groups and specific interactions with the counter ions. Counter ions which associate with the fixed ionic groups are preferred by the resin. An almost unlimited variety of resins with different fixed ionic groups and different compositions and degrees of crosslinking of the matrix can be prepared.

Certain coals are natural weak-acid cation exchangers. Others can be transformed into ion exchangers by chemical "activation." The most important activation treatment is sulfonation which leads to strong-acid cation exchangers.

Many other natural and synthetic materials can act as ion exchangers. From still others, ion exchangers can be prepared by introducing fixed ionic groups (for example, by sulfonation) or by crosslinking. Two such products which can be used for special purposes are ion-exchange paper and phosphorylated cotton.

The most important ion exchangers are the synthetic resins which are superior to the other materials in their chemical and mechanical stability, ion-exchange capacity, ion-exchange rate, and versatility. Inorganic ion exchangers have a higher thermal stability and resistance to radiation. All other materials have little, if any, practical importance.

REFERENCES

1. "Activit," N. V. Octrooien Maatschappij, F. Patent 778,922, 1935.
2. "Activit," N. V. Octrooien Maatschappij, F. Patent 828,222, 1938.
3. Adler, H., G. Klein, and F. K. Lindsay, *Ind. Eng. Chem.*, **30**, 163 (1938).
3a. Alberti, G., and G. Grassini, *J. Chromatog.*, **4**, 83 (1960).
4. Amphlett, C. B., L. A. McDonald, and M. J. Redman, *Chem. & Ind.*, **1956**, 1314; *J. Inorg. & Nuclear Chem.*, **6**, 220, 236 (1958).

5. Amphlett, C. B., *Intern. Conf. Peaceful Uses of Atomic Energy*, 2d Conf., Geneva, **28**, 63 (1958).

6. Barrer, R. M., U.S. Patent 2,413,134, 1946.

7. Barrer, R. M., *J. Chem. Soc.*, **1948**, 127, and 2158; **1950**, 2342.

8. Barrer, R. M., and E. A. D. White, *J. Chem. Soc.*, **1951**, 1267; **1952**, 1561.

9. Barrer, R. M., and N. McCallum, *J. Chem. Soc.*, **1953**, 4029.

10. Barrer, R. M., and L. Hinds, *J. Chem. Soc.*, **1953**, 1879.

11. Barrer, R. M., J. W. Baynham, and N. McCallum, *J. Chem. Soc.*, **1953**, 4035.

12. Barrer, R. M., and J. S. Raitt, *J. Chem. Soc.*, **1954**, 4641.

13. Barrer, R. M., and D. C. Sammon, *J. Chem. Soc.*, **1955**, 2838.

14. Barrer, R. M., and D. M. MacLeod, *Trans. Faraday Soc.*, **51**, 1290 (1955).

15. Barrer, R. M., W. Buser, and W. F. Grütter, *Helv. chim. Acta*, **39**, 518 (1956).

*16. Barrer, R. M., and J. D. Falconer, *Proc. Roy. Soc. (London)*, **A236**, 227 (1956).

17. Barrer, R. M., and J. W. Baynham, *J. Chem. Soc.*, **1956**, 2882.

*18. Barrer, R. M., *Proc. Chem. Soc.*, **1958**, 99; *Brit. Chem. Eng.*, **4**, 267 (1959).

19. Barrer, R. M., J. W. Baynham, F. W. Bultitude, and W. M. Meier, *J. Chem. Soc.*, **1959**, 195.

20. Behrmann, A. S., and H. Gustafson, *Ind. Eng. Chem.*, **30**, 1011 (1938).

*21. Beutner, R., "Die Entstehung elektrischer Ströme in lebenden Geweben," Ferd. Enke, Stuttgart, 1920.

22. Bhatnagar, M. S., and P. C. Nigam, *J. Appl. Chem.*, **1**, 517 (1951).

23. Blake, C. A., C. F. Baes, Jr., K. B. Brown, C. F. Coleman, and J. C. White, *Intern. Conf. Peaceful Uses of Atomic Energy*, 2d Conf., Geneva, **28**, 289 (1958).

24. Bonhoeffer, K. F., M. Kahlweit, and H. Strehlow, *Z. Elektrochem.*, **57**, 614 (1953); *Z. physik. Chem. (Frankfurt)*, **1**, 21 (1954).

25. Borromite Comp. of America (Y. K. Lee), U.S. Patent 1,472,011, 1923.

26. Borrowman, G., U.S. Patent 1,994,682, 1935.

27. Breck, D. W., W. G. Eversole, R. M. Milton, T. B. Reed, and T. L. Thomas, *J. Am. Chem. Soc.*, **78**, 5963 (1956).

28. Brothers, J. A., R. G. Hart, and W. G. Mathers, *J. Inorg. & Nuclear Chem.*, **7**, 85 (1958).

29. Broughton, D. B., and D. B. Carson, *Petrochem. Refining*, May, 1959, p. 18.

30. Cerrai, E., and C. Testa, *J. Chromatog.*, **5**, 442 (1961).

*31. Corte, H., in Ullmann's Encyclopädie der technischen Chemie, vol. 8, p. 801, Urban & Schwarzenberg, Munich-Berlin, 1957.

32. Daul, G. C., J. D. Reid, and R. M. Reinhardt, *Ind. Eng. Chem.*, **46**, 1042 (1954).

33. DeBrünn, P., Ger. Patent 274,650, 1914.

34. DeBrünn, P., Ger. Patents 270,324, 1914; 342,968, 1921.

35. Deuel, H., *Helv. chim. Acta*, **30**, 1269 (1947).

36. Deuel, H., K. Hutschneker, and J. Solms, *Z. Elektrochem.*, **57**, 172 (1953).

37. Deuel, H., and H. Neukom, *Advances in Chem. Ser.*, **11**, 51 (1954).

*38. Deuel, H., and K. Hutschneker, *Chimia*, **9**, 49 (1955).

39. Electric Smelting and Aluminum Co. (A. H. Cowles), U.S. Patent 1,745,844, 1930.

40. Ellenburg, J. Y., G. W. Leddicotte, and F. L. Moore, *Anal. Chem.*, **26**, 1045 (1954).

41. Engel, P. N., Ger. Patent 583,974, 1933.

42. Estes, J. H. (The Texas Co.), U.S. Patent 2,847,280, 1958.

43. Forslind, E., *Acta Polytech. Nr.* 115, Chem. M. Ser., **3**, No. 5 (1952); *Chem. Abstr.*, **47**, 10949 (1953).

44. Foster, M. D., *Bull. Geol. Soc. Am.*, **63**, 1250 (1952).

45. Gans, R., *Jahrb. preuss. geol. Landesanstalt (Berlin)*, **26**, 179 (1905).

---

* Reviews are marked with asterisks.

46. Gans, R., Ger. Patent 174,097, 1906.

47. Gans, R., *Jahrb. preuss. geol. Landesanstalt (Berlin)*, **34**, 242 (1913).

48. General Zeolite Co., Ger. Patent 588,740, 1933.

48a. Gindin, L. M., P. I. Bobikov, E. F. Kouba, and A. V. Bugaeva, *Zhur. Neorg. Khim.*, **5**, 1868 (1960).

49. Goetz, P. C. (Permutit Co.), U.S. Patent 2,260,971, 1941.

50. Greene-Kelly, R., *J. Colloid Sci.*, **11**, 77 (1956); *Trans. Faraday Soc.*, **52**, 1281 (1956).

*51. Griessbach, R., "Austauschadsorption in Theorie und Praxis," pp. 1–42, Akademie-Verlag G.m.b.H., Berlin, 1957.

52. Guthrie, J. D., *Ind. Eng. Chem.*, **44**, 2187 (1952).

53. Guyer, A., M. Ineichen, and P. Guyer, *Helv. chim. Acta*, **40**, 1603 (1957).

54. Hale, D. K., *Chem. & Ind.*, **1955**, 1147.

55. Heimann, H., and R. Ratner, *Bull. Research Council Israel*, **3**, 96 (1953).

*56. Hendricks, S. B., *Ind. Eng. Chem.*, **37**, 625 (1945).

*56a. Hersh, C. K., "Molecular Sieves," Reinhold Publishing Corporation, New York, 1961.

57. Hess, H. V., and W. A. Ray (The Texas Co.), U.S. Patent 2,885,368, 1959.

58. Hofmann, U., K. Endell, and D. Wilm, *Z. Krist., Mineral Petrog.*, Abt. **A86**, 340 (1933).

*59. Hofmann, U., *Angew. Chem.*, **68**, 53 (1956).

60. I. G. Farbenindustrie, F. Patent 814,808, 1937.

61. I. G. Farbenindustrie, F. Patent 817,881, 1937.

62. Irving, H., and D. N. Edgington, *Proc. Chem. Soc.*, **1959**, 360.

63. Jenny, H., *J. Phys. Chem.*, **36**, 2217 (1932); **40**, 501 (1936).

64. Jurgens, J. F., J. D. Reid, and J. D. Guthrie, *Textile Research J.*, **18**, 42 (1948).

65. Karšulin, M., and V. Stubičan, *Monatsh.*, **85**, 343 (1954); *Chem. Abstr.*, **48**, 13507 (1954).

66. Kember, N. F., and R. A. Wells, *Nature*, **175**, 512 (1955).

66a. Knight, C. S., *Nature*, **188**, 739 (1960).

67. Kraus, K. A., and H. O. Phillips, *J. Am. Chem. Soc.*, **78**, 249 (1956).

68. Kraus, K. A., T. A. Carlson, and J. S. Johnson, *Nature*, **177**, 1128 (1956).

69. Kraus, K. A., and H. O. Phillips, *J. Am. Chem. Soc.*, **78**, 694 (1956).

70. Kraus, K. A., H. O. Phillips, T. A. Carlson, and J. S. Johnson, *Intern. Conf. Peaceful Uses of Atomic Energy*, 2d Conf., Geneva, **28**, 3 (1958).

70a. Larsen, E. M., and D. R. Vissers, *J. Phys. Chem.*, **64**, 1732 (1960).

71. Lautsch, W., *Die Chem.*, **57**, 149 (1944).

72. Lautsch, W., G. Manecke, and W. Broser, *Z. Naturforschung.*, **8b**, 232 (1953).

73. Lederer, M., *Anal. Chim. Acta*, **12**, 142 (1955).

74. Lederer, M., and S. Kertes, *Anal. Chim. Acta*, **15**, 226 (1956).

75. Lemberg, J., *Z. deut. geol. Ges.*, **22**, 355 (1870); **28**, 519 (1876).

75a. Lewandowski, A., *Anal. Chim. Acta*, **23**, 317 (1960).

76. Lewis, C. J., *Ind. Wastes*, **2**, 137 (1957); *Chem. Abstr.*, **51**, 18500 (1957).

77. Liebknecht, O., U.S. Patents 2,191,060 and 2,206,007, 1940; Ger. Patent 736,926, 1951.

78. Liebknecht, O., U.S. Patent 2,378,307, 1945.

79. Mahlman, H. A., G. W. Leddicotte, and F. L. Moore, *Anal. Chem.*, **26**, 1939 (1954).

*80. Marshall, C. E., "The Colloid Chemistry of the Silicate Minerals," Academic Press, New York, 1949.

81. Massatsch, C. (Permutit A. G.), Ger. Patents 363,704 and 366,088, 1922.

---

* Reviews are marked with asterisks.

82. Mattson, S., *Kgl. Landbruks-Högsk. Ann.*, **15**, 308 (1948).
83. Merriam, C. N., Jr., and H. C. Thomas, *J. Chem. Phys.*, **24**, 993 (1956).
84. Merz, E., *Z. Elektrochem.*, **63**, 288 (1959).
85. M'Even, M. B., and M. I. Pratt, *Trans. Faraday Soc.*, **53**, 535 (1957).
86. Milton, R. M. (Union Carbide Corp.), U.S. Patents 2,882,243 and 2,882,244, 1959.
87. Mohan Rao, G. J., and S. C. Pillai, *J. Indian Inst. Sci.*, **A36**, 70 (1954).
88. Mongar, I. L., and A. Wassermann, *Discussions Faraday Soc.*, **7**, 118 (1949); *J. Chem. Soc.*, **1952**, 492, 500, 510.
89. Moore, F. L., *Anal. Chem.*, **29**, 1660 (1957); **30**, 908 (1958).
90. Muendel, C. H., and W. A. Selke, *Ind. Eng. Chem.*, **47**, 374 (1955).
91. Norrish, K., *Discussions Faraday Soc.*, **18**, 120 (1954).
92. Norrish, K., and J. P. Quirk, *Nature*, **173**, 255 (1954).
93. Permutit A. G., Ger. Patents 279,630, 1914; 376,545, 383,321 and 383,322, 1923; 656,731, 1938.
94. Permutit A. G., Ger. Patents 295,623, 1916; 371,796, 1923; 580,711, 1933; 639,280, 1936; 693,706, 1940.
95. Permutit A. G., Ger. Patent 300,209, 1917.
96. Permutit A. G., Ger. Patents 437,809, 1926; 641,216, 1937; 662,230, 1938.
97. Permutit A. G., Brit. Patent 478,134, 1938.
98. Permutit Co. (W. H. Bruce and R. Riley), U.S. Patent 2,139,299, 1938.
99. Phillips & Pain, Etabl., F. Patent 47,578, 1937.
100. Podschus, E., U. Hofmann, and K. Leschewski, *Z. anorg. allgem. Chem.*, **228**, 305 (1936).
101. Reed, T. B., and D. W. Breck, *J. Am. Chem. Soc.*, **78**, 5972 (1956).
102. Riedel A. G., Ger. Patents 186,630 and 192,156, 1907; 200,931, 1908.
103. Rosenheim, Artur R. (inventor O. Liebknecht), Ger. Patent 463,719, 1928.
104. Roy, M. M., and R. C. Basu Roy, *Naturwissenschaften*, **42**, 15, 177 (1955).
105. Roy, M., *J. Appl. Chem.*, **6**, 335 (1956).
106. Schindewolf, U., *Z. Elektrochem.*, **62**, 335 (1958).
107. Schmidt, O., *Z. physik. Chem.*, **133**, 263 (1928).
108. Schwab, G. M., and K. Jockers, *Angew. Chem.*, **50**, 546 (1937).
109. Schwab, G. M., and G. Dattler, *Angew. Chem.*, **50**, 691 (1937).
110. Sensel, E. E. (The Texas Co.), U.S. Patent 2,841,471, 1958.
111. Singer, F., Thesis, Techn. Hochschule, Berlin, 1910.
112. Slabaugh, W. H., *J. Am. Chem. Soc.*, **74**, 4462 (1952); *J. Phys. Chem.*, **58**, 162 (1954).
113. Smit, P. ("Activit" N.V.), U.S. Patent 2,191,063, 1940.
114. Smit, P. ("Activit" N.V.), Holl. Patent 75,953, 1954.
115. Smith, M. C., *Water Works Eng.*, **90**, 1600 (1937).
116. Socony-Vacuum Oil Co., Ger. Patent 896,189, 1953.
117. Sollner, K., I. Abrams, and C. W. Carr, *J. Gen. Physiol.*, **25**, 7 (1941).
118. Specker, H., and H. Hartkamp, *Z. anal. Chem.*, **140**, 167 (1953).
119. Staatsmijnen in Limburg, Directie van de, Brit. Patents 678,486, 1952; 695,232, 1953.
120. Stach, H., Ger. Patent 752,369, 1951.
121. Stach, H., GDCh Hauptvers. Hamburg, 1953; *Angew. Chem.*, **65**, 564 (1953).
*122. Stach, H., in Ullmann's Encyklopädie der technischen Chemie, vol. 8, p. 804, Urban & Schwarzenberg, Munich-Berlin, 1957.
123. Standard Oil Co., Ger. Patent 900,812, 1953.

---

* Reviews are marked with asterisks.

124. Stout, P. R., *Proc. Soil Sci. Soc. Am.*, **4,** 177 (1939).

125. Tiger, H. L., and P. C. Goetz (Permutit Co.), U.S. Patent 2,069,564, 1937.

126. Umland, F., *Z. Elektrochem.*, **60,** 711 (1956).

127. United Water Softeners Ltd., Brit. Patent 450,574, 1936.

*128. Walton, H. F., *J. Franklin Inst.*, **232,** 305 (1941).

129. Wayne Tank & Pump Co., Ger. Patent 416,543, 1925.

130. Wiegner, G., *J. Landwitsch.*, **60,** 111, 197 (1912).

131. Wiegner, G., *Trans. Soc. Chem. Ind.*, **50,** 65T (1931).

132. Wright, M. L., *Trans. Faraday Soc.*, **49,** 95 (1953); **50,** 89 (1954).

133. *Chem. Eng. News*, Jan. 25, 1960, part 2, p. 66.

* Reviews are marked with asterisks.

3

Preparation

The first synthetic ion exchangers, inorganic alumosilicates, were prepared more than half a century ago. Much effort has since been invested in developing ion exchangers of similar and different types. Today, synthetic organic resins have become the most efficient and most widely used ion exchangers. A great variety of such resins with different properties are available or have been described in the literature. This chapter deals almost exclusively with organic resins; the preparation of other types of ion exchangers has been outlined in the previous chapter.

Table 3-1. Trade names and manufacturers of ion-exchange resins

Trade name	Manufacturer
Amberlite	Rohm & Haas Co., Philadelphia, Pa.
De-Acidite	The Permutit Co., Ltd., London, England
Dowex	Dow Chemical Co., Midland, Mich.
Duolite	Chemical Process Co., Redwood City, Calif.
Imac	Industrieele Mij. Activit N.V., Amsterdam, Netherlands
Ionac*	Ionac Co. Ltd., New York, N.Y.
Lewatit	Farbenfabriken Bayer, Leverkusen, Germany (West)
Nalcite†	National Aluminate Corp., Chicago, Ill.
Permutit	Permutit Co., New York, N.Y.
	Permutit A. G., Berlin-Schmargendorf, Germany (West)
Permutite	Phillips & Pain-Vermorel, Paris, France
Resex, Resanex	Jos. Crosfield & Sons Ltd., Warrington, Lancs., England
Wofatit	VEB Farbenfabrik Wolfen, Wolfen, Kr.Bitterfeld, Germany (East)
Zeo-Karb	The Permutit Co. Ltd., London, England
Zerolit‡	United Water Softeners, London, England

* Product of Permutit Co., marketed by Ionac Co.

† Product of Dow Chemical Co., marketed by Nat. Aluminate Corp. There is no difference between corresponding Dowex and Nalcite resins.

‡ Product of Permutit Co. Ltd., marketed by United Water Softners.

Ion-exchange resins can be obtained from various companies. The largest manufacturing companies and the trade names of their resins are listed in Table 3-1. (The trade names do *not* designate specific types of resins.)

The preparation of high-performance ion exchangers is no simple matter. Even the duplication of syntheses which are described in the scientific and patent literature requires experience and know-how. Therefore, most companies and laboratories prefer to buy ion exchangers ready-made instead of preparing their own. For these reasons, no experimental details will be given. This chapter is not intended to serve as a "cookbook" but, rather, to make the reader acquainted with the principles of different syntheses. A guide of this sort will be useful to the chemist who is faced with the problem of preparing his own resin for specific purposes. The physical chemist may skip this chapter without loss in continuity.

The chemical structures shown in this chapter are hypothetical. As yet, the resin structures have not been exhaustively established by degradative or other classical methods. Furthermore, the structures of the polymers do not represent repeating identical units since the sequence of the monomeric components in the copolymers is essentially random.

3-1. PRINCIPLES

The synthesis of an ion-exchange resin must yield a three-dimensional, crosslinked matrix of hydrocarbon chains carrying fixed ionic groups. This can be achieved by various methods. Monomeric organic electrolytes can be polymerized in such a way that a crosslinked network is formed. As an alternative, the matrix can be built from nonionic monomers; the fixed ionic groups are then introduced into the completed network. It is also possible to introduce ionic groups while the polymerization is still in progress.

The resin should be insoluble, but able to swell to a limited extent. This requires a proper adjustment of the degree of crosslinking. Linear, noncrosslinked polyelectrolytes are soluble. On the other hand, polymers which are too highly crosslinked cannot swell. The mobility of the counter ions in such resin is so low that ion exchange no longer occurs. Hence, the polymerization must be carried out in such a way that crosslinks are formed at appropriate intervals. Two examples may serve to illustrate this point.

1. Polycondensation of *p*-substituted phenol with formaldehyde yields linear polymers

$$\text{(3-1)}$$

No crosslinking occurs because the para position (to the OH group) is occupied and the meta position is inaccessible to the aldehyde. However, if unsubstituted phenol is added, a crosslinked polymer may be obtained

$$(3\text{-}2)$$

The degree of crosslinking can be adjusted by varying the content of phenol (and excess formaldehyde) in the reaction mixture.

2. Polymerization of styrene yields linear polystyrene

$$(3\text{-}3)$$

However, if divinylbenzene is added, a crosslinked matrix is obtained [199]

$$(3\text{-}4)$$

The degree of crosslinking can be adjusted by varying the divinylbenzene content of the reaction mixture.

In the polycondensation process, the incorporation of a trifunctional molecule (unsubstituted phenol) results in a branching of the chain. In the addition polymerization, the incorporation of a molecule with two unsaturated groups (divinylbenzene) results in the formation of a link between two chains.

Actually, it is only in the case of addition polymerization that the degree of crosslinking can be adjusted as easily as the equations given above seem to indicate. This is one of the advantages of addition polymerization. Polycondensation is a much more complex process. Here, the structure of the products depends not only on the composition of the reaction mixture, but also on the experimental conditions such as reaction time, temperature, etc.

With the reactions (3-2) and (3-4) crosslinked matrices have been formed. The remaining task is to introduce fixed ionic groups. This can be achieved by substitution during or after polymerization, or by starting out from monomers which carry ionic groups.

The specific examples given in the following sections will show that, indeed, most ion-exchange resins are prepared according to one of the two methods indicated above. The more recent addition polymers have almost completely replaced the earlier condensation polymers.

3-2. CATION EXCHANGERS

The condensation product of phenol and formaldehyde [reaction (3-2)] is a cation exchanger, though an extremely weak one (the dissociation constant of the phenolic OH groups is about $1.3 \cdot 10^{-10}$ mole/liter). As an ion exchanger it has no practical importance. However, the discovery of its ion-exchange properties by Adams and Holmes [4], in 1935, led to the synthesis of the first high-performance ion-exchange resins. The two English chemists recognized and solved the problem of introducing more efficient fixed ionic groups, i.e., anionic and cationic groups with higher acid and base strengths.

Today, a broad scale of cation exchangers with fixed ionic groups of different character and different acid strength are available. The most common products are strong-acid resins with sulfonic acid groups and weak-acid resins with carboxylic acid groups

$$-SO_3^- \quad \text{and} \quad -COO^-$$

Even with only these two groups, resins of various acid strengths can be made since the dissociation constants are affected by the nature and configuration of the units to which the groups are attached. For example, arylsulfonic acids are stronger than alkylsulfonic acids. Recently, other cation exchangers with different properties and acid strengths have been developed. These resins carry phosphonic, phosphinic, arsonic, and selenonic acid groups:

$$-PO_3^{2-} \quad -HPO_2^- \quad -AsO_3^{2-} \quad -SeO_3^-$$

Many ion-exchange resins contain two or more different types of fixed ionic groups. Such resins are called "bifunctional" or "polyfunctional."

Furthermore, resins carrying ionic groups with high selectivities for certain counter ions have been prepared. These materials will be discussed in Sec. 3-2c.

a. Condensation Polymers

The earliest cation-exchange resin was a condensation product of phenol and formaldehyde [4,5]. Other monovalent or polyvalent phenols [4,5,209, 210], e.g., resorcinol and naphthol or natural tannins [4,173] with phenolic groups can be used instead of phenol, and other aldehydes instead of formaldehyde. Only the phenolic OH groups can act as fixed ionic groups. Accordingly, the resins have a very low acid strength.

Groups with higher acid strength can be introduced by various methods. The simplest method is *sulfonation* of the phenol prior to polymerization [72,123,130,157,173,209]

$$ (3\text{-}5) $$

The phenolsulfonic acid can be polymerized without being isolated from the sulfonation mixture [130,209]. It is true that sulfonation gives predominantly *p*-sulfonic acid. Nevertheless, highly crosslinked products can be obtained by allowing sufficient time for the polymerization. The mechanism of this crosslinking is not altogether clear. Most likely sulfone bridges are formed, or phenolsulfonic acid is partially hydrolyzed by formaldehyde [113a].

Alternatively, the polymerization can be performed in alkaline solution [123,130,157, 173]. In this case, unsubstituted phenol is added to obtain the desired degree of crosslinking [see reaction (3-2)].

Phenolsulfonic acid resins are easily prepared even with simple laboratory equipment. They are bifunctional since they contain both strong-acid sulfonic and weak-acid phenolic groups. Amberlite IR-100 and Dowex 30 were resins of this type. They are no longer available.

Dihydroxynaphthalenedisulfonic acid [73] and similar compounds have been used instead of phenolsulfonic acid, and other aldehydes have been used instead of formaldehyde. Because of their phenolic groups, the resins are only moderately resistant to alkali and dissolved oxygen. Resins with improved chemical stability are obtained by using phenol ethers such as anisole instead of phenol [79,94]. These resins have the additional advantage of being monofunctional.

When used in H$^+$ form at temperatures above 60°C, the resins may lose sulfonic acid groups by thermal hydrolysis. Other cationic forms are more stable.

Weak-acid resins with *carboxylic groups* can be prepared by a similar method. Suitable monomers are salicylic acid [164,205] and 1,3,5-resorcylic acid [11,110]

$$\text{(phenol-COOH)} + \text{(phenol)} \xrightarrow{\text{H}_2\text{CO}} \cdots \qquad (3\text{-}6)$$

$$\text{(HO-phenol-COOH)} \xrightarrow{\text{H}_2\text{CO}} \cdots \qquad (3\text{-}7)$$

In the second example no phenol is required because all ortho and para positions of the phenolic component are accessible to the aldehyde. Wofatit C (no longer available) was a resin of this type.

The resins described so far contain fixed ionic groups directly attached to aromatic rings. Resins carrying fixed ionic groups on side chains can also be made.

The alkaline condensation of phenolate, sodium sulfite, and formaldehyde yields a resin with *methylenesulfonic acid groups* [10,100,108,137]

$$\text{(phenolate)}, \ \text{Na}_2\text{SO}_3 \xrightarrow{\text{H}_2\text{CO}} \cdots \qquad (3\text{-}8)$$

This resin has a somewhat weaker acidity, but a higher thermal stability than the phenolsulfonic resins.

Wofatit P and Amberlite IR-1 (no longer available) were resins of this type.

Weak-acid resins which carry carboxylic acid groups on side chains have been prepared from *phenoxyacetic acid* [7,13,75,76,119] and similar compounds [75,76,201]

$$(3\text{-}9)$$

As a rule, unsubstituted phenol is added to enhance polymerization. Instead of phenol, other materials such as resorcinol may be used [76]. In this case, the first step of reaction (3-9) leads to resorcinol-mono-O-acetic acid or, with excess of chloroacetic acid, to resorcinol-di-O-acetic acid

In this way it is possible to introduce two ionic groups per aromatic ring. Resins of this type have a slightly higher acid strength than those with carboxyl groups attached directly to the aromatic rings. Lewatit CNO is a resin of this type.

Recently, the preparation of condensation polymers with *phosphonic acid groups* has been described [208]:

$$PCl_3 \xrightarrow[205°C]{H_2CO} Cl\!-\!CH_2\!-\!POCl_2 \xrightarrow{NaOH} Cl\!-\!CH_2\!-\!PO_3^{2-}(Na^+)_2$$

$$(3\text{-}10)$$

Substituted phenols can be used instead of phenol. The polycondensation can also be carried out in alkaline medium. The resins are of medium acid strength.

Duolite C-65 is a phenolic resin with phosphonic acid groups.

Likewise, resins with *arsonic acid groups* can be prepared by condensation of substituted phenols with aldehydes [40,42,204], for example:

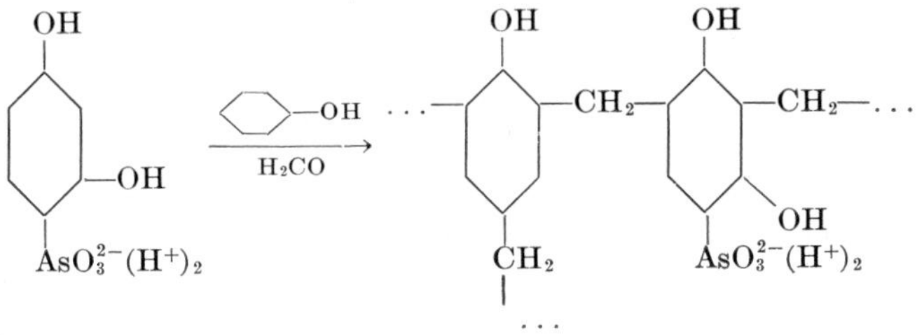

$$(3\text{-}11)$$

In the syntheses mentioned so far, the ionic groups are introduced into the phenolic component. Instead, the aldehyde can be used as the carrier. In particular, *benzaldehyde-2,4-disulfonic acid* has proved to be useful [209]. Condensation with phenols and formaldehyde yields products of about the following structure:

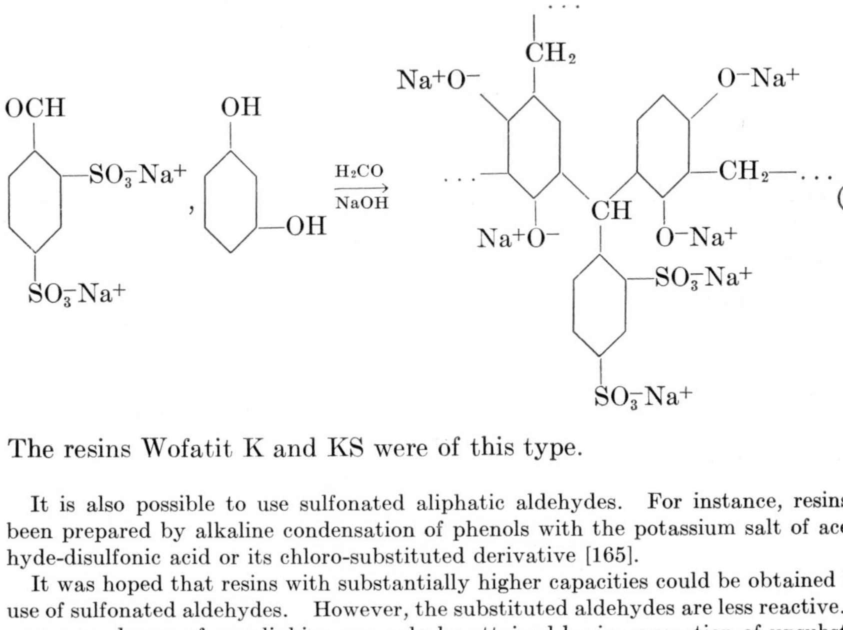

$$(3\text{-}12)$$

The resins Wofatit K and KS were of this type.

It is also possible to use sulfonated aliphatic aldehydes. For instance, resins have been prepared by alkaline condensation of phenols with the potassium salt of acetaldehyde-disulfonic acid or its chloro-substituted derivative [165].

It was hoped that resins with substantially higher capacities could be obtained by the use of sulfonated aldehydes. However, the substituted aldehydes are less reactive. The necessary degree of crosslinking can only be attained by incorporation of unsubstituted phenols. Thus the gain in capacity is almost nullified.

Ionic groups can also be introduced after polymerization. Condensation polymers with arylsulfonic acids groups have been prepared by sulfonation of phenolic resins [109, 122] and various Friedel-Crafts condensation products [77,161]. Carboxylic acid groups have been introduced into phenolic resins by heating with bicarbonate and carbon dioxide under pressure [111] and by treatment with chloroacetic acid [7,119]; see reaction (3-9).

The resins mentioned so far either are monofunctional or contain additional phenolic groups which are inactive except at very high pH. However, *bifunctional resins* containing both sulfonic and carboxylic acid groups have also been prepared. They are readily obtained by condensation of appropriate monomers [93,95], for example,

$$(3\text{-}13)$$

A resin of this type is Lewatit CNS.

Occasionally, polycondensation is carried out in the presence of substances such as polyalcohols [39] or phenol ethers which are incorporated into the matrix and affect the behavior of the resin. For example, phenolic resins can be made to swell more strongly, and the volume change which accompanies conversion of weak-acid resins from the H^+ form to other forms can be reduced.

Recently, cation exchangers with *silicone framework* have been described. For example, an ion exchanger of this type can be prepared by formation of a mixed gel from benzyltriolsilane-*p*-sulfonic acid

and silicic acid [185]. It is claimed that these products have a higher thermal stability than the conventional organic resins.

b. Addition Polymers

Most of the present ion-exchange resins are addition copolymers prepared from vinyl monomers. These polymers have a higher chemical and thermal stability than their forerunners, the condensation polymers. Also, addition polymerization has the advantage that the degree of crosslinking and the particle size of the resins are more readily adjusted.

The most important resins of this type are *crosslinked polystyrenes with sulfonic acid groups* which have been introduced after polymerization by treatment with concentrated sulfuric acid or chlorosulfonic acid [1,2,22,48, 51–53,169,213]. As a rule, divinylbenzene is used as the crosslinking agent

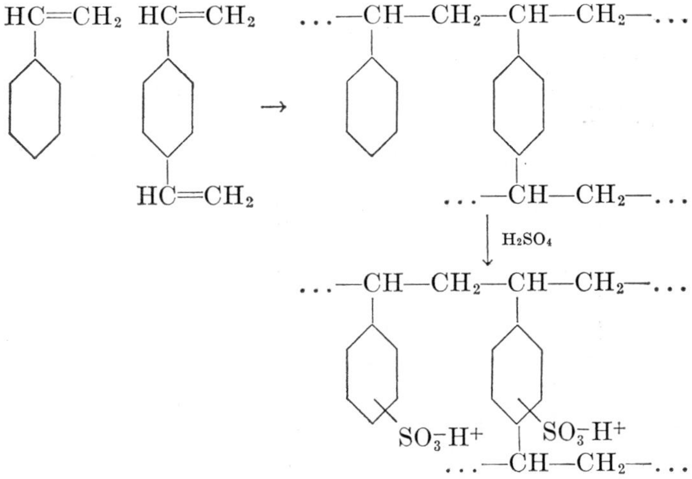

$$
HC{=}CH_2 \quad HC{=}CH_2 \qquad \ldots{-}CH{-}CH_2{-}CH{-}CH_2{-}\ldots
$$

$$(3\text{-}14)$$

Amberlite IR-120, Dowex 50, Nalcite HCR, Permutit Q, Duolite C-20 and C-25, and Lewatit S-100 are resins of this type.

Pure divinylbenzene is not readily accessible. Hence the resins are prepared with a commercial product consisting of a mixture of the different divinylbenzene isomers (about 40 to 55 per cent) and ethylstyrene (about 45 to 60 per cent). Ethylstyrene is also incorporated into the matrix.

By varying the divinylbenzene content, the degree of crosslinking can be adjusted in a simple and reproducible manner. The *nominal DVB content* is used to indicate the degree of crosslinking; it refers to mole per cent of pure divinylbenzene (not of the commercial product) in the polymerization mixture. General-purpose ion exchangers contain between 8 and 12 per cent DVB. For special purposes, resins with as little as 0.25 per cent DVB and as much as 25 per cent DVB have been prepared. Resins with low DVB content swell strongly and are soft and gelatinous. Resins with very high DVB content can swell hardly at all and are tough and mechanically more stable.

The copolymer beads are prepared by the so-called *pearl polymerization* technique [99,222]. The monomers (from which polymerization inhibitors have been removed) are mixed, and a polymerization catalyst such as benzoyl peroxide is added. The mixture is then added to a thoroughly agitated aqueous solution which is kept at the temperature required for polymerization (usually 85 to 100°C). The mixture forms small droplets which remain suspended. A suspension stabilizer (gelatin, polyvinyl-alcohol, sodium oleate, sodium methacrylate, magnesium silicate, etc.) in the aqueous phase prevents agglomeration of the droplets. The size of the droplets depends chiefly on the nature of the suspension stabilizer, the viscosity of the solution, and the agitation, and can be varied within wide limits. The polymer is obtained in the form of fairly uniform spherical beads (see Fig. 3-1). For most purposes, a bead size of 0.1 to 0.5 mm is preferred, but beads from 1 μ to 2 mm in diameter can be prepared without major difficulties. A simple laboratory setup for pearl polymerization is shown in Fig. 3-2.

FIG. 3-1. Styrene-divinylbenzene pearl polymer. (*Microphotography, enlargement* 1:25. *From Ullmann's Encyklopädie der technischen Chemie, 3d ed., vol. 8, p. 808, Urban & Schwarzenberg, Munich-Berlin, 1957.*)

It is possible to use partially prepolymerized instead of monomeric styrene. It seems that beads prepared in this way are mechanically more resistant, but are less homogeneous.

The polymerization can be carried out in such a way that so-called "popcorn" polymers are obtained [22,103]. These are spongy products of very high porosity and large surface area. Popcorn polymers tend to form when small resin particles, which act as polymerization seeds, are added to the reaction mixture.

The *sulfonation* of the resins presents no problems if proper precautions are taken. Sulfonation progresses from the outer shells toward the center of the particles and is accompanied by considerable swelling and evolution of heat. The matrix is strained rather severely, and the beads may crack. Such disintegration can be avoided by letting the beads swell, prior to sulfonation, in solvents such as toluene, nitrobenzene, methylenechloride, or trichloroethane [27,213]. Similar strains develop when the sulfonated beads are transferred into a dilute aqueous solution or pure water. Therefore it is advisable to transfer the beads at first into a highly concentrated

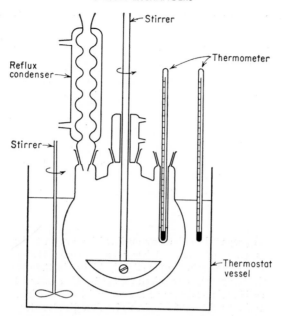

Fig. 3-2. Simple laboratory setup for pearl polymerization.

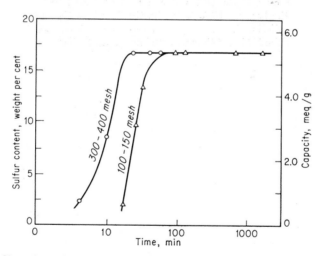

Fig. 3-3. Sulfonation of crosslinked polystyrene. The sulfur content and the ion-exchange capacity of the (washed and dried) product are shown as a function of sulfonation time for two different particle sizes. Both curves reach the same final value which corresponds to complete monosubstitution of all benzene rings. Conditions: resin with 5 per cent DVB; sulfonation with concentrated sulfuric acid at 100°C. *From K. W. Pepper* [169].

electrolyte solution which causes less swelling (see Sec. 5-2) and then to dilute the solution stepwise [213].

Sulfonation with concentrated sulfuric acid or chlorosulfonic acid results in practically complete monosulfonation of all benzene rings including those of the divinylbenzene and ethylstyrene components, provided that sufficient time for the reaction is allowed; double substitution does not occur under the usual conditions. These conclusions are based on chemical analyses which show that the reaction stops when, on the average, one group is introduced per benzene ring [169]; see Fig. 3-3. Also, it has been shown that sulfonation of (soluble) linear polystyrene and polymerization of pure p-styrenesulfonic acid give products with identical infrared spectra [96a]. This is additional evidence for complete and exclusive monosulfonation, preferably in the para position.

Ion-exchange resins prepared in the way outlined here seem to be neither completely uniform nor strictly monofunctional. It has been presumed that pearl polymerization leads to beads in which the crosslinking is slightly higher in the outer shells than in the center and that at the temperature required for sulfonation (about 100°C at least in the initial stage) a few carboxylic acid groups are formed by oxidation. As claimed by its manufacturers, the resin Duolite C-25 is free of these disadvantages [1]. The resin is supposedly uniform in crosslinking and more porous than the usual styrene-divinyl-benzene copolymers of equal DVB content. It can be sulfonated at a somewhat lower temperature (85°C) by sulfuric acid and can be transferred immediately into water without damage to the beads. Unfortunately, the details of the preparation procedure have so far not been disclosed.

A number of other similar ion exchangers are known in which styrene has been replaced by one of its derivatives such as methylstyrene, vinylanisole [103], or phenylacetylene [52]. Likewise, divinylbenzene may be replaced by another crosslinking agent with at least two unsaturated groups, for example, divinylacetylene [51] or butadiene [103].

The ion-exchange capacity of the resins is not quite so readily varied as the degree of crosslinking. Incomplete sulfonation leads to products which are not uniform and tend to crack. However, it is possible to incorporate styrene derivatives such as 2,5-dichloro-styrene which are sulfonated much more slowly than styrene itself. Thus the capacity can be adjusted by varying the 2,5-dichlorostyrene content [80]. Another method which is based on a quite different preparation procedure will be discussed later (see page 40).

"Flash sulfonation" (i.e., short exposure to sulfuric or chlorosulfonic acid) and sulfonation with sulfur trioxide [96] lead to resins which carry sulfonic acid groups at the particle surfaces only. Such resin have been used for special purposes.

Sulfonation is the least expensive but by no means the only way of introducing fixed ionic groups into crosslinked polystyrene. Recently, several styrene-type cation exchangers with *phosphinic, phosphonic,* and *arsonic acid groups* have been described.

Phosphorus trichloride can be condensed with the benzene rings in the presence of a Friedel-Crafts catalyst. *Phosphinic acid groups* are formed by hydrolysis under mild conditions [126] and *phosphonic acid groups* by oxidation with chlorine prior to hydrolysis [3,40,151] or with nitric acid after hydrolysis (crosslinking is not shown) [126].

...—CH—CH$_2$—...   ...—CH—CH$_2$—...   ...—CH—CH$_2$—...

$$\xrightarrow[\text{AlCl}_3]{\text{PCl}_3} \quad \text{PCl}_2 \qquad \xrightarrow{\text{H}_2\text{O}} \quad \text{HPO}_3^-\text{H}^+$$

$\downarrow$ Cl$_2$ $\qquad$ $\downarrow$ HNO$_3$ $\qquad$ (3-15)

...—CH—CH$_2$—...   ...—CH—CH$_2$—...

PCl$_4$ $\qquad\xrightarrow{\text{H}_2\text{O}}\qquad$ PO$_3^{2-}$(H$^+$)$_2$

The resins Duolite C-62 (phosphinic groups) and C-63 (phosphonic groups) are of this type.

Phosphorus thiochloride, PSCl$_3$, may be used instead of phosphorus trichloride. In this case, *thiophosphonic acid groups*, —PSO$_2^{2-}$(H$^+$)$_2$, are formed [152].

Resins with methylenephosphinic acid groups have also been prepared. Here, cross-linked polystyrene is chloromethylated (see page 52), treated with phosphite esters, and hydrolyzed [41,65,127,150].

Bifunctional resins containing both phosphonic and sulfonic acid groups have been obtained by sulfonation of phosphonic acid resins [126,150,151].

The introduction of *arsonic acid groups* is somewhat cumbersome. So far, only one preparation method has been described (crosslinking is not shown) [40,204]:

...—CH—CH$_2$—...   ...—CH—CH$_2$—...

$$\xrightarrow[\text{AlCl}_3]{\text{ClCO}-\langle\;\rangle-\text{AsCl}_2}$$

CO—$\langle\;\rangle$—AsCl$_2$

H$_2$O$_2$ $\Big|$ NaOH $\qquad$ (3-16)

...—CH—CH$_2$—...

CO—$\langle\;\rangle$—AsO$_3^{2-}$(Na$^+$)$_2$

Selenonic acid groups, in contrast to arsonic acid groups, can be introduced directly by treatment with selenic acid [26]. The reaction is carried out in concentrated sulfuric acid with cupric or silver selenide catalysts. The temperature can be kept so low that sulfonation does not occur.

In the syntheses described so far, the ionic groups are introduced *after* polymerization. An interesting alternative is the introduction of the groups into one of the monomers *before* they are polymerized [159,216–221]. Examples are given below.

$$C_2H_5- \bigcirc \xrightarrow{ClSO_3H} C_2H_5- \bigcirc -SO_2Cl$$

$$C_2H_5- \bigcirc -SO_2- \bigcirc -C_2H_5$$

$$\downarrow Br_2/CCl_4 \quad (UV\text{-light})$$

$$BrCH_2CH_2- \bigcirc \xrightarrow{ClSO_3H} BrCH_2CH_2- \bigcirc -SO_2Cl,$$

$$BrCH_2CH_2- \bigcirc -SO_2- \bigcirc -CH_2CH_2Br$$

$$\swarrow NH_3 \qquad KOH \searrow CH_3OH$$

$$BrCH_2CH_2- \bigcirc -SO_2NH_2,$$

$$BrCH_2CH_2- \bigcirc -SO_2- \bigcirc -CH_2CH_2Br$$

$$CH_2{=}CH- \bigcirc -SO_3^-K^+$$

$$KOH \mid C_2H_5OH \qquad\qquad DVB \mid (CH_3)_2NCHO$$

$$\text{(3-17)}$$

$$CH_2{=}CH- \bigcirc -SO_2NH_2,$$

$$CH_2{=}CH- \bigcirc -SO_2- \bigcirc -CH{=}CH_2$$

$$\downarrow (CH_3)_2NCHO$$

$$\xrightarrow[HCl]{NaNO_2}$$

In the preparation of p-sulfonamidostyrene, distyrenesulfone is obtained as by-product [219]. If not isolated, it will act as a crosslinking agent in subsequent polymerization. In contrast, the (purified) potassium p-styrenesulfonate must be crosslinked with divinylbenzene or a similar agent. The polymerization is carried out in dimethyl-formamide, as a rule with styrene added. Instead of the potassium salt, an ester of styrenesulfonic acid can be used [85].

These preparation procedures are more troublesome and far more expensive than sulfonation of crosslinked polystyrene. Furthermore, the capacity of the products is lower because the benzene rings of the crosslinking agent carry no ionic groups. However, ion exchangers prepared in this way have two advantages which may well warrant their use in scientific investigations:

1. The products are strictly monofunctional because they contain exclusively styrene-p-sulfonic acid groups. The danger of oxidative formation of carboxylic acid groups has been eliminated.

2. Not only the degree of crosslinking, but also the capacity can be varied independently by choice of the relative amounts of the three reactants—sulfonated monomer, styrene, and crosslinking agent [218].

The most widely used weak-acid cation exchangers are prepared by a very similar method, i.e., by copolymerization of an organic acid or acid anhydride [46] and a crosslinking agent. As a rule, *acrylic* or *methacrylic acid* [47,74,78,101] is used in combination with divinylbenzene [47], ethylene-dimethacrylate [101], or similar compounds with at least two vinyl groups.

$$
\begin{array}{ccc}
CH_3 & & CH_3 \\
| & DVB & | \\
C{=}CH_2 & \xrightarrow{\quad} & \ldots-C-CH_2-CH-CH_2-\ldots \\
| & & | \\
COOH & & COOH
\end{array}
\qquad (3\text{-}18)
$$

$$\ldots-CH-CH_2-\ldots$$

The pearl polymerization technique (see page 35) can be used if esters instead of the water-soluble acids are polymerized. The esters are hydrolyzed after polymerization [21,60].

Resins of this type are Amberlite IRC-50, Permutit H-70, Duolite CS-101, and Wofatit CP 300.

The capacity of the resins can be varied by incorporating appropriate amounts of non-dissociating vinyl monomers (styrene, etc.) or by partial hydrolysis* of the ester copoly-

---

* In contrast to sulfonation, hydrolysis of small and not too highly crosslinked resin beads can be performed in such a way that the reaction is slow as compared with the

mers [60]. Resins with residual ester groups cannot be exposed to strong acids or bases without change in capacity.

Bifunctional resins containing both sulfonic and carboxylic acid groups can be prepared by sulfonation of acrylic and methacrylic acid polymers [82,83].

Cation-exchange resins can also be prepared from *polyvinylalcohol*. Sulfonation is the most convenient and inexpensive means of introducing fixed ionic groups [43]. Apparently, semiesters are formed:

$$\ldots-\overset{|}{\underset{OH}{C}}H-CH_2-\ldots \quad \xrightarrow{H_2SO_4} \quad \ldots-\overset{|}{\underset{O-SO_3^-H^+}{C}}H-CH_2-\ldots \tag{3-19}$$

Resins of this type, which include the commercial product CFB-P (Chem. Fabrik Budenheim, Germany), have a lower acid strength than other resins with sulfonic acid groups.

Arylsulfonic acid groups can be introduced by condensation of polyvinylalcohol with benzaldehyde and subsequent sulfonation [129].

Polyvinylalcohol can be phosphorylated by reaction with phosphorus oxychloride followed by hydrolysis [12,58], by reaction with phosphoric acid containing excess phosphorus pentachloride [12,58,81], and by treatment with phosphoric acid and urea [58].

$$\tag{3-20}$$

The ionic groups are attached to the matrix by ester links. Crosslinking occurs apparently by formation of di-esters involving two adjacent chains. The soluble linear inter-

---

diffusion of the agent within the bead. Thus the agent is evenly distributed throughout the bead before significant hydrolysis occurs. In this way, rather uniform products can be prepared.

mediate has also been used for introducing ionic groups into cellulose derivatives such as paper and cotton [58].

Polyvinylalcohol has also been condensed with arsenic acid and with boric acid [12].

Resins carrying esters such as —O—SO$_3$H and —O—PO$_3^{2-}$ as fixed ionic groups lose their capacity when exposed to hydrolyzing agents.

c. Specific Cation Exchangers

Even the common general-purpose cation exchangers are somewhat selective; i.e., they prefer certain counter-ion species to others. Many attempts have been made to obtain higher selectivities and to develop resins which prefer one particular (or at least not more than a few) counter-ion species very strongly to all others. Such resins are said to be "specific" for the preferred counter ions.

The basic idea in the development of such resins was this. It was correctly assumed that resins will prefer counter ions which tend to associate with the fixed ionic groups or with components of the matrix. A cation which forms strong complexes with, or is precipitated by, a certain reagent should thus be preferred by a resin into which this reagent has been incorporated (see also page 162). The behavior of weak-acid resins confirms the validity of this conclusion. Anions of weak acids, by definition, tend to associate with H$^+$ ions, forming weakly dissociated complexes or precipitates; resins with weak-acid groups, in fact, have a marked preference for H$^+$ ions.

The first attempt to put this idea into practice was made by Skogseid [189]. He synthesized a resin containing groups with a configuration similar to that of *dipicrylamine:*

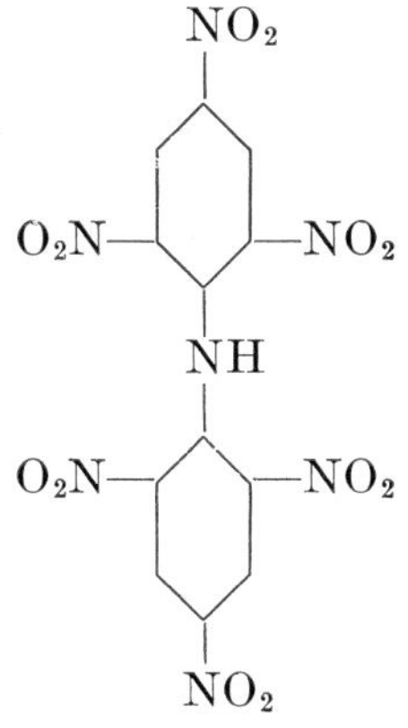

Dipicrylamine is known to be a specific precipitating agent for K$^+$ ions. The affinity of the resin for K$^+$ ions is, indeed, considerably greater than that of other cation-exchange resins (see also page 162).

The resin was prepared from polystyrene by nitration, reduction, condensation with picrylchloride, and renewed nitration:

$$(3\text{-}21)$$

The product has a very low acid strength.

Many compounds which form *chelates* with metal cations have been incorporated into resins by polycondensation with phenols and aldehydes. Examples are: anthranilic acid [86,114] (specific for zinc and other transition metal ions),

$$(3\text{-}22)$$

o-aminophenol [86,168], anthranilic acid-diacetic acid [20], m-phenylene-diglycine [86], and m-phenylenediaminetetraacetic acid [20]

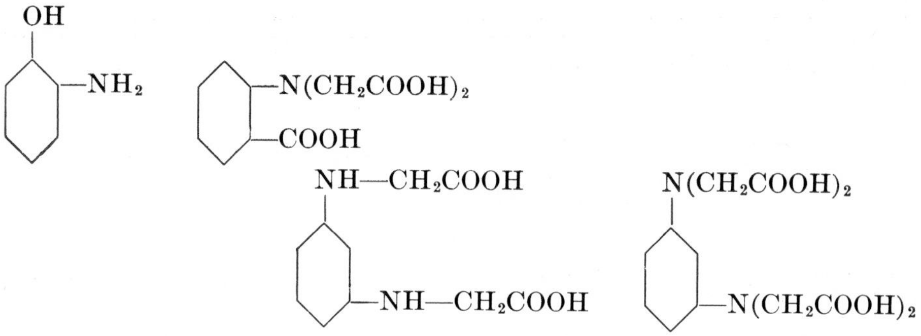

$$OH$$

[chemical structures]

—NH$_2$ —N(CH$_2$COOH)$_2$
            —COOH

NH—CH$_2$COOH   N(CH$_2$COOH)$_2$

—NH—CH$_2$COOH   —N(CH$_2$COOH)$_2$

The latter three compounds can be prepared from chloroacetic acid and anthranilic acid or *m*-phenylenediamine. Many resins with other chelating groups have been described [188a].

Chelating agents can also be introduced into styrene-type resins. Ion exchangers of this type are mechanically and chemically more stable than the condensation polymers. Various methods of preparing resins with *iminodiacetic acid groups* are given as examples [171] (crosslinking is not shown).

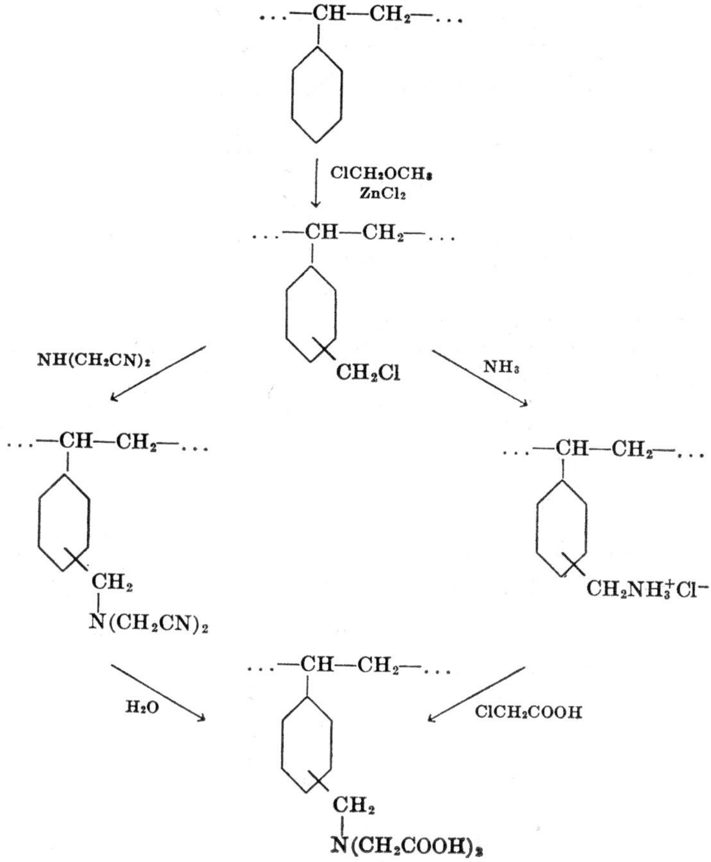

$$\cdots-CH-CH_2-\cdots$$

ClCH$_2$OCH$_3$
ZnCl$_2$

$$\cdots-CH-CH_2-\cdots$$

CH$_2$Cl

NH(CH$_2$CN)$_2$ NH$_3$

$$\cdots-CH-CH_2-\cdots$$

CH$_2$
N(CH$_2$CN)$_2$

$$\cdots-CH-CH_2-\cdots$$

CH$_2$NH$_3^+$Cl$^-$

H$_2$O   ClCH$_2$COOH   (3-23)

$$\cdots-CH-CH_2-\cdots$$

CH$_2$
N(CH$_2$COOH)$_2$

Alternatively, the iminodiacetic acid group can be introduced into monomeric styrene which is then copolymerized with divinylbenzene or a crosslinking agent such as

$$CH_2{=}CH{-}\hexagon{-}\underset{\underset{CH_2COOH}{|}}{CH_2{-}N{-}CH_2}{-}\hexagon{-}CH{=}CH_2$$

The latter can be prepared from chloromethylated styrene and glycine
[158,160].

The first steps of the syntheses—chloromethylation and amination—are
discussed in more detail in Sec. 3-3b.

In their complexing tendency the resins are similar to ethylenediaminetetraacetic acid (EDTA).

A resin with iminodiacetic acid groups, Dowex A-1, has recently become
commercially available.

Many other specific resins have been prepared. Only a few examples can be given.
Hydroxamic acid groups have been introduced into a resin with carboxylic acid groups
(crosslinking is not shown) [44,45]:

$$(3\text{-}24)$$

This resin is specific for Fe^{3+} ions. Resins with *mercapto groups* (preparation on page
555) prefer Hg^{2+} ions [32,88]. A resin with *chromotropic acid groups* preferring Ti^{4+} has
been made [121]. Agents such as *β-naphthol* have been introduced by coupling with
diazotized resins [87,166]; see reaction (12-2), page 554. Resins containing *chlorophyll*
and *haemin derivatives* or similar compounds form extremely strong chelates with ions
such as Fe^{3+} [30,132]. In fact, the chelated counter ions are held so strongly that they
can hardly be exchanged. However, such resins can act as redox ion exchangers (see
page 555).

Cation exchangers with *optically active groups* have been prepared by condensation of
D- and L-*β-(p-oxyphenyl)-butyric acid* and of N-*p-toluylsulfonyl-L-tyrosine* with formaldehyde [31].

$$HO{-}\hexagon{-}\underset{\underset{CH_3}{|}}{CH}{-}CH_2{-}COOH,$$

$$HO{-}\hexagon{-}CH_2{-}\underset{\underset{NH{-}SO_2{-}\hexagon{-}CH_3}{|}}{CH}{-}COOH$$

Racemization of the groups can be avoided. However, attempts to use such resins for separating amine racemates have been unsuccessful.*

One unattractive feature is common to all specific ion exchangers. The desired strong affinity for a certain counter ion is attained by introducing groups with which the counter ion tends to associate. An undesired consequence of such an association is that the mobility of the counter ion in the resin is greatly reduced. The gain in selectivity must be paid for by a loss in ion-exchange rate. This effect is observed even with the common weak-acid resins which exchange H^+ ions at a considerably lower rate than the strong-acid resins. Also, resins with extreme specificity are difficult to regenerate (except when the preferred counter ion is readily displaced by H^+) and may even hold chelated counter ions so obstinately that ion exchange no longer occurs. Hence, for any application one should choose the resin carefully, seeking a reasonable compromise between selectivity, ease of regeneration, and rate of ion exchange.

3-3. ANION EXCHANGERS

Anion exchange was developed almost exclusively with synthetic organic resins. No anion exchangers with satisfactory properties were available before anion-exchange resins were invented. Since that day, the superiority of the resins has never been challenged.

The first organic anion exchangers were among the earliest ion exchange resins. The first patents by Adams and Holmes described not only cation exchangers, but also anion exchangers with weak-base amino groups [6]

$$-NH_3^+ \qquad \diagdown NH_2^+$$

Later, resins with strong-base quaternary ammonium groups were prepared:

$$-N^+- \qquad -N^+(CH_3)_3, \text{ etc.}$$

The most recent anion exchangers include resins with strong-base quaternary phosphonium groups and tertiary sulfonium groups:

$$-P^+- \qquad \diagdown S^+-$$

---

* Anion exchangers with optically active groups gave better results; see p. 57.

The earlier ion-exchange resins were condensation polymers. These resins have been almost completely replaced by the more stable addition polymers. This is true for anion exchangers as well as for cation exchangers. However, even the best strong-base addition polymers prepared so far cannot compete with the cation exchangers with respect to chemical and thermal stability and useful resin life. A remedy is difficult to find because the potential ionic groups are inherently less stable. In view of this lack of stability, it is not surprising that undesired side reactions in the course of the preparation are often encountered. In most cases, the syntheses are not as simple as the reaction patterns given in the following may seem to indicate. Nevertheless, anion exchange, in former times a somewhat neglected stepchild, has lately received much more attention.

a. Condensation Polymers

The first anion-exchange resins were prepared from *aromatic amines* such as *m*-phenylenediamine by condensation with formaldehyde [6,120,178,206].

$$(3\text{-}25)$$

The aldehyde reacts with the amino groups. Secondary and even tertiary amino groups are formed, and the resins thus are polyfunctional. Not only the degree of crosslinking but also the base strength of the resin depend on the relative amount of formaldehyde used.

Amino groups which are directly attached to benzene rings are very weakly basic. The base strength of the resins can be enhanced by alkylation, for example, with dimethylsulfate [106,155].

$$(3\text{-}26)$$

The aldehyde can be partly or completely replaced by saccharides which also react with the amino groups. The presence of hydroxyl groups improves the swelling properties of the resin [178,206].

Aliphatic polyamines, which have the advantage of being not quite so weakly basic as the aromatic amines, can also be condensed with aldehydes [29,71,180,202,215]. Tetraethylenepentamine,

$$NH_2—C_2H_4—NH—C_2H_4—NH—C_2H_4—NH—C_2H_4—NH_2$$

has been used extensively. As a rule, a phenol or aromatic amine is added to facilitate the condensation [71,215]. A resin prepared from diethylene-triamine, phenol, and formaldehyde may have a structure such as

$$\cdots—\overset{\displaystyle OH}{\underset{\displaystyle \overset{|}{CH_2}}{\bigcirc}}—CH_2—NH—C_2H_4—NH—C_2H_4—\overset{}{\underset{\displaystyle \overset{|}{CH_2}}{N}}—CH_2—\overset{\displaystyle OH}{\bigcirc}—CH_2—\cdots$$

Other agents which can be used instead of, or in addition to, the aldehyde are polyhaloparaffins [91,107,124] such as dichloroethane, and α-halo-β-γ-epoxides such as epichlorohydrin [8,28,67,68,135,136,139,174,200]. Condensation takes place by reactions such as

$$—NH_2 + ClCH_2CH_2Cl + H_2N\diagup \rightarrow —NH_3^+—CH_2CH_2—N\overset{+}{H}\diagup + 2Cl^-$$

$$(3-27)$$

$$—NH_2 + ClCH_2—\underset{\diagdown O\diagup}{CH_2—CH_2} + HN\diagup \rightarrow$$

$$—NH_3^+—CH_2—\underset{\displaystyle \overset{|}{OH}}{CH}—CH_2—N\diagup + Cl^- \quad (3-28)$$

The haloepoxides are particularly strong condensing agents and react even with tertiary amino groups. Thus resins with strong-base quaternary ammonium groups can be obtained. Condensation products of polyethyleneimine and epichlorohydrin are readily prepared even with simple laboratory equipment [139]. These resins have structures such as

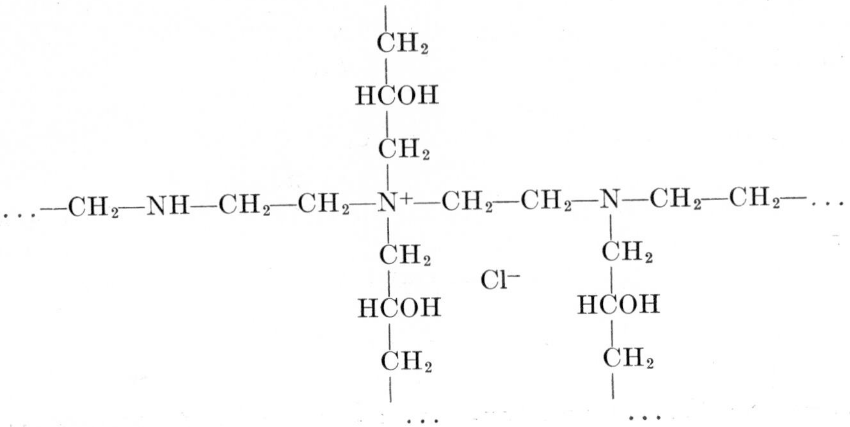

$$
\begin{array}{ccc}
& CH_2 & \\
& | & \\
& HCOH & \\
& | & \\
& CH_2 & \\
& | & \\
\cdots -CH_2-NH-CH_2-CH_2-N^+-CH_2-CH_2-N-CH_2-CH_2-\cdots & \\
& | \qquad\qquad\quad | & \\
& CH_2 \qquad\qquad CH_2 & \\
& | \quad Cl^- \quad | & \\
& HCOH \qquad\qquad HCOH & \\
& | \qquad\qquad\quad | & \\
& CH_2 \qquad\qquad CH_2 & \\
& | \qquad\qquad\quad | & \\
& \cdots \qquad\qquad\quad \cdots &
\end{array}
$$

All these resins are polyfunctional.

A large number of modified amine resins have been prepared by adding substances such as furfural [202], α-β-unsaturated ketones [124,175], or saccharides [202] to the condensation mixture.

Basic condensation polymers have also been prepared with *ammonia* or *ammonium salts*. Anhydrous ammonia can be condensed under pressure with dihaloparaffins or with epichlorohydrin [70,117]. Condensation of phenol and formaldehyde in the presence of ammonium sulfate gives an anion-exchange resin [18].

Many other condensation polymers with anion-exchange properties have been made. The syntheses include condensation of heterocyclic nitrogen compounds such as pyridine with haloepoxides [174]; condensation of urea and urea derivatives with aldehydes [9,15,66,116,131,138,176,179,203]; condensation of phenols, aldehydes, and nitroparaffins, followed by reduction of the nitro groups [188].

Recently, anion-exchange resins with *quaternary phosphonium groups* [198] and *tertiary sulfonium groups* [59,134,194] have been prepared.

Monomeric phosphonium or sulfonium salts with at least one phenolic substituent can be condensed with formaldehyde. For example,

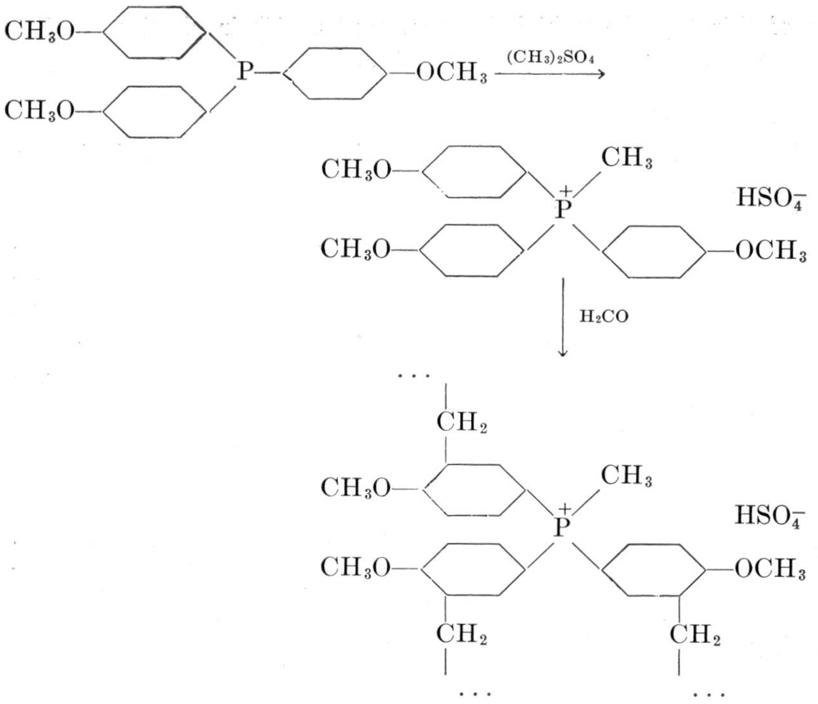

CH_3O-⬡$-$ CH_3O-⬡$-$ $P-$⬡$-OCH_3$ $\xrightarrow{(CH_3)_2SO_4}$

CH_3O-⬡ CH_3O-⬡ $\overset{+}{P}$ CH_3 ⬡$-OCH_3$ HSO_4^-

$\downarrow H_2CO$

$$(3\text{-}29)$$

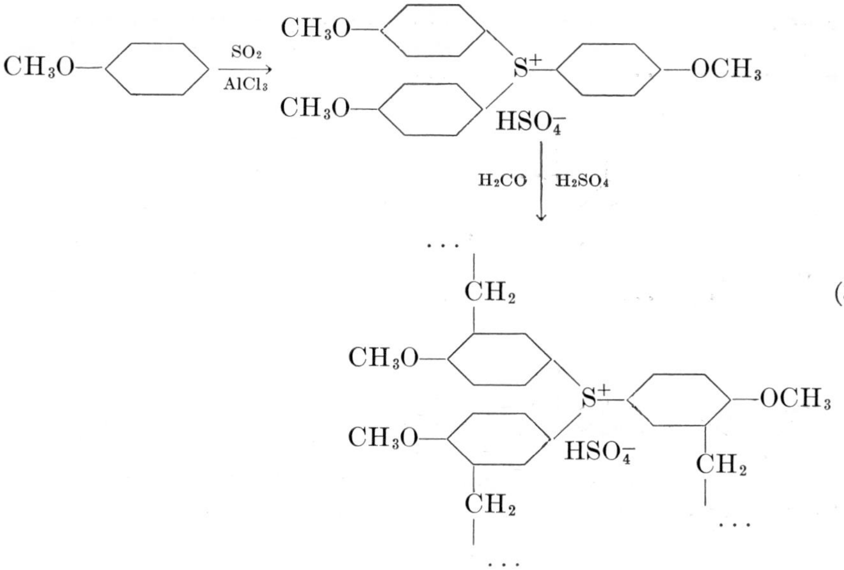

$\cdots$
CH_2
CH_3O-⬡
CH_3O-⬡ $\overset{+}{P}$ CH_3 ⬡$-OCH_3$ HSO_4^-
CH_2 CH_2
$\cdots$ $\cdots$

CH_3O-⬡ $\xrightarrow[AlCl_3]{SO_2}$ CH_3O-⬡ CH_3O-⬡ S^+ ⬡$-OCH_3$ HSO_4^-

$H_2CO \mid H_2SO_4$
$\downarrow$

$$(3\text{-}30)$$

$\cdots$
CH_2
CH_3O-⬡
CH_3O-⬡ S^+ ⬡$-OCH_3$
HSO_4^- CH_2
CH_2 $\cdots$
$\cdots$

As a rule, phenol is added to facilitate condensation.

Other methods of preparation include quaternization of polymers containing phosphine groups [198], and chlorination and subsequent alkylation or arylation of polymeric sulfides in the presence of aluminum chloride [194].

Resins of this type have high base strengths. Their physicochemical properties have not yet been studied in detail.

b. Addition Polymers

With the development of styrene-type anion exchangers, a significant advance was made. The most important advantages of these more recent addition polymers are the following. Monofunctional resins, both weak- and strong-base types, can be made, and the degree of crosslinking can be adjusted in a relatively simple and reproducible manner without affecting the base strength of the ionic groups. In comparison, most of the earlier condensation polymers are polyfunctional, and their crosslinking and base strength are interdependent since the amino groups take part in the condensation.

The most important anion exchangers are made from *crosslinked styrene* pearl polymers [14,19,23,24,49,61–64,98,104,105,125,145–149,170,181,182, 212,214]. The preparation of these polystyrene beads has been described earlier (see page 35). Various styrene derivatives (methylstyrene [61,62], vinylanisole [104,105], etc.) and crosslinking agents other than divinyl-benzene (vinylacrylate, etc. [125]) can also be used.

The basic groups can be introduced in a number of different ways. Most anion exchangers are prepared by chloromethylation of the polystyrene beads and subsequent treatment with ammonia or primary, secondary, or tertiary alkyl amines (crosslinking is not shown):

$$...—CH—CH_2—...$$

$$\downarrow \; ClCH_2OCH_3 \atop ZnCl_2$$

$$...—CH—CH_2—...$$

$$CH_2Cl$$

$$N(CH_3)_3 \swarrow \qquad \searrow NH_3$$

$$...—CH—CH_2—... \qquad\qquad ...—CH—CH_2—...$$

$$CH_2N^+—CH_3Cl^- \atop \underset{CH_3}{\overset{CH_3}{|}} \qquad\qquad CH_2NH_3^+Cl^-$$

(3-31)

The reaction of the chloromethylated intermediate with ammonia or with primary or secondary amines leads to weak-base resins with primary, secondary, and tertiary amino groups [23,63,98,104,146,147,170].   The reaction with a tertiary amine (quaternization) yields a strong-base resin with quaternary ammonium groups [19,24,64,98,105,145,147,148,170,181,212].

The *chloromethylation* of the polystyrene is a Friedel-Crafts condensation, catalyzed by anhydrous aluminum, zinc, or stannous chloride.   For two reasons, the reaction is somewhat more difficult to control than sulfonation: the reaction may proceed beyond monosubstitution, and a side reaction may occur [170]:

$$\cdots-\langle\ \rangle-CH_2Cl + \langle\ \rangle-\cdots \rightarrow$$

$$\cdots-\langle\ \rangle-CH_2-\langle\ \rangle-\cdots + HCl \quad (3\text{-}32)$$

This side reaction results in an additional crosslinking and, since the methylene bridges cannot react with amines, in a lower capacity of the final product. Usually the side reaction is suppressed as far as possible.   In a few cases, however, it has been used intentionally for crosslinking purposes [182].

Certain precautions must be taken in order to obtain a uniform degree of chloromethylation (and crosslinking) throughout the entire bead.   The beads should be fully swollen in chloromethylether before the reaction is initiated by addition of the catalyst [19,147,170].   Otherwise the degree of substitution will be higher in the outer shells than in the center.   The capacity of the final product can be adjusted, within certain limits, by varying the reaction time and thus the degree of chloromethylation.   The chloromethylation can also be carried out with other agents such as aliphatic α-ω-dichlorides [145,146] or formaldehyde and hydrochloric acid [145,146, 214].

The *quaternization* of chloromethylated resins with tertiary alkyl amines takes place smoothly and quantitatively.   Almost any amine can be used, except very bulky molecules which are unable to penetrate the crosslinked resin.   The reaction can be carried out with aqueous or organic solutions. The reaction with an aqueous amine is facilitated by prior treatment of the beads with swelling agents such as dioxane which are miscible with water. The two most common strong-base resins are made with trimethylamine and dimethylethanolamine, respectively, and contain the ionic groups:

$$-CH_2-\overset{\overset{\displaystyle CH_3}{|}}{\underset{\underset{\displaystyle CH_3}{|}}{N^+}}-CH_3 \qquad -CH_2-\overset{\overset{\displaystyle CH_3}{|}}{\underset{\underset{\displaystyle CH_3}{|}}{N^+}}-C_2H_4OH$$

Resins of the first type are Dowex 1, Amberlite IRA-400, Permutit S-1, Nalcite SBR, Duolite A-42, and De-Acidite FF (The Permutit Co., London). Resins of the second type are Dowex 2, Amberlite IRA-410, Permutit S-2, Nalcite SAR, and Duolite A-40. The resins Amberlite IRA-401 and 411 differ from the standard types 400 and 410 only by having a lower DVB content.

The treatment of the chloromethylated intermediate with *secondary alkyl amines* leads to monofunctional weak-base resins with tertiary amino groups [170]. By treatment with ammonia and primary alkyl amines, polyfunctional weak-base resins with primary, secondary, and tertiary amino groups are obtained. The primary amine can react with two and ammonia even with three chloromethyl groups [170]:

$$
\begin{array}{cc}
\ldots\mathrm{-CH_2Cl} & \ldots\mathrm{-CH_2}\diagdown \\[2mm]
+\ \mathrm{H_2N-C_2H_5} \rightarrow & \mathrm{NH^+-C_2H_5 + 2Cl^- + H^+} \\[2mm]
\ldots\mathrm{-CH_2Cl} & \ldots\mathrm{-CH_2}\diagup
\end{array}
$$

$$(3\text{-}33)$$

Additional crosslinking results if the chloromethyl groups belong to different chains. Occasionally, polyamines such as tetraethylenepentamine are used [146,170,181]. They can react in a similar way with two or more chloromethyl groups.

The resins Amberlite IR-45, Dowex 3, Nalcite WBR, and Duolite A-14 are polyfunctional weak-base anion exchangers of this type. De-Acidite G is a monofunctional resin with tertiary amino groups.

Strong-base resins with *quaternary phosphonium groups* can be obtained by letting the chloromethylated polymer react with a tris-dialkylaminophosphine [149], for example,

$$(3\text{-}34)$$

Resins with a very similar configuration can be prepared in a somewhat different way. This procedure, frequently patented but seldom used, consists of copolymerization of alkylstyrenes such as dimethylstyrene with crosslinking agents, preferably divinylbenzene, and chlorination of the side chains, followed by quaternization or amination as before [61,62,148]:

$$\ldots-CH-CH_2-CH-CH_2-\ldots$$
$$-CH_2N^+(CH_3)_3Cl^-$$
$$\ldots-CH_2-CH-\ldots \quad CH_2N^+(CH_3)_3Cl^-$$

$$N(CH_3)_3 \uparrow$$

$$CH{=}CH_2 \quad \ldots-CH \quad CH_2-CH-CH_2-\ldots \quad \ldots-CH-CH_2-CH-CH_2-\ldots$$
$$-CH_3 \quad \xrightarrow{DVB} \quad -CH_3 \quad \xrightarrow[\text{UV-Light}]{Cl_2/CCl_4} \quad -CH_2Cl$$
$$CH_3 \quad \ldots-CH_2-CH-\ldots \quad CH_3 \quad \ldots-CH_2-CH-\ldots \quad CH_2Cl \quad (3\text{-}35)$$

$$NH_3 \downarrow$$

$$\ldots-CH-CH_2-CH-CH_2-\ldots$$
$$-CH_2NH_3^+Cl^-$$
$$\ldots-CH_2-CH-\ldots \quad CH_2NH_3^+Cl^-$$

In contrast to the procedure (3-31), the crosslinking agent remains without ionic groups, but more groups can be introduced into the other components. At the same time, the procedure provides a simple means of adjusting the capacity by incorporation of varying amounts of a third monomer (styrene) which is not chlorinated. However, a serious disadvantage is that the chlorination of the side chains is somewhat difficult to control and may proceed beyond monosubstitution, thus giving a lower capacity since dichloromethyl groups do not react with ammonia or amines.

Weak-base groups can also be introduced into crosslinked polystyrene by nitration and subsequent reduction [14,49,190] (crosslinking is not shown).

$$\ldots-CH-CH_2-\ldots \quad \ldots-CH-CH_2-\ldots \quad \ldots-CH-CH_2-\ldots$$
$$\xrightarrow{HNO_3} \quad \xrightarrow{Na_2S_x} \quad (3\text{-}36)$$
$$NO_2 \quad NH_2$$

This method is, of course, not restricted to polystyrene. Resins of this type carry amino groups directly attached to the benzene rings and have very low base strengths. They have little practical importance, except as intermediates in the preparation of resins with particular groups [cf. syntheses (3-21) and (12-2)].

Crosslinked polystyrenes are by no means the only addition polymers into which basic groups can be introduced. Many other vinyl polymers have been used. A few examples are given in the following.

Anion exchangers have been made from acrylic and methacrylic acid by polymerization in the presence of polyamines [183,187] and by treatment of the crosslinked polymeric esters with polyamines [69]:

$$
\ldots\text{—CH—CH}_2\text{—}\ldots
$$

$$
\underset{\text{COOC}_2\text{H}_5}{|}
$$

$$
\text{HN(C}_2\text{H}_4\text{NH}_2)_2
$$

$$
\text{HN(C}_2\text{H}_4\text{NH}_2)_2
$$

$$
\text{HC}{=}\text{CH}_2
$$

$$
\underset{\text{COOH}}{|}
$$

$$
\ldots\text{—CH—CH}_2\text{—}\ldots
$$

$$
\underset{\text{CO}}{|}
$$

$$
\text{NH—C}_2\text{H}_4\text{—NH—C}_2\text{H}_4\text{—NH} \qquad (3\text{-}37)
$$

$$
\underset{\text{CO}}{|}
$$

$$
\ldots\text{—CH}_2\text{—CH—}\ldots
$$

These are weak-base resins and are polyfunctional.

Crosslinked polyacrylonitrile can be hydrogenated to the polyamine using Raney nickel catalyst [56]. The result is a monofunctional and weak-base resin. By quaternization with an alkylhalide it can be transformed into a strong-base resin (crosslinking is not shown):

$$
\ldots\text{—CH—CH}_2\text{—}\ldots \xrightarrow[\text{NH}_3]{\text{Ni,H}_2} \ldots\text{—CH—CH}_2\text{—}\ldots \xrightarrow{\text{C}_2\text{H}_5\text{Br}} \ldots\text{—CH—CH}_2\text{—}\ldots \qquad (3\text{-}38)
$$

with side groups CN; CH$_2$—NH$_2$; and CH$_2$—N$^+$(C$_2$H$_5$)$_3$ Br$^-$ respectively.

In a similar manner, anion exchangers can be prepared from crosslinked copolymers of alicyclic vinyl compounds carrying amino or cyano groups on side chains [57]. An example is the copolymerization of vinyl-cyanocyclohexane and divinylbenzene followed by hydrogenation and quaternization.

Also, linear polyacrylonitrile has been used as a starting material. After hydrogenation it is crosslinked with dihalohydrocarbons such as dichloroethane [56].

Another possibility is given by the amination of crosslinked polyvinylchloroalkyl-ether [55], for example,

$$
\text{HC}{=}\text{CH}_2
$$

$$
\underset{\text{C}_2\text{H}_4\text{Cl}}{\overset{\text{O}}{|}} \xrightarrow{\text{DVB}}
$$

$$
\ldots\text{—CH—CH}_2\text{—CH—CH}_2\text{—}\ldots \xrightarrow{\text{N(CH}_3)_3}
$$

with O—C$_2$H$_4$Cl and ...—CH$_2$—CH—... groups

$$
\ldots\text{—CH—CH}_2\text{—CH—CH}_2\text{—}\ldots \qquad (3\text{-}39)
$$

with O—C$_2$H$_4$—N$^+$(CH$_3$)$_3$ Cl$^-$ and ...—CH$_2$—CH—... groups

Weak- and strong-base resins can be obtained.

Methylvinylketone yields a crosslinked resin when copolymerized with divinylbenzene or similar agents. Formamide groups are then introduced by heating with ammonium formate, formamide, or formic acid and an amine. These groups are subsequently hydrolyzed with hydrochloric acid [102]. A weak-base resin is obtained.

At an elevated temperature, polyvinylalcohol reacts with pyridine and pyridine derivatives to give weak-base anion exchangers [195].

The preparation of strong-base resins from polymers with phosphine and sulfide groups has already been mentioned (see page 51).

Instead of introducing active groups into crosslinked resins, it is possible to polymerize monomeric bases with unsaturated groups or salts of such bases. Many resins have been prepared in this way. However, none of them has found widespread use. Only a few examples are given.

Weak-base resins have been obtained by polymerizing vinylpyridine or vinylquinoline with crosslinking agents such as divinylacetylene, vinylcyclohexene, etc. [50,54,153].

A monofunctional strong-base resin is obtained by copolymerization of p-dimethylamidostyrene with a crosslinking agent, followed by quaternization [128].

$$ \text{(3-40)} $$

Strong-base resins can also be prepared by polymerization of quaternary ammonium salts with unsaturated substituents [17,33–38]. For example

$$ \text{(3-41)} $$

No crosslinking agent is required if the reactant contains more than two unsaturated groups.

For special applications, anion exchangers with many different kinds of ionic groups have been made. Perhaps the most interesting of these are resins with *optically active groups*. For example, the carboxylic acid groups of a cation exchanger have been converted to the carboxychloride [see reaction (3-24)] and then esterified with optically active bases such as quinine [92]. With resins of this kind, optically active isomers of mandelic acid have been enriched [92]. However, the separation efficiency is not very impressive.

This comprehensive, but by no means exhaustive, survey illustrates the immense variety of syntheses by which anion exchangers with widely differing properties can be obtained. The structure and the degree of crosslinking of the matrix can be varied in any resin. In anion exchangers, even the fixed ionic groups can be varied in a systematic manner by introducing different substituents at the nitrogen, phosphorus, or sulfur atom. This versatility is an advantage which has so far not been fully exploited. On the other hand, the chemical and thermal stability of the anion exchangers does not match that of the cation exchangers. This is particularly true for the most important anion exchangers, the strong-base resins with quaternary ammonium groups. This configuration is not very stable, especially in the presence of hydroxyl ions. Deterioration results from the well-known Hofmann degradation.* Strong-base anion exchangers which are free of this disadvantage have yet to be discovered.

3-4. AMPHOTERIC ION EXCHANGERS

Materials which contain both acidic and basic groups are called amphoteric. Various ion exchangers of this type have been prepared, but applications have been found for only a few.

Several resins which have already been described are amphoteric. Condensation products of amines and phenols (page 49) contain phenolic OH groups of very low acid strength in addition to the primary, secondary, and tertiary amino groups. In this case, the basic character prevails. A considerable number of the specific cation exchangers, for example, the resins with iminodiacetic acid groups (see page 45), contain weak-base groups in addition to carboxylic acid groups. Here, the acidic character prevails. Occasionally, resins intended for use as sorbents have been equipped with both weak-acid and weak-base groups, with the main purpose of guaranteeing sufficient swelling in alkaline as well as in acidic media [29] (see also page 122). All these materials can act as cation exchangers at pH values above their isoelectric point, and as anion exchangers at pH values below this point.

Several amphoteric resins with strong-acid groups have been prepared. However, most of these products were not crosslinked and thus were insoluble only within a narrow pH range [16,207]. Crosslinking, though not attempted, should not be difficult.

More recently, crosslinked amphoteric resins with aminoalkylphosphonic and -carboxylic acid groups have been prepared [141,205a], for example by copolymerization of ethyleneimine-N-ethylphosphonic acid esters or the corresponding carboxylic acid esters with β,β'-di(ethyleneimino)diethylbenzene and subsequent hydrolysis of the ester groups [141].

A resin containing both strong-base and strong-acid groups was described a few years ago [197]. It is prepared by copolymerization of styrene, vinylchloride, and a crosslinking agent, followed by quaternization and sulfonation of the product.

---

* The mechanism and the rate of resin degradation have recently been studied in more detail with a typical strong-base resin, Amberlite IRA-400 [19a]. Parallel to the Hofmann degradation (loss of strong-base groups by liberation of tertiary amine) a hydrolysis reaction transforms strong-base to weak-base groups and liberates methanol. Note also that the salt forms are more stable than the OH$^-$ form.

$$HC{=}CH_2, HC{=}CH_2 \qquad \xrightarrow{DVB} \qquad \ldots{-}CH{-}CH_2{-}CH{-}CH_2{-}\ldots$$

(with Cl substituent and benzene rings)

$$\Big\downarrow N(CH_3)_3 \qquad\qquad (3\text{-}42)$$

$$\ldots{-}CH{-}CH_2{-}CH{-}CH_2{-}\ldots \qquad \xleftarrow{H_2SO_4} \qquad \ldots{-}CH{-}CH_2{-}CH{-}CH_2{-}\ldots$$

with $N^+(CH_3)_3Cl^-$ and $SO_3^-H^+$ groups, and $N^+(CH_3)_3Cl^-$

The physicochemical properties of this interesting resin have so far not been studied.

The most recent and most important amphoteric resins are the so-called "snake-cage polyelectrolytes." These products are conventional cation or anion exchangers within which linear polycations or polyanions, respectively, have been formed by polymerization [97]. For example, a snake-cage polyelectrolyte can be prepared by converting a strong-base anion exchanger (Dowex 1) to the acrylate form and then polymerizing the acrylate anions in the resin. The resin Retardion 11-A-8 (Dow Chemical Co.) is a commercial product of this type. The linear chains of the poly-counter ions are so intricately intertwined with the crosslinked matrix that they cannot be displaced by other counter ions; they are trapped like snakes in a cage.

One feature distinguishes the snake cage polyelectrolytes from other amphoteric resins: the ionic groups of the poly-counter ions are not attached to the matrix. Thus the charges of the poly-counter ions and of the matrix have more freedom to move relative to one another, and hence, may neutralize one another. As a consequence, it is not necessary for the resin to contain mobile counter ions (or counter ions to the poly-counter ions) to remain electrically neutral, provided that the charges of the fixed ionic groups and the poly-counter ions are properly balanced. The resins are excellent reversible sorbents for electrolytes. They are used for separations by "ion retardation" (see Sec. 9-5).

3-5. PARTICLE SHAPE AND SIZE, MACRORETICULAR RESINS, AND SUPPORTED ION EXCHANGERS

In most applications, ion exchangers are used as coherent gels in the form of small particles of about 0.1 to 1 mm in diameter. Such particles are readily prepared by the methods described in the preceding sections.

Addition polymers are usually prepared by the pearl polymerization technique which gives spherical beads of variable particle size (see page 35).

Of course, polymerization in aqueous suspension is possible only if the monomers are insoluble in water. This is not always the case. However, water-soluble monomers such as acrylic acid can be made insoluble, for example, by esterification. The ester groups are then hydrolyzed after polymerization. Alternatively, the "water-in-oil" technique can be used. Here, the copolymer is formed exclusively from hydrophilic monomers. The droplets of the polymerization mixture are suspended in an inert organic solvent in which the monomers are insoluble.

Of course, addition polymers can also be prepared by bulk-phase polymerization. The solid product is then ground to obtain the desired particle size.

Condensation polymers are usually obtained in the form of a gelatinous mass which is dried and ground (see Fig. 3-4). However, spherical beads

FIG. 3-4. Ion-exchange condensation polymer after drying and grinding. (*Microphotography, enlargement* 1:25. *From Ullmann's Encyklopädie der technischen Chemie, 3d ed., vol.* 8, *p.* 808, *Urban & Schwarzenberg, Munich-Berlin,* 1957.)

can also be obtained by a water-in-oil pearl polymerization with the precondensed and viscous, but still liquid reaction mixture [72,133,136,137].

For certain applications, ion exchangers having higher porosities, special geometric forms, or particular mechanical properties are needed. For example, for use in the nonpolar solvents, highly porous materials are preferable because ordinary ion-exchange resins hardly swell in such solvents and thus give very low rates of ion exchange or catalytic reactions. Certain continuous ion-exchange processes operate with infinite belts which must be flexible and have a high tensile strength. Ion-exchange electrodialysis requires thin membranes with large surface areas and excellent mechanical stabilities. In many such cases, the ordinary coherent ion-exchange gels are unsatisfactory.

Highly porous, so-called *macroreticular* ion-exchange resins can be prepared by a variation of the conventional pearl-polymerization technique. An organic solvent which is a good solvent for the monomers, but a poor solvent for the polymer, is added to the polymerization mixture. As polymerization progresses, the solvent is squeezed out by the growing copolymer regions. In this way, one can obtain spherical beads with wide pores (several hundred angström units) which guarantee access to the interior of the beads even when nonpolar solvents are used [177]. The new Amberlyst ion-exchange resins are of this type.

Large, mechanically strong, and highly porous ion-exchanger pellets have also been prepared by cementing small ion-exchanger particles together with an inert binder, for example, with a phenolic resin [112], or by impregnating an adequately strong and stable porous support such as pumice [172]. As a rule, the support is impregnated with a precondensed liquid reaction mixture. The condensation is then completed *in situ*. The impregnation technique has also been used for preparing ion-exchange papers and infinite ion-exchanger belts from cotton (see page 19). The preparation of ion-exchanger membranes is described in the next section.

3-6. ION-EXCHANGER MEMBRANES

The term ion-exchanger "membrane" is commonly used in a very broad sense and comprises solid films, foils, disks, ribbons, tubes, plugs, etc., in short, any material that can be used as a separating wall between two solutions.

The first resinous ion-exchanger membranes were prepared about ten years ago. Within an unusually short time they have become valuable tools and the object of a great variety of scientific studies. There is no lack of potential plant-scale applications. Here, however, membranes with large surface area, high mechanical stability, and long useful life are needed. These requirements are not easily met.

For scientific purposes, the so-called "homogeneous" membranes are preferred. These are coherent, unsupported gels. For practical applications, reinforced or "heterogeneous" membranes offer the advantage of higher mechanical strength. These membranes are supported by inert carriers or binders. Membranes can also be prepared by evaporation and impregnation techniques. These different preparation procedures will be outlined below. The following discussion includes the precursors of the resinous membranes.

The preparation of mechanically stable ion-exchanger membranes is somewhat difficult. So far, only very few membranes are commercially available. Details of their preparation are kept secret by the manufacturers. Hence the following description is necessarily incomplete.

a. Collodion and Mineral Membranes

The resinous ion-exchanger membranes had early precursors. Collodion and mineral membranes were prepared and studied more than thirty years ago. The discovery of the ion-exchange properties of such membranes by Teorell and K. H. Meyer in 1935 (see page 377) coincided with the synthesis of the first ion-exchange resins.

Collodion membranes are prepared by dissolving collodion in ether-alcohol mixtures, pouring the solution onto a smooth, inert surface, and evaporating the solvent under carefully controlled conditions. The membranes are then detached from the surface and washed with water or an aqueous solution. The pore width of the membranes can be adjusted by varying the drying time [142,154,156,191]. The commercial "ultra-filters" are relatively porous materials of this type. Collodion membranes are weak-acid cation exchangers. The ion-exchange capacity of untreated collodion is very low (of the order of 10^{-3} meq/g). It can be increased by treatment with caustic before or after membrane formation [191]. Caustic causes partial degradation of the collodion which, in turn, is oxidized by the degradation products. The preparation of impregnated collodion membranes is described in Sec. 3-6f.

Zeolite membranes can be prepared from flawless, translucent zeolite crystals by careful grinding [143]. Only very few zeolites, for example, apophyllite, are found in the form of crystals of adequate size.

Clay membranes can be prepared by evaporation of electrodialyzed clay suspensions followed by drying at about 500°C [144].

All these membranes have either low capacities or low permeabilities, and are no longer used for ion-exchange work.

b. "Homogeneous" Membranes

In a few fortunate cases, the preparation of ion exchangers by polymerization can be performed without much difficulty in such a way that the product is obtained in "membrane" form, i.e., as a film, foil, ribbon, etc. This is true, for example, for condensation products of phenolsulfonic acid or its derivatives and formaldehyde [79,113,115,118,140] (see page 30) and of polyethyleneimine and epichlorohydrin [139] (see page 50). Homogeneous cation- and anion-exchanger membranes can be prepared by condensation of these monomers on mercury or acid-resistant plates or by heating a pre-condensed, viscous reaction mixture between glass plates. These are strong-acid or strong-base membranes and have often been used for scientific studies. The membranes are translucent, an indication that inhomogeneities, if any, are smaller than the wavelength of visible light ($<4,000$ A).

In a similar way, anion-exchanger membranes have been prepared by condensing melamine, guanidine carbonate, and formaldehyde (see page 50) [193], and tertiary sulfonium salts with formaldehyde (see page 50) [196].

The sulfonation of crosslinked polystyrene foils is not impossible [140,184]. However, difficulties are encountered because sulfonation produces so much strain that the foil tends to crack (see page 36). Foils made with partially prepolymerized instead of monomeric styrene appear to be less sensitive. Also, less strain develops if very thin films are used. Such films have been prepared by evaporation of solutions of linear polystyrene and subsequent crosslinking by irradiation with a cobalt-60 source [186]. Membranes have also been prepared from sulfonated monomers. For example, propyl-*p*-styrenesulfonate has been copolymerized with styrene and divinylbenzene and then hydrolyzed [85].

The ion-exchanger membranes manufactured by the Asahi Chemical Company (Tokyo) are homogeneous membranes prepared from partially prepolymerized styrene-divinylbenzene mixtures.

For industrial applications, *reinforced membranes* have been prepared by polymerization on supporting wide-mesh plastic tissues [115]. The membranes Nepton CR-51, CR-61 (cation exchangers), and AR-111 (anion exchanger), manufactured by Ionics Inc., Cambridge, Mass., are of this type. The tissue must be elastic and should adhere to the ion-exchange material, so that bending and changes in swelling do not cause the material to peel off or to crack.

c. "Heterogeneous" Membranes

The so-called "heterogeneous" membranes are prepared by embedding colloidal ion-exchanger particles in an inert binder which provides sufficient mechanical strength. Polyethylene, polystyrene, phenolic resins, polymethacrylates, synthetic rubber, wax, and many other materials have been used as binders.

Heterogenous membranes can be prepared by rolling colloidal ion-exchange materials into an inert plastic foil under pressure and, if necessary, at an elevated temperature [25]. Thermoplastic resins can be mixed in powder form with the ion exchanger; the mixture is then compressed or rolled to give membranes [167,224,225]. In another procedure, the binder is dissolved in a suitable solvent, the colloidal ion exchanger is suspended in the viscous solution, the solvent is removed by evaporation, and the remaining mass is compressed [223]. Finally, colloidal ion-exchanger particles can be compressed to give a porous disk; the disk is immersed under vacuum in, say, styrene; when the vacuum is removed, the atmospheric pressure forces the styrene into the disk where it is subsequently polymerized. The surfaces of such membranes must be ground to provide free access to the ion-exchange material [225].

A necessary requirement for heterogeneous membranes is that the ion-exchanger particles be in contact with one another, rather than be separated by the binder. Therefore the volume percentage of ion-exchange material should be made as high as is compatible with the required mechanical strength. Most heterogeneous membranes contain from 50 to 75 per cent ion-exchange material.

Heterogeneous membranes can be made from almost any ion exchanger, whereas the list of materials from which homogeneous membranes can be prepared is rather restricted. However, the properties of heterogeneous membranes are not ideal: the electric conductivity is lower and the (undesired) permeability for electrolytes is higher than those of the homogeneous membranes. It is likely that the heterogeneous membranes will disappear as homogeneous membranes with comparable mechanical strength become available.

The membranes Amberplex A-1, Permaplex A-10 (both anion exchangers), Amberplex C-1, and Permaplex C-10 (both cation exchangers) are heterogeneous. The Amberplex membranes are no longer available.

d. "Interpolymer" Membranes

Thin membranes with a rather uniform structure and favorable mechanical properties have recently been prepared by a novel method [89,90,162,

211]. The films are obtained by evaporation of a solution containing a linear polyelectrolyte and a linear inert polymer. The films are insoluble in water or aqueous solutions, even though no crosslinking has occurred. Apparently the chains of the water-soluble polyelectrolyte and the water-insoluble inert polymer are so intricately intertwined with one another that the hydrophilic polyelectrolyte cannot be leached out. The following polymers have been used: dynel (copolymer of vinylchloride and acrylonitrile) as the inert polymer, polystyrenesulfonic acid for strong-acid membranes, a copolymer of maleic-acid anhydride and vinylmethylether for weak-acid membranes, and polyvinylimidazol quaternized with methyliodide for strong-base membranes. The solvent must dissolve the hydrophilic polyelectrolyte as well as the hydrophobic inert polymer. Dimethylformamide and dimethylsulfoxide can be used. The relative amounts of the two polymers can be varied within certain limits. Thus membranes of different capacities can be prepared.

In a similar manner, strong-acid membranes were prepared much earlier from collodion and polystyrenesulfonic acid [163,192].

The Nalfilm membranes manufactured by the National Aluminate Corp. are believed to be interpolymer membranes.

e. Graft-copolymer Membranes

Recently, graft polymerization has been used successfully for preparing ion-exchanger membranes [43a]. This new and very promising technique yields thin membranes with outstanding mechanical and good electrochemical properties. Polyethylene films are impregnated with styrene or styrene-divinylbenzene mixtures and are then exposed to γ radiation from a cobalt-60 source. This irradiation causes styrene and divinylbenzene to be grafted onto the polyethylene base. Styrene contents of 60 mole per cent and higher can be obtained, but the optimum seems to lie at 30 to 50 mole per cent. Strong-acid cation-exchanger membranes are obtained by sulfonation of the graft copolymer (see page 36), and strong-base and weak-base anion-exchanger membranes by chloromethylation and subsequent quaternization or amination (see page 52). Alternatively, anion-exchanger membranes can be prepared by grafting vinylpyridine onto polyethylene films; the resulting copolymer can be quaternized to give a strong-base membrane [43a].

Membranes of this type are more heterogeneous than the "homogeneous" membranes and more homogeneous than the "heterogeneous" ones. In the graft-copolymer membranes, microscopic regions of crystalline polyethylene and of substituted polystyrene alternate, but are smaller and more intricately linked to one another than in the ordinary heterogeneous membranes.

Graft-copolymer membranes are now commercially available. The membranes AMFion A-60, A-104, and A-104B (anion exchangers) and C-60, C-103, C-103C, and C-313 (cation exchangers, manufactured by American Machine and Foundry Company) are of this type.

f. Impregnated Membranes

Microporous membranes with sufficient mechanical strength are readily prepared from substances such as collodion (see Sec. 3-6a). For most purposes, however, the ion-exchange capacity of these materials is too low.

Strong-acid and strong-base groups can be introduced into such membranes by impregnating with soluble polyelectrolytes. The swollen membrane sorbs polyelectrolytes from aqueous solutions. Subsequent drying reduces the capability of the membrane to swell, so that the polyelectrolytes are trapped. Good results have been obtained with polystyrenesulfonic acid for cation-exchanger membranes and with poly-2-vinyl-N-methylpyridiniumbromide for anion-exchanger membranes [84,163,192].

These membranes are readily prepared and convenient for laboratory use. However, they tend to lose capacity when in constant use and are chemically less stable than resinous membranes.

SUMMARY

Ion-exchange resins consist of a crosslinked hydrocarbon matrix which carries acidic or basic groups. The matrix can be formed by polycondensation or by addition polymerization. Addition polymers are chemically more stable and have almost completely replaced the earlier condensation polymers. The fixed ionic groups are introduced either into one of the monomers or, after polymerization, into the crosslinked resin.

Most of the earlier cation-exchange resins were condensation products of phenol derivatives and aldehydes. Sulfonic (strong-acid), carboxylic (weak-acid), or phosphonic acid groups (intermediate acidity) are usually introduced into the phenolic component. However, sulfonated aldehydes have also been used.

The most important cation exchangers are sulfonation products of crosslinked polystyrene (strong acid), and crosslinked copolymers of acrylic or methacrylic acid (weak acid). Phosphonic acid groups have also been introduced into polystyrene.

Bifunctional cation exchangers which contain two types of ionic groups can be prepared.

Cation exchangers with specific preference for certain cations can be made by introducing groups which form strong complexes, preferably chelates, with these cations. Resins with chelating iminodiacetic acid groups have now become commercially available.

Most of the earlier anion-exchange resins were condensation products of aromatic or aliphatic amines and aldehydes, dihaloparaffins, or haloepoxides (epichlorohydrin). Most of these resins contain primary, secondary, and tertiary amino groups and are weak-base and polyfunctional materials.

The most important anion exchangers are crosslinked polystyrenes into which strong- or weak-base groups have been introduced by chloromethylation and subsequent amination. Reaction with tertiary alkyl amines gives strong-base quaternary ammonium groups, and reaction with primary or secondary alkyl amines or ammonia gives weak-base amino groups.

Anion exchangers with strong-base quaternary phosphonium and tertiary sulfonium groups have also been made.

Many other types of cation and anion exchangers have been prepared. These include resins with optically active groups.

Amphoteric ion exchangers contain both acidic and basic groups. Snake-cage polyelectrolytes are a novel variety of amphoteric resins. They are prepared from conventional ion exchangers by polymerization of monomeric counter ions within the resin.

For special purposes, ion exchangers in the form of pellets, belts, etc., have been prepared by cementing ion-exchanger particles together with an inert binder or by impregnating suitable supporting carriers.

Ion-exchanger membranes have been prepared by various methods. Homogeneous membranes are coherent gels. They can be reinforced by incorporating supporting wide-mesh plastic tissues. Only relatively few ion exchangers can be prepared in the form of such membranes. Heterogeneous membranes are prepared by incorporating colloidal ion-exchanger particles into an inert binder. "Interpolymer" membranes are obtained by evaporation of a solution containing a linear polyelectrolyte and a linear inert polymer. Graft-copolymer membranes are prepared by impregnating plastic films with monomers such as styrene, grafting these monomers onto the film material by γ irradiation, and then introducing fixed ionic groups. Ion-exchanger membranes can also be made by impregnating collodion films with polyelectrolytes.

REFERENCES

1. Abrams, I. M., *Ind. Eng. Chem.*, **48**, 1469 (1956).
2. Abrams, I. M. (Chemical Process Co.), Brit. Patent 785,157, 1957.
3. Abrams, I. M. (Chemical Process Co.), U.S. Patent 2,844,546, 1958.
4. Adams, B. A., and E. L. Holmes, *J. Soc. Chem. Ind. (London)*, **54**, 1 T (1935).
5. Adams, B. A., and E. L. Holmes, Brit. Patent 450,308, 1936.
6. Adams, B. A., and E. L. Holmes, Brit. Patent 450,309, 1936; U.S. Patent 2,151,883, 1939.
7. Akihara, T., Jap. Patent 845, 1953.
8. Alm, A. V. (American Cyanamid Co.), U.S. Patent 2,586,770, 1952.
9. American Cyanamid Co. and W. W. Triggs, Brit. Patent 575,266, 1946.
10. American Cyanamid Co., Brit. Patent 648,281, 1952.
11. Ashida, K., *Chem. High Polymers (Tokyo)*, **10**, 27 (1953); *Chem. Abstr.*, **48**, 9585 (1954).
12. Ashida, K., *Chem. High Polymers (Tokyo)*, **10**, 117 (1953); *Chem. Abstr.*, **48**, 14042 (1954).
13. Ashida, K., *Chem. High Polymers (Tokyo)*, **10**, 490 (1953); *Chem. Abstr.*, **49**, 9839 (1955).
14. L'Auxiliaire des chemins de fer et de l'industrie, and G. V. Austerweil, F. Patent 832,866, 1938.

15. L'Auxiliaire des chemins de fer et de l'industrie, and G. V. Austerweil, F. Patent 49,745, 1939.
16. Azorlosa, J. L. (Hercules Powder Co.), U.S. Patent 2,592,107, 1952.
17. Barney, A. L. (E. I. Du Pont de Nemours), U.S. Patent 2,677,679, 1954.
18. Bauman, W. C., and G. B. Heusted (The Dow Chemical Co.), U.S. Patent 2,601,202, 1952.
19. Bauman, W. C., and R. McKellar (The Dow Chemical Co.), U.S. Patent 2,614,099, 1952.
19a. Baumann, E. W., J. Chem. Eng. Data, **5**, 376 (1960).
20. Blasius, E., and G. Olbrich, Z. Anal. Chem., **151**, 81 (1956).
21. Bodamer, G. W. (Rohm & Haas Co.), U.S. Patent 2,597,437, 1952.
22. Bodamer, G. W. (Rohm & Haas Co.), U.S. Patent 2,597,438, 1952.
23. Bodamer, G. W. (Rohm & Haas Co.), U.S. Patent 2,597,439, 1952.
24. Bodamer, G. W. (Rohm & Haas Co.), U.S. Patent 2,597,440, 1952.
25. Bodamer, G. W. (Rohm & Haas Co.), U.S. Patents 2,681,319 and 2,681,320, 1954.
26. Boresch, C. (Farbenfabriken Bayer), Ger. Patent 942,624, 1956.
27. Boyer, R. F. (The Dow Chemical Co.), U.S. Patent 2,500,149, 1950.
28. Bradley, D. F., and A. Rich, J. Am. Chem. Soc., **78**, 5898 (1956).
29. Braithwaite, D. G., and J. S. D'Amico (National Aluminate Corp.), U.S. Patent 2,582,098, 1952.
30. Broser, W., and W. Lautsch, Naturwissenschaften, **38**, 208 (1951).
31. Bunnett, J. F., and J. L. Marks, J. Am. Chem. Soc., **74**, 5893 (1952).
32. Burke, W. J. (E. I. Du Pont de Nemours), U.S. Patent 2,418,497, 1947.
33. Butler, G. B., and R. L. Bunch, J. Am. Chem. Soc., **71**, 3120 (1949).
34. Butler, G. B., and F. L. Ingley, J. Am. Chem. Soc., **73**, 895 (1951).
35. Butler, G. B., and R. L. Goette, J. Am. Chem. Soc., **74**, 1939 (1952).
36. Butler, G. B., R. L. Bunch, and F. L. Ingley, J. Am. Chem. Soc., **74**, 2543 (1952).
37. Butler, G. B., and R. A. Johnson, J. Am. Chem. Soc., **76**, 713 (1954).
38. Butler, G. B., and R. L. Bunch, U.S. Patent 2,687,382, 1954.
39. Centrale Suiker Mij., N. V., and L. J. Kantebeen, Brit. Patent 654,391, 1951.
40. Chemical Research Laboratory, Teddington, Middlesex, Report of the Director, 1952, p. 65.
41. Chemical Research Laboratory, Teddington, Middlesex, Report of the Director, 1953, p. 38.
42. Chemical Research Laboratory, Teddington, Middlesex, Report of the Director, 1956, p. 43.
43. Chemische Fabrik Budenheim, Brit. Patent 727,476, 1955.
43a. Chen, W. K. W., R. B. Mesrobian, D. S. Ballantine, D. J. Metz, and A. Glines, J. Polymer Sci., **23**, 903 (1957).
44. Cornaz, J. P., and H. Deuel, Experientia, **10**, 137 (1954).
45. Cornaz, J. P., K. Hutschneker, and H. Deuel, Helv. chim. Acta, **40**, 2015 (1957).
46. D'Alelio, G. F. (General Electric Co.), U.S. Patent 2,340,110, 1944.
47. D'Alelio, G. F. (General Electric Co.), U.S. Patent 2,340,111, 1944.
48. D'Alelio, G. F. (General Electric Co.), U.S. Patent 2,366,007, 1944.
49. D'Alelio, G. F. (General Electric Co.), U.S. Patent 2,366,008, 1944.
50. D'Alelio, G. F. (Koppers Co.), U.S. Patent 2,623,013, 1952.
51. D'Alelio, G. F. (Koppers Co.), U.S. Patent 2,631,127, 1953.
52. D'Alelio, G. F. (Koppers Co.), U.S. Patent 2,644,801, 1953.
53. D'Alelio, G. F. (Koppers Co.), U.S. Patent 2,645,621, 1953.
54. D'Alelio, G. F. (Koppers Co.), U.S. Patent 2,683,124, 1954.
55. D'Alelio, G. F. (Koppers Co.), U.S. Patent 2,683,125, 1954.
56. D'Alelio, G. F. (Koppers Co.), U.S. Patent 2,697,079, 1954.
57. D'Alelio, G. F. (Koppers Co.), U.S. Patent 2,697,080, 1954.

58. Daul, G. C., J. D. Reid, and R. M. Reinhardt, *Ind. Eng. Chem.*, **46**, 1042 (1954).
59. DeJong, G. J. (Stamicarbon N. V.), U.S. Patent 2,713,038, 1955.
60. Deuel, H., K. Hutschneker, and J. Solms, *Z. Elektrochem.*, **57**, 172 (1953).
61. Dow Chemical Co., Brit. Patent 679,852, 1952.
62. Dow Chemical Co., Brit. Patent 679,853, 1952.
63. Dow Chemical Co., Brit. Patent 683,399, 1952.
64. Dow Chemical Co., Brit. Patent 683,400, 1952.
65. Drake, L. R. (The Dow Chemical Co.), U.S. Patent 2,764,562, 1956.
66. Dudley, J. R. (American Cyanamid Co.), U.S. Patent 2,467,523, 1949.
67. Dudley, J. R., and L. A. Lundberg (American Cyanamid Co.), U.S. Patent 2,469,-683, 1949.
68. Dudley, J. R. (American Cyanamid Co.), U.S. Patent 2,469,684, 1949.
69. Dudley, J. R. (American Cyanamid Co.), U.S. Patent 2,582,194, 1952.
70. Du Pont de Nemours & Co., E. I., Brit. Patent 548,107, 1942.
71. Eastes, J. W. (Resinous Products & Chemical Co.), U.S. Patent 2,354,671, 1944.
72. Evers, W. L. (Rohm & Haas Co.), U.S. Patent 2,518,420, 1950.
73. Farbenfabriken Bayer and H. Passing, R. Bauer, and D. Delfs, Ger. Patent 824,391, 1951.
74. Farbenfabriken Bayer, Ger. Patent Application K 4386, 1942.
75. Farbenfabriken Bayer, Ger. Patents 829,498, 1952; 898,080, 1953.
76. Farbenfabriken Bayer, and H. Lauth, Ger. Patent 871,964, 1953.
77. Farbenfabriken Bayer, Brit. Patent 717,276, 1954.
78. Farbenfabriken Bayer, Brit. Patent 719,330, 1954.
79. Farbenfabriken Bayer, K. Haagen, and F. Helfferich, Ger. Patent 971,729, 1959; U.S. Patent 2,882,247, 1959.
80. Feinland, R., D. E. Baldwin, and H. P. Gregor, *J. Polymer Sci.*, **10**, 445 (1953).
81. Ferrel, R. E., H. S. Olcott, and H. Fraenkel-Conrat, *J. Am. Chem. Soc.*, **70**, 2101 (1948).
82. Ferris, A. H. (Rohm & Haas Co.), U.S. Patent 2,678,306, 1954.
83. Ferris, A. H., and W. R. Lyman (Rohm & Haas Co.), U.S. Patent 2,678,307, 1954.
84. Gottlieb, M. H., R. Neihof, and K. Sollner, *J. Phys. Chem.*, **61**, 154 (1957).
85. Graydon, W. F., and R. J. Stewart, *J. Phys. Chem.*, **59**, 86 (1955).
86. Gregor, H. P., M. Taifer, L. Citarel, and E. I. Becker, *Ind. Eng. Chem.*, **44**, 2834 (1952).
87. Gregor, H. P., 13th *Congr. Intern. Pure Appl. Chem.*, Stockholm, 1953; Ref.: *Angew. Chem.*, **66**, 143 (1954).
88. Gregor, H. P., D. Dolar, and G. K. Hoeschele, *J. Am. Chem. Soc.*, **77**, 3675 (1955).
89. Gregor, H. P., H. Jacobson, R. C. Shair, and D. M. Wetstone, *J. Phys. Chem.*, **61**, 141 (1957).
90. Gregor, H. P., and D. M. Wetstone, *J. Phys. Chem.*, **61**, 147 (1957).
91. Griessbach, R., E. Meier, and H. Wassenegger (I. G. Farbenindustrie), Ger. Patent 742,355, 1943.
92. Grubhofer, N., and L. Schleith, *Naturwissenschaften*, **40**, 508 (1953); *Z. Physiol. Chem.*, **296**, 262 (1954).
93. Haagen, K., *Z. Elektrochem.*, **57**, 178 (1953).
94. Haagen, K. (Farbenfabriken Bayer), U.S. Patent 2,692,866, 1954.
95. Haagen, K. (Farbenfabriken Bayer), U.S. Patent 2,729,607, 1956.
96. Hale, D. K., *Manchester Roy. Inst. Symp.*, 1952; Ref.: *Nature*, **170**, 150 (1952).
96a. Hart, R., and R. Janssen, *Makromol. Chem.*, **43**, 242 (1961).
97. Hatch, M. J., J. A. Dillon, and H. B. Smith, *Ind. Eng. Chem.*, **49**, 1812 (1957).
98. Hawdon, A. R., R. P. Linstead, and S. L. S. Thomas, Brit. Patent Appl. 7,732, 1950.
99. Hohenstein, W. P., and H. Mark, *J. Polymer Sci.*, **1**, 127 (1946).

100. Holmes, E. L., U.S. Patent 2,191,853, 1940.
101. Howe, P. G., and J. A. Kitchener, *J. Chem. Soc.*, **1955**, 2143.
102. Hwa, J. C. H. (Rohm & Haas Co.), U.S. Patent 2,597,491, 1952.
103. Hwa, J. C. H. (Rohm & Haas Co.), U.S. Patent 2,597,492, 1952.
104. Hwa, J. C. H. (Rohm & Haas Co.), U.S. Patent 2,597,493, 1952.
105. Hwa, J. C. H. (Rohm & Haas Co.), U.S. Patent 2,597,494, 1952.
106. I. G. Farbenindustrie, F. Patent 820,969, 1937.
107. I. G. Farbenindustrie, Brit. Patent 489,173, 1938.
108. I. G. Farbenindustrie, Ger. Patent 734,279, 1943.
109. I. G. Farbenindustrie, Ger. Patent 747,664, 1944.
110. I. G. Farbenindustrie, Ger. Patent 764,618, 1945.
111. I. G. Farbenindustrie, Ger. Patent 766,121, 1945; new number 919,666, 1954.
112. I. G. Farbenindustrie, Ger. Patent Application 74,991, 1943.
113. Ishibashi, N., T. Seiyama, and W. Sakai, *J. Electrochem. Soc. Japan*, **22**, 684 (1954); *Chem. Abstr.*, **49**, 9415 (1955).
113a. Jakubovic, A. O., *J. Chem. Soc.*, **1960**, 4820.
114. Jenckel, E., and H. v. Lillin, *Kolloid Z.*, **146**, 159 (1956).
115. Juda, W., and W. A. McRae, U.S. Patents 2,636,851 and 2,636,852, 1953.
116. Kaiser, D. W. (American Cyanamid Co.), U.S. Patent 2,596,930, 1952.
117. Kalle Co., Ger. Patent Appl. K 164,647, 1942.
118. Kasper, A. A. (Ionics Inc.), U.S. Patent 2,702,272, 1955.
119. Kawabe, H., S. Fujita, and M. Yanagita, *Rept. Sci. Res. Inst. (Tokyo)*, **9**, 397 (1952); *Chem. Abstr.*, **48**, 7817 (1954).
120. Kirkpatrick, W. H. (National Aluminate Corp.), U.S. Patent 2,106,486, 1938.
121. Klyachko, V. A., U.S.S.R. Patent 105,753, 1957.
122. Konami, T., and K. Nishioka (Kirashiki Rayon Co.), Jap. Patent 3796, 1954.
123. Kressman, T. R. E., and J. A. Kitchener, *J. Chem. Soc.*, **1949**, 1190.
124. Kressman, T. R. E. (Permutit Co. Ltd.), U.S. Patent 2,570,822, 1951.
125. Kressman, T. R. E., and E. I. Akeroyd (Permutit Co. Ltd.), Brit. Patent 694,778, 1953.
126. Kressman, T. R. E., and F. L. Tye (Permutit Co. Ltd.), Brit. Patent 726,918, 1955.
127. Kressman, T. R. E., and F. L. Tye (Permutit Co. Ltd.), Brit. Patent 726,925, 1955.
128. Kropa, E. L. (American Cyanamid Co.), U.S. Patent 2,663,702, 1953.
129. Kuriyama, S., and C. Yamashita, Jap. Patent 5383, 1952.
130. Kuwada, T., A. Misono, S. Yoshikawa, and Y. Osawa, *J. Chem. Soc. Japan, Ind. Chem. Sect.*, **55**, 625 (1952); *Chem. Abstr.*, **48**, 6049 (1954).
131. Kuwada, T., S. Yoshikawa, and T. Kubotera, *J. Chem. Soc. Japan, Ind. Chem. Sect.*, **57**, 676 (1954); *Chem. Abstr.*, **49**, 8526 (1955); Jap. Patent 6045, 1953.
132. Lautsch, W., W. Broser, U. Döring, and H. Zoschke, *Naturwissenschaften*, **38**, 210 (1951).
133. Lešek, F., M. Sytař, and R. Chromeček, *Zhur. Prikl. Khim.*, **33**, 1745 (1960).
134. Lindenbaum, S., G. E. Boyd, and G. E. Myers, *J. Phys. Chem.*, **62**, 995 (1958).
135. Lundberg, L. A., and J. R. Dudley (American Cyanamid Co.), U.S. Patent 2,469,-692, 1949.
136. Lundberg, L. A. (American Cyanamid Co.), U.S. Patent 2,610,156, 1952.
137. Lundberg, L. A. (American Cyanamid Co.), U.S. Patent 2,610,170, 1952.
138. Lundberg, L. A. (American Cyanamid Co.), U.S. Patent 2,620,315, 1952.
139. Manecke, G., and K. F. Bonhoeffer, *Z. Elektrochem.*, **55**, 475 (1951).
140. Manecke, G., *Z. physik. Chem.*, **201**, 1 (1952).
141. Manecke, G., and H. Heller, *Angew. Chem.*, **72**, 523 (1960).
142. Manegold, E., and K. Solf, *Kolloid Z.*, **55**, 273 (1931).
143. Marshall, C. E., *J. Phys. Chem.*, **43**, 1155 (1939).
144. Marshall, C. E., and W. E. Bergman, *J. Phys. Chem.*, **46**, 52 (1942).

145. McBurney, C. H. (Rohm & Haas Co.), U.S. Patent 2,591,573, 1952.

146. McBurney, C. H. (Rohm & Haas Co.), U.S. Patent 2,591,574, 1952.

147. McMaster, E. L. (The Dow Chemical Co.), U.S. Patent 2,616,877, 1952.

148. McMaster, E. L., R. M. Wheaton, and J. R. Skidmore (The Dow Chemical Co.), U.S. Patents 2,631,999, 2,632,000, and 2,632,001, 1953.

149. McMaster, E. L., and H. Tolksmith (The Dow Chemical Co.), U.S. Patent 2,764,-560, 1956.

150. McMaster, E. L., and W. K. Glesner (The Dow Chemical Co.), U.S. Patent 2,764,-561, 1956.

151. McMaster, E. L., and W. K. Glesner (The Dow Chemical Co.), U.S. Patent 2,764,-563,1956.

152. McMaster, E. L., and W. K. Glesner (The Dow Chemical Co.), U.S. Patent 2,764,-564, 1956.

153. Meier, R. L., and W. E. Elwell (California Research Corp.), U.S. Patent 2,469,295, 1949.

154. Meyer, K. H., and J. F. Sievers, *Helv. chim. Acta*, **19**, 665 (1936).

155. Michael, M. W. (American Cyanamid Co.), U.S. Patent 2,543,666, 1951.

156. Michaelis, L., *Kolloid Z.*, **62**, 2 (1933).

157. Misono, A., and S. Yoshikawa, Jap. Patent 2245, 1953.

158. Mock, R. A., C. A. Marshall, and L. R. Morris (The Dow Chemical Co.), U.S. Patent 2,910,445, 1959.

159. Moralli, J., *Bull. soc. chem. France*, **1953**, 1044.

160. Morris, L. R. (The Dow Chemical Co.), U.S. Patent 2,875,162, 1959.

161. Nakamura, Y., K. Fujiwara, and K. Yaegashi, *J. Chem. Soc. Japan, Ind. Chem. Sect.*, **55**, 603 (1952); *Chem. Abstr.*, **48**, 6049 (1954).

162. National Aluminate Corp. (H. P. Gregor and H. I. Patzelt), Brit. Patent 835,137, 1960.

163. Neihof, R., *J. Phys. Chem.*, **58**, 916 (1954).

164. Ohtsuka, Y., and S. Umezawa, *J. Chem. Soc. Japan, Ind. Chem. Sect.*, **55**, 230 (1952); *Chem. Abstr.*, **47**, 10766 (1953).

165. Otto, J. A. (Allied Chemical & Dye Corp.), U.S. Patent 2,590,449, 1952.

166. Parrish, J. R., *Chem. & Ind. (London)*, **1955**, 386.

167. Patnode, H. W., and M. R. J. Wyllie (Gulf Res. Dev. Co.), U.S. Patent 2,614,976, 1952.

168. Pennington, L. D., and M. B. Williams, *Ind. Eng. Chem.*, **51**, 759 (1959).

169. Pepper, K. W., *J. Appl. Chem.*, **1**, 124 (1951).

170. Pepper, K. W., H. M. Paisley, and M. A. Young, *J. Chem. Soc.*, **1953**, 4097.

171. Pepper, K. W., and D. K. Hale, in "Ion Exchange and Its Applications," p. 13, Society of Chemical Industry, London, 1955.

172. Permutit Co. Ltd. and E. L. Holmes, L. E. Holmes, and W. G. Prescott, Brit. Patent 506,291, 1939.

173. Permutit Co. Ltd. and E. L. Holmes, and L. E. Holmes, Brit. Patent 588,380, 1947.

174. Permutit Co. Ltd. and T. R. E. Kressman, Brit. Patent 643,943, 1950.

175. Permutit Co. Ltd. and T. R. E. Kressman, Brit. Patent 655,554, 1951.

176. Permutit Co. Ltd. and T. R. E. Kressman, Brit. Patent 660,130, 1951.

177. Permutit Co. Ltd. and J. R. Millar, Brit. Patent 849,122, 1960.

178. Phillips & Pain, Etabl., F. Patent 819,433, 1937.

179. Phillips & Pain, Etabl., F. Patent 990,563, 1951.

180. Resinous Products & Chemical Co., Brit. Patent 556,622, 1943.

181. Resinous Products & Chemical Co., F. Patent 988,486, 1951.

182. Rohm & Haas Co., Brit. Patent 670,348, 1952.

183. Rohm & Haas Co., Brit. Patent 718,168, 1954.

184. Roth, H. H. (The Dow Chemical Co.), U.S. Patent 2,604,461, 1952.

185. Runge, F., and W. Zimmermann, *J. prakt. Chem.*, **1**, 283 (1954).

186. Schmid, G., *J. chim. phys.*, **55**, 163 (1958).
187. Schneider, H. J. (Rohm & Haas Co.), U.S. Patent 2,675,359, 1954.
188. Scott, M. J., and E. F. Jackson (Monsanto Chemical Co.), U.S. Patent 2,531,863, 1950.
188a. Seidl, J., and J. Stamberg, *Chem. & Ind.*, **1960**, 1190.
189. Skogseid, A., Dissertation, Oslo, 1948; A. Skogseid (Norsk Hydro-Electrisk Kv.), Norw. Patent 72,583, 1947; U.S. Patent 2,592,350, 1952.
190. Skogseid, A. (Norsk Hydro-Electrisk Kv.), Ger. Patent 876,913, 1953.
191. Sollner, K., *J. Phys. Chem.*, **49**, 47 (1945).
192. Sollner, K., and R. Neihof, *Arch. Biochem. Biophys.*, **33**, 166 (1951).
193. Spiegler, K. S., in "Ion Exchanges Technology," F. C. Nachod and J. Schubert (eds.), p. 118, Academic Press, Inc., New York, 1956.
194. Staatsmijnen in Limburg, Directie van de, Holl. Patents 72,245, 73,798, 1953; Holl. Patent 75,968, 1954.
195. Staatsmijnen in Limburg, Directie van de, Brit. Patent 697,503, 1953; Holl. Patent 73,922, 1954.
196. Staatsmijnen in Limburg, Directie van de, Holl. Patent 73,966, 1954.
197. Stach, H., *Angew. Chem.*, **63**, 263 (1951).
198. Stamicarbon N. V., Holl. Patent 75,705, 1954.
199. Staudinger, H., and E. Husemann, *Ber. dtsch. chem. Ges.*, **68**, 1618 (1935).
200. Stroh, G. R. (American Cyanamid Co.), U.S. Patent 2,515,142, 1950.
201. Suda, H., and R. Oda, *J. Chem. Soc. Japan, Ind. Chem. Sect.*, **57**, 506 (1954); *Chem. Abstr.*, **49**, 4907 (1955).
202. Sussman, S. (Permutit Co.), U.S. Patent 2,518,956, 1950.
203. Swain, R. C. (American Cyanamid Co.), U.S. Patent 2,251,234, 1941.
204. Thomas, S. L. S., and J. I. Jones (Natl. Research Development Corp.), Brit. Patent 762,085, 1956.
205. Umezawa, S., and Y. Ohtsuka (Nippon Penicillin Sci. Ass.), Jap. Patent 1598 (1953).
205a. United Kingdom Atomic Energy Authority (J. Kennedy), Brit. Patent 855,009, 1960.
206. United Water Softeners and E. L. Holmes, Brit. Patent 472,404, 1937.
207. Urbain, O. M., and W. R. Stemen (C. H. Lewis Co.), U.S. Patent 2,275,210, 1942.
208. Walsh, E. N., T. M. Beck, and A. D. F. Toy, *J. Am. Chem. Soc.*, **78**, 4455 (1956).
209. Wassenegger, H. (I. G. Farbenindustrie), Ger. Patent 733,679, 1943.
210. Wassenegger, H., and E. Meier (I. G. Farbenindustrie), Ger. Patent 745,387, 1943.
211. Wetstone, D. M., and H. P. Gregor, *J. Phys. Chem.*, **61**, 151 (1957).
212. Wheaton, R. M., and W. C. Bauman, *Ind. Eng. Chem.*, **43**, 1088 (1951).
213. Wheaton, R. M., and D. F. Harrington, *Ind. Eng. Chem.*, **44**, 1796 (1952).
214. Wheaton, R. M., and D. F. Harrington (The Dow Chemical Co.), U.S. Patent 2,642,417, 1953.
215. Whittaker, D., and G. G. Allen (Imperial Chem. Ind. Ltd.), U.S. Patent 2,588,784, 1952.
216. Wiley, R. H., and C. C. Ketterer, *J. Am. Chem. Soc.*, **75**, 4519 (1953).
217. Wiley, R. H., N. R. Smith, and C. C. Ketterer, *J. Am. Chem. Soc.*, **76**, 720 (1954).
218. Wiley, R. H., and S. F. Reed, Jr., *J. Phys. Chem.*, **60**, 533 (1956).
219. Wiley, R. H., and J. M. Schmitt, *J. Am. Chem. Soc.*, **78**, 2169 (1956).
220. Wiley, R. H., and S. F. Reed, Jr., *J. Am. Chem. Soc.*, **78**, 2171 (1956).
221. Wiley, R. H., and J. M. Schmitt, *J. Polymer Sci.*, **27**, 587 (1958).
222. Winslow, F. H., and W. Matreyek, *Ind. Eng. Chem.*, **43**, 1108 (1951).
223. Woermann, D., K. F. Bonhoeffer, and F. Helfferich, *Z. physik. Chem. (Frankfurt)*, **8**, 265 (1956).
224. Wyllie, M. R. J., and H. W. Patnode, *J. Phys. Chem.*, **54**, 204 (1950).
225. Wyllie, M. R. J., and S. L. Kanaan, *J. Phys. Chem.*, **58**, 73 (1954).

4

Capacity

From a practical point of view, an ion exchanger can be considered as a reservoir of exchangeable counter ions. These counter ions are put to use in ion-exchange operations and, hence, the counter-ion content (or the potential for taking up counter ions) is one of the most important characteristics of an ion exchanger. This is all the more true since the counter-ion content of a given amount of material is given essentially by the amount of fixed charges which must be balanced by the counter ions, and thus is essentially constant, i.e., independent of the particle size and shape and of the nature of the counter ion.

Ion exchangers are characterized in a quantitative manner by their *capacity* which, in common usage, is defined as the number of counter-ion equivalents in a specified amount of the material. Actually, this simple definition is not sufficient and will have to be qualified later in the discussion. Considerable confusion has arisen from the fact that, at least in the past, different authors had different concepts of the capacity and used different definitions and units. Hence, capacity data stated without a rigorous definition or a description of how they were obtained should be accepted with reservations.

In this book, a whole chapter is devoted to the capacity of ion exchangers. The detailed description of this one aspect is intended to make the reader acquainted not only with the maze of different definitions and methods of determination, but also with the behavior of the fixed ionic groups as the unique and most important components of the ion exchangers.

4-1. DEFINITIONS AND UNITS

Capacity and related data are primarily used for two purposes: for characterizing ion-exchange materials and for use in the numerical calculation of ion-exchange operations. In the first case, the capacity should be defined, if possible, in such a way that it is a characteristic constant of the material and is independent of the experimental conditions.　In the second case, it is usually more practical to use other definitions or quantities which reflect the effect of the operating conditions.　A glossary of the most common definitions is given in Table 4-1.　The various definitions are illustrated in the following discussion.

Table 4-1. Capacity definitions

	Definition	Remarks
Capacity (maximum capacity, ion-exchange capacity)	Number of ionogenic groups per specified amount of ion exchanger	Constant used for characterizing ion exchangers
Scientific weight capacity....	Units: meq/g dry H^+ or Cl^- form	
Technical volume capacity...	Units: eq/liter packed bed in H^+ or Cl^- form and fully water-swollen. Other units: eq/ft³ bed, lb CaO/ft³ bed, etc.	
Apparent capacity (effective capacity)	Number of *exchangeable* counter ions per specified amount of ion exchanger. Common units: meq/g dry H^+ or Cl^- form (apparent weight capacity)	Is lower than maximum capacity when ionogenic groups are incompletely ionized; depends on experimental conditions (pH, solution concentration, etc.)
Sorption capacity.............	Amount of solute, taken up by sorption rather than by ion exchange, per specified amount of ion exchanger	Depends on experimental conditions
Useful capacity..............	Capacity utilized when equilibrium is not attained	Depends on experimental conditions (ion-exchange rate, etc.)
Breakthrough capacity (dynamic capacity)	Capacity utilized in column operations	Depends on operating conditions
Concentration of fixed ionic groups	Number of fixed ionic groups in meq/cm³ swollen resin (molarity) or per gram solvent in resin (molality)	Depends on experimental conditions (swelling, etc.). Used in theoretical treatment of ion-exchange phenomena

Weight capacity.　The accepted way of characterizing the capacity of an ion exchanger is by giving the number of ionogenic groups contained in the *"specific amount"* of the material.　The specific amount is defined as the amount which weighs one gram when the material is completely converted to the H^+ or Cl^- form* and is devoid of sorbed solutes and solvents.　So

---

* The capacity of anion exchangers refers to the Cl^- form rather than the OH^- form because the dry weight of the latter is more difficult to determine (see Sec. 5-9c).

rigorous a definition is necessary because the weight of a given amount of the ion exchanger depends on the experimental conditions, for example, on its ionic form. The characteristic constant obtained in this way is usually called the (scientific) *weight capacity* and is expressed in milliequivalents per gram.

The weight capacity of the common ion-exchange resins is of the order of several milliequivalents per gram.

> *Example.* Styrene-divinylbenzene copolymers, when completely monosulfonated and in H^+ form, consist predominantly of units

$$...-CH-CH_2-...$$

$$SO_3^- H^+$$

> (see page 35). Each unit, $C_8H_8O_3S$, has the formula weight 184.2 and carries one fixed ionic group. Accordingly, the theoretical weight capacity is about $1,000/184.2 = 5.43$ meq/g. Actually, the resins also contain sulfonated divinylbenzene and ethylstyrene units with equivalent weights of 210.2 and 212.2, respectively. The capacity of, say, a resin with 8 per cent DVB and 4 per cent ethylstyrene thus is slightly lower, namely, 5.35 meq/g.

With styrene-type cation exchangers, the values predicted in this way agree remarkably well with both experimental capacity determinations and analytical determinations of the sulfur content (see also Fig. 3-3). Furthermore, the dry-weight capacity depends very little on the degree of crosslinking since the crosslinking agent (divinylbenzene) is also sulfonated and differs not very much from the styrene units in its equivalent weight.

The capacities of most other resins are of the same order of magnitude (about 9.0 meq/g for crosslinked polyacrylic acid, 2.5 to 4.0 meq/g for styrene-type anion exchangers with methylenetrimethylammonium groups, etc.). In most cases, however, the capacity is not as readily predicted as for sulfonated polystyrenes. In styrene-type anion exchangers, for example, not every benzene ring carries one ionic group. In phenolsulfonic-acid resins, as a rule, only every second or third benzene ring carries a sulfonic acid group. Analytical determinations of the sulfur content of such resins can also be misleading because sulfur may be present in the form of (non-ionic) sulfone groups, $R-SO_2-R$.

The capacities of inorganic ion exchangers fall in the same range. For example, zirconium phosphates with capacities up to 12 meq/g have been prepared. For chabazite, $(Ca,Na)[Si_2AlO_6]_2 \cdot 6H_2O$, the equivalent weight of the (hypothetical) H^+ form is 234.2, and the theoretical weight capacity thus 4.22 meq/g. Most other materials have lower capacities.

In clays, an unambiguous distinction between sorbed and structurally bound water is hardly possible. Here, the capacity is usually given in milliequivalents per gram of "backbone," i.e., of material left after ignition in air minus weight of exchangeable counter ions. Ignition is accompanied by an irreversible loss of structurally bound water.

Note also that capacity data supplied by resin manufacturers occasionally refer to "air dry" material which usually still contains about 5 to 10 per cent water. Accordingly, these values are slightly lower than the scientific weight capacities.

Volume capacity. For technical applications and design purposes, the number of exchangeable counter ions in, say, an ion-exchange column and the size of this column are the pertinent variables. Here, it is more practical to define the capacity as the number of ionogenic groups per unit *volume of packed bed.* This so-called technical volume capacity is usually given in equivalents per liter of (fully swollen) bed. Other units such as equivalents per cubic foot, pounds of CaO or $CaCO_3$ per cubic foot, etc., are also used.

The volume occupied by a given amount of the ion exchanger depends on the experimental conditions (ionic form of the resin, composition of the solution with which the resin is in contact, etc.). The volume capacity usually refers to a settled bed which is in H^+ or Cl^- form, contains no sorbed solutes, and is fully water-swollen. In this case, the following interrelation between the scientific weight capacity and the technical volume capacity holds:

$$Q_{vol} = (1 - \beta)\bar{\rho} \frac{100 - W}{100} Q_{weight} \qquad (4\text{-}1)$$

where Q_{vol} = volume capacity in equivalents per liter packed bed; Q_{weight} = scientific weight capacity in milliequivalents per gram; β = fractional void volume of the packing; W = water content of the resin in weight per cent; $\bar{\rho}$ = density of the swollen resin in grams per cubic centimeter.

Sometimes, however, the volume capacity is defined as referring to a bed under the operating conditions. This value is, in most cases, somewhat higher since the bed usually contracts when being treated with electrolyte solutions or solvents other than water.

The volume capacity depends on the water content of the ion exchanger and, hence, on the degree of crosslinking, even in the case of styrene-type resins. A weakly crosslinked resin swells more strongly and thus has a lower capacity per unit volume.

Example. Sulfonated polystyrenes have a weight capacity of about 5.4 meq/g (see page 74). A resin with 10 per cent DVB, in H^+ form, free of sorbed solutes, and fully water-swollen has a density $\bar{\rho} = 1.25$ g/cm^3 and a water content $W = 46.8$ % wt [24]. The fractional void volume of a packed bed may be taken as $\beta = 0.40$. According to Eq. (4-1), the volume capacity is

$$Q_{vol} = (1 - 0.40) \cdot 1.25 \frac{100 - 46.8}{100} 5.4 = 2.2 \text{ eq/liter bed}$$

In comparison, the data for a resin with 2 per cent DVB are $\bar{\rho} = 1.09$ g/cm^3 and $W = 76.5\%$ wt [24]. The volume capacity thus is

$$Q_{vol} = (1 - 0.40) \cdot 1.09 \, \frac{100 - 76.5}{100} \, 5.4 = 0.83 \text{ eq/liter bed}$$

Concentration of fixed ionic groups. The weight or volume capacity is an excellent means of characterizing an ion exchanger, but a rather inconvenient one to use in the theoretical treatment of ion-exchange phenomena. What are needed here are quantities which reflect the condition (swelling state, etc.) of the resin in the particular process which is being studied. Such a quantity is the *concentration of the fixed ionic groups*, usually given in milliequivalents per gram of solvent in the resin (weight normality, molality) or per milliliters of swollen gel* (volume normality, molarity). The concentration of the fixed ionic groups refers to the particular state of the resin under the given experimental conditions and thus is inherently a variable rather than a characteristic constant. As a rule, its value even changes in the course of, say, an ion exchange since the latter is usually accompanied by a change in swelling.

In the theoretical treatment of ion exchangers, two different models are commonly used. The treatment of diffusion and other rate phenomena is usually based on the concept that the ion-exchanger gel can be considered as a *quasi-homogeneous phase* (see Chaps. 6, 7, 8, 9, and 12). Here, the most appropriate concentration unit is the molarity. In the treatment of swelling, sorption, and ion-exchange equilibria it is often more practical to use the *sponge model* which pictures the ion-exchanger gel as a heterogeneous system consisting of the inert matrix and the "pore" liquid (see Chap. 5). Here, the most appropriate concentration unit is the molality. Of course, the units in any such treatment should be used consistently for all species.

In the definition of the concentration of fixed ionic groups, the question arises whether or not undissociated ionogenic groups should be included (see also Sec. 4-2). In the theoretical treatment, association can be accounted for either in the definition of the concentrations (i.e., not counting associated species as ions) or in the definition of the activity coefficients (in this case, the ionic concentrations include associated species). One or the other approach may be more expedient in any particular case.

The concentration of fixed ionogenic groups (associated groups included) in a resin which is in an arbitrary ionic form and contains arbitrary amounts of sorbed solutes is related to the (scientific) weight capacity by

$$\bar{m}_R = \frac{100 - W}{W \left(1 + \sum_i Q_i - M_{ref}10^{-3}Q_{weight}\right)} \, Q_{weight} \qquad (4\text{-}2)$$

$$X = \bar{\rho} \, \frac{100 - W}{100 \left(1 + \sum_i Q_i - M_{ref}10^{-3}Q_{weight}\right)} \, Q_{weight} \qquad (4\text{-}3)$$

---

* In contrast to the technical volume capacity which refers to unit volume of packed bed, the interstitial void is *not* included.

where $\bar{m}_R$ = molality of fixed groups in milliequivalents per gram; X = molarity of fixed groups, in milliequivalents per cubic centimeter; $\bar{p}$ = density of the resin in grams per cubic centimeter; W = solvent content of the resin in weight, per cent; Q_i = amount of species i in the "specific amount" of resin, in grams; M_{ref} = atomic weight of reference ion (1 for cation exchangers, 35.5 for anion exchangers); the summation is carried out over counter ions and sorbed solutes, if any.

Example. The concentration of fixed ionic groups in a sulfonated polystyrene with 10 per cent DVB, in Na^+ form and free of sorbed solutes, can be calculated from the following data: Q_{weight} = 5.33 meq/g; W = 44.0% wt; $\bar{p}$ = 1.31 g/cm^3. The specific amount of the resin contains $22.99 \cdot 10^{-3} \cdot Q_{weight}$ = 0.12 g Na^+ and no sorbed solutes (22.99 is the atomic weight of Na). Thus $\sum_i Q_i = 0.12$ g. One obtains

$$\bar{m}_R = \frac{100 - 44.0}{44.0(1 + 0.12 - 5.33 \cdot 10^{-3})} \, 5.33 = 6.1 \text{ meq/g solvent}$$

$$X = \frac{1.31(100 - 44.0)}{100(1 + 0.12 - 5.33 \cdot 10^{-3})} \, 5.33 = 3.5 \text{ meq/cm}^3 \text{ resin}$$

The dependence of the molality and molarity of fixed ionic groups on the degree of crosslinking in a typical resin is shown in Fig. 4-1.

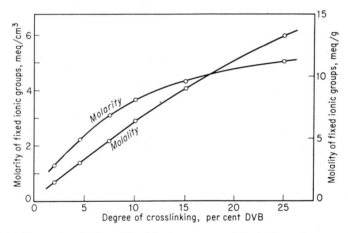

FIG. 4-1. Molality and molarity of fixed ionic groups and their dependence on the (nominal) degree of crosslinking. Resins: sulfonated styrene-divinylbenzene copolymers in H^+ form, fully water-swollen. *Calculated from experimental data of K. W. Pepper, D. Reichenberg, and D. K. Hale* [24].

Apparent capacity. From a practical point of view, the number of counter ions which can be taken up or exchanged is more important than the number of ionogenic groups. For example, weak-acid or weak-base groups may be incompletely ionized and thus partly inoperative. The *apparent* or *effective* capacity, expressed in terms of exchangeable counter ions, depends on the experimental conditions. A more detailed discussion is given in Sec. 4-2.

Ion-exchange capacity, sorption capacity, and over-all sorptive capacity. An ion exchanger in, say, Na^+ form can sorb electrolytes such as

NaCl from solutions. The Na^+ content of a resin which contains sorbed NaCl is higher than its content of fixed ionic groups. The usual capacity definitions refer to ion exchangers which are free of sorbed solutes (see page 7); counter ions taken up by sorption are not included. One can stress this point by declaring these capacities explicitly as *ion-exchange capacities.* Beyond their ion-exchange capacity, ion exchangers have a *sorption capacity* for electrolytes and other solutes. The sum of the two may be called "overall sorptive capacity." The sorption capacity, in contrast to the (appropriately defined) ion-exchange capacity, depends strongly on the nature of the solute and the experimental conditions such as solution concentration, type of solvent, etc. Sorption equilibria are discussed in Sec. 5-3.

The distinction between ion-exchange and sorption capacity loses much of its sharpness when the difference between the two phenomena is not clear-cut. For example, a weak-base anion exchanger in the free-base form takes up acids without exchanging ions:

$$\overline{R—NH_2} + H^+ + Cl^- \rightarrow \overline{R—NH_3^+} + \overline{Cl^-} \tag{4-4}$$

The phenomenon (4-4) is, in fact, sorption rather than ion exchange. The anion exchanger in the free-base form can be described as having a low apparent ion-exchange capacity and a correspondingly high apparent sorption capacity for acids. However, it is usually more expedient to characterize the resin by its maximum ion-exchange capacity which is attained when all ionogenic groups are ionized. This capacity value is constant and, when converted to milliequivalents per specific amount, is identical with the scientific weight capacity.

Useful Capacity; Breakthrough Capacity. Ion exchange occurs at a finite rate. This rate may be so low that the full capacity of an ion exchanger cannot be utilized in an actual operation. The "useful" capacity may thus be lower than the (equilibrium) ion-exchange capacity.

Many ion-exchange operations are carried out in columns. As a rule, the operation is discontinued at breakthrough, before the bed has come to complete equilibrium with the feed. The capacity which is utilized until breakthrough occurs is called the *breakthrough* (or *dynamic*) *capacity.* The breakthrough capacity and its dependence on the operating conditions is discussed in Secs. 9-1 and 9-9.

General remarks. The various capacities can, of course, be expressed in different concentration units. For example, the apparent capacity can be given in milliequivalents per unit weight of dry or swollen resin, per unit volume of resin or bed, etc. Note that dimensions such as milliequivalents per gram or milliequivalents per cubic centimeter are not sufficient for identifying the concentration units since they can refer to swollen or dry resin or bed, to different ionic forms of the resin, etc.

The notation chosen in this section is hardly more than an attempt to arrive at an interconsistent set of definitions. As yet, a uniform notation has not been generally accepted. In many earlier publications, the term "capacity" has been used indiscriminately for one or the other of the quantities defined above. A meaningful comparison of literature data can only be made when the capacities given are defined in the same way and are converted to the same concentration units.

4-2. APPARENT CAPACITY AND ITS DEPENDENCE ON EXPERIMENTAL CONDITIONS

The apparent capacity is a phenomenological quantity which indicates how many counter ions the ion exchanger can take up under specified conditions. From the practical point of view, it matters little whether the uptake is by ion exchange or by sorption or what chemical mechanisms are involved.

The apparent capacity (expressed in terms of exchangeable counter ions) and the scientific weight capacity (expressed in terms of ionogenic groups in the resin) are not necessarily equivalent, even when electrolyte sorption is insignificant. Only when they are ionized do the ionogenic groups act as fixed charges which must be balanced by counter ions. Groups which are (and remain) nonionized do not contribute to the apparent capacity. Strong-acid and strong-base groups are, by definition, practically completely ionized under any conditions. The apparent capacity of resins with such groups thus is essentially constant and equivalent to the scientific weight capacity. In contrast, weak-acid and weak-base groups are predominantly nonionic at low and high pH, respectively. The apparent capacity of resins with such groups thus depends on the pH. For example, weak-acid resins can take up fewer Na^+ ions from acid than from alkaline solutions [4], and weak-base resin can take up fewer Cl^- ions from alkaline than from acid solutions.

The degree of ionization of the ionogenic groups depends on the acid or base strength of the groups, i.e., on their pK value, and on the pH in the resin. Acid groups become predominantly nonionic when the pH drops below the pK value of the groups [see Eq. (4-12)]. The opposite holds for base groups.* The apparent capacity of cation exchangers thus falls off when the pH in the resin drops below the pK of the groups. The same is true for anion exchangers when the pH rises above the pK of the groups.

The pH in the resin usually differs from that in the external solution (see also page 85) and depends on other factors besides the external pH. Suppose that the external solution contains a strong electrolyte such as NaCl. The Na^+ ions can enter the resin, displacing (free) H^+ ions from the resin:

$$Na^+ + \overline{H^+} \rightarrow H^+ + \overline{Na^+} \tag{4-5}$$

thus raising the internal pH. It follows from the LeChâtelier principle that, at a given pH in the external solution, the exchange (4-5) is enhanced when the concentration of Na^+ in the external solution is increased. The apparent capacity of the resin for cations such as Na^+ thus not only depends

---

* The pK value of a weak-base group, for example, RNH_2, is defined as the negative logarithm of the equilibrium constant of the reaction $RNH_3^+ \rightleftharpoons RNH_2 + H^+$; $pK_{resin} \equiv - \log ([RNH_2][H^+]/[RNH_3^+])$.

on the pH of the external solution but also increases with increasing concentration of Na^+ in the solution. Of course, the same is true for the capacity of weak-base resins for anions. The apparent capacities of resins with weakly ionized groups also depend on the nature of the counter ion; a greater affinity of the counter ion for the resin results in a greater "driving force" for the uptake by an exchange such as (4-5) and in a higher apparent capacity of the resin for this ion.

The apparent capacity of weak-acid and weak-base resins for ions which form weak bases and weak acids, respectively, is usually rather low, even when the pH in the resin is favorable for ionization of the ionogenic groups [3,23]. A weak acid is substantially dissociated only at a pH which is *higher* than the pK of the acid. The basic groups of an anion exchanger are substantially ionized only at a pH which is *lower* than the pK of the groups. The presence of acid anions as counter ions is only possible when there is an overlap of the pH ranges in which the acid and the groups are ionized, i.e., when

$$pK_{acid} < pK_{resin} \qquad (4-6)$$

This fact may be illustrated by a case in which the condition (4-6) is not met. Consider the uptake of borate ions ($pK_{acid} \approx 9$) by a weak-base resin with amino groups ($pK_{resin} \approx 8$). At an (internal) pH below 8, the amino groups are ionized, but boric acid is not. Hence the electric charge of the groups must be balanced by anions other than borate. Borate anions in substantial amounts can only exist at a pH above 9, but in this range the fixed groups are not ionized. Thus, neither at high nor at low pH do the ionogenic groups contribute to the uptake or retention of boric acid or borate anions. Similar rules hold for cation exchangers. Here, the condition which corresponds to (4-6) is

$$pK_{base} > pK_{resin} \qquad (4-7)$$

The apparent capacity of anion exchangers for anions of polyvalent acids is also pH dependent, at least when expressed in terms of moles of acid taken up. Phosphoric acid may serve as an example. The pK values of this acid are $pK_1 \cong 2$; $pK_2 \cong 7$; $pK_3 \cong 12$. Hence, at an (internal) pH above 12, the predominant species in the resin is PO_4^{3-} which balances the charges of *three* fixed ionic groups. At lower pH, the species HPO_4^{2-} and $H_2PO_4^-$ become predominant. These species balance the charges of only *two* and *one* fixed groups, respectively. A resin in, say, $H_2PO_4^-$-form thus contains three times as much phosphate as when in PO_4^{3-} form [21,23], provided that no other effects interfere. This interesting phenomenon and its consequences will be discussed in more detail in Sec. 5-3f.

Polyfunctional ion exchangers contain ionogenic groups which differ in their pK values. Here, the various effects produced by the different groups are superimposed on one another [20,23]. The apparent capacities for various counter ions and the pH depend-ence are readily derived from the discussion in the preceding paragraphs.

In a few exceptional cases, the apparent capacity is limited by the size of the counter ion. For example, zeolites exclude counter ions which are too large to fit into the chan-nels of the alumosilicate framework. With ion-exchange resins, such effects become noticeable only if the degree of crosslinking is very high or if the counter ion is very large [5,25]. This "sieve action" is discussed in more detail in Secs. 5-4b and f.

The apparent capacities of weak-acid and weak-base resins are also a function of tem-perature. As a rule, the pK values of both acid and base groups decrease with increasing temperature. Thus, at higher temperature, the apparent capacity of weak-acid resins is usually higher and that of weak-base resins lower [14].

The complex dependence of the apparent capacity on the experimental conditions makes this quantity rather unsuitable for resin characterization. Apparent capacity data are meaningful only when accompanied by a detailed description of the experimental conditions (pH alone is insufficient). A better way of characterizing a resin is by giving its (scientific) weight capacity and the pK of its ionogenic groups. For monofunctional strong-acid and strong-base resins, the pK value is not needed since the apparent capacity is practically constant. For polyfunctional resins, the capacity contributions of the various groups and their pK values should be given. This information is sufficient for estimating the apparent capacity under any particular set of experimental conditions (see page 87). The scientific weight capacity and the pK values can be determined by pH titration of the resin. This technique is described in Secs. 4-4 and 4-5d.

4-3. pH TITRATION

Ion-exchange resins are polyelectrolyte gels. Cation exchangers in H^+ form and anion exchangers in OH^- form can be considered as insoluble acids and bases. In many respects, they act like their soluble counterparts. In particular, they can be titrated with standard bases and acids. In such a titration, the ion exchanger remains insoluble, but comes to equilibrium with the solution to which the titrant is added. The neutralization of the resin acid or base can be observed by recording the pH of the supernatant solution while the titration is in progress. Such a "pH titration curve" can be evaluated to give the number of ionogenic groups and their pK value. This procedure is very similar, though not quite as simple, as in the case of dissolved acids and bases. The pH titration curve, first used by Griessbach [13] is an excellent means of characterizing an ion exchanger [1–3,7,8,10–15].

A correct interpretation of pH titration curves can only be given when the mechanism is well understood. In the following, the mechanism of pH titrations is discussed in detail.*

---

* For the sake of simplicity, a "progressive" titration is described. This procedure is the common one for dissolved acids and bases. For ion exchangers, however, other techniques are more practical (see Sec. 4-5c).

a. Straight Titration

Suppose that a monofunctional, strong-acid cation exchanger is titrated with a standard NaOH solution. The resin, completely converted to the H^+ form, is placed in water to which the titrant is added. Upon addition of NaOH, the ion exchange

$$\overline{H^+} + Na^+ \rightarrow \overline{Na^+} + H^+ \qquad (4\text{-}8)$$

takes place. The H^+ ions released by the resin combine at once with the OH^- ions of the added base

$$H^+ + OH^- \rightarrow H_2O \qquad (4\text{-}9)$$

According to the Le Châtelier principle, the neutralization of the H^+ ions in the solution drives the ion exchange (4-8) essentially to completion, i.e., the

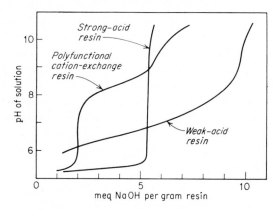

Fig. 4-2. pH titration curves of various cation-exchange resins.

Na^+ ions added are practically completely taken up by the resin as long as the latter still contains H^+ ions. The amount of H^+ ions released by the resin is stoichiometrically equivalent to the amount of NaOH added. Hence the pH of the supernatant aqueous phase remains essentially unchanged. However, as soon as all H^+ ions have been displaced from the resin by Na^+, the pH of the solution rises sharply with further addition of NaOH. The titration curve is similar to that of a dissolved strong acid, except that the initial pH of the aqueous phase is much higher since the H^+ ions of the acid groups are in the resin rather than in the aqueous phase. The number of acid equivalents—and thus the capacity of the resin—can be calculated from the amount of titrant added up to the point where the steep rise in pH occurs. For example, the weight capacity of the strong-acid resin in Fig. 4-2 is 5.3 meq/g.

The titration curve of a monofunctional, weak-acid resin has a somewhat different shape (see Fig. 4-2). The initial pH of the aqueous phase is slightly higher because the acid groups are weakly dissociated. For the same reason, the resin is reluctant to exchange its H^+ ions for Na^+ ions, so that the ion exchange (4-8) remains incomplete. Hence, the pH in the aqueous phase rises noticeably even in the early stages of the titration. With increasing concentrations of Na^+ and OH^- in the solution, the ion exchange (4-8) is driven more and more to completion. The pH rises sharply when the resin is completely converted to the Na^+ form. The (maximum) capacity of the resin can be calculated as before from the amount of titrant added up to this point. For example, the capacity of the weak-acid resin in Fig. 4-2 is 9.7 meq/g.

The titration curve of a polyfunctional cation exchanger containing both strong- and weak-acid groups shows steps (see Fig. 4-2). In the early stages of the titration, the pH in the resin is still low and the weak-acid groups are undissociated and thus inactive. Therefore, the initial part of the titration curve resembles that of a monofunctional strong-acid resin. The pH in the aqueous phase rises steeply when the strong-acid groups are completely converted to the Na^+ form. Upon further addition of NaOH, the weak-acid groups are titrated as described in the previous paragraph. The (maximum) capacities of both the strong- and weak-acid groups can be calculated from the two points on the curve at which the pH rises sharply. The capacity of the strong-acid groups of the polyfunctional cation exchanger in Fig. 4-2 is 1.9 meq/g, that of the weak-acid groups is 3.5 meq/g.

The pH titration curves of anion exchangers are analogous, except that the pH of the aqueous phase changes in the opposite direction.

Many polyfunctional ion exchangers, particularly the weak-base resins and ion-exchange coals, contain different ionogenic groups with a whole spectrum of pK values. Here, the steps in the titration curve are smeared out, and the curve has a gradual and fairly uniform slope over a wide pH range. Individual groups can be identified only by special techniques.

b. Titration with Added Salt

Ion exchangers are often titrated in the presence of a dissolved salt such as NaCl. Such a salt has little effect on the titration curves of dissolved acids and bases, but it changes the titration curves of resins. When a strong-acid resin in H^+ form is placed in a solution of, say, NaCl, the ion exchange (4-8) begins even before NaOH is added, and the solution becomes acidic. The pH which the solution attains at this stage depends on the amount of NaCl added, on the ratio of solution volume to resin weight, and on the capacity and nature of the resin. With addition of NaOH, the solution is progressively neutralized and, at the same time, the ion exchange (4-8) is driven to completion. The titration curve thus shows a gradual rise in the early stages of the titration and a steep rise at the point of complete neutralization of the resin. The presence of the salt results in a lower and slightly more sloping curve in the early titration stages. Otherwise the curve is unchanged. In particular, the capacity of the resin can be calculated as before (see Fig. 4-3, upper left; note that the coordinates in this figure are different from those in Fig. 4-2).

Other ion exchangers behave in an analogous manner. With resins having groups of very low acid or base strength, the pH change produced by added salt is less drastic since little or no ion exchange occurs with a neutral salt solution (see Fig. 4-3, lower right).

4-4. DETERMINATION OF pK VALUES

Titration curves in which the pH of the aqueous phase is plotted as a function of the amount of titrant added (see Fig. 4-2) show quantitatively the capacity of the ion exchanger. However, pK values cannot be obtained directly from such curves. First, the relation between the pK of the ionogenic groups in the resin and the pH of the aqueous phase must be established. In the following, a simple relation is derived which leads to "apparent" pK values. Later, a more rigorous treatment is outlined. The discussion is restricted to weak-acid and weak-base groups. For strong-acid and strong-base groups, the equations give only an upper or lower limit for the pK value. Here, however, the exact pK is of little practical significance since the groups are almost completely ionized even at very low and very high pH. For the sake of simplicity, the derivations are given for a cation exchanger. With a few obvious changes they can also be applied to anion exchangers.

a. "Apparent" pK Values

The pK value of an acid group RH is defined as the negative logarithm of the equilibrium constant K of the dissociation equilibrium (square brackets are used for concentrations).

$$\frac{[\overline{R^-}][\overline{H^+}]}{[\overline{RH}]} = K \qquad\qquad pK \equiv -\log K \qquad (4\text{-}10)^*$$

The degree of dissociation α and the pH in the resin are defined by

$$\alpha \equiv \frac{[\overline{R^-}]}{[\overline{R^-}] + [\overline{RH}]} \qquad\qquad \overline{pH} \equiv -\log [\overline{H^+}] \qquad (4\text{-}11)$$

From Eqs. (4-10) and (4-11) one obtains

$$\overline{pH} = pK - \log \frac{1 - \alpha}{\alpha} \qquad (4\text{-}12)$$

---

* The dissociation constant has the dimension of a concentration. Hence the numerical values of K and pK depend on the concentration unit which is used. The same is true for $\overline{pH}$. As a rule, the molality scale (moles per gram solvent in the resin) is used.

Note that this equation involves the pH *in the resin*. The pH in the external solution is usually quite different [16].

The second term in Eq. (4-12) vanishes when $\alpha = 0.5$. In weak-acid resins, the amount of (free) H^+ ions is insignificant as long as ionized groups are present, so that $\alpha = 0.5$ corresponds to 50 per cent conversion of the resin from the H^+ form to the, say, Na^+ form. Thus the (apparent) pK of the groups is equal to the internal pH when the resin is half converted:

$$pK = \overline{pH} \qquad (\alpha = 0.5) \qquad (4\text{-}13)$$

The pK of strong-acid groups is, of course, smaller than the pH at 50 per cent conversion because, at this stage, the degree of dissociation is much larger than 0.5.

The pH in the resin must now be related to the pH in the solution. As a first approximation, it can be assumed that the concentration ratio $[Na^+]/[H^+]$ is the same in the ion exchanger and in the aqueous phase:

$$[\overline{H^+}] = [H^+][\overline{Na^+}]/[Na^+] \qquad (4\text{-}14)$$

In this approximation, specific interactions, swelling pressure effects, etc., are neglected (see Sec. 5-4b).

At 50 per cent conversion, the Na^+ concentration in the resin is

$$[\overline{Na^+}] = \frac{[\overline{X}]}{2} \qquad (\alpha = 0.5) \qquad (4\text{-}15)$$

where $[\overline{X}] \equiv [\overline{RH}] + [\overline{R^-}]$ is the total concentration of (dissociated and undissociated) ionogenic groups. One obtains from Eqs. (4-13) to (4-15)

$$pK = pH + \log [Na^+] - \log \frac{[\overline{X}]}{2} \qquad (\alpha = 0.5) \qquad (4\text{-}16)$$

The corresponding relation for weak-base anion exchangers, when titrated with HCl, is

$$pK = pH - \log [Cl^-] + \log \frac{[\overline{X}]}{2} \qquad (\alpha = 0.5) \qquad (4\text{-}17)$$

Equation (4-16) can be used for computing pK values of weak-acid cation exchangers from pH titrations. The uptake of Na^+ in milliequivalents per specific amount of the resin is plotted as a function of the pH of the aqueous phase (see Fig. 4-3). This curve has a plateau which corresponds to the (scientific) weight capacity, i.e., to complete conversion of the resin to the Na^+ form. The point of half conversion is readily located. The pH and the Na^+ concentration in the aqueous phase and the concentration of ionogenic groups in the resin, all at the point of half conversion, are determined and inserted in Eq. (4-16). Experimental details are given in Sec. 4-5d.

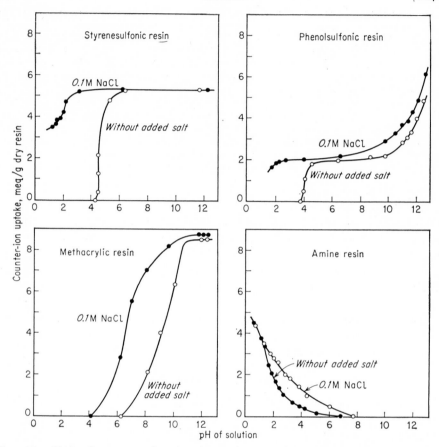

FIG. 4-3. pH titration curves of various ion-exchange resins, measured with and without added salt.   In contrast to Fig. 4-2, the counter-ion uptake is plotted versus the pH of the aqueous phase.   The ratio of solution volume to resin dry-weight is 150 ml : 1 g.   *From N. E. Topp and K. W. Pepper* [27], *and D. K. Hale and D. Reichenberg* [15].

Table 4-2. Apparent pK values of ionogenic groups in resins

Cation exchangers		Anion exchangers	
Ionogenic group	Apparent pK	Ionogenic group	Apparent pK
—SO_3H	< 1	—$N(CH_3)_3OH$	> 13
—PO_3H_2 pK$_1$	2–3	—$N(C_2H_4OH)(CH_3)_2OH$	> 13
pK$_2$	7–8	—NH_2	7–9
—COOH	4–6	—NH—	7–9
—$\langle\!\!\!\bigcirc\!\!\!\rangle$—OH	9–10	—$\langle\!\!\!\bigcirc\!\!\!\rangle$—$NH_2$	5–6

Example. The pK value of the ionogenic groups in the polymethacrylic acid resin in Fig. 4-3, lower left, can be calculated in the following way. The scientific weight capacity corresponds to the plateau of the curve and is 9.2 meq/g. The point of half conversion thus is at 4.6 meq/g Na^+ uptake. The corresponding external pH, in the titration with 0.1 M NaCl added, is 6.4. The concentration of Na^+ in the solution is approximately 0.1 M (changes by ion exchange and by the addition of titrant compensate one another approximately at this point; analytical determination is required for more accurate calculations). The water content of the half-converted resin (determined separately) is about 60% wt. Hence, the concentration of ionogenic groups $[\overline{X}]$ at half conversion is $9.2(100 - 60)/60 = 6.1$ meq/g water, and the (molal) pK is

$$\mathrm{pK} = 6.4 + \log 0.1 - \log 3.05 = 4.9$$

The pK values of weak-base anion exchangers are calculated in an analogous manner from Eq. (4-17).

The pK values of the different groups in polyfunctional ion exchangers can also be calculated, provided that the values differ sufficiently so that the titration curve shows distinct steps. Here, the point of half conversion of the respective groups, i.e., the half height of the respective step must be located.

Apparent capacities under given experimental conditions can be estimated by reversing the calculation procedure. The concentration of an arbitrary univalent counter ion A^+ in a weak-acid resin is

$$[\overline{A^+}] = \alpha[\overline{X}] \tag{4-18}$$

provided that the resin is partly converted to the A^+ form. From Eqs. (4-12) and (4-18) and a relation which corresponds to Eq. (4-14), one obtains

$$\log \frac{1 - \alpha}{\alpha^2} = \mathrm{pK} - \mathrm{pH} + \log[\overline{X}] - \log[A^+] \tag{4-19}$$

The degree of dissociation α is calculated from this equation and is then used to obtain the apparent weight capacity $Q_{app} = \alpha Q_{weight}$.

Example. A polymethacrylic acid resin with $Q_{weight} = 9.0$ meq/g, pK $= 4.8$, and a water content of 45% wt in H^+ form and 65% wt in Na^+ form is equilibrated with a large excess of 0.02 M NaCl solution of pH 6.0. With an average water content of 55% wt, the concentration of ionogenic group is $[\overline{X}] \approx 9.0 \cdot 45/55 = 7.4$ meq/g water. It follows that

$$\log \frac{1 - \alpha}{\alpha^2} \approx 4.8 - 6.0 + \log 7.4 - \log 0.02 = 1.37$$

$$\alpha \approx 0.19$$
$$Q_{app} \approx 0.19 \cdot 9.0 = 1.7 \text{ meq/g}$$

The estimate is conservative, particularly at low degrees of dissociation, because electrolyte sorption has not been taken into account. Furthermore, this simple method fails if A^+ associates with the fixed ionic groups or is the cation of a weak base.

Equations (4-16), (4-17), and (4-19) are derived with a number of simplifying assumptions and thus give only approximate results. However, they are sufficient for most practical applications. The apparent pK values which are obtained in this way are in reasonable agreement with those of the analogous soluble acids and bases.

In many publications, the attempt has been made to compute pK values of ionogenic groups from conventional titration curves (pH of the aqueous phase versus amount of titrant added) by use of the Henderson-Hasselbach equation [3,7,10,11,14]:

$$\text{pH} = \text{pK} - \log \frac{1 - \alpha}{\alpha} \qquad (4\text{-}20)$$

A more careful consideration shows that, here, two implicit assumptions are made. It is assumed, first, that the pH in the resin and in the aqueous phase are the same, and, second, that the resin is half converted when half the amount of titrant required for complete conversion is added to the aqueous phase. As a rule, neither assumption holds. The failure of Eq. (4-20) is demonstrated by the fact that it leads to pK values which depend strongly on the amount of salt added.

b. Intrinsic pK Values

A more rigorous treatment has recently been given by Katchalsky [18,22] who extended his theory of linear polyelectrolytes [17,19] to ion-exchange resins. However, even this approach is based on several simplifying assumptions which hold only for highly swollen gels, i.e., for weakly crosslinked resins.

Katchalsky derives his equations from a model. The matrix with fixed ionic groups is pictured as a crosslinked network of chains which consist of rigid, rod-shaped segments carrying one ionogenic group each (see Sec. 5-1, Fig. 5-3). The chains coil statistically. A "chain" is defined as a network unit between two crosslinks. Every chain consists (on the average) of Z segments. The number Z thus characterizes the degree of crosslinking. Katchalsky's theory includes the effects of the electrostatic forces acting within the gel and of the configurational entropy of the matrix, which both affect the degree of ionization of the ionogenic groups. The theory can also be applied to swelling and sorption equilibria (see Sec. 5-2e).

Katchalsky's theory leads to the following relation between the "intrinsic" pK value $\text{pK}°$ of a weak-acid cation exchanger and the pH of the external solution:

$$\text{pK}° = \text{pH} + \log \frac{1 - \alpha}{\alpha} - \frac{0.434}{kTn_m} \left(\frac{\partial F_{el}}{\partial \alpha} \right)_{\bar{V},\bar{\kappa}} - \log \frac{m_-\gamma_-}{\bar{m}_-\bar{\gamma}_-} \qquad (4\text{-}21)$$

where k = Boltzmann constant; T = absolute temperature; n_m = number of segments in the gel; $\bar{V}$ = gel volume; m_i = molality of species i; subscript $-$ refers to the (univalent) co-ion; quantities with bars refer to the interior of the gel; γ_i = molal activity coefficient of species i.

In this equation, F_{el} is the (Helmholtz) electrostatic free energy of the gel, for which the model gives

$$F_{el} = \frac{n_p \nu^2 e^2}{\epsilon h_0 (\bar{V}/\bar{V}_0)^{1/3}} \ln \left[1 + \frac{6(\bar{V}/\bar{V}_0)^{1/3}}{\bar{\kappa} h_0} \right] + B \qquad (4\text{-}22)$$

where ϵ = dielectric constant; h_0 = chain length in the unstretched gel; $\bar{V}_0$ = volume of the unstretched gel; n_p = number of chains in the gel; B = constant [irrelevant for the differentiation in Eq. (4-21)]

and $\bar{\kappa}$ is the reciprocal of the radius of the Debye-Hückel ionic cloud surrounding the fixed ionic groups:

$$\bar{\kappa}^2 = \frac{4\pi e^2 \sum_i z_i \bar{m}_i}{\epsilon k T} \qquad (4\text{-}23)$$

where e = charge of the electron; z_i = valence of species i; the summation is carried out over counter ions and co-ions.

The ratio $\gamma_-/\bar{\gamma}_-$ of the activity coefficients of the co-ion in Eq. (4-21) cannot be measured directly and must be approximated.

Outline of the Derivation. Equilibrium between the gel and the external solution is attained when the (Gibbs) free energy of the system is at its minimum. This minimum is found by computing the free energy as a function of the variables in Eq. (4-21). The free energy is split into two additive terms. The first term is the "ideal free energy of mixing." The second term accounts for deviations from ideality and results in the correction term by which Eq. (4-21) differs from the simple approach given before. This term involves the configurational entropy of the matrix and the electrostatic forces acting within the gel, and is evaluated by the use of statistical thermodynamics. It is assumed that the electric field surrounding the fixed ionic groups is adequately described by the Debye-Hückel theory. The electrostatic free energy of a chain is calculated by summation of the contributions from all single fixed ionic groups at the most probable distance from one another [17,19]. The electrostatic free energy of the chains is, of course, a function of the degree of dissociation and of the coiling of the chains. The electrostatic free energy of the gel is obtained by summation of the contributions from all chains. It is assumed that these contributions are additive, i.e., that the chains do not interact with one another. The free energy of contraction of the uncharged network is considered as negligible in comparison to the electrostatic free energy of the chains. Of course, the last two assumptions are valid only for highly swollen, weakly crosslinked gels.

Equation (4-21) differs from the simple approximation given before by the correction term which involves the electrostatic free energy of the gel. It is interesting to analyze the physical meaning of this term. The (dissociated) ionic groups on the chains are at a short distance from one another. The counter ions are attracted by the resulting high charge density and form an ionic atmosphere which surrounds the chain. Neighboring ionic groups are partially shielded from one another by the surrounding counter ions. This shielding is, of course, most effective when the ionic groups are far apart and when the gel contains a large amount of sorbed electrolyte, i.e., when the gel is predominantly in the (undissociated) H^+ form, and when the electrolyte concentration in the external solution is high. Neighboring groups which are incompletely shielded repel one another electrostatically and thus tend to stretch the coiled chain. However, stretching increases the free energy of the network. The gel tends to reduce this additional tension by neutralizing the fixed charges by more complete association with

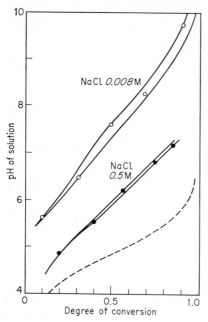

FIG. 4-4. Calculated and observed pH titration curves for a weakly crosslinked polymethacrylic-acid gel ($Z = 200$), with 0.008 M and 0.5 M NaCl added. The experimental values are shown as circles. The solid curves are calculated from Eq. (4-21) by use of $pK_{resin} = 4.86$, and with two different assumptions about the single activity coefficient ratio. The broken curve is calculated from the Henderson-Hasselbach equation (4-20). *From I. Michaeli and A. Katchalsky* [22].

H^+ ions. Hence, at the same "intrinsic" pK, the degree of dissociation of an acid group in the gel is smaller than in a dissolved monomer. This effect is strongest when the shielding of the fixed ionic groups is least efficient, i.e., when the resin is almost completely converted to the salt form and when the electrolyte concentration in the external solution is low.

The apparent pK value is calculated from the observed degree of dissociation, without accounting for this electrostatic effect. Hence, the apparent pK is higher than the intrinsic one (lower for anion exchangers). In extreme cases, the difference may amount to more than one pH unit.

To be sure, the intrinsic pK is better defined than the apparent one. However, when the intrinsic pK is used in calculations, the electrostatic free energy must be taken into account consistently. The use of the apparent pK thus is usually more convenient for practical purposes.

Katchalsky's theory has been confirmed by measurements with weakly crosslinked polymethacrylic-acid gels [18,22]. A comparison of calculated and observed pH values obtained with two different concentrations of added salt is shown in Fig. 4-4. The calculated values are based on the intrinsic pK of 4.86, as measured directly with dissolved linear polymethacrylic acid.

4-5. EXPERIMENTAL METHODS

Any measurements with resins as shipped by the manufacturer give, as a rule, unreliable and unreproducible results. Such resins should be thoroughly "conditioned" by repeated exchange cycles and extensive washing.   Conditioning and equilibration of ion exchangers is described in more detail in Sec. 5-9.

a. Capacity Determination

Capacities of strong-acid and strong-base ion exchangers are readily determined by direct methods which are described in this section.   These methods are less reliable when applied to ion exchangers with weak-acid or weak-base groups.   Here, a better way of determining the (maximum) capacity is by pH titration (see Secs. 4-5c and 4-3).

Various techniques for capacity determinations have been developed [9,12,14,20,26].   A convenient procedure for strong-acid cation exchangers is described in the following. A sample (about 15 g) of the ion exchanger is completely converted to the H^+ form by treatment with a liberal excess of 1 to 2 M HCl in a column, on a filter, or by repeated batch equilibration (see Sec. 5-9b), until the acid remains free of metal cations.   The resin is then washed with deionized water to remove sorbed HCl, until the water remains free of Cl^-.   About 10 g of the resin is centrifuged to remove adherent liquid (see Sec. 5-9b), weighed, and placed in a small laboratory column (see Fig. 8-2).   A known amount of standard 0.1 N NaOH (about 50 ml/g of resin), followed by about two bed volumes of deionized water, is passed through the column at a low flow rate (ca. 5 bed volumes per hour, less for highly crosslinked resins).   The effluent is collected.   The amount of NaOH should be in moderate excess (about twofold) over the total capacity of the bed to guarantee complete conversion to the Na^+ form.   The deionized water serves to remove interstitial and sorbed NaOH.   The excess of NaOH is back-titrated in the effluent with standard 0.1 N HCl.   The remaining 5 g of the ion exchanger are used for determining the water content (see Sec. 5-9c).   The scientific weight capacity is

$$Q_{weight} = \frac{100}{100 - W} \frac{\text{amount of NaOH} - \text{titrant used [meq]}}{\text{weight of swollen resin [g]}}$$

The result can be checked by reconverting the bed, which is now in Na^+ form, to the H^+ form in essentially the same way as before.   Standard 0.1 N HCl is used, and the excess of HCl is back-titrated with 0.1 N NaOH.   The excess of HCl should be larger (about fivefold) since equilibrium is less favorable for reconversion.

The capacity of strong-base anion exchangers can be determined in an analogous manner.   The resin is converted to the OH^- form, washed to remove excess NaOH, and placed in the column.   Standard 0.1 N HCl (about twofold excess) is passed through the column, and the excess acid is back-titrated with 0.1 N NaOH.   The weight and water content of the sample are determined with the resin in the Cl^- form.   Capacity determinations by reconversion to the OH^- form are impractical because an inconveniently large excess of NaOH would be required.

Capacities can also be determined by converting weighed samples from the H^+ form (or OH^- form) to the Na^+ form (or Cl^- form) by repeated batch equilibrations with a liberal excess of about 1 M NaCl (see Sec. 5-9b) and titrating the liberated H^+ (or OH^-) in the combined decanted solutions.   This procedure is more lengthy and is mainly used for membranes and other types of resins which cannot be placed in columns.

The technical volume capacity is usually determined with larger samples of the resin. The packed volume of the fully swollen ion exchanger in the H^+ form or Cl^- form is measured in a calibrated cylinder under water.

For practical purposes, the following rapid routine determinations give sufficiently accurate results even for polyfunctional, weak-acid and weak-base resins [6].

Cation Exchangers, Total Capacity (strong- and weak-acid groups).   About 5 g of the resin are converted to the H^+ form and washed as above.   About 1 g is weighed into a dry 250-ml Erlenmeyer flask.   Exactly 200 ml of standard 0.1 N NaOH in 5% wt NaCl solution are added.   After standing overnight in the stoppered flask, 50-ml aliquots of the supernatant solution are back-titrated to the phenolphthalein end point with standard 0.1 N HCl. The remaining 4 g of the resin are used for determining the water content (drying overnight at 60°C under vacuum or at 110°C under atmospheric pressure).

Cation Exchangers: Capacity of the Strong-acid Groups. About 5 g of the resin are pretreated as above. The sample is then leached on a filter with exactly 1 liter of 4% wt neutral Na_2SO_4 solution fed from a dropping funnel. The filtrate is collected in a dry flask. Next, 100-ml aliquots of the filtrate are titrated to the phenolphthalein end point with standard 0.1 N NaOH.

Anion Exchangers. About 10 g of the resin are converted completely to the Cl^- form by treatment with a liberal excess of 1 N HCl and washed with ethanol until the effluent is neutral to methyl orange. About 5 g are weighed, placed on a filter, and leached with exactly 1 liter of 1% wt aqueous ammonia fed from a dropping funnel. The filtrate is collected in a dry flask and is neutralized. Titration of 100-ml aliquots with standard 0.1 N $AgNO_3$ gives the *capacity of the weak-base groups.* Now, the filter with the sample is leached with exactly 1 liter of 4% wt Na_2SO_4 solution. The effluent is collected in another dry flask and is neutralized. Titration of 100-ml aliquots gives the *capacity of the strong-base groups.* The remaining 5 g of the resin is used in determining the water content (drying overnight at 50°C under vacuum or at 80°C under atmospheric pressure).

The scientific weight capacity is

$$Q_{weight} = \frac{\text{solution volume} \times \text{meq of titrant used}}{\text{volume of aliquot} \times (100 - W) \times \text{wet weight of sample}}$$

where W = water content in weight per cent.

The techniques described above are adapted to the common ion-exchange resins and cannot be applied in all cases. For example, most inorganic ion exchangers are not sufficiently resistant to acids and bases. Here, the capacity can be determined by neutral ion exchange (K^+ for Na^+, etc.). In other cases, the rate of ion exchange is so low that conversion requires too much time. Here, the capacity can be determined by destructive chemical analysis of the material.

For plant applications, the breakthrough capacity is often determined directly in laboratory-scale experiments which simulate the operating conditions of the plant [1,2,14,26,28].

b. Determination of the Concentration of Ionogenic Groups

The concentration of ionogenic groups in an ion exchanger can be calculated from the scientific weight capacity by use of Eq. (4-2) or (4-3). The ionic composition of the ion exchanger, the amounts of sorbed solutes, and the solvent content must be known. The determination of these quantities is described in Sec. 5-9.

c. pH Titration

The principle of the pH titration has been described in Sec. 4-3. Prior to use, the ion exchanger is completely converted to the H^+ form (or OH^- form) and is washed with water to remove excess acid or base.

The pH titration is often carried out as described in Sec. 4-3. A sample of the ion exchanger (about 1 g) is weighed, placed in water or in a NaCl solution (about 50 ml), and is titrated with standard 0.1 N NaOH (or HCl). The pH of the supernatant solution is measured with a glass electrode and a calomel reference electrode after every addition of titrant. However, this procedure is rather lengthy since sufficient time must be allowed for establishment of equilibrium between the ion exchanger and the solution before the pH is measured. Too rapid titrations give erroneous results which can be recognized by hysteresis phenomena.

The following technique is more practical [15,27]. A number of samples (about 1 g each) of the ion exchanger are weighed into dry flasks.   To the different samples, successively larger amounts of standard NaOH (or HCl) are added.   Deionized water is then added as required to keep the ratio of solution volume to resin weight constant (say, 100 ml solution per gram of ion exchanger).   Equilibrium is established by shaking the stoppered flasks until the pH of the solution attains a constant final value.   Equilibration requires usually less than an hour for ion exchangers with strongly ionized groups, and up to several weeks for materials with low ion-exchange rates.   The titration curve is obtained by plotting the pH of the solution versus the amount (in milliequivalents per specific amount of the ion exchanger) of titrant added.

Titrations in the presence of salt are carried out in essentially the same way.   NaCl is added to each sample in such a way that the concentration of Cl^- is the same in all solutions.   The shape of the titration curve depends on the salt concentration and on the ratio of solution volume to resin weight.   Therefore, these quantities must be kept constant and should be stated together with the results.

d. Determination of pK Values

The calculation of pK values from pH titration data has been described in Sec. 4-4. The pH titration is carried out as described in the second part of the preceding section. In addition to the pH of the solutions, the uptake of Na^+ (or Cl^-) by the resin samples must be determined.   This can be done by separating the ion exchanger from the solution (see Sec. 5-9b) and determining the uptake after displacement of the ion by H^+, or OH^- [12].   A more rapid, but less reliable method is the determination of the stoichiometrically equivalent amount of H^+ (or OH^-) displaced from the ion exchanger in the course of the equilibration.   This determination can be made by titration or back-titration of the solution to pH 7 [27].

The evaluation of Eq. (4-16) or (4-17) also requires the concentration of Na^+ (or Cl^-) in the solution and the water content of the half-converted ion exchanger.   The counterion concentration in the solution is obtained from a material balance (meq added NaCl + meq added NaOH − meq Na^+ in resin = meq Na^+ in solution; the volume change of the solution is insignificant).   The water content of the ion exchanger must be determined separately.

The method gives useful results only in the presence of dissolved salt (0.1 to 1.0 N).

SUMMARY

The capacity of ion exchangers is defined in terms of the number of ionogenic groups in the material and is usually given in milliequivalents per gram of dry H^+ form or Cl^- form of the resin (scientific weight capacity) or per milliliter of swollen resin bed (technical volume capacity). The capacity, when defined in this way, is a characteristic constant of the material. The common ion-exchange resins have weight capacities between 2 and 10 meq/g.

In the theoretical treatment of ion-exchange phenomena, the concentration of fixed ionic groups is more convenient to use than the capacity. The concentration of fixed ionic groups, given in milliequivalents per milliliter swollen resin or per gram of solvent in the resin, depends on the experimental conditions and may even change in the course of an ion exchange.

Other definitions of the capacity are possible and useful.   The apparent (or effective) capacity is defined as the number of exchangeable counter ions in the material and is important for practical applications.   In resins with strong-acid or strong-base groups, the number of exchangeable counter ions is practically equivalent to the number of ionogenic groups. Deviations are found in ion exchangers with weakly ionized groups. Here, the apparent capacity depends on the pK value of the groups and on the experimental conditions, particularly on the pH and the concentration of the solution. Weak-acid groups are not ionized and thus are inactive at low pH. The same is true for weak-base groups at high pH.

The best way of characterizing ion exchangers is by giving their (scientific) weight capacity and the pK of their ionogenic groups. Both these quantities can be determined by pH titration. Apparent capacities under any given experimental conditions can be estimated from these data.

REFERENCES

1. Bauman, W. C., *Ind. Eng. Chem.*, **38**, 46 (1946).
2. Bauman, W. C., J. R. Skidmore, and R. H. Osmun, *Ind. Eng. Chem.*, **40**, 1350 (1948).
*3. Bauman, W. C., in "Ion Exchange," F. C. Nachod (ed.), p. 45, Academic Press, Inc., New York, 1949.
4. Boyd, G. E., J. Schubert, and A. W. Adamson, *J. Am. Chem. Soc.*, **69**, 2818 (1947).
5. Deuel, H., J. Solms, and L. Anyas-Weisz, *Helv. chim. Acta*, **33**, 2171 (1950).
6. Fisher, S., and R. Kunin, *Anal. Chem.*, **27**, 1191 (1955).
7. Fisher, S., and R. Kunin, *J. Phys. Chem.*, **60**, 1030 (1956).
8. Gregor, H. P., and J. I. Bregman, *J. Am. Chem. Soc.*, **70**, 2370 (1948).
9. Gregor, H. P., J. I. Bregman, F. Gutoff, R. D. Broadley, D. E. Baldwin, and C. G. Overberger, *J. Colloid Sci.*, **6**, 20 (1951).
10. Gregor, H. P., J. Belle, and R. A. Marcus, *J. Am. Chem. Soc.*, **76**, 1984 (1954).
11. Gregor, H. P., L. B. Luttinger, and E. M. Loebl, *J. Phys. Chem.*, **59**, 366 (1955).
12. Gregor, H. P., M. J. Hamilton, J. Becher, and F. Bernstein, *J. Phys. Chem.*, **59**, 874 (1955).
13. Griessbach, R., *Ver. deut. Chemiker, Beih.*, **31**, 1 (1939); *Angew. Chem.*, **52**, 215 (1939).
*14. Griessbach, R., "Austauschadsorption in Theorie und Praxis," pp. 245–250, 270–273, 395–398, Akademie-Verlag G. m. b. H., Berlin, 1956.
15. Hale, D. K., and D. Reichenberg, *Discussions Faraday Soc.*, **7**, 79 (1949).
16. Honda, M., *J. Am. Chem. Soc.*, **73**, 2943 (1951); *Japan Analyst*, **1**, 122 (1952); *Chem. Abstr.*, **47**, 4688 (1953).
17. Katchalsky, A., and S. Lifson, *J. Polymer Sci.*, **11**, 409 (1953).
*18. Katchalsky, A., *Progr. Biophys.*, **4**, 1 (1954).
19. Katchalsky, A., and I. Michaeli, *J. Polymer Sci.*, **15**, 69 (1955).
20. Kressman, T. R. E., and J. A. Kitchener, *J. Chem. Soc.*, **1949**, 1190.
21. Kunin, R., and R. J. Myers, *J. Am. Chem. Soc.*, **69**, 2874 (1947).
22. Michaeli, I., and A. Katchalsky, *J. Polymer Sci.*, **23**, 683 (1957).
23. Myers, R. J., J. W. Eastes, and D. Urquhart, *Ind. Eng. Chem.*, **33**, 1270 (1941).
24. Pepper, K. W., D. Reichenberg, and D. K. Hale, *J. Chem. Soc.*, **1952**, 3129.
25. Richardson, R. W., *Nature*, **164**, 916 (1949).
26. Stach, H., *Angew. Chem.*, **63**, 263 (1951).
27. Topp, N. E., and K. W. Pepper, *J. Chem. Soc.*, **1949**, 3299.
28. Zimmermann, M., *Angew. Chem.*, **64**, 107 (1952).

---

* Surveys are marked with asterisks.

5

Equilibria

For more than half a century, equilibria between ion exchangers and solutions have been the subject of numerous experimental and theoretical investigations. Most of the earlier investigations were made with inorganic ion exchangers and centered on the study of ion-exchange equilibria, i.e., on the distribution of different competing counter-ion species between the ion exchanger and a solution. Swelling and sorption equilibria received little attention until organic ion-exchange resins, in which these phenomena are more important and more obvious, were invented and studied.

Most of the initial theoretical work consisted in attempts to describe ion-exchange equilibria by empirical equations. Insight into the basic physical factors grew only gradually. Accumulated experience and the knowledge of these factors provided the basis for the development of various models by which, within limits, the behavior of ion exchangers can be predicted. This more recent phase of theoretical evolution owes much of its success to the development of ion-exchange resins. The synthesis of resins provided, for the first time, the means of varying properties such as structure, capacity, degree of crosslinking, etc., systematically and independently. Thus it became possible to investigate separately the effects of the various physical factors.

In recent years, several theories for equilibria between ion exchangers and solutions have been developed. They are in good agreement with experimental results. Thus the theoretical knowledge has reached a rather advanced stage. Nevertheless, to give a tangible and yet exact interpretation of the theoretical aspects, as attempted in this book, is more difficult for equilibria than for other ion-exchange phenomena. The appropriate means of describing equilibria is thermodynamics. Rigorous thermodynamics, however, is inherently abstract. An interpretation in terms of the pertinent physical forces requires the introduction of a model. Yet, the properties of any particular model are reflected not only in the form of the equations obtained, but usually also in the physical interpretation to which these equations lead. This explains the coexistence, confusing at first sight, of a number of quite diverse theoretical approaches. They all have their merits, and in the final analysis the differences are usually seen to be semantical rather than fundamental.

In this chapter, various theories of swelling, sorption, and ion-exchange equilibria are discussed. In particular, the attempt is made to give tangible explanations of the phenomena and their physical causes and to assist the reader in acquiring a "feel" which may help him in selecting the most appropriate theory for his specific purposes. The discussion is preceded by a brief survey outlining the fundamentals of the different theoretical approaches.

5-1. THEORETICAL APPROACHES AND MODELS

Equilibria between ion exchangers and solutions can be described by means of rigorous thermodynamics. This treatment is quite general and requires, in principle, no model and no assumptions about the mechanisms of the phenomena. The problem can be attacked in different ways. The form of the equations which are obtained depends on the choice of the components of the system and of the standard and reference states. The various equations are, of course, equivalent to one another. In the most typical theories of this group, the components are taken to be the "resinates" (i.e., the salts of the macromolecular, solid ion-exchanger acid or base), the dissolved electrolytes, and the solvent, and the standard and reference states of the resinates are taken to be the respective mono-ionic forms of the ion exchanger. The first approach of this kind dates back to Kielland [167] in 1935, and the first rigorous treatment was given by Gaines and Thomas [99] in 1953. These theories will be outlined in Sec. 5-4g.

The rigorous and abstract thermodynamic treatment is "correct" and universal, but it yields a minimum of information about the physical causes of the phenomena to which it is applied. Also, its practical value is restricted because, in most cases, the quantities involved cannot be determined by independent measurements, nor can they be predicted without using non-thermodynamic assumptions. Therefore, models with particular properties resembling those of the ion exchanger have been introduced for deriving equations which reflect the action of various physical forces. With such models, the effects of particular properties on the behavior of the system can be analyzed. The more refined and complex the model, the more information of this kind may be obtained. In this way, the prediction of equilibria from known fundamental data of the solvent and the solutes and independent measurements of certain properties of the ion exchanger may come within the range of the theory. However, every commitment to a model with particular properties means a deviation from rigorous thermodynamics in its strictest sense.   The general formulations of abstract thermodynamics are universal, whereas relations derived from specific models are meaningful only when the pertinent properties of the actual system are adequately represented by the model.

The first models of ion exchangers were not of the type described above. Kielland [167], Vanselow [291], and many of their successors have pictured ion exchangers as solid solutions of the alumosilicates or resinates.   Bauman [19], in 1947, introduced the concept that ion exchangers are concentrated aqueous electrolytes in which one ionic species is immobile.   These models are, in essence, not more than interpretations.   They do not lead to

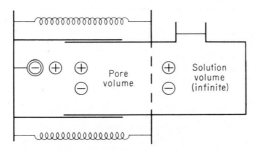

Fig. 5-1. Gregor's model of the ion exchanger.   The matrix is represented by elastic springs which are stretched when the resin swells.   *From H. P. Gregor* [109].

new equations which reflect the action of physical forces; they lead beyond the formal treatment only in that they help to visualize the system and suggest conclusions by analogy (for example, the application of Harned's empirical rule for activities in concentrated electrolytes).   A rather non-committal approach of this kind is, of course, the best when little is known about details of the mechanisms.

The first model which reflects any of the particular properties of ion-exchange resins was introduced by Gregor [109].   According to this model, the matrix of the resin is a network of elastic springs.   When the resin swells, the network is stretched and exerts a pressure on the internal "pore" liquid (Fig. 5-1), as the skin of an inflated toy balloon exerts a pressure on the air inside.   The "swelling pressure" in the resin affects swelling, sorption, and ion-exchange equilibria.   In the thermodynamic treatment of this model, the components of the system are usually taken to be the matrix with fixed ionic groups, the various mobile ionic species, and the solvent.   Solvation shells have been considered by Gregor as being part of the ions, and by others as belonging to the solvent.   Gregor's choice is thermodynamically less well defined, but it brings out more clearly the physical action of the swelling pressure (see pages 117 and 172).

Gregor's model can explain, as least qualitatively, the selectivity sequence of the alkali ions and other rules in systems in which the swelling-pressure effect is not overshadowed by the action of other forces. The model cannot explain the striking selectivities which are often found and usually attributed to specific interactions, such as "ion-pair formation," between the fixed ionic groups and the preferred counter ion. Several theories have been developed in which such interactions, either chemical or merely electrostatic, are the essential feature (see pages 173, 198, and 199).

Gregor's model is purely mechanical. Swelling pressure is the only particular property considered. Electrostatic interactions are not included. More recently, Lazare and Gregor [191] have suggested a refined model in

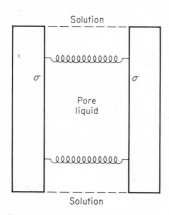

which such forces also have their place (see Fig. 5-2). This model pictures the ion-exchange resin as a series of planar plates parallel to one another and interconnected by elastic springs. The plates carry an (uniform) electric surface charge and, hence, repel one another electrostatically, stretching the elastic springs. The liquid between the plates—representing the pore liquid in the actual exchanger—has a surplus charge of opposite sign. The (continuous) charge in the liquid is assumed to obey a Poisson-Boltzmann distribution, i.e., the charge is largest at the surface of the plates and smallest halfway between the plates. The electrostatic repulsion between neighboring plates is calculated from the one-dimensional theory of the stability of lyophobic colloids by Verwey and Overbeek [293]. The equations derived from this model are rather complex and difficult to evaluate. So far, the model has only been applied to swelling and electrolyte-sorption equilibria (see pages 118 and 145).

Fig. 5-2. Lazare and Gregor's refined model which includes electrostatic interactions. The matrix is represented by parallel plates which are interconnected by elastic springs and carry uniform electric surface charges, σ. *According to L. Lazare, B. R. Sundheim, and H. P. Gregor* [191].

Both Gregor's models may be called "macroscopic." They do not involve the single ion as a discrete particle, and the elasticity of the springs which represent the matrix is purely mechanical. In contrast, the models proposed by Katchalsky [162,163,214] and by Harris and Rice [241,241a] are based on considerations on a molecular scale. Both these models, which are similar in many points, were originally developed for linear polyelectrolytes and were later extended to include crosslinked gels. The matrix with fixed ionic groups is represented by crosslinked chains consisting of rigid, rod-shaped segments carrying one ionogenic group each. The segments are interconnected by universal joints (Fig. 5-3). The elasticity of the matrix is not mechanical but, rather, it is due to the increase in entropy which accompanies the coiling of the chains because a coiled configuration can be realized in a larger number of ways than a stretched one.

(The macroscopically observed "mechanical" elasticity of materials with network structure, such as rubber, is actually due to this effect, not to stretching of atomic bonds or widening of bond angles.) The configurational entropy is computed by use of the statistical theory of the elasticity of nonpolar, macromolecular networks developed chiefly by Flory, Rehner, and Kuhn [89]. Both models also include electrostatic forces, in particular the repulsion between neighboring fixed ionic groups. In solutions of linear polyelectrolytes, this force is known to stretch the chains. In the computation of the electrostatic interactions, Rice and Harris's treatment differs from Katchalsky's. The former assume that the distribution of fixed

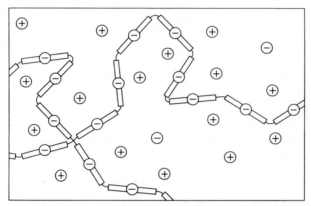

Fig. 5-3. Katchalsky's molecular model. The matrix is represented by a crosslinked network of chains which consist of rigid, rod-shaped segments carrying one electric charge each. Rice and Harris use essentially the same model.

ionic groups within the exchanger is practically uniform, and consider interactions only between nearest neighbors, without differentiating between groups on the same and on adjacent chains. In Katchalsky's treatment, which is restricted specifically to weakly crosslinked resins, interactions between all groups on one and the same chain are calculated, whereas interactions between neighboring chains are disregarded. Another difference between the two approaches is that Rice and Harris's model includes ion pair formation, whereas Katchalsky's does not. The application of the models is outlined in Secs. 4-4b, 5-2e, 5-3c, and 5-4g.

Quite a variety of other approaches and models have been developed and used. The conclusions derived from such models are as diverse as the models themselves. It is obvious that the equations of a theory can reflect the effects of only those properties with which the model has been equipped. Different theories, when applied to the same phenomenon, may well attribute the observed effect to quite different physical causes. The theories of ion exchange are no exception.

Thus we are confronted with a large number of theories, some of them mutually exclusive, which have little in common beyond the phenomenon they describe. Yet, they can hardly be classified as "correct" or "incorrect." A theory cannot be dismissed a priori as fallacious if the treatment is consistent, i.e., if no contradictory assumptions are made, no necessary consequences of the postulated model are omitted, and no effect is counted twice. Whether the theory is realistic and useful is quite another question. It is generally understood that a theory should adequately represent experimental results and that a model should give a reasonable explanation of the physical causes of the phenomena. Yet the way in which this aim is achieved is often viewed with a less critical attitude. Certain theories involve several parameters which can be chosen freely or within wide limits so as to fit the experimental results. It is known that a function with five parameters can be fitted to the shape of, say, an elephant. Thus, an agreement between experiment and theory achieved by such methods does not prove the value of the latter. A better criterion for the usefulness of a theory is its ability to predict the behavior of a system from fundamental data or independent measurements. As a rule, such predictions can only be made if the model is realistic, i.e., if the decisive features of the actual system are adequately represented. The behavior of ion exchangers in general depends on factors of an almost overwhelming variety. In any particular system, one or the other of these factors may be the most important, and, accordingly, one or the other theory is the most appropriate. The ideal theory is universal and uses only known or accessible fundamental data of the components. For equilibria with ion exchangers, such a theory does not yet exist, and if it could ever be developed, it would be (to quote Glueckauf) an "elephantine affair of unmanageable complexity."

5-2. SWELLING

Ion exchangers, both inorganic and organic, are able to sorb solvents in which they are placed. While taking up solvent, the ion exchanger usually expands, or "swells." This is particularly true for ion-exchange resins. Ion exchangers swell to only a limited degree; an equilibrium is attained beyond which swelling does not proceed. This section deals with such swelling equilibria, particularly those of ion-exchange resins in aqueous media. The behavior of crystalline ion exchangers is briefly outlined at the end of this section. Swelling in nonaqueous and mixed solvents will be discussed in Sec. 10-2, and the kinetics of swelling in Sec. 6-6b.

a. Principles and General Rules

Ion-exchange resins can swell in water and polar solvents, but only to a limited degree. The resins are built from (monomeric) units which carry ionogenic groups. These groups, as well as the ions which they form, tend to surround themselves with polar solvent molecules. Monomers with such

groups are thus soluble in polar solvents. Polymerization does not interfere with the solubility as long as the polymers formed are linear. For
example, linear polystyrenesulfonic acid and polyacrylic acid are water-
soluble.* Ion-exchange resins, however, are crosslinked. In such resins,
the dissolution process gets under way, driven by the affinity of the ionogenic groups and ions for the polar solvent. The coiled and packed chains
of the matrix unfold and make room for solvent molecules, but the chains
cannot separate completely because they are interconnected by crosslinks.
As a result, the resins swell but do not dissolve.

The behavior of linear and crosslinked polyelectrolytes is analogous to that of nonionic
resins. For example, linear polystyrene is soluble in solvents, such as toluene, which have
a high affinity for styrene. Crosslinked styrene-divinylbenzene copolymers swell in
toluene, but are not dissolved. This fundamental principle was first recognized and
demonstrated by Staudinger [280] in 1935. The essential difference between nonpolar
and ion-exchange resins is that the former, in contrast to the latter, swell much more
strongly in nonpolar than in polar solvents.

Several exchangers have been prepared without the addition of a specific crosslinking
agent. Nevertheless they are insoluble. In many cases, crosslinking seems to occur
because of complex side reactions. In relatively weakly hydrophilic materials, crosslinking may be unnecessary because hydrogen bonds and London forces between the chains
are sufficient to prevent dissolution in water.

Swelling equilibrium is a balance of opposing forces. The tendency of
the polar and ionic constituents of the resin to surround themselves with
solvent and thus to stretch the matrix meets with an increasing resistance
by the latter. Equilibrium is attained when the elastic forces of the matrix
balance the dissolution tendency.

The various forces can be analyzed in the light of the models which have
been described in the previous section. First, there is the tendency of the
fixed and mobile ions to form solvation shells. This effect appears most
clearly in Gregor's model in which the solvation shells are considered as
being part of the ions. Second, the interior of the ion exchanger, as a
highly concentrated solution of ions, has a tendency to dilute itself by
taking up additional solvent. In the macroscopic models, this effect
appears as an osmotic pressure difference between the interior of the resin
and the external solution. In the molecular models, the effect appears
as the free energy of mixing. A third expanding force is found in the models
which include electrostatic interactions. Neighboring fixed ionic groups
repel one another electrostatically and thus tend to stretch the chains of the
matrix (see also page 90). Of course, interactions between the solvent
and the matrix can also occur, particularly if the solvent is organic (see
Sec. 10-2). All these expanding forces decrease as swelling progresses: the
solvation tendency with approaching completion of the solvation shells, the

---

* Sulfonation of polystyrene may lead to a product which is crosslinked by sulfone
bridges. Such products are insoluble [247].

osmotic pressure difference or free energy of mixing with increasing dilution of the "pore liquid," and the electrostatic repulsion between fixed ionic groups with increasing distance between the groups.

The counteracting contractive force of the elastic matrix is symbolized by elastic springs in the macroscopic models, and appears essentially as a gain in configurational entropy accompanying the coiling of the chains in the molecular models. The contractive force, no matter whether mechanical or statistical, increases with increasing expansion of the network.

The models can be used for a quantitative treatment of swelling equilibria (see Sec. 5-2d). Anticipating the most important results in a qualitative way, one can readily deduce from the models these general rules; the extent of swelling depends on the following factors:

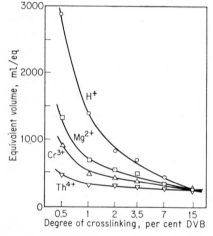

FIG. 5-4. Dependence of swelling on the degree of crosslinking and the counterion valence. The equivalent volumes of various ionic forms of styrene-type cation exchangers are shown as a function of the nominal DVB content. *From experimental data by C. Calmon* [49].

Nature of the Solvent. Polar solvents are, as a rule, better swelling agents than the nonpolar since they interact more strongly with the ions and polar groups in the resin. A more detailed discussion is given in Sec. 10-2.

Degree of Crosslinking. Highly crosslinked resins have a reduced ability to swell [63,110,229,284]; see Fig. 5-4. The greater number of links makes the network more rigid. In the macroscopic models the "springs" are harder, while in the molecular models the chains are shorter and, hence, the loss in configurational entropy accompanying a given expansion is greater.*

Nature of the Fixed Ionic Groups. The greater the affinity of the groups for the (polar) solvent, the more strongly does the resin swell. In particular, resins swell more strongly when their ionogenic groups are completely ionized (see also below).

Capacity. A high-capacity ion-exchange resin contains ions in higher concentration. Therefore, the tendency of the pore liquid to dilute itself and the resulting swelling are more pronounced than with a low-capacity resin [193].

---

* Note that the term "degree of crosslinking," as commonly used, refers to the nominal mole per cent of the crosslinking agent rather than to a measured quantity. Hence, only qualitative comparisons between resins of the same type can be made. Also, certain types of matrices may be inherently more rigid than others.

Nature of the Counter Ion. The effect of the counter ion on swelling equilibria is somewhat complex. Various factors must be considered. In moderately and highly crosslinked resins, in which most of the solvent is present in the form of solvation shells, the *size* and *solvation tendency* of the counter ion are most important [109]. The resin expands when a counter ion is replaced by another one which, in its solvated state, occupies more room (with ions of different valences, the ionic volumes must, of course, be compared on an equivalent rather than molar basis). For example, the sequence of increasing resin volumes of the alkali-ion forms of most cation exchangers is $Cs^+ < Rb^+ < K^+ < Na^+ < Li^+$ [110,115,229]. This sequence is the same as that of the hydrated ionic volumes. However, in very highly crosslinked resins, solvation may remain incomplete. Here, the sequence may be partly or completely reversed since Li^+ is the smallest and Cs^+ the largest ion when not solvated. In weakly crosslinked resins, which contain large amounts of "free" solvent (i.e., solvent not in the form of solvation shells), the *valence* of the counter ion is, as a rule, the most important factor [49]. The tendency to take up free solvent depends on the number of counter ions in the resin. This number is cut in half when univalent counter ions are replaced by bivalent ones. The osmotic pressure difference in the macroscopic models, and the free energy of mixing in the molecular models become correspondingly smaller. Ionic-size and solvation effects in these highly swollen gels are relatively unimportant. Thus, weakly crosslinked resins swell less when the valence of the counter ion is high (see Fig. 5-4). Note that, often, the opposite holds in moderately and highly crosslinked resins since the polyvalent ions are usually more strongly hydrated (see the crossovers in Fig. 5-4).

Ion-pair Formation and Association. Swelling of a resin is reduced when counter ions and fixed groups associate or form complexes. Such localization of the counter ions reduces, in the macroscopic models, the tendency to form solvation shells and the osmotic activity and, in the molecular models, it reduces the free energy of mixing. For example, weak-acid resins swell less in H^+ form than in alkali-ion forms [5,155,163,164,214]; see Fig. 5-13. Weak-base resins swell less in free-base than in chloride form, whereas the opposite usually holds for strong-acid and strong-base resins.

Concentration of the Solution. Resins which are equilibrated with electrolyte solutions swell more strongly when the solution concentration is low [49,63,110,229]; see Fig. 5-5. Any increase in solution concentration reduces the osmotic pressure difference between the interior of the resin or, in the molecular models, the free energy of mixing. Thus the "driving force" for solvent uptake is smaller.

These rules can be briefly summarized as follows. Swelling is favored by:

Polar solvents
Low degree of crosslinking of the resin

High capacity of the resin
Strong solvation tendency of the fixed ionic groups
Large and strongly solvated counter ions
Low valence of the counter ion
Complete dissociation in the resin
Low concentration of the external solution

These rules are of considerable practical importance, especially for column operations. The osmotic pressure difference (or the so-called "swelling pressure") is usually large and may exceed 1,000 atm. An ion-exchange

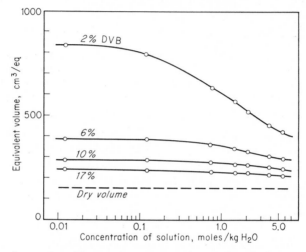

FIG. 5-5. Dependence of swelling on the concentration of the solution. The curves show the equivalent volumes of the NH_4^+ forms of styrene-type cation exchangers of various DVB contents in equilibrium with NH_4Cl solutions. *From experimental data by H. P. Gregor, F. Gutoff, and J. I. Bregman* [110].

column can burst when the resin swells. An excessive shrinking of the material in a column is equally undesirable because it favors channeling, particularly at the column walls (see Sec. 9-10a).

b. Water of Hydration and "Free" Water

In the qualitative discussion in the preceding section, a distinction has been made between "free" solvent and solvent bound in the form of solvation shells. In fact, in Gregor's first model [109], solvation is one of the most important features. To be sure, the distinction between free and bound solvent is thermodynamically ill-defined and to a certain degree arbitrary, but it greatly helps in understanding and explaining quite a number of phenomena, at least in a semiquantitative way (see, for example, pages 117, 158, and 172). In this section, hydration in ion exchangers and various methods of estimating hydration numbers are briefly discussed.

Attempts of predicting, from purely theoretical considerations, ionic hydration in as complex a system as the interior of an ion-exchange resin are, at best, highly speculative. However, conclusions can be drawn from various experimental observations. The following experimental evidence is available.

The water uptake by an initially dry ion-exchange resin is accompanied, in its early stages, by a volume contraction of the total system (resin plus external solution); later, water is taken up without any significant volume change of the system [229,230]. Since it is known that, as a rule, ionic hydration shells are more tightly packed than free water, it can be concluded that (primary) hydration shells are formed as long as the total system contracts, whereas additional water is taken up as free water. Hydration numbers in ion exchangers can be estimated in this way [230].

> *Example.* In sulfonated styrene-type cation exchangers, about 0.6 gram water is found to be more tightly packed than ordinary free water, whereas additional water taken up is not [229]. The 0.6 gram water is presumably bound as hydration shells. Accordingly, since the scientific weight capacity of the resins is 5.3 meq/g, each —SO$_3$H group is hydrated by about $0.6/5.3 \cdot 0.018 \approx 6$ water molecules [230].

Similar results are obtained with resins in other ionic forms [110,229]. The hydration numbers estimated in this way do not depend on the degree of crosslinking [229], provided, of course, that the degree of crosslinking is low enough to permit uptake of free water beyond the water of hydration.

A more detailed study has been made by Glueckauf [105] who calculated enthalpies and entropies of water sorption from vapor-sorption isotherms at different temperatures (see also page 116) and interpreted these results in terms of successive association equilibria between the ions and water molecules in the resin:

$$\overline{M^+} + \overline{H_2O} \rightleftharpoons \overline{M^+\cdot H_2O}$$
$$\overline{M^+\cdot(H_2O)} + \overline{H_2O} \rightleftharpoons \overline{M^+\cdot(H_2O)_2}, \text{ etc.} \tag{5-1}$$

Glueckauf defines water of hydration as those water molecules which are bound with equilibrium constants greater than unity. He concludes that, first, the sulfonate group is hydrated by one water molecule and that cation hydration then follows.* Hydration numbers of various cations (extrapolated to infinite swelling of the resin) obtained in this way are shown in Table 5-1.

Less direct evidence has been obtained by various other measurements [65,111,207,230,240]. The results do not differ greatly from the values in Table 5-1.

---

* Recent infrared-spectroscopy results [304], however, indicate that even the first water molecule goes to the cation rather than to the sulfonate group.

Table 5-1. Hydration numbers of cations (extrapolated to infinite swelling) in sulfonated styrene-type cation exchangers

Ion	Hydration number	Ion	Hydration number
H^+	3.9	Be^{2+}	7.0
Li^+	3.3	Mg^{2+}	7.0
Na^+	1.5	Ca^{2+}	5.2
K^+	0.6	Sr^{2+}	4.7
Cs^+	0	Ba^{2+}	2.0
Ag^+	0.3	Hg^{2+}	4.5
NH_4^+	0.4		

From E. Glueckauf and G. P. Kitt [105].

The free-water content does not necessarily parallel the total water content nor the expansion of the resin. For example, swelling of a resin increases when a counter ion is replaced by another counter ion which, in its hydrated state, is larger. The higher swelling pressure in the more strongly swollen resin squeezes free water out of the resin, thus reducing the free-water content. Swelling and total water content of the alkali-ion forms of strong-acid cation exchangers, in accordance with this picture, *increase* in the sequence $Cs^+ \leq Rb^+ < K^+ < Na^+ < Li^+$, whereas the free-water content *decreases* in this same sequence [47,109,111]; see also Fig. 5-6.

Many experimental results are more readily explained in terms of the free-water content than of the total water content of the resins. For example, the diffusion coefficients of sorbed nonelectrolytes in cation exchangers in the various alkali-ion forms increase, as a rule, with increasing free-water

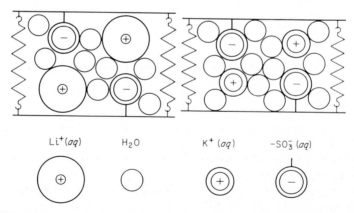

$Li^+(aq)$ H_2O $K^+ (aq)$ $-SO_3^- (aq)$

FIG. 5-6. Free water and water of hydration in the fully swollen Li^+ and K^+ forms of a cation exchanger (*schematic*). Because of the stronger hydration of the Li^+ ion, the Li^+ form has the larger equivalent volume and total water content, but because of the higher swelling pressure (more strongly stretched elastic springs) the Li^+ form has the lower free-water content. *From W. Buser* [47].

content, although the total water content varies in the opposite way [111];
see also Sec. 6-8.

c. Water-vapor Sorption Isotherms

The discussion has been restricted so far to swelling and solvent uptake
by resins which are placed in the liquid solvent. Additional information
about the properties of the resins can be obtained from measurements of

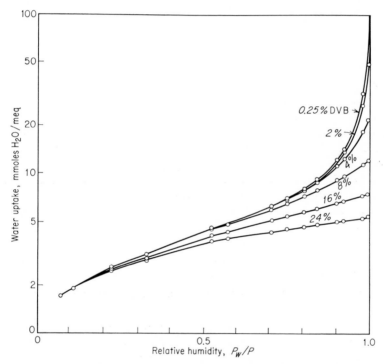

Fig. 5-7. Water-vapor sorption isotherms of ion-exchange resins. The curves show the
water uptake of the H$^+$ forms of styrene-type cation exchangers of various degrees of
crosslinking as a function of the relative humidity of the gas phase. *From G. E. Boyd
and B. A. Soldano* [40].

solvent-vapor uptake from gas phases at various partial pressures of the
solvent [40,76,76a,115,190]. As a rule, the results are given in the form of
vapor-sorption isotherms in which (at constant temperature) the solvent
uptake is shown as a function of the relative saturation of the gaseous phase.

Vapor-sorption isotherms are conveniently measured by the isopiestic
technique (see Sec. 5-9d).

Water-vapor sorption isotherms of sulfonated styrene-type cation
exchangers of various degrees of crosslinking are given in Fig. 5-7. The
curves show that the water uptake at low relative humidity is almost
independent of the degree of crosslinking. In this range, about two to four

water molecules per ionogenic group are taken up and are probably bound as hydration shells. At high relative humidity, the resins take up much more (free) water. Here, the degree of crosslinking has a pronounced effect.

This behavior is readily explained. At low relative humidity, the water uptake and, hence, the swelling pressure are small and the decisive factor is

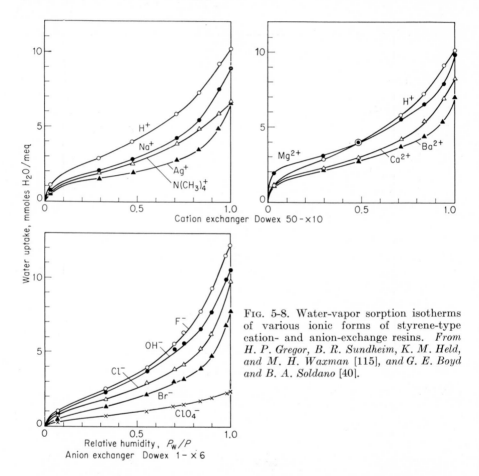

FIG. 5-8. Water-vapor sorption isotherms of various ionic forms of styrene-type cation- and anion-exchange resins. *From H. P. Gregor, B. R. Sundheim, K. M. Held, and M. H. Waxman* [115], *and G. E. Boyd and B. A. Soldano* [40].

the hydration tendency of the ionogenic groups (which is independent of the degree of crosslinking). At high relative humidity, hydration is complete, and the uptake of free water depends strongly on the swelling pressure which, at equal water uptake, is higher in the more tightly crosslinked resins.

A series of curves such as those shown in Fig. 5-7 can be used for calculating swelling pressures (see page 110).

Water-vapor sorption isotherms of cation and anion exchangers in various ionic forms are shown in Fig. 5-8. For counter ions of equal valence, the curves are similar in shape. The water uptake is higher throughout for the more strongly hydrated species. With large organic cations such as $N(C_2H_5)_4^+$, the water uptake at high relative humidity is conspicuously low. Here, the organic substituents occupy room which would otherwise be free for water molecules. Polyvalent cations are usually strongly hydrated, but are less efficient in producing free-water uptake (see page 103). Accordingly, the water uptake at low relative humidity is high, but rises less steeply with increasing relative humidity once hydration is complete. This effect is particularly noticeable in weakly crosslinked resins.

d. Quantitative Treatment

Swelling equilibria can be accurately described by thermodynamic relations. However, these relations involve quantities which cannot be calculated from fundamental data. Hence, quantitative predictions can only be made when either empirical relations or results of swelling measurements are used. Nevertheless, valuable information about essential features of the resins can be obtained in this way.

Various models can be applied to swelling equilibria. In this section, Gregor's simple model of the elastic matrix (see page 97) is used.* Other approaches are briefly outlined in the next section.

Swelling pressure and solvent activity. The "pore" liquid in an ion-exchange resin is subject to the contractive forces of the matrix and thus is under a higher pressure than the external solution. The pressure difference between the pore liquid and the solution is called the "swelling pressure":

$$\Pi \equiv \bar{P} - P \qquad (5-2)$$

where Π = swelling pressure; $\bar{P}$ = pressure in the resin; P = pressure in the external solution.

The swelling pressure affects the solvent uptake and thus the solvent activity in the resin. For a resin which is in equilibrium with pure solvent (solvent activity in the external phase $a_w = 1$), the following relation is obtained

$$\Pi v_w = -RT \ln \bar{a}_w \qquad (5-3)$$

where v_w = partial molar volume of the solvent; $\bar{a}_w$ = solvent activity in the resin.

Derivation. The general thermodynamic condition for equilibrium between two different phases is that the chemical potential of every component† be equal in both phases:

$$(\mu_i)_1 = (\mu_i)_2 \qquad (5-4)$$

Here, subscripts 1 and 2 refer to the two phases. The chemical potential μ_i of the com-

---

* The basic principle of this model was first formulated by Procter [234,235] as early as 1916.

† This statement is only true for components in Gibbs' sense, i.e., not for ions; see also pp. 140 and 141.

ponent i is defined by

$$\mu_i \equiv \left(\frac{\partial G}{\partial n_i}\right)_{P, T, n_j, n_k, \ldots} \tag{5-5}$$

where G = free energy; n_i = number of moles of species i; P = pressure; T = absolute temperature; subscripts j, k, . . . refer to the components other than i.

The pressure dependence of the chemical potential is

$$\frac{\partial \mu_i}{\partial P} = \frac{\partial}{\partial P}\left(\frac{\partial G}{\partial n_i}\right) = \frac{\partial}{\partial n_i}\left(\frac{\partial G}{\partial P}\right) = \frac{\partial V}{\partial n_i} = v_i \tag{5-6}$$

where V = volume; v_i = partial molar volume of the species i, defined by

$$\left(\frac{\partial V}{\partial n_i}\right)_{P, T, n_j, n_k, \ldots} \equiv v_i$$

For the sake of simplicity, it will be assumed that the partial molar volumes are constant, i.e., independent of composition and pressure.   At least for the solvent this assumption holds fairly well within a wide range of experimental conditions.*   Furthermore, it is assumed that the chemical potential (in isothermal systems) can be split into two additive terms of which one depends on composition only, the other on pressure only. The chemical potential μ_i of an arbitrary species i in a solution with molality m under the pressure P then is

$$\mu_i(P,m) = \mu_i(P^0,m) + (P - P^0)v_i \tag{5-7}$$

where P^0 = standard pressure, preferably taken as 1 atm.

The activity a_i of species i is defined by

$$\mu_i(P,m) = \mu_i^0(P) + RT \ln a_i \tag{5-8}$$

where μ_i^0 = chemical potential of species i in the standard state.

By combining Eqs. (5-7) and (5-8) one obtains

$$\mu_i(P,m) = \mu_i^0(P^0) + RT \ln a_i + (P - P^0)v_i \tag{5-9}$$

Equation (5-9) is applied to the solvent.   The standard and reference states are taken to be pure solvent under atmospheric pressure.   Thus

$$\mu_w = \mu_w^0(P^0) \tag{5-10}$$

when the resin is in equilibrium with pure solvent under atmospheric pressure (subscript w refers to the solvent).   Equation (5-3) is obtained from Eqs. (5-4), (5-9), (5-10), and (5-2).

Determination of swelling pressures.   Swelling pressures are difficult to measure directly.   The most convenient way of calculating swelling pressures is from vapor-sorption isotherms measured with a series of resins of different crosslinking [40,115]; see Fig. 5-7.   This method is based on the following argument.

---

* If the pressure dependence of the partial molar volumes is taken into account, the quantity v_i in the equations to follow must be replaced by $\frac{1}{\Pi}\int_{P^0}^{P} v_i \, dP$.

The chemical potential of the solvent in the gas phase is

$$(\mu_w)_g = \mu_w^0(P) + RT \ln \frac{P_w}{P} \tag{5-11}$$

where P = vapor pressure of solvent (at saturation); P_w = partial pressure of the solvent; deviations from ideality in the gas phase are disregarded.

It follows from Eqs. (5-4), (5-9), and (5-11) that, in equilibrium between the resin and the gas phase,

$$RT \ln \frac{P_w}{P} = \Pi v_w + RT \ln \bar{a}_w \tag{5-12}$$

Two resins of equal structure but with different degrees of crosslinking are compared at equal total gas pressures and equal solvent contents of the resins. The partial pressures of the solvent must, of course, be different if the solvent contents of the resins are to be equal. Equation (5-12) applies to the equilibria with both resins. Furthermore, the vapor pressure P and the internal solvent activity $\bar{a}_w$ are the same [granted that the dependence of the chemical potential on pressure affects only the first term in Eq. (5-8)]. Thus it follows from Eq. (5-12) that

$$RT \ln \frac{P_w}{P'_w} = (\Pi - \Pi')v_w \tag{5-13}$$

Quantities with prime refer to equilibrium with the second resin.

In a fictitious resin with no crosslinking at all, the swelling pressure Π' would be zero. By comparison, at equal solvent content, with this fictitious resin, the swelling pressure Π of the original resin could be calculated from Eq. (5-13). In practice, either a very weakly crosslinked resin (0.25 per cent DVB) is used for the comparison, or the difference $\Pi - \Pi'$ is determined for a series of comparison resins with different degrees of crosslinking and is extrapolated to zero crosslinking of the comparison resin.

The isopiestic comparison method is only applicable if the degree of crosslinking can be varied without significant change in structure and weight capacity, so that, at equal solvent content, the differences in the chemical potentials of the solvent in the different resins are exclusively due to the differences in swelling pressure.

Example. The swelling pressure in the fully water-swollen cation exchanger with 16 per cent DVB crosslinking in Fig. 5-7 is calculated in the following way. The comparison resin with 0.25 per cent DVB crosslinking reaches the same water content at $P_w/P = 0.78$. Furthermore, $R = 0.0821$ liter atm mole^{-1} deg^{-1}; $T = 298°$; $v_w = 0.018$ liter/mole. The swelling pressure of the resin with 16 per cent DVB thus is

$$\Pi = \frac{0.0821 \cdot 298}{0.018} \ln \frac{1.0}{0.78} \cong 340 \text{ atm}$$

Swelling pressures in equilibrium with pure water $(P_w/P = 1)$, calcu-lated from the isotherms in Fig. 5-7 by use of Eq. (5-13), are shown in Fig. 5-9. The swelling pressure varies almost linearly with the (nominal) DVB content.

Elasticity of the matrix. The swelling pressure is a result of the con-tractive forces of the elastic matrix. These forces increase when the matrix is expanded. With styrene-type cation and anion exchangers it has been

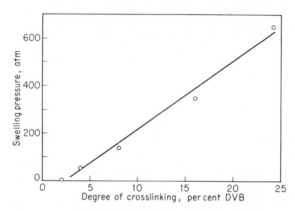

FIG. 5-9. Swelling pressure and degree of crosslinking. With styrene-type cation exchangers there is a practically linear relation between swelling pressure and nominal DVB content. The values in the diagram are for resins in H^+ form. *From experimental data by H. P. Gregor* [115], *and G. E. Boyd* [40].

found that the swelling pressure of a given resin is a linear function of the equivalent volume of the resin [40,109,110]:

$$\bar{V}_e = a\Pi + b \qquad (5\text{-}14)$$

where $\bar{V}_e$ = equivalent volume of the resin.

The empirical constants a and b are characteristic for the resin and are independent of the ionic form and the relative humidity (see Fig. 5-10). The constant b is the volume of the unstrained resin and is essentially independent of crosslinking. The constant a reflects the elastic properties and is larger for more highly crosslinked resins. The linear relation between $\bar{V}_e$ and Π shows that the chains of the matrix behave, indeed, like ideal elastic springs. This behavior proves that the model with the elastic matrix is realistic and useful. However, it is doubtful whether the relation (5-14) holds for other than styrene-type resins (see also Sec. 5-2f). Conditions as favorable for a theoretical treatment as in styrene-divinylbenzene copolymers are rarely found. Here, the reactivities of the two monomers are so similar that the divinylbenzene is incorporated essentially at random. Thus the copolymer has a certain mesh-width distribution, but no gross inhomogene-ities. Incidentally, this fact is the only justification for using the nominal

DVB content in extrapolations and other mathematical operations which require a quantitative measure for the degree of crosslinking [289].

Osmotic coefficients.   Since the swelling pressure in a given resin is a function of the equivalent volume of the resin alone, irrespective of the ionic form, one is justified in attributing the differences in the osmotic

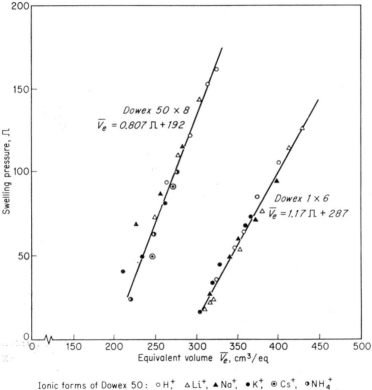

Ionic forms of Dowex 50: $\circ H^+$, $\triangle Li^+$, $\blacktriangle Na^+$, $\bullet K^+$, $\circledcirc Cs^+$, $\circ NH_4^+$
Ionic forms of Dowex 1 : $\circ OH^-$, $\triangle F^-$, $\blacktriangle CL^-$, $\bullet Br^-$

FIG. 5-10. Equivalent volume of the ion exchanger and swelling pressure.   With styrene-type ion-exchange resins a linear relation between equivalent volume and swelling pressure is found.   This relation is independent of the swelling state and the nature of the counter ion.   The diagram shows experimental data for Dowex 50-X 8 (cation exchanger) and Dowex 1-X 6 (anion exchanger) with various counter ions and at different relative humidities.   *From G. E. Boyd and B. A. Soldano* [40].

behavior of the various ionic forms exclusively to differences in the osmotic activity of the counter-ion species.

The osmotic activity of a "resinate" AR can be described in terms of the osmotic coefficient ϕ_{AR} which is defined by

$$\ln \bar{a}_w = - \frac{\nu_{AR}\phi_{AR}\bar{m}_{AR}M_w}{1{,}000} \qquad (5\text{-}15)$$

where ν_{AR} = number of ions into which AR dissociates; $\bar{m}_{AR}$ = internal molality (millimoles of AR per gram of solvent in the resin); M_w = molecular weight of the solvent,

that is, in the same way as the osmotic coefficient of dissolved electrolytes. For the latter, the value of ν can be obtained by extrapolation to infinite dilution, where the solution is ideal ($\phi = 1$). For resins, this extrapolation is impossible because, even in very strongly swollen gels, the charge density at the chains of the matrix remains high, so that an approximation to ideal behavior cannot be expected. Hence, Eq. (5-15) defines only the product $\nu_{AR}\phi_{AR}$. It has been found that the osmotic products $\nu_{AR}\phi_{AR}$ of resins are rather similar to the osmotic coefficients ϕ_{AY} of corresponding soluble electrolytes, provided that the latter are completely dissociated [115]. For example, the comparison of toluenesulfonic acid with (weakly cross-linked) sulfonated styrene-type resins in H^+ form shows that the osmotic coefficients are similar over a considerable molality range if one chooses $\nu_{C_7H_7SO_3H} = 2$ and $\nu_{HR} = 1$. The agreement obtained with $\nu_{HR} = 1$ shows that the fixed ionic groups have little, if any, osmotic activity. Of course, at low molality (strong swelling of the resin) the osmotic coefficients of the resins are anomalous because the matrix retains a high local charge density and prevents swelling beyond a certain limit.

The osmotic coefficients of dissolved strong electrolytes (which parallel those of the strongly dissociated resinates) have been studied extensively and are tabulated [131,245]. For salts of a common anion, the coefficients usually increase with increasing Debye-Hückel parameter a^0 which gives the distance of closest approach between ions of opposite sign. For the most common univalent ions, this sequence is

$$Ag^+ < K^+ < Na^+ < Li^+ < H^+$$

Swelling of strong-acid resins increases in the same sequence. The sequence of the radii of the hydrated ions is the same, with the exception of ions such as Ag^+ and Tl^+ which are strongly polarized and thus have abnormally low a^0 values.

Swelling and vapor-sorption equilibria can be predicted when the osmotic coefficient (as a function of the internal molality) and the characteristic constants a and b of the resin are known. The system is completely described by Eqs. (5-12), (5-14), (5-15), and a correlation between the resin volume and the solvent content.

The missing link in the quantitative theoretical prediction of swelling equilibria from fundamental data is that no universal theory for predicting osmotic coefficients has so far been developed. This gap has been partly bridged by empirical correlations [see, for example, Eq. (5-109)]. However, the range of validity of these relations is still uncertain. These difficulties are not astonishing since the treatment is based on a simple model. All properties and forces which are not represented by the model are necessarily reflected in the osmotic coefficients. This is equally true for concentrated electrolyte solutions. The theory of swelling equilibria thus encounters the same difficulties as the theory of concentrated electrolytes in general.

Swelling in solutions. Swelling equilibria with solutions can be treated in a similar way. It must be taken into account that both the resin and the solution contain solutes. The solvent activity in the liquid phase thus is no longer unity, and Eq. (5-3) must be replaced by

$$\Pi v_w = -RT \ln \frac{\bar{a}_w}{a_w} \tag{5-16}$$

Similarly, Eq. (5-15) must be replaced by

$$-\ln \bar{a}_w = \frac{\phi \sum_i \bar{m}_i M_w}{1,000} \tag{5-17}$$

Summation is carried out over all mobile species.

In the correlation between resin volume and solvent content, the space occupied by sorbed solutes must be taken into account. The distribution of the solutes between the resin and the solution is also needed. Such sorption equilibria are discussed in Sec. 5-3.

Strong electrolytes in particular are rather strongly excluded by the resins. Hence, addition of a strong electrolyte lowers a_w more than $\bar{a}_w$. As a result, the osmotic pressure difference becomes smaller, and the resin swells less than in pure solvent.

Thermodynamic functions. Vapor-sorption isotherms can be used to calculate the *free energy of swelling* [41,76,76a,115,190,284]. The free-energy change ΔG_1 with addition of one mole of dry resin to an infinite amount of solvent vapor of relative humidity P_w/P

$$\text{Resin (dry)} + n\text{H}_2\text{O}(P_w) \rightarrow \text{resin} \cdot n\text{H}_2\text{O}(P_w) \tag{5-18}$$

is

$$\Delta G_1 = -RT \int_0^{P_w/P} n \, d \ln \frac{P_w}{P} \tag{5-19}$$

The free-energy change ΔG_2 accompanying the transfer of n moles of solvent from pure solvent under the pressure P into an infinite amount of resin which is in equilibrium with solvent vapor of relative humidity P_w/P

$$n\text{H}_2\text{O}(P) \rightarrow n\text{H}_2\text{O}(P_w) \tag{5-20}$$

is

$$\Delta G_2 = nRT \ln \frac{P_w}{P} \tag{5-21}$$

The (integral) free energy of swelling is the sum of both contributions:

$$\Delta G_1 = \Delta G_1 + \Delta G_2 = - RT \int_0^{P_w/P} n \, d \ln \frac{P_w}{P} + nRT \ln \frac{P_w}{P} \quad (5\text{-}22)$$

The *heat of swelling* ΔH can be determined by direct measurement [76,190] or from the temperature coefficient of swelling [115,284]. The general thermodynamic relation between ΔG and ΔH is

$$\Delta G = \Delta H - T \, \Delta S \quad (5\text{-}23)$$

Equations (5-22) and (5-23) can be used for calculating the *entropy of swelling* ΔS from the vapor-sorption isotherm and the heat of swelling [76,76a,115,190,284]. The entropy of swelling is chiefly given by the configurational entropy of the matrix. An expansion of the matrix involves uncoiling of the chains. Thus a less probable configuration with lower entropy is attained. This entropy loss is particularly great in highly crosslinked resins. In addition, other factors such as mixing and solvation effects contribute to the entropy of swelling.

The free energy, heat, and entropy of swelling of a representative cation-exchange resin are shown in Fig. 5-11.

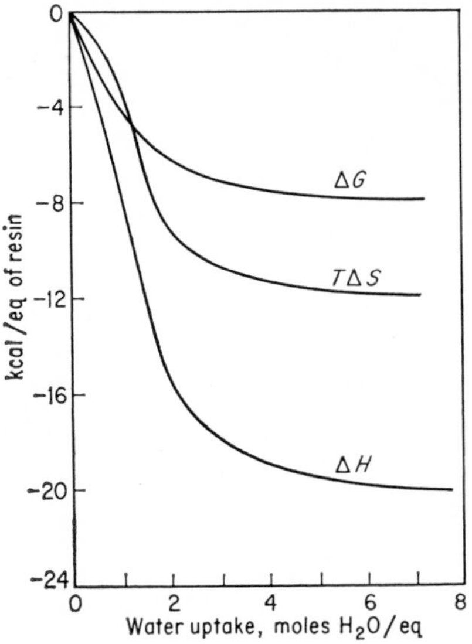

FIG. 5-11. Free energy, heat, and entropy of swelling. The diagram gives experimental values of the (integral) free-energy, heat, and entropy changes accompanying the water uptake by a dry resin (styrene-type cation exchanger of 13 per cent DVB in H^+ form; temperature 25°C). *From B. R. Sundheim, M. H. Waxman, and H. P. Gregor* [284].

e. Other Approaches and Models

Other approaches and models can be used for the quantitative treatment of swelling equilibria. For materials such as zeolites and clays, which have a rigid rather than elastic framework, Gregor's model is, of course, inappropriate. Here, a noncommittal thermodynamic treatment which is not based on a model with specific properties seems the best approach. Such a treatment is outlined in a later section (see page 196). For ion-exchange resins, other models have been used which account, at least partially, for the various forces which are responsible for the differences in the osmotic activities of the resinates. The introduction of osmotic coefficients is thus avoided. However, the theories involve other parameters which, as a rule, are not readily accessible. Also, the applicability of the theories is restricted by the assumptions which are made. Such approaches are outlined in the following.

Solvation effects. Gregor based his original treatment [109] on the idea that solvation is one of the most important factors which determine swelling and ion-exchange equilibria. As components of the system he chose the matrix with *solvated* fixed ionic groups, the *solvated* mobile ions, and the *free* solvent. He assumed that the system behaves ideally, except for solvation effects. It is true that the distinction between free solvent and solvation shells is thermodynamically ill-defined and somewhat arbitrary. Nevertheless, this approach helps to explain a number of empirical rules in a semiquantitative way (see also pages 145 and 172).

With Gregor's choice of the components, the osmotic pressure difference between the pore liquid and the external liquid (pure solvent) is given by

$$\Pi = - \frac{RT}{v_w} \ln \bar{N}_w^* = - \frac{RT}{v_w} \ln \frac{q_w^*}{q_w^* + 1} \qquad (5\text{-}24)$$

Quantities referring to free solvent and solvated ions are denoted with asterisks; $\bar{N}_w^*$ = mole fraction of free solvent in the pore liquid; q_w^* = number of moles of free solvent in one equivalent of resin.

This equation, in which deviations from ideality except for solvation effects are neglected, takes the place of Eq. (5-3) and is derived in an analogous way. The equivalent volume of the resin (in A form) is given by

$$\bar{V}_e = \bar{q}_w^* v_w + \frac{v_A^*}{|z_A|} + \bar{v}_R^* \qquad (5\text{-}25)$$

where v_A^* = molar volume of solvated counter ion A; $\bar{v}_R^*$ = equivalent volume of matrix with solvated fixed ionic groups; z_A = electrochemical valence of A.

Equations (5-24) and (5-25), in combination with the empirical relation

$$\bar{V}_e = a\Pi + b \qquad (5\text{-}14)$$

give a complete description of the system. Swelling and solvent uptake of the various ionic forms can be predicted from the empirical constants a, b, and $\bar{v}_R^*$ (which are the same for all ionic forms) and the solvated counterion volumes.

In this treatment, solvation effects appear explicitly in the equations, whereas in the previous (and more rigorous) treatment they were disguised in the osmotic coefficients. The larger the solvated counter ion, the larger is the equivalent volume of the resin (see Fig. 5-12) and the swelling pressure, and the smaller is the free-solvent content (see also Fig. 5-6).

The treatment can be extended to include swelling in contact with solutions (see also page 115). This is done in essentially the same way as in the more rigorous treatment which was described before.   Gregor's approach can also be used for calculating differences in solvated counter-ion volumes. It has been shown that the difference $v_A^* - v_B^*$ is twice the difference $(\bar{V}_e)_{AR} - (\bar{V}_e)_{BR}$, extrapolated to zero crosslinking, of the equivalent volumes of the respective ionic forms [237].

This simple approach is quite satisfactory in explaining swelling equilibria in systems in which, indeed, solvation is the most important factor. This is true, for example, for the alkali-ion forms of sulfonated styrene-type cation exchangers.   Of course, the treatment must fail when effects other than solvation become important.

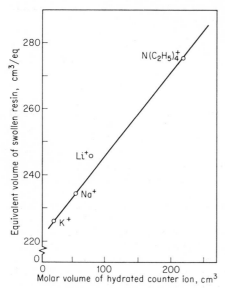

FIG. 5-12. Swelling and equivalent volume of the hydrated counter ion. In systems in which solvation is the most significant factor, there is an approximately linear relation between the equivalent volume of the swollen resin and the equivalent volume of the hydrated counter ion. (Resin: Dowex 50-X10, solutions: 0.001 M chlorides.) *From H. P. Gregor* [109].

Incomplete dissociation of the fixed ionogenic groups. Various models include explicitly the effect of incomplete dissociation of the fixed ionogenic groups by treating the non-ionized groups as separate species. Such approaches are particularly suited to describe swelling of weak-acid resins, in which the fixed ionic groups can associate with H^+ ions (see, for example, Katchalsky's theory in Sec. 4-4b).   An interesting feature of these resins is that, by responding with swelling or shrinking to pH changes in the external solutions, they can convert chemical energy into mechanical energy ("mechanochemical systems" [5,164]).

Electrostatic effects. The refined model of Lazare and Gregor [191] includes, as an additional feature, the electrostatic forces within the resin (see Sec. 5-1). However, beyond the implication that the resin can be adequately represented by such a plate model, the treatment involves several assumptions and one free parameter, namely, the charge density at the plate surfaces. The equations are rather complicated and can be evaluated only numerically. For details, the reader is referred to the original publication [191].

In the molecular models (see below), the electrostatic effects are accounted for in a different way.

Molecular models. The fundamental properties of the molecular models have already been described in Sec. 5-1. In the following, the application to swelling equilibria is briefly outlined.

The *model of Harris and Rice* [132,241,241a] has been designed for resins of moderate and high degrees of crosslinking. Chemical interaction (ion-pair formation) between fixed ionic groups and counter ions is included, and electrostatic interactions between neighboring fixed ionic groups on the same and on adjacent chains are computed. Swelling equilibria are calculated in the following way. Equilibrium is attained when the free energy of the system is at its minimum. The free energy is split into three additive terms: a chemical contribution arising from ion-pair formation, a configurational contribution arising from the statistical properties of the (uncharged) matrix and from the free energy of mixing, and a third contribution comprising electrostatic interactions and the free energy of permutation of ionized and nonionized ionogenic groups. The chemical contribution is calculated with the assumption that ion-pair formation between the fixed ionic groups and the counter ion can be expressed in terms of an "intrinsic binding constant" of the association equilibrium. The configurational contribution is calculated by use of Flory's theory of the elasticity of macromolecular networks [89]. This theory is extended by including a correction for the finite length of the chains. The third contribution is calculated from a lattice model rather than from the chain model; it is assumed that the ionogenic groups are uniformly distributed, occupying sites in a spatial lattice. Electrostatic interactions between nearest neighbors are calculated by use of the Debye-Hückel theory for the various "microscopic" states of the gel, i.e., for the various possible distributions of the ion pairs. A partition function is then formed by combining all microscopic states according to their free energy in essentially the same way as in the statistical lattice theories of liquids [141]. The total free energy of the system is obtained as a function of the number of ion pairs and of the gel volume. Several simplifying assumptions are made in the derivations. The resulting equations are rather complicated. The interested reader is referred to the original publication [241].

The equations derived from this model contain several quantities which cannot be measured. This is particularly true for the "coordination number of the ionogenic groups" in the postulated lattice, the dielectric constant in the gel, and the intrinsic binding constants of the ion pairs. Here, Rice and Harris make the following assumptions [241]. The coordination number in the lattice is taken as 10; this is somewhat less than in the densest packing of spheres (coordination number 12). The dielectric constant of the gel is assumed to be quite low, even lower than the average of the constants for water ($\epsilon = 80$) and the organic matrix ($\epsilon \approx 2$). In addition, Rice and Harris operate with an "effective" dielectric constant which is assumed to be about 2 to 4 at a minimum distance of about 5 A from a fixed ionic group and which increases linearly with the distance from the group until it attains the macroscopic value at a distance of about 12 A. The intrinsic binding constants for alkali-ion forms of resins with sulfonic acid groups are assumed to be of the order of 10 to 100. Such values would give little ion-pair formation in solutions of ordinary monomeric sulfonates. In the resins, however, a considerable extent of ion-pair formation is calculated because the dielectric constant is low and the electrostatic interaction between neighboring fixed charges favors ion-pair formation.

One characteristic feature of this model is the interrelation between ion-pair formation, electrostatic interactions, and expansion of the matrix. Neighboring fixed ionized groups repel one another electrostatically. This repulsion tends to stretch the matrix, thus decreasing the configurational entropy. Hence, increased ion-pair formation, which neutralizes fixed charges, decreases the free energy of the gel (see also page 90).

Comparisons between the model and actual systems (H^+ form and alkali-ion forms of sulfonated styrene-type cation exchangers) have been made by introducing numerical values for the various parameters in the equations [241]. Good qualitative agreement has been obtained. In particular, the model correctly predicts that swelling increases with decreasing degree of crosslinking and solution concentration and with increasing capacity of the resin. It is interesting to analyze the relation between swelling and the ionic form of the resin. According to the model, the counter ion with the stronger tendency to form ion pairs causes less swelling. It can be assumed that counter ions which can approach the fixed ionic groups more closely are bound more strongly. In this way, the model accounts for the empirical relation between swelling and the Debye-Hückel parameter a^0 (see page 114). Note that, in Gregor's model, this same effect is attributed to a quite different physical cause, namely, to the larger size of the (solvated) ion with the larger a^0 value.*

For weakly crosslinked, strongly swollen gels this model must fail. Here, the distance between adjacent chains can become very great, so that the lattice model used for the computation of the electrostatic interactions becomes unrealistic. The behavior of resins of this type is more adequately described by *Katchalsky's model* [162,163,214]; see also Sec. 4-4b. This model has been developed primarily for weakly crosslinked, weak-acid resins. Electrostatic interactions are calculated on the basis of the chain model for fixed ionic groups on one and the same chain only. Furthermore, it is assumed that the

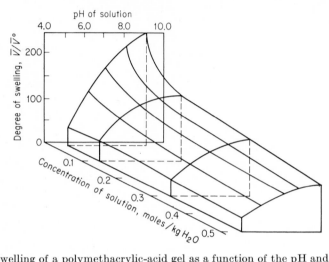

Fig. 5-13. Swelling of a polymethacrylic-acid gel as a function of the pH and the concentration of the solution (NaCl). *From I. Michaeli and A. Katchalsky* [214].

"salts" of the fixed acid groups are completely dissociated, whereas the resinous "acid" is very weakly dissociated. Katchalsky's equations have been given in Sec. 4-4b. They can be used for calculating the degree of swelling $\bar{V}/\bar{V}_0$ as a function of the pH and the salt concentration of the external solution. An example is shown in Fig. 5-13.

Katchalsky's theory cannot be applied to highly crosslinked resins because interactions between neighboring chains are disregarded. Thus the two molecular models supplement one another in a fortunate way.

f. Ion Exchangers with Particular Structure

The discussion in the previous sections is based on models in which the structure of the resins is tacitly assumed to be uniform. The almost ideally elastic behavior of styrene-divinylbenzene matrices [see Eq. (5-14)] justifies the use of such models for resins of this type. However, for many other, less common ion exchangers the models with the elastic or statistically

---

* A serious objection to the explanation of differences in swelling by differences in the extent of ion-pair formation alone is the fact that cation exchangers with sulfonic acid groups, as a rule, swell more strongly when in H^+ form then when in an alkali-ion form. Yet it is very unlikely that the crosslinked sulfonic acids would dissociate more strongly than their alkali salts.

coiled matrix are unrealistic. Peculiarities of a few typical ion exchangers of such types are briefly discussed in this section.

Resins with inhomogeneous structure. Most condensation polymers, and perhaps even a few additional polymers, have a structure which is inhomogeneous in colloidal dimensions. The condensation product of phenolsulfonic acid and formaldehyde (see page 30) has been thoroughly studied in this respect. Studies of the polycondensation reaction indicate that, first, condensation nuclei are formed. The nuclei then grow to give submicroscopic, very tightly crosslinked grains. Only in the last stage of the reaction do these submicroscopic grains coalesce to form a coherent gel. Resins with satisfactory properties are obtained if the polycondensation is stopped as soon as the grains are sufficiently, but not too tightly, linked with one another. Such resins consist of highly crosslinked "islands" which are embedded in regions of low crosslinking. This hypothesis is in good agreement with experimental stress-strain diagrams and results of measurements of strain birefringence and diffusion phenomena [169,261]. When a resin of this type swells, the regions of low crosslinking expand, whereas the "hard" islands remain essentially unchanged. Most of the fixed ionic groups—and thus most of the counter ions—are concentrated in the hard islands. Hence, differences in valence and hydration of the counter ions have less effect on the swelling behavior than in uniformly built resins of comparable water content (see Table 5-2). Of course, activities, swelling pressures, osmotic coefficients, etc., can be defined for such resins also. Actually, they would represent suitable mean values for the whole resin phase. However, their relations to other physical quantities such as hydra-

Table 5-2. Water contents of various ionic forms of sulfonated styrene-type and phenol-formaldehyde-type cation exchangers

Counter ion	Dowex 50* ($\approx 11\%$ DVB) % wt	Phenolsulfonic acid resins[†]	
		Higher crosslinking, % wt	Lower crosslinking, % wt
H^+	50.2	59.0	68.7
Li^+	49.9	59.5	69.1
Na^+	44.3	58.7	68.6
K^+	38.8	55.1	64.2
NH_4^+	41.5	58.0	67.6
Ag^+	23.7		
Mg^{2+}	48.3	55.7	65.7
Ca^{2+}	44.7	54.5	67.0
Sr^{2+}	40.3	55.1	67.5
Ba^{2+}	34.7	52.6	60.2
Al^{3+}		57.7	68.2

* From data by H. P. Gregor [110].
[†] From G. Manecke [202].

tion numbers, equivalent volumes, configurational entropies, etc., are more complex than in the simple homogeneous models.

Similar effects are observed with many other resins.

Certain ion-exchange materials have an even more coarse structure than the ordinary condensation polymers. For example, for collodion membranes a "bubble" structure has been established by electron micrographs. The pore liquid is contained in microscopic interconnected bubbles in the compact material [200,279]. In such a case, the definition of the ion exchanger (including pore liquid) as one thermodynamic phase is, of course, unrealistic.

Amphoteric ion exchangers. Swelling of amphoteric resins with both weak-acid and weak-base groups is a function of the pH of the solution and shows a characteristic minimum near the isoelectric point of the resin. Here, the active groups of both types are practically undissociated, so that the osmotic pressure difference is small. When the pH is increased or decreased, either the acid or the base groups dissociate, thus increasing the number of osmotically active particles within the resin. The result is an increase in swelling in either case.

Crystalline ion exchangers. Natural and synthetic *zeolites* have a rather rigid framework structure. The (dehydrated) crystals have interstices in which solvent molecules can be accommodated [7,11,14,15,17,138] without much change in the external volume of the crystal. The amount of solvent which a crystal can take up depends on the available internal volume and, hence, also on the volume occupied by the counter ions. As a rule, the water content of a wet zeolite decreases with increasing (crystalline) radius of the counter ion. In many cases, however, not only the size of the counter ion affects the solvent uptake since exchange of one counter ion for another is often accompanied by a slight distortion of the crystal lattice. Table 5-3 shows a comparison of experimental values for some representative zeolites in various ionic forms.

Table 5-3. Water contents of various zeolites in different ionic forms

Counter ion	Chabazite, % wt	Analcite, % wt	Basic cancrinite, % wt	Basic sodalite, % wt
Li^+	21.8		9.8	10.9
Na^+	20.3	8.1	6.1	9.2
K^+	17.1	1.5		
Rb^+	13.6	1.9		
NH_4^+		1.5		
Ag^+	15.7	8.6	3.7	5.2
Tl^+	9.2	0.5		
Ca^{2+}	22.2			
Sr^{2+}	20.7			
Ba^{2+}	19.3			

From R. M. Barrer [7,11,14].

Zeolites are polar and hydrophilic materials and thus have a higher affinity for polar than for nonpolar solvents.   However, the (empty) interstices in the crystal lattice are readily filled even with nonpolar solvent molecules.   The uptake of liquid solvent by a zeolite is mainly governed by steric effects rather than by chemical affinities.*   The rigid and regular lattice acts as a "molecular sieve," preventing the access of molecules which are too large [9,15,17].   For example, dehydrated chabazite takes up n-paraffins and CHF_2Cl, but not isoparaffins, aromatics, CF_3Cl, and CF_4 [9]; see Fig. 5-14.   The amount of solvent taken up is chiefly determined by the available intracrystalline void volume.   Both the width of the channels in the lattice and the intracrystalline void volume can be determined rather accurately from solvent-sorption measurements [15].   Both these quantities depend on the ionic form and the hydration state of the zeolite.

Montmorillonites and other crystalline ion exchangers with *layer structure* swell anisotropically.   They are able to take up solvent which is accommodated in between the lattice layers.   Solvent uptake increases the interlayer distance, but leaves the structure of the layers themselves practically unchanged   [137–139,148,149,165,217, 224,225].   In the early stages of swelling, the interlayer distance increases stepwise ("crystalline swelling") rather than continuously [224,225].   Lattice forces which must be overcome by the solvation tendency of the intersticial counter ions seem to be responsible for this effect.   In montmorillonite, stable interlayer distances of about 9.5, 12.4, 15.4, 19.0, and 22.5 A have been found by X-ray diffraction (see Table 5-4).   These spacings are common to almost all ionic forms.   The change from one stable interlayer distance to another requires a certain activation energy.   This fact results in hysteresis phenomena which are typical of "crystalline swelling" (see Fig. 5-15).   With

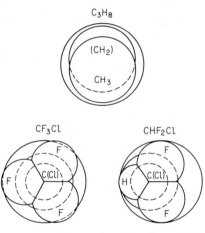

Fig. 5-14. Sieve action of zeolites.   Dehydrated chabazite can accommodate CHF_2Cl and normal paraffins, but excludes CF_3Cl and isoparaffins.   *From R. M. Barrer and D. W. Brook* [9].

monovalent and strongly hydrated counter ions such as Na^+ and Li^+, the stage of crystalline swelling is finally overcome.   Beyond 40 A, the interlayer distance increases continuously, and the material behaves like a gel.   With other counter ions such as K^+, NH_4^+, Mg^{2+}, Ca^{2+}, Al^{3+}, etc., swelling comes

---

* Of course, competitive sorption of components of mixed solvents depends on chemical affinities.   Polar molecules such as H_2O, H_2S, NH_3, etc., are preferentially taken up [17].

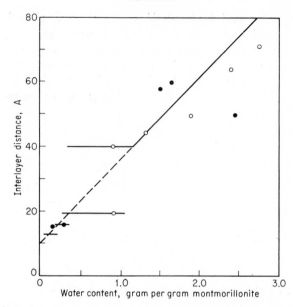

FIG. 5-15. Crystalline swelling of ion exchangers with layer structure.   Ion exchanger: Wyoming bentonite; the interlayer distances were calculated from X-ray-diffraction data by Norrish [225] (○) and Hendricks [137] and Mooney [217] (●).   *From K. Norrish and J. P. Quirk [225].*

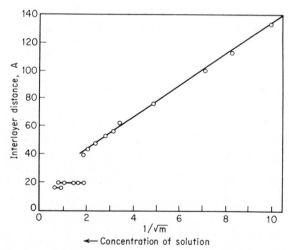

FIG. 5-16. Crystalline swelling of ion exchangers with layer structure.   Swelling of Wyoming bentonite in NaCl solutions as a function of the solution concentration.   *From K. Norrish and J. P. Quirk [225].*

to a stop at one of the stable crystalline interlayer distances [224]. The dependence of swelling on the concentration of the external solution is shown in Fig. 5-16.

Table 5-4. Observed interlayer distances (in Angstrom units) of various ionic forms of montmorillonite

Counter ion									
H^+	Li^+	Na^+	K^+	NH_4^+	Cs^+	Mg^{2+}	Ca^{2+}	Sr^{2+}	Ba^{2+}
≈ 10	9.5	9.5	10.0	10		9.5	9.5	9.5	9.8
12.4	12.4	12.4	12.4	?	≈ 12			≈ 12.0	≈ 12.0
15.4	15.4	15.4	15.0	15		15.4	15.4	≈ 15.5	≈ 15.5
19.0	19.0	19.0				19.2	18.9	?	18.9
22.4	22.5								

From K. Norrish [224].

5-3. SORPTION OF SOLUTES

Ion exchangers can sorb solutes from solutions with which they are in contact. As a rule, sorption of a solute is a reversible phenomenon, i.e., the solute can be removed from the ion exchanger by washing with pure solvent. However, a few cases of irreversible sorption are known (see page 130).

The sorption behavior of strong electrolytes is quite different from that of weak and nonelectrolytes. The latter two are sorbed by ion exchangers in a similar way as by usual nonionic adsorbents. Strong electrolytes, in contrast, are subject to the electrostatic forces arising from the presence of fixed ionic groups and counter ions in the resin. The result is a Donnan-type sorption equilibrium which is unique for ionic sorbents.

The discussion in this section centers on sorption equilibria between ion-exchange resins and aqueous solutions. The behavior of other materials is briefly outlined. Sorption from nonaqueous and mixed solvents is discussed in Sec. 10-4, and the kinetics of sorption in Sec. 6-6a. Definitions of the quantities which are used in this and later chapters are given in the following introductory section.

a. Sorption Isotherms and Distribution Coefficients

Sorption equilibria are best described in terms of sorption isotherms and distribution coefficients.

Sorption isotherms describe, in the form of functions or diagrams and for a given constant temperature, the dependence of the equilibrium concentration of the solute in the sorbent on the concentration in the external solution. For usual sorbents, it is customary to give the concentration of the solute in the sorbent per unit weight of (blank) sorbent.

For ion exchangers, it is preferable to relate the concentrations in both phases—ion exchanger and solution—either to unit weight of the solvent in the phase or to unit volume of the phase. With this convention, the sorption isotherm is either of the two functions

$$\bar{m}_i = f(m_i) \tag{5-26}$$
$$\bar{C}_i = g(C_i) \tag{5-27}$$

where m_i = concentration of solute i in millimoles per gram solvent (molality); C_i = concentration of solute i in moles per liter (molarity); quantities with bars refer to the sorbent phase; $\bar{C}_i$ relates to unit volume of the swollen sorbent.

The molal isotherm (5-26) is appropriate when the "sponge" model for the ion exchanger is used, i.e., when a distinction between pore liquid and matrix is made. The molar

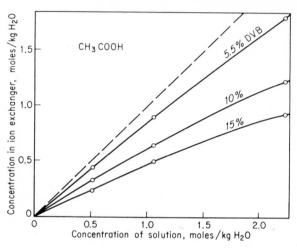

FIG. 5-17. Representative molal sorption isotherms of a solute. The isotherms are negatively curved. Sorbents: styrene-type cation exchangers of various degrees of crosslinking, in H⁺ form; solute: acetic acid. *From D. Reichenberg and W. F. Wall* [240].

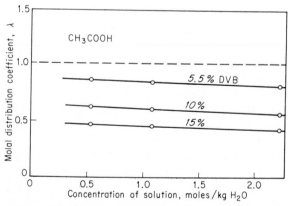

FIG. 5-18. Representative distribution coefficients of a solute. The coefficients are calculated from the experimental data in Fig. 5-17. *From D. Reichenberg and W. F. Wall* [240].

isotherm (5-27) is used when the sorbent is treated as a single, quasi-homogeneous phase. Representative molal sorption isotherms are shown in Fig. 5-17.

The *distribution coefficient* of a solute is defined as the ratio of the concentrations of the solute in the sorbent and in the solution:

$$\lambda_i \equiv \frac{\bar{m}_i}{m_i} \tag{5-28}$$

$$\lambda_i' \equiv \frac{\bar{C}_i}{C_i} \tag{5-29}$$

where λ_i = molal distribution coefficient; λ_i' = molar distribution coefficient.

The distribution coefficient corresponds to one point on the sorption isotherm, giving the ratio of the ordinate value to the abscissa value at this particular point. Only in the case of a linear isotherm is the distribution coefficient independent of concentration. The molal distribution coefficients corresponding to the isotherms in Fig. 5-17 are shown in Fig. 5-18.

Molarities C_i and molalities m_i can be interconverted if the solvent content and density of the sorbent and the density of the solution are known:

$$\bar{m}_i = \frac{100}{W\bar{p}}\,\bar{C}_i \qquad \bar{C}_i = \frac{W\bar{p}}{100}\,\bar{m}_i \tag{5-30}$$

$$m_i = \frac{C_i}{\rho - C_iM_i/1,000} \qquad C_i = \frac{m_i\rho}{1 + m_iM_i/1,000} \tag{5-31}$$

and, hence,

$$\lambda_i' = \frac{W\bar{p}}{100\rho}\left(1 + \frac{m_iM_i}{1,000}\right)\lambda_i \qquad \lambda_i = \frac{100}{W\bar{p}}\left(\rho - \frac{C_iM_i}{1,000}\right)\lambda_i' \tag{5-32}$$

where W = solvent content in weight per cent; $\bar{p}$ = density of swollen sorbent at equilibrium; ρ = density of the solution; M_i = molecular weight of the solute.

For practical purposes the uptake $\bar{Q}_i$ of solute in terms of, say, millimoles per gram of dry and blank sorbent can be calculated from the distribution coefficient:

$$\bar{Q}_i = \frac{m_i\lambda_i W}{100 - W - m_i\lambda_i WM_i/1,000} \tag{5-33}$$

b. Sorption of Nonelectrolytes

A quantitative theory for nonelectrolyte sorption by ion exchangers has not yet been developed. However, various general rules emerge more or less clearly from the wealth of experimental results. These rules can be explained qualitatively in terms of physical forces and interactions, and, with due caution, qualitative predictions of sorption equilibria can be made.

In the absence of interactions of any kind, it should be expected that the (molal) concentrations of the solute in the sorbent and in the external solution are equal, i.e., that the molal distribution coefficient is unity. It is hardly surprising that such a behavior is rarely found. The various interactions which cause deviations from ideality are discussed in the following.

Ionic Solvation and Salting Out. The fixed ionic groups and counter ions in the ion exchanger form solvation shells and thus tie up solvent molecules; only a fraction of the total internal solvent is "free" (see Sec. 5-2b), and only the free solvent is available for dissolving the nonelectrolyte (at least, provided that the latter does not displace solvent from the ionic solvation shells). In the absence of other interactions one must expect the nonelectrolyte concentrations in the *free* solvent to be the same in the resin and in the solution. The molality, which refers to the *total* solvent including ionic solvation shells, thus is lower in the resin than outside where all the solvent is free. The nonelectrolyte is "salted out," in essentially the same way as in liquid-liquid distribution equilibria when a soluble salt is added to one liquid phase [208,230,240].

Salting-out effects are obviously most pronounced when only a small fraction of the solvent in the resin is free. This is the case when the resin is highly crosslinked and the counter ions are strongly hydrated (see Sec. 5-2b). With salting out as the predominant effect, the molal distribution coefficient of the solute thus decreases with increasing degree of crosslinking (see Fig. 5-18) and increasing solvation number of the counter ion.

If salting out is the predominant effect, sorption of the nonelectrolyte solute can be enhanced by adding an electrolyte to the external solution. Electrolyte addition results in salting out in the solution also and thus counteracts salting out in the ion exchanger. This principle is used in separations by "salting-out chromatography" [243a]; see Sec. 9-7e.

Sorption of acetic acid* by sulfonated styrene-type resins can be explained quantitatively by the salting-out effect: it is found that the distribution of the solute between the free solvent in both phases is uniform under all conditions, if four water molecules are assigned to each —SO_3H group as its hydration shell [240]. Unfortunately, a situation as simple as this is an exception. In most cases, other effects overshadow the salting-out effect.

Interactions with Counter Ions; Salting In and Complex Formation. In certain systems, exactly the opposite of salting out is observed. For example, it is known that addition of acids increases rather than decreases the solubilities of a number of organic compounds such as aliphatic alcohols in water [240,272]. The mechanism which is responsible for such effects, occasionally called "salting in," is not yet altogether clear. Analogous effects are observed with ion-exchange resins. For example, aliphatic alcohols are salted in by strong-acid cation exchangers in H^+ form, i.e., sorbed with distribution coefficients greater than unity (see also Fig. 5-19), but are salted out by the same resins when in alkali-ion forms [240].

If such salting in is the predominant effect, sorption of the nonelectrolyte solute can be reduced by adding an acid as solubilizer to the external solution. This principle is used in separations by "solubilization chromatography" [272]; see Sec. 9-7e.

---

* It is true that acetic acid is a weak electrolyte rather than a nonelectrolyte, but under the experimental conditions its dissociation is negligible.

Interactions between the nonelectrolyte and the counter ions become even more obvious when inorganic counter ions are replaced by *organic ions* such as $N(C_2H_5)_4^+$. Sorption of organic nonelectrolytes with hydrocarbon groups from aqueous solutions is, as a rule, greatly increased by such a replacement. Certain inorganic ion exchangers will sorb larger nonpolar organic molecules only after organic counter ions have been introduced [12,108]. On the other hand, sorption of distinctly hydrophilic nonelectrolytes such as sugars is usually reduced when inorganic counter ions are replaced by organic ones.

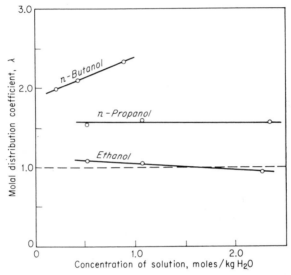

FIG. 5-19. Sorption of alcohols by a strong-acid resin in H^+ form (sulfonated polystyrene with 5.5 per cent DVB). The molal distribution coefficients are larger than unity and increase with increasing carbon number of the alcohol. *From D. Reichenberg and W. F. Wall* [240].

The most striking effects are observed when the solute forms strong *complexes* or even *chelates* with the counter ions. For example, ammonia and organic amines are very strongly sorbed by cation exchangers with Ag^+, Cu^{2+}, Ni^{2+}, or other transition-metal counter ions [135,136,282]; see also Fig. 5-27 and Sec. 5-7. These ions readily shed their solvation shells to form stable amine complexes. The resins take up amines even from very dilute solutions until the coordinative valences of the metal ion are saturated. Other examples are sorption of polyhydric compounds (glycols, carbohydrates, etc.) and carbonyl compounds which form addition products with borate and bisulfite anions, respectively, by anion exchangers in the borate [166,255] or bisulfite form [253]. Furthermore, anion exchangers in the Br^- and I^- forms are excellent sorbents for molecular Br_2 and I_2, respectively, which form complexes such as Br_3^- and I_3^- with the counter ion in the resin [303].*

London and Dipole Interactions. Sorption of organic nonelectrolytes with hydrocarbon groups by ion-exchange resins with hydrocarbon matrices is likely to be affected by two kinds of interactions. First, sorption is, as a rule, favored by *London interactions* between the solute and the matrix [51,199,240]. However, these forces are usually weak. A second and stronger contribution may come from *dipole-dipole interactions* of the polar solvent molecules with one another and with polar groups of the solute. The consequence of such interactions is that the hydrocarbon groups tend to coagulate or to be squeezed out of the polar solution onto a phase boundary. In solutions, this effect is strikingly demonstrated by soap-micelle formation and detergent action. Both the London and the dipole interactions favor local adsorption of the hydrocarbon groups of the solute on the matrix and thus enhance sorption of the nonelectrolyte. Both interactions are, of course, more pronounced when the hydrocarbon group of the solute is larger (provided that the polar group remains the same). Hence, in homologous series such as ethanol, propanol, n-butanol, or acetic acid, propionic acid, n-butyric acid, the distribution coefficient usually increases with increasing molecular weight of the solute (see Fig. 5-19) [231,232,240], at least as long as sorption is not limited by molecular size effects (see farther below).

London forces are specific interactions and depend on the molecular structure of the solute and the matrix. Different types of resins may widely differ in their sorption behavior. According to the ancient rule *"similia similibus solvuntur,"* a high affinity and thus strong sorption may be expected when the chemical configurations of the solute and the matrix are similar. Indeed, as a rule, styrene- and phenol-type ion exchangers sorb aromatic compounds more strongly than aliphatic compounds of comparable molecular weight. In particular, phenols and many phenol derivatives are extremely strongly sorbed by resins with aromatic groups [2,52,297]; see Table 5-5. The distribution coefficient for phenol is even much higher when the solution is more dilute. Large molecules with strong affinity for the resin, for example, certain dyes such as alizarin and indigo sulfonates, may be held irreversibly [123].

Molecular Size, Swelling Pressure, and "Sieve Action." The molecular size of the solute, in combination with the degree of crosslinking of the resin, may considerably affect the sorption behavior. The interior of the swollen resin is under a rather high *swelling pressure* which tends to squeeze solvent and solute molecules out of the resin. Larger molecules are more strongly

---

* Molecular iodine, however, is very strongly sorbed by anion-exchange resins in other ionic forms also [254]. Thus, complex formation with I^- ions is not the only cause for sorption by resins in I^- form.

affected. This becomes evident when Eq. (5-16), used earlier for the solvent, is applied to the nonelectrolyte solute

$$\Pi v_N = -RT \ln \frac{\bar{a}_N}{a_N} \tag{5-34}$$

A given swelling pressure Π reduces the internal activity $\bar{a}_N$ of a species N more drastically if the partial molar volume v_N of the species is large. The equilibrium swelling pressure, in turn, is high if the resin is highly crosslinked.

Table 5-5. Molal distribution coefficients of various nonelectrolytes sorbed by cation and anion exchangers from solutions containing 50 g of solute per liter

Solute	Cation exchanger		Anion exchanger	
	Dowex 50-X8		Dowex 1-X7.5	Dowex 1-X8
	H^+ form	Na^+ form	Cl^- form	SO_4^{2-} form
Ethyleneglycol	0.67	0.63		
Diethyleneglycol	....	0.67		
Triethyleneglycol	0.74	0.61		
Ethylenediamine	....	0.57		
Tetraethylenepentamine	....	0.66		
Sucrose	0.24			
D-Glucose	0.22			
Glycerol	0.49	0.56	1.12	
Acetic acid	0.71			
Acetone	1.20	....	1.08	0.66
Formaldehyde	0.59	....	1.06	1.02
Methanol	0.61	....	0.61	
Phenol	3.08	....	17.7	

From R. M. Wheaton and W. C. Bauman [297].

With resins of moderate crosslinking and smaller nonelectrolyte molecules, this swelling-pressure effect is rather small and is often overshadowed by other interactions which favor sorption of larger molecules (for example, see Fig. 5-19). However, with increasing size of the solute molecule or increasing degree of crosslinking, the effect becomes more important. The distribution coefficients in homologous series may thus have maximum values at medium molecular sizes.

Sorption of even larger molecules is limited by still another restriction, namely, by the purely mechanical *sieve action* of the matrix. Molecules which are too large for passing through the meshes of the matrix are excluded by the resin.

Of course, sieve action does not impose a sharp limit on the molecular size of the solute since the mesh width of the matrix is not uniform. Swelling-pressure and sieve effects thus are difficult to distinguish. Also, the sorption rate becomes very low when the molecular size of the solute approaches the critical range. Hence, uptake of large molecules under ordinary experimental conditions may be low because sorption equilibrium, no matter how favorable, is not attained.

The (average) mesh width of fully swollen resins is about 6 to 30 A, depending on the degree of crosslinking and the ionic form [100a,121,129,181,182]. As a rule, the common styrene-type ion-exchange resins with 8 to 12 per cent DVB crosslinking sorb simple phenyl and naphthyl derivatives, glucose, di- and tripeptides, etc., without much steric hindrance. Larger molecules such as phenolphthalein, streptomycin, quinine, etc., find sufficient room only in resins with a lower degree of crosslinking [186,188].

Sieve action and its dependence on the ionic form of the resin is strikingly demonstrated by the behavior of weak-acid resins which swell much more strongly in alkali-ion forms than in the H^+ form. The H^+ form of the resin does not sorb medium-sized molecules such as methylene blue, whereas the alkali form does. Such molecules are "trapped" by the shrinking matrix when, after sorption, the alkali counter ion is replaced by H^+ [154]. Elution is only possible after reconversion to the alkali-ion form.

Dependence on the Solution Concentration. The uptake of the solute by the resin increases with increasing concentration of the solution. The (molal) distribution coefficient, however, usually decreases, i.e., the sorption isotherm has negative curvature. This is particularly true for solutes which are very strongly sorbed even from dilute solutions. Sorption of phenol by phenolic resins [2], and of ammonia by resins in Ag^+ or Cu^{2+} form [282] are typical examples. Here, saturation of the resin is almost complete at relatively low solution concentrations, so that the isotherm flattens out after an initial steep rise. However, in a number of cases, isotherms with positive curvature (distribution coefficient increasing with increasing concentration) are found [240]; see, for example, the curve for *n*-butanol in Fig. 5-19.

The negative curvature of the isotherms is even stronger when the internal solute concentration is given per unit weight of dry and blank sorbent [see Eq. (5-33)] since swelling and solvent content decrease with increasing solution concentration. Usually, a Langmuir or Freundlich isotherm can be fitted reasonably well to the experimental results.

Dependence on Temperature and Pressure. The effect of *temperature* on sorption equilibria is complex and has not yet been studied systematically. Not only the heat of the actual sorption process is involved, but also the temperature dependence of swelling, solvation, and, in some cases, of the dissociation of ion pairs or complexes in the resin. Usually, the temperature dependence of sorption is small. In cases of strong specific sorption the temperature coefficient is likely to be negative, i.e., sorption is smaller at higher temperatures.

The effect of *pressure* on sorption of solutes has so far received very little attention. However, one may expect that the pressure dependence is insignificant since sorption usually occurs without much change in volume of the total system (ion exchanger plus solution).

Survey. The considerations above can be summarized as follows. Sorption is quite generally favored by specific interactions between the solute and the matrix, fixed ionic groups, or counter ions of the ion exchanger, and is discouraged by salting out caused by counter ions and fixed ionic groups. Specific interactions may arise from a number of causes, particularly from structural similarity of solute and ion exchanger (London forces) and from complex formation of solute molecules with the counter ions. Both specific interaction and salting out become stronger when the degree of crosslinking of the ion exchanger is increased and the temperature is lowered. London forces may result in stronger sorption of larger molecules. However, sorption of large molecules is adversely affected by the swelling pressure in the resin, and molecules which exceed a critical size are excluded by sieve action. The dependence of sorption on the solution concentration is usually well described by a Langmuir or Freundlich isotherm, i.e., the amount of solute in the sorbent increases and the distribution coefficient decreases with increasing concentration.

Sorption by ion exchangers of particular structure. The rules quoted above apply chiefly to ion-exchange resins. Other types of ion-exchange materials may behave differently. A few peculiarities will be mentioned briefly.

Natural and synthetic *zeolites* have a regular and rather rigid crystal lattice and, hence, show a strikingly sharp sieve action [9,17]; see Fig. 5-14. It is true that dry zeolites can sorb gaseous or liquid nonelectrolytes; however, there is usually very little sorption of nonelectrolytes from aqueous solutions, because water is preferred by the hydrophilic lattice and by the counter ions. From nonaqueous solutions, polar molecules such as NH_3, H_2S, etc., are taken up in preference to less polar ones.

Montmorillonites and other crystalline ion exchangers with layer structure can sorb nonelectrolytes even from aqueous solutions, particularly when the inorganic counter ions have been replaced by organic ones [108].

"Tailor-made" *silica gels* with high sorption specificities for various larger organic molecules have been prepared by forming the gels in the presence of the respective organic compounds which are subsequently eluted. For a considerable period of time, the gel retains a "form memory"; in preference to others, the gel sorbs the compound around which it has been molded during the solidification [25,61,77]. With resinous ion-exchanger gels, such phenomena have never been observed and are unlikely to occur because the hydrocarbon matrix is too flexible and elastic.

c. Sorption of Strong Electrolytes

Equilibria of ion exchangers with solutions of electrolytes are more complex than with those of nonelectrolytes. The ion exchanger contains counter ions, say, species A. Upon equilibration with an electrolyte solution containing other counter ions, say, species B, ion exchange occurs, and the ion exchanger is partially converted to the B form. Such "ion-exchange equilibria" are discussed in Sec. 5-4. Only in exceptional cases can electrolytes BY (where Y is the co-ion) be sorbed by ion exchangers in A form without ion exchange (see Sec. 5-3f). In the following, sorption of electrolytes AY by ion exchangers in A form will be studied.

There are two essential aspects in which electrolyte sorption differs from nonelectrolyte sorption. First, the ion exchanger contains counter ions A even prior to sorption; the additional, sorbed ions A are indistinguishable from the original ones. Second, the mobile ions A and Y are subject to the electrostatic forces in the system. Electrolyte sorption is best understood when the effect of the electric forces is analyzed and the ions A and Y are treated as separate species (without artificial distinction between "original" and "sorbed" counter ions in the ion exchanger). The electrolyte uptake is, of course, stoichiometrically equivalent to the co-ion uptake since electroneutrality requires that the co-ions which enter the ion exchanger be accompanied by an equivalent amount of counter ions.

The Donnan potential. First, the origin of the electrostatic forces in the system will be studied. Suppose that a cation exchanger (containing no sorbed electrolyte) is placed in a dilute solution of a strong electrolyte. There are considerable concentration differences between the two phases; the cation concentration is larger in the ion exchanger, whereas the (mobile) anion concentration is larger in the solution. If the ions carried no electric charges, these concentration differences would be levelled out by diffusion. However, such a process would disturb electroneutrality since, actually, the ions are charged. Migration both of cations into the solution and of anions into the ion exchanger results in an accumulation of positive charge in the solution and of negative charge in the ion exchanger. The first few ions which diffuse thus build up an electric potential difference between the two phases. This so-called "Donnan potential" pulls cations back into the (negatively charged) ion exchanger and anions back into the (positively charged) solution. An equilibrium is established in which the tendency of the ions to level out the existing concentration differences is balanced by the action of the electric field. In the ion exchanger, the counter-ion concentration thus remains much higher and the co-ion concentration much lower than in the external solution.

The situation with anion exchangers is analogous. Here, of course, the Donnan potential has the opposite sign.

The electric potential difference between ion exchangers and dilute solutions can attain very high values. Yet, this does not mean that in either the ion exchanger or the solution deviations from electroneutrality detectable by chemical analysis can occur. Migration of just a few ions is sufficient to build up so strong an electric field counteracting any further migration that deviations from electroneutrality remain far below the limit of accuracy of any method, except for the measurement of the electric field itself. Thus, for all practical purposes, the condition of electroneutrality must be considered as still valid.*

The Donnan potential has one immediate consequence for electrolyte sorption; it repels co-ions from the ion exchanger and thus prevents the internal co-ion concentration from rising beyond an equilibrium value which is usually much smaller than the concentration in the external solution. Co-ion uptake and electrolyte sorption are equivalent because of the electroneutrality requirement. Hence, *the electrolyte is, at least partially, excluded by the ion exchanger.* This *Donnan exclusion* is a unique feature of electrolyte sorption by ionic sorbents.

Electrolyte-sorption equilibria have a formal resemblance to equilibria in systems such as

$$A^+, Y^-, H_2O \left| \begin{array}{c} \text{membrane} \\ \text{impermeable for } R^- \end{array} \right| A^+, Y^-, R^-, H_2O \qquad (5\text{-}35)$$

in which a membrane permeable for all species except for R^- is between two solutions, AY and AY + AR. In both systems, one ionic species (the fixed ionic groups, or the R^- ions) is restricted to one of the two phases. The resulting equations for the distribution of the mobile species and the electric potential difference in both systems are formally identical. The behavior of membrane systems such as (5-35) was first elucidated by F. G. Donnan [78], in 1911. In his honor, such membrane equilibria are called *Donnan equilibria* and the electric potential differences between the two solutions *Donnan potentials.* Because of the formal analogies, the terms Donnan equilibrium and Donnan potential are now also applied to sorption equilibria of strong electrolytes and phase boundary potentials between ion exchangers and solutions.

The first application of the Donnan concept to ion exchangers was made as early as 1929 by Mattson [209], a Swedish soil scientist. However, only with the work of Bauman [19], Boyd [39], Gregor [109], and Glueckauf [104], almost twenty years later, has this important concept found general acceptance.

In this book, the Donnan concept is used in the qualitative and quantitative discussion of electrolyte sorption and ion-exchange equilibria and of membrane phenomena.

General rules. Anticipating the results of the quantitative treatment in a later part of this section (page 140), one can deduce the most important rules for electrolyte sorption in a qualitative way. The key to the understanding of the sorption behavior is the Donnan potential and its action on the ions. A qualitative discussion, based mainly on the Donnan concept, is given in the following.

Electrolyte sorption is best expressed in terms of the distribution of the

---

* For deviations from electroneutrality in the immediate vicinity of the phase boundary, see footnote to p. 267.

co-ion, since electrolyte uptake and co-ion uptake are stoichiometrically equivalent and no co-ions are present in the ion exchanger prior to sorption. The effect of the Donnan potential on the co-ion distribution explains the characteristic features of Donnan-type equilibria.

Dependence on Capacity, Degree of Crosslinking, Solution Concentration, and Ionic Valences. It has been shown above that the Donnan potential partially excludes the co-ions from the ion exchanger. The higher the Donnan potential (in absolute value), the stronger is the exclusion, i.e., the smaller is the electrolyte uptake. The Donnan potential, in turn, depends on the ionic concentrations and valences. Equilibrium is attained when the action of the Donnan potential balances the tendency of the counter ions to diffuse out into the solution. This tendency, and thus the Donnan potential, is greater when the concentration difference between the ion exchanger and the solution is larger; the absolute value of the Donnan potential increases with decreasing external and increasing internal counter-ion concentration, and so does the efficiency of electrolyte exclusion. The internal (molal) counter-ion concentration is high when the resin has a high ion-exchange capacity and is highly crosslinked and thus not strongly swollen. Consequently, *the efficiency of electrolyte exclusion increases with decreasing solution concentration and with increasing capacity and degree of crosslinking of the ion exchanger.*

The dependence on the solution concentration is particularly interesting and unique for Donnan-type equilibria. According to the rule deduced above, the distribution coefficient of the co-ion is very low at low concentrations and rises with increasing concentration. Thus the sorption isotherm has a strong *positive* curvature, quite in contrast to the ordinary, negatively curved Langmuir and Freundlich isotherms (see Fig. 5-20).

The force with which an electric field acts on an ion is proportional to the ionic charge. Hence, the Donnan potential required to balance the tendency of the counter ions to diffuse into the solution is smaller when the valence of the counter ions is higher. Because of the smaller Donnan potential, electrolyte exclusion is less efficient. On the other hand, a given Donnan potential excludes the co-ions more efficiently when the co-ion valence is higher. Consequently, *electrolyte exclusion is more efficient with counter ions of low valence and co-ions of high valence.* For example, Na_2SO_4 is more strongly excluded by a cation exchanger than NaCl, and NaCl is more strongly excluded than $CaCl_2$. For an anion exchanger, the sequence is the opposite.

Ionic-size Effects, Swelling Pressure, and Sieve Action. The effects of molecular size, swelling pressure, and sieve action in nonelectrolyte sorption have been discussed in the previous section. The same rules apply to electrolyte sorption. Here, however, swelling-pressure effects are usually much less important than the Donnan exclusion which was discussed above (see also the calculation on page 143). Sieve action prevents polyelectrolytes from being sorbed by moderately and highly crosslinked resins [72].

Interactions with the Fixed Ionic Groups and the Matrix. Various kinds of interactions in the ion exchanger can strongly affect electrolyte sorption. Association or ion-pair formation between the *counter ions and the fixed*

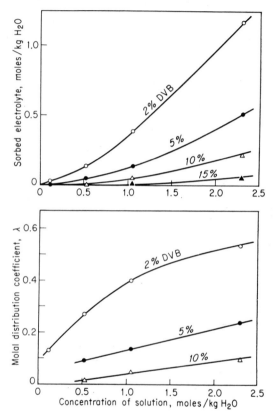

FIG. 5-20. Electrolyte sorption as a function of the solution concentration. The upper diagram gives the sorption isotherms, the lower diagram the distribution coefficients for sorption of HCl by styrene-type cation exchangers of various degrees of crosslinking. The isotherms are positively curved. Electrolyte exclusion is most efficient with highly crosslinked resins and dilute solutions. *From experimental data by K. W. Pepper, D. Reichenberg, and D. K. Hale* [229].

ionic groups localizes the counter ions in the ion exchanger and thus reduces the Donnan potential and the efficiency of electrolyte exclusion. For example, weak-acid cation exchangers in H^+ form are very little ionized and, hence, do not exclude acids [239]. (Salts or bases convert the ion exchanger to the salt form which is dissociated and excludes electrolytes.) The acids are taken up in essentially the same way as by nonionic sorbents, i.e., according to a Langmuir- or Freundlich- rather than a Donnan-type isotherm. The same is true for sorption of bases by weak-base anion exchangers.

Even more conspicuous deviations from the Donnan-type sorption behavior are found when *multivalent counter ions* associate strongly with the fixed ionic groups. In such cases, the rules for Donnan exclusion may even be reversed. Thorium ions, which are bound rather tightly by many cation exchangers, may serve as an example. It seems that the thorium ions, Th^{4+} or ThO^{2+}, associate with the fixed ionic groups:

$$\overline{-R^-} + \overline{ThO^{2+}} \rightarrow \overline{-RThO^+} \qquad (5\text{-}36)$$

The thorium form of a cation exchanger thus contains positive fixed complexes, $-RThO^+$, instead of negative fixed ionic groups, $-R^-$. The

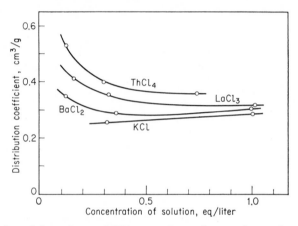

FIG. 5-21. Sorption of electrolytes of different valences by a cation exchanger (membrane Nepton CR-61). Electrolytes with counter ions of higher valences are less efficiently excluded. (The concentrations in the resin phase refer to unit weight of the resin.) *From experimental data by N. W. Rosenberg, J. H. B. George, and D. W. Potter* [246].

charge of these positive fixed complexes must be compensated by mobile ions such as Cl^-. The chloride ion, strictly speaking the co-ion, must act the part of the counter ion for the fixed complex $-RThO^+$. As a consequence, the cation exchanger behaves like an anion exchanger, the Donnan potential reverses its sign, and the distribution coefficient of Cl^- increases with *decreasing* concentration of the solution [246]; see Fig. 5-21. Phenomena of this kind, though usually less pronounced, are the rule with cation exchangers containing trivalent or quadrivalent counter ions. Note that such resins, actually transformed into anion exchangers, can sorb limited amounts of other electrolytes such as NaCl without exchanging their multivalent cations.

Strong specific interactions may also occur between the *co-ions* and the fixed ionic groups or the matrix. Such interactions provide a "driving force" which attracts co-ions to the ion exchanger and thus counteracts electrolyte exclusion. For example, cupric, silver, zinc, and mercuric salts are strongly sorbed by weak-base anion exchangers with amino groups which form amine complexes with the metal co-ion [1,185,250].

Interactions between Mobile Ions. Electrolyte sorption is also affected by interactions between counter ions and co-ions, particularly by *complex formation.* Uptake of anionic complexes such as $[ZnCl_4]^{2-}$ by anion exchangers is a typical example. Metals which, in cationic form, are excluded by anion exchangers can duck the Donnan barrier by entering the exchanger in the form of anionic complexes. Similarly, species such as chloride ions which, in anionic form, are excluded by cation exchangers can enter the ion exchanger in the form of cationic complexes $[ZnCl]^{+}$, $[CuCl]^{+}$, etc. Complex formation of this kind thus reduces the efficiency of Donnan exclusion of the electrolyte. These important phenomena are discussed in detail in Sec. 5-6.

The fact that incomplete dissociation of an electrolyte with a multivalent counter ion results in stronger sorption was recognized as early as 1922 by Günther-Schulze [124], long before detailed theories for equilibria with ion exchangers had been developed. Günther-Schulze measured sorption of bivalent-metal chlorides by permutites and used his results for calculating "self-complexing" constants, i.e., the constants for the associations $Cu^{2+} + Cl^{-} \rightarrow CuCl^{+}$, etc. This work has received little attention, although it anticipated much of the later development. The basic idea is correct, though Günther-Schulze's experimental technique and his simple theory are not quantitatively satisfactory. The calculation of complex-stability constants from ion-exchange and sorption equilibria will be discussed in Sec. 5-6.

A special situation is encountered if the counter ion in the ion exchanger is multivalent and can *associate with* H^{+} *or* OH^{-} *ions.* For example, counter ions such as SO_4^{2-} or PO_4^{3-} in anion exchangers can form the species HSO_4^{-}, HPO_4^{2-}, and $H_2PO_4^{-}$. Anion exchangers in these forms can sorb acids, even acids with other anions, without exchanging their original counter anions. Such "site sharing" is discussed in Sec. 5-3f.

Dependence on Temperature and Pressure. The dependence of electrolyte sorption on temperature and pressure has not yet been studied systematically. The theoretical arguments which can be presented are essentially the same as for nonelectrolyte sorption (see page 132), i.e., it should be expected that highly specific sorption decreases with increasing temperature, and that pressure has little, if any, effect.

Survey. These general rules can be summarized as follows. Strong electrolytes, in contrast to nonelectrolytes, are excluded, to varying degrees, by ion exchangers. This electrolyte exclusion is favored by low concentration of the solution, high capacity and crosslinking of the ion exchanger, low valence of the counter ion, high valence of the co-ion, and large molar volume of the electrolyte. Electrolyte exclusion can be partially or completely offset by association, complex formation, or similar interactions between the ions of the electrolyte and the fixed ionic groups or the matrix, and by association of mobile ions with one another.

Quantitative treatment. Sorption equilibria can be accurately described by means of abstract Gibbsian thermodynamics. In Gibbs' thermodynamics, a system may be built only from independent components which are accessible in an isolated state. With ion exchangers, for example, the components may be taken to be the "resinates," the electrolyte, and the solvent (but not individual ions!). The equations derived in this way do not contain the Donnan potential explicitly. In this book, a slightly different course is chosen. The components are taken to be the matrix with fixed ionic groups, the various mobile ionic species, and the solvent.* Such a procedure is quite common in electrochemistry and has also been adopted by Donnan [78,79] and many of his successors. The advantage of this approach is that a sounder understanding of the physical causes of the phenomena is obtained.

Thermodynamics with individual ions is, in certain respects, a somewhat controversial matter. Ions are not independent components in Gibbs' sense because they must always be accompanied by other ions of opposite charge and, hence, cannot be isolated. The existence of ions cannot be proven by purely thermodynamic means. The choice of ionic species as components of the system already implies a concrete conception of the structure of matter, a concept which goes beyond the confines of Gibbs' abstract thermodynamics. Nevertheless, the introduction of discrete ionic species and their individual properties (partial molar volumes, activities, etc.) does not invalidate the rigor of a thermodynamic treatment. To be sure, from the point of view of abstract thermodynamics, the quantities referring to individual ionic species are undefined and fictitious; they "do not exist because they can never be measured" (by thermodynamic means). It is their very inaccessibility which makes their use in thermodynamics possible; whenever an actual macroscopic measurement is made, only the net effect of several such fictitious quantities is noted. The individual ionic quantities cancel or combine of necessity in such a way that they can equally well be expressed in terms of truly Gibbsian components. Thus, in thermodynamic expressions, any differences arising from the choice of the components are always merely formal.

These facts are generally recognized. The controversial aspect is the interpretation rather than the derivation of the equations. The apostles of rigorous thermodynamics allow the use of quantities referring to individual ionic species as fictitious quantities, but they object to interpreting them as physical realities. The same is true for "single" potential differences (such as the Donnan potential between the ion exchanger and the solution) which are thermodynamically equally undefined. As far as the interpretation of the equations is concerned, the treatment in this book follows others in adopting a different attitude. Tangible explanations in terms of physical forces rather than thermodynamic rigor are sought. For this purpose, the premise is accepted that properties of individual ions and single potential differences, though thermodynamically ill-defined, are physical realities.

Ions carry electric charges and are subject to the electric forces within the system. Thus, the equilibrium distribution of an ionic species between

---

* Note that ionic species are not *independent* components. Their concentrations are interrelated by the electroneutrality condition, without which the system is not completely described.

two phases is affected by the electric potential difference between the phases. In equilibrium, the electrochemical potential η_i of the ionic species i is the same in both phases

$$(\eta_i)_1 = (\eta_i)_2 \tag{5-37}$$

This relation takes the place of Eq. (5-4) which is valid for electrically neutral components only. The electrochemical potential differs from the chemical potential μ_i by a term which depends on the electric potential of the phase:

$$\eta_i = \mu_i + z_i \mathfrak{F} \varphi \tag{5-38}$$

where z_i = electrochemical valence of the species i (negative for anions, zero for nonelectrolytes); $\mathfrak{F}$ = Faraday constant; φ = electric potential.

Equation (5-37), in combination with Eqs. (5-38), (5-9), and (5-2), can be used for deriving the following relation for the Donnan potential, E_{Don}, i.e., for the electric potential difference $\bar{\varphi} - \varphi$ between the ion exchanger and the solution

$$E_{Don} \equiv \bar{\varphi} - \varphi = \frac{1}{z_i \mathfrak{F}} \left(RT \ln \frac{a_i}{\bar{a}_i} - \Pi v_i \right) \tag{5-39}$$

where a_i = activity of species i; Π = swelling pressure; v_i = partial molar volume of species i.

This relation holds for any mobile ionic species present in the system.* When applied to the counter ion, it clearly reflects the dependence of the Donnan potential on the concentration (or activity) difference between the ion exchanger and the solution and on the counter-ion valence. When applied to the co-ion, it shows the dependence of co-ion exclusion on the Donnan potential and the co-ion valence (see page 136).

The application of Eq. (5-39) to sorption of a strong electrolyte AY by an ion exchanger in A form requires the following additional relations. One mole of the electrolyte dissociates to give v_A moles of ions A and v_Y moles of ions Y. Hence,

$$z_A v_A = -z_Y v_Y \tag{5-40}$$

and the partial molar volume of the electrolyte is

$$v_{AY} = v_A v_A + v_Y v_Y \tag{5-41}$$

Combining the two equations (5-39) for both mobile species A and Y with Eqs. (5-40) and (5-41), one obtains

$$RT \ln \left[\left(\frac{a_A}{\bar{a}_A} \right)^{v_A} \left(\frac{a_Y}{\bar{a}_Y} \right)^{v_Y} \right] = \Pi v_{AY} \tag{5-42}$$

In contrast to Eq. (5-39) which involves single ion activities and the partial

---

* It is assumed that the partial molar volume is constant. For nonconstant v_i, see footnote to p. 110.

molar volume of an ion, Eq. (5-42) contains only quantities which are thermodynamically defined. This becomes apparent when the product of cation and anion single activities is replaced by the mean activity, $a_\pm$:

$$a_A^{\nu_A} a_Y^{\nu_Y} = (a_\pm)_{AY}^\nu \qquad\qquad \nu \equiv \nu_A + \nu_Y \qquad\qquad (5\text{-}43)$$

With this replacement and with substitution of the swelling pressure by use of Eq. (5-3), Eq. (5-42) becomes

$$\left(\frac{\bar{a}_\pm}{a_\pm}\right)^\nu = \left(\frac{\bar{a}_w}{a_w}\right)^{\nu_{AY}/\nu_w} \qquad\qquad (5\text{-}44)$$

This relation is a general thermodynamic formulation of the Donnan equilibrium.

An explicit relation for the concentration of the sorbed electrolyte in the ion exchanger can be derived from Eq. (5-44) by use of the electroneutrality condition. The mean activity $a_\pm$ and the ionic molalities are interrelated by*

$$a_\pm^\nu = m_A^{\nu_A} m_Y^{\nu_Y} \gamma_\pm^\nu \qquad\qquad (5\text{-}45)$$

$$\bar{a}_\pm^\nu = \bar{m}_A^{\nu_A} \bar{m}_Y^{\nu_Y} \bar{\gamma}_\pm^\nu \qquad\qquad (5\text{-}46)$$

Equation (5-46) can be considered as a definition of the mean molal activity coefficient $\bar{\gamma}_\pm$ of the electrolyte in the ion exchanger. The electroneutrality conditions in the ion exchanger and the solution are

$$|z_A|\bar{m}_A = \bar{m}_R + |z_Y|\bar{m}_Y \qquad\qquad (5\text{-}47)$$

$$|z_A|m_A = |z_Y|m_Y \qquad\qquad (5\text{-}48)$$

where $\bar{m}_R$ = molality of the (univalent) fixed ionic groups.

Substituting the ionic activities in Eq. (5-44) by use of Eqs. (5-45) to (5-48), one obtains

$$\left(\frac{\bar{m}_Y}{m_Y}\right)^{\nu_Y} = \left(\frac{|z_Y|m_Y}{|z_Y|\bar{m}_Y + \bar{m}_R}\right)^{\nu_A} \left(\frac{\gamma_\pm}{\bar{\gamma}_\pm}\right)^\nu \left(\frac{\bar{a}_w}{a_w}\right)^{\nu_{AY}/\nu_w} \qquad (5\text{-}49)$$

For $\nu = 2$, i.e., for 1,1-valent, 2,2-valent, etc. electrolytes, Eq. (5-49) can be solved for $\bar{m}_Y$:

$$|z_Y|\bar{m}_Y = \left[\frac{\bar{m}_R^2}{4} + (z_Y m_Y)^2 \left(\frac{\gamma_\pm}{\bar{\gamma}_\pm}\right)^2 \left(\frac{\bar{a}_w}{a_w}\right)^{\nu_{AY}/\nu_w}\right]^{1/2} - \frac{\bar{m}_R}{2} \qquad (5\text{-}50)$$

---

* The definitions (5-45) and (5-46) of the mean (molal) activities imply the following choice of the standard and reference states in the ion exchanger and the solution. The standard state is a solution or pore liquid in which the mean molal activity $a_\pm$ of the electrolyte AY is unity. The reference state is a solution or ion-exchanger phase of infinite dilution. The reference state of the ion exchanger is fictitious; it cannot be realized since swelling is limited and the local concentration of ions along the chains remains high even when the resin is very strongly swollen. This fact, however, does not exclude such a normalization.

The distribution coefficient of the co-ion (or of the sorbed electrolyte) is accordingly

$$\lambda_{AY} \equiv \frac{\bar{m}_Y}{m_Y} = \left[\left(\frac{\bar{m}_R}{2z_Y m_Y} \right)^2 + \left(\frac{\gamma_\pm}{\bar{\gamma}_\pm} \right)^2 \left(\frac{\bar{a}_w}{a_w} \right)^{v_{AY}/v_w} \right]^{\frac{1}{2}} - \frac{\bar{m}_R}{2|z_Y|m_Y} \quad (5\text{-}51)$$

For very dilute solutions $(m_Y \ll \bar{m}_R)$, Eq. (5-50) reduces to

$$\bar{m}_Y \cong m_Y^2 \left(\frac{|z_Y|}{\bar{m}_R} \right) \left(\frac{\gamma_\pm}{\bar{\gamma}_\pm} \right)^2 \left(\frac{\bar{a}_w}{a_w} \right)^{v_{AY}/v_w} \quad (5\text{-}52)$$

The internal co-ion concentration should thus be expected to decrease in proportion to the square of the concentration of the external solution when the latter is greatly diluted, provided that the last two factors on the right-hand side of Eq. (5-52) remain approximately constant. In ion-exchange resins, however, the factor $(\gamma_\pm/\bar{\gamma}_\pm)^2$ increases with dilution of the solution (see page 144).

Equation (5-49) in combination with the relations for solvent uptake and swelling pressure (see Sec. 5-2d) gives a complete description of the distribution of the mobile ionic species and the solvent.

The interested reader will have no difficulty in deriving the rules regarding the dependence of electrolyte sorption on the solution concentration, the molality of fixed ionic groups, and the ionic valences (see page 136) from Eq. (5-49). It can also be shown that the effect of swelling pressure and ionic size is usually small. In Eq. (5-49), this effect appears in the factor $(\bar{a}_w/a_w)^{v_{AY}/v_w}$ which can be substituted according to Eq. (5-16) by

$$\left(\frac{\bar{a}_w}{a_w} \right)^{v_{AY}/v_w} = \exp\left(-\frac{\Pi v_{AY}}{RT} \right) \quad (5\text{-}53)$$

The partial molar volumes of most electrolytes are of the order of 15 to 40 cm^3/mole. Let us consider an extreme case, where the swelling pressure is increased from 0 to 500 atm. Inserting $R = 0.082$ liter atm mole^{-1} deg^{-1} and $T \approx 300°$, one sees that the expression (5-53) is only decreased from unity to about 0.5, whereas the factor $\bar{m}_R/m_Y$ in Eq. (5-49) may vary over several orders of magnitude.

All other effects such as complex formation and association are not immediately evident from Eq. (5-49). These effects are only reflected in the behavior of the activity coefficients, unless complexes, ion pairs, etc., are treated as separate species. Without knowledge of the activity coefficients, sorption equilibria cannot be quantitatively predicted. The situation is essentially the same as in swelling equilibria where the lack of a theory for predicting osmotic coefficients is the missing link (see page 114). The particular behavior of activity coefficients in ion exchangers is discussed in the following.

Activity coefficients of sorbed electrolytes. One peculiar property of the mean activity coefficient $\bar{\gamma}_\pm$ in ion-exchange resins [as defined in accordance with Eq. (5-8) or (5-54)] has received much attention and stirred up many controversies. The mean molal activity coefficients of aqueous electrolytes approach unity, by virtue of the choice of the reference state, when the solution is infinitely diluted. In contrast, the mean molal activity coefficients in ion-exchange resins are reported to drop to rather small values when the external solution is greatly diluted [19,63,106,110,117,171, 198,220]. In other words, the internal co-ion concentration does not drop as sharply with dilution of the external solution as one might expect on the basis of Eq. (5-52).

The reality of this effect has often been doubted because, first, no thermodynamic reason for the anomalous behavior is apparent and, second, errors can easily arise in the very delicate measurements on which the establishment of the effect hinges, namely, in the determinations of very low co-ion contents of resins in solutions in which the co-ion concentration is much higher (see Sec. 5-9f). However, careful measurements have confirmed the anomality at least in part.

It seems that a satisfactory explanation has now been found by Freeman [91] who attributes the reported anomalous behavior of the activity coefficients to two causes. The first is the analytical error caused by retention of liquid films by the resin beads (this error can be avoided by special precautions [259]). The second cause is additional, non-Donnan-type electrolyte sorption by impurities in the resins. In anion exchangers, for example, a small number of carboxylic groups may act as such an impurity which sorbs a stoichiometric amount of acid even from extremely dilute solutions. A very small number of such groups—usually much less than 1 per cent of the regular fixed ionic groups—is sufficient to affect the apparent activity coefficient very strongly in the low concentration range where the "regular" Donnan-type sorption is extremely small. Of course, the nature and number of extraneous groups and thus the extent of "impurity-bound" electrolyte sorption depend on the conditions of resin preparation and may even vary from batch to batch of nominally the same resin. Accordingly, the reproducibility of electrolyte sorption from dilute solutions is rather poor, and numerical values of apparent activity coefficients in this concentration range are of little practical value.

After applying a correction for sorption of the impurity-bound electrolyte, Freeman finds that the logarithm of the mean activity coefficient of the sorbed electrolyte now varies linearly with the internal co-ion concentration. This result can be thermodynamically explained in terms of specific interactions [45,257]. Even after correction for the impurity-bound electrolyte, the limiting value of the activity coefficient extrapolated to infinite dilution of the external solution may well be somewhat smaller than unity. This is not surprising since the high charge density along the matrix chains and electrostatic repulsion between neighboring fixed ionic groups favor ionic association [163,191,198]; see Sec. 4-4b.

In ion exchangers with inhomogeneous structure, the peculiar decrease of the apparent activity coefficients with dilution of the external solution can have still another cause. The characteristic "island" structure of condensation polymers has been described earlier (see Sec. 5-2f). In such resins, the highly swollen regions of low crosslinking and low concentration of fixed charges exert little Donnan exclusion and thus can sorb electrolytes even from rather dilute solutions. However, it is unlikely that the sorption behavior of the much more uniform styrene-type resins has this cause.

It is interesting to note that with zeolites, which have a completely regular and rather rigid framework structure, the anomalous effect is *not* observed. Rather, the mean activity coefficient of the sorbed electrolyte is essentially independent of the solution concentration, i.e., electrolyte sorption obeys an ideal Donnan isotherm [16]. With the zeolites, in fact, all the above-mentioned causes for the anomalous behavior—extraneous sorbing groups, stretching of the matrix because of repulsion between nonneutralized neighboring fixed charges, and inhomogeneities—are absent.

Other theoretical approaches and models

Omission of Swelling-pressure Effects. The thermodynamic treatment of electrolyte sorption can equally well be based on a model in which the pressure difference between the interior of the ion exchanger and the external solution is ignored [30,201]. Swelling-pressure effects then do not appear explicitly, but are disguised in the activity coefficients. In such a treatment, the activity is defined by

$$\mu_i(P,m) = \mu_i^0(P^0) + RT \ln a_i \tag{5-54}$$

rather than by Eq. (5-8). One obtains for the Donnan potential and the Donnan equilibrium

$$E_{\mathrm{Don}} = \frac{RT}{z_i \mathfrak{F}} \ln \frac{a_i}{\bar{a}_i} \tag{5-55}$$

$$\bar{a}_\pm = a_\pm \tag{5-56}$$

$$(|z_Y| \bar{m}_Y + \bar{m}_R)^{\nu_A}(|z_Y| \bar{m}_Y)^{\nu_Y} = (|z_Y| m_Y)^\nu \left(\frac{\gamma_\pm}{\bar{\gamma}_\pm}\right)^\nu \tag{5-57}$$

These relations are simpler than the corresponding Eqs. (5-39), (5-44), and (5-49) and will be used in later chapters where swelling-pressure effects are unimportant. Note that, in these equations, the definition of the activities and activity coefficients is slightly different from the definition in the previous part of this section.

Models Including Solvation Effects. In Gregor's original approach [109], the components of the system are taken to be the *solvated* ions, the *free* solvent, and the matrix with solvated fixed ionic groups (see page 117). With this choice of the components, the swelling pressure becomes a much more important factor since the molar volumes of the solvated species are considerably larger than their partial molar volumes. This approach provides a convenient and useful approximation for systems in which the deviations from ideality are primarily caused by solvation effects. The simple treatment fails for equilibria with very dilute solutions and for cases in which effects other than solvation become important.

Models Including Electrostatic Interactions. The refined model suggested by Lazare and Gregor [191] can be applied to electrolyte sorption (see pages 98 and 118). The equations derived from this model are rather complex. The interested reader is referred to the original publication [191]. Theoretical calculations with this model lead to internal mean activity coefficients which decrease when the external solution is greatly diluted.

Katchalsky's model [163,214] for weakly crosslinked gels (see page 88) can also be applied to electrolyte sorption. Activity coefficients in the gel are calculated from the relation

$$kT \ln \, \gamma_i = \frac{\partial F_{el}}{\partial n_i} \qquad (5\text{-}58)$$

With Eq. (4-22), Katchalsky obtains

$$-kT \ln \, \bar{\gamma}_i = \frac{\nu^2 e^2 \bar{m}_R}{e h_0 [(\bar{V}/\bar{V}_0)^{1/3} + \bar{\kappa} h_0/6] \Sigma z_i^2 \bar{m}_i} \qquad (5\text{-}59)$$

The mean activity coefficient decreases with dilution of the solution since the shielding parameter $\bar{\kappa}$ appears in the denominator. Katchalsky's theory is not applicable to moderately and highly crosslinked gels.

Harris and Rice's model has not yet been extended to include electrolyte sorption.

Ion exchangers of particular structure. Certain peculiarities which are found with various different types of ion exchangers are briefly discussed in the following.

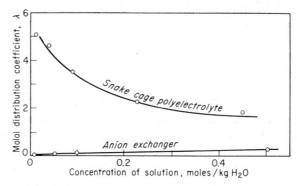

FIG. 5-22. Distribution coefficients for sorption of NaCl by a snake-cage polyelectrolyte (Dowex 2-X8-polyacrylate) and by an anion exchanger (Dowex 2-X8, Cl⁻ form). *From M. J. Hatch, J. A. Dillon, and H. B. Smith* [133].

Zeolites can sorb electrolytes from solutions, provided that no exclusion by sieve action occurs. It is interesting to note that, at great dilution, the internal co-ion concentration does indeed approach proportionality to the square of the external concentration [16]. The mean activity coefficient in zeolites thus does not show the abnormal behavior which is found in ion-exchange resins.

Sorption by *amphoteric ion exchangers* with weak-acid and weak-base groups depends strongly on the pH of the solution. The distribution coefficient is at its maximum near the isoelectric point of the ion exchanger. Here, both the acid and base groups are essentially nonionized, and Donnan exclusion is insignificant. When the pH of the solution is increased or decreased, either the acid or the base groups dissociate and cause Donnan exclusion.

The behavior of *snake-cage polyelectrolytes* (see Sec. 3-4) is completely different from that of the usual ion-exchanger gels. Electrolytes are, in general, much more strongly sorbed than nonelectrolytes [133]; see Fig. 5-22.

The fixed ionic charges are electrically balanced by the poly-counter ions which cannot leave the gel. Therefore the Donnan potential remains small and the chief cause for electrolyte exclusion is absent. It seems that electrolyte sorption is enhanced by interactions between the sorbed ions and the ionic groups of the resin and the poly-counter ion. The resins can distinguish between different electrolytes.

d. Simultaneous Sorption of Electrolytes and Nonelectrolytes

The previous sections have shown that ion exchangers are very poor sorbents for strong electrolytes but, as a rule, good sorbents for nonelectrolytes. From mixed solutions, nonelectrolytes are taken up in preference to electrolytes (at least, unless particular effects such as sieve action interfere). The preference of the resins for nonelectrolytes can be used for separations [22,297]; see "ion exclusion," Sec. 9-4.

There is little mutual interference between electrolyte and nonelectrolyte sorption, provided that the solution is reasonably dilute. The preference of the resin for the nonelectrolyte thus is strongest when electrolyte exclusion is most efficient, i.e., when the capacity and crosslinking of the resin and the co-ion valence are high and the external electrolyte concentration and the counter-ion valence are low (see page 136). For example, 1,2-valent electrolytes are more efficiently separated from nonelectrolytes by cation exchangers, and 2,1-valent electrolytes by anion exchangers.

The preference of the resin for the nonelectrolyte N can be expressed quantitatively by the separation factor, α_{AY}^{N}, which is defined by

$$\alpha_{AY}^{N} \equiv \frac{\bar{m}_N m_Y}{m_N \bar{m}_Y} \tag{5-60}$$

[see also Eq. (5-70)]. This factor can be calculated from the relations for the two sorption equilibria. Electrolyte sorption is described by Eq. (5-57) (swelling-pressure effects are accounted for in the activity coefficients). The corresponding relation for nonelectrolyte sorption is

$$\bar{m}_N \bar{\gamma}_N = m_N \gamma_N \tag{5-61}$$

For low electrolyte concentrations ($m_{AY} \ll \bar{m}_R$), one obtains

$$\alpha_{AY}^{N} = \left(\frac{\bar{m}_R}{|z_Y| m_Y} \right)^{\nu_A / \nu_Y} \frac{\gamma_N}{\bar{\gamma}_N} \left(\frac{\bar{\gamma}_\pm}{\gamma_\pm} \right)^{\nu / \nu_Y} \tag{5-62}$$

Note that the activity coefficients in Eq. (5-62) are for electrolyte-nonelectrolyte mixtures and are not identical to those in systems with only one of these species. Thus, Eq. (5-62) does not permit accurate predictions of the separation factor to be made from separate measurements of electrolyte and nonelectrolyte sorption. However, the equation correctly reflects the effects of the most important variables.

In systems with solutions of moderate or high concentrations, sorptions of electrolytes and nonelectrolytes affect one another, of course, to a considerable extent. Electrolytes can act, for example, either as salting-out agents or else as solubilizers for nonelectrolytes (see page 128). On the other hand, the effects of massive addition of nonelectrolytes on electrolyte sorption have so far received little attention and are of less practical importance.

Snake-cage polyelectrolytes, in contrast to ordinary ion-exchange resins, are very good sorbents for electrolytes (see page 146). From mixed solutions, electrolytes are sorbed in preference to nonelectrolytes. This effect can be used for separations [133]; see "ion retardation," Sec. 9-5.

e. Sorption of Weak Electrolytes

Weak electrolytes are little affected by Donnan exclusion and thus are sorbed in essentially the same way as nonelectrolytes. Acetic acid, for example, is sorbed by cation exchangers in H^+ form (see Fig. 5-17) and by anion exchangers in acetate form. This sorption is almost completely nonionic since the high concentration of H^+ or acetate ions in the ion exchangers suppresses the dissociation of the acid [240]. In a similar way, weak bases such as ammonia, pyridine, and piperidine are sorbed by anion exchangers in OH^- or free-base form and by cation exchangers in ammonium, pyridinium, or piperidinium form. Resins may take up weak electrolytes by nonionic sorption well in excess of their ion-exchange capacity. Earlier reports of abnormally high "capacities" of anion exchangers for weak organic acids can be explained in this way [26,62,66,231,232,240, 256].

The dissociation of weak electrolytes and, hence, their uptake by ion exchangers depend on the pH of the solution [26]. This pH dependence can be used for elution. For example, weak acids which are taken up in undissociated form by cation exchangers in H^+ form are most efficiently eluted with alkali; the resin and the acid are neutralized by the alkali, and the (dissociated) salt of the acid is expelled by the Donnan effect [295].

Weak electrolytes can also be sorbed, without simultaneous ion exchange, by resins containing multivalent counter ions. This phenomenon is discussed in the next section.

f. "Site Sharing"

Electrolytes are usually excluded from ion exchangers by the Donnan effect, and equilibration of an ion exchanger with a solution containing a counter ion which is different from that in the ion exchanger usually results in counter-ion exchange. However, both these rules are not universally valid. Exceptions are found, for example, with ion exchangers containing multivalent counter ions which can associate with H^+ or OH^- ions. Anion exchangers in sulfate and phosphate forms may serve as examples. Such resins contain the counter ions SO_4^{2-} or PO_4^{3-}, and can take up sulfuric or phosphoric acid by the following mechanisms [20,172,212,219]:

$$
\begin{array}{ccc}
\text{—R}^+ & & \text{—R}^+ \quad \text{HSO}_4^- \\
& \text{SO}_4^{2-} + \text{H}_2\text{SO}_4 \quad \rightarrow & \\
\text{—R}^+ & & \text{—R}^+ \quad \text{HSO}_4^-
\end{array}
\qquad (5\text{-}63)
$$

or

$$
\begin{array}{ccc}
\text{—R}^+ & & \text{—R}^+ \quad \text{H}_2\text{PO}_4^- \\
\text{—R}^+ & \text{PO}_4^{3-} + 2\text{H}_3\text{PO}_4 \quad \rightarrow & \text{—R}^+ \quad \text{H}_2\text{PO}_4^- \\
\text{—R}^+ & & \text{—R}^+ \quad \text{H}_2\text{PO}_4^-
\end{array}
\qquad (5\text{-}64)
$$

where —R$^+$ is a fixed ionic group of the resin.

The uptake of acid lowers the internal pH. As a consequence, the counter ions associate partly with the H$^+$ ions of the penetrating acid. This association decreases the charge of the original counter ions, and ionic groups of the resin become available for holding the anions of the penetrating acid. The net effect is an uptake of acid without exchange of original counter ions. This mechanism has been called "site sharing" [212].

The sorbed acid can be eluted from the resin by washing thoroughly with pure solvent. Washing results in an increase of the internal pH and thus in a reversal of the process (5-63) or (5-64). Since strong-base anion-exchange resins prefer polyvalent anions such as PO_4^{3-}, SO_4^{2-}, CrO_4^{2-}, etc., very strongly to OH$^-$, it is also possible to elute the sorbed acid with dilute NaOH, without displacing significant amounts of the original counter ions from the resin [3a].

Completely dissociated salts such as Na_2SO_4 cannot be taken up by site sharing since they do not bring in H$^+$ ions which can associate with the anion in the resin. Site sharing can thus be used for separating polyvalent acids from their salts [20,172]. For example, a strong-base anion exchanger in SO_4^{2-} form sorbs H_2SO_4, but excludes Na_2SO_4. On the other hand, sulfates which can form complex counter ions such as $UO_2(SO_4)_3^{4-}$ are sorbed [3,270].

Site sharing is not restricted to sorption of acids which have their anion in common with the anion exchanger. For example, anion exchangers in PO_4^{3-} form can take up limited amounts of acetic acid by site sharing without exchanging phosphate ions [21,212,285]:

$$
\begin{array}{ccc}
\text{—R}^+ & & \text{—R}^+ \quad \text{H}_2\text{PO}_4^- \\
\text{—R}^+ & \text{PO}_4^{3-} + 2\text{HAc} \quad \rightarrow & \text{—R}^+ \quad \text{Ac}^- \\
\text{—R}^+ & & \text{—R}^+ \quad \text{Ac}^-
\end{array}
\qquad (5\text{-}65)
$$

Of course, phosphate ions are eventually replaced by acetate ions when the resin is treated with a great excess of acetic acid. The sorbed acid can be eluted as described above.

A necessary condition for acid sorption by site sharing is that an H$^+$ ion of the penetrating acid associate with the counter ion in the resin. Hence, the pK of the penetrating acid (the pK_1 in the case of a polybasic acid) must be lower than the highest pK of the multivalent acid anion in the resin. A higher site-sharing capacity is attained if the pK of the penetrating acid is lower than the second-highest pK of the (in this case at least trivalent) anion in the resin. On the other hand, the pK of the penetrating acid should be higher than the pK_1 of the anion in the resin since, otherwise,

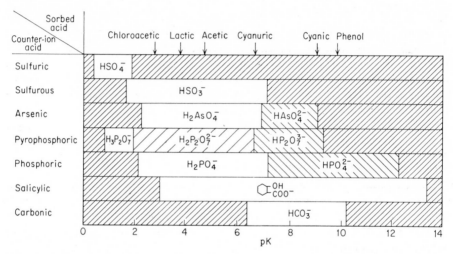

Fig. 5-23. Operative pK ranges for site sharing with various polyvalent-acid counter ions. Acids with pK values which fall in the clear or lightly shaded areas can be sorbed by site sharing. The protonated counter-ion species formed are shown in the respective fields. Acids with pK values which fall in the strongly shaded areas cannot be sorbed by site sharing, either (on the right) because protonation does not occur, or (on the left) because the original acid counter ion is displaced by ion exchange. *From R. E. Meeker and D. B. Luten* [212].

this anion will form undissociated acid which is no longer electrostatically held by the fixed charges. The condition for site sharing thus is [212]

$$(pK_1)_{\text{counter ion}} < pK_{\text{sorbed acid}} < (pK_n)_{\text{counter ion}} \qquad (5\text{-}66)$$

Anion exchangers in PO_4^{3-} form may serve as an example. The pK values of phosphoric acid are $pK_1 \approx 2$, $pK_2 \approx 7$, and $pK_3 \approx 12$. Very weak acids with pK > 12 are not taken up by site sharing since they cannot donate protons even to PO_4^{3-} ions. From weak acids with pK values between 7 and 12, the PO_4^{3-} ions can accept one proton, forming HPO_4^{2-} ions and thus vacating every third site for the anions of the weak acid; hence, the site-sharing capacity of the resin for such acids is about one-third of the ion-exchange capacity. From acids with pK values between 2 and 7, the PO_4^{3-} ions can accept two protons, forming $H_2PO_4^-$ ions and thus vacating two out of three sites; hence, the site-sharing capacity for such acids is about two-thirds of the ion-exchange capacity. Strong acids with pK < 2 displace phosphate from the resin because undissociated H_3PO_4 is formed.

A table showing the pK ranges for site-sharing sorption by anion exchangers in various ionic forms is given in Fig. 5-23. Site sharing is not restricted to uptake of acids by anion exchangers. Other systems, however, have not yet been systematically studied.

5-4. ION-EXCHANGE EQUILIBRIA

Ion-exchange equilibrium is attained when an ion exchanger is placed in an electrolyte solution containing a counter ion which is different from that in the ion exchanger. Suppose that the ion exchanger is initially in the, say, A form and that the counter ion in the solution is B. Counter-ion exchange occurs, and the ion A in the ion exchanger is partially replaced by B:

$$\bar{A} + B \rightleftharpoons \bar{B} + A \qquad (5\text{-}67)$$

(see also Fig. 1-1). In equilibrium, both the ion exchanger and the solution contain both competing counter ion species, A and B.

The exchange (5-67) is, as a rule, reversible. Thus it makes no difference from which side equilibrium is approached, that is, whether A is exchanged for B, or B for A. The final equilibrium distribution of the counter ions is the same in either case, provided that the amounts of all the components in the system are the same.*

The concentration ratio of the two competing counter-ion species in the ion exchanger is usually different from that in the solution; as a rule, the ion exchanger selects one species in preference to the other. This *selectivity* and its physical causes are the main topic of this section.

Ion-exchange equilibria are of great practical and theoretical importance and have been studied ever since ion exchangers were recognized as such. Most of the earlier theories are, in essence, descriptions of ion-exchange equilibria by empirical or semiempirical equations. Only in the last fifteen years have consistent theories been developed which provide essentially correct descriptions of the phenomena and their physical causes. The discussion in this section is based on these approaches. Earlier theories and other theoretical treatments are briefly outlined in Sec. 5-4g. As far as possible the discussion is kept in general terms. Emphasis is on the behavior of ion-exchange resins in contact with aqueous solutions. Peculiarities which are observed with other types of ion exchangers and with non-aqueous and mixed solvents are briefly reviewed in Secs. 5-4f and 10-4, respectively. The discussion is preceded by a short section in which

---

* In a few exceptional cases, metastable equilibria exist in addition to the true thermodynamic equilibrium. Here, the final distribution can depend on the initial composition of the ion exchanger (see p. 189).

definitions of the various quantities used for describing ion-exchange equilibria are given.

a. Ion-exchange Isotherm, Separation Factor, Selectivity Coefficient, and Equilibrium Constant

Ion-exchange equilibrium can be characterized by the *ion-exchange isotherm*. This isotherm is a graphical representation which, in principle, covers all possible experimental conditions at a given temperature. Any specific set of experimental conditions (solution concentration, relative amounts of the counter ions, etc.) corresponds to one point on the isotherm surface. Equilibrium can also be described in terms of a quantity such as the *separation factor, selectivity coefficient,* or *distribution coefficient.* As a rule, these quantities vary with experimental conditions. Thus any specific value of one of these quantities corresponds to only one point on the isotherm surface. There are no fixed rules as to which quantity should be used for describing equilibrium. The chemist is free to choose the quantity which best fits his purposes. However, it is important that unambiguous definitions be given. Considerable confusion has arisen from inadequate definitions and from the deplorable lack of a uniform notation. Ion-exchange isotherms and the various characteristic quantities are discussed in the following paragraphs.

Ion-exchange Isotherm. The *ion-exchange isotherm* shows the ionic composition of the ion exchanger as a function of the experimental conditions. Various ways of representation can be used. As a rule, the equivalent ionic fraction,* $\bar{x}_A$, of the counter ion A in the ion exchanger is plotted as a function of the equivalent ionic fraction x_A in the solution, while the other variables are kept constant. The equivalent ionic fraction is defined by

$$x_A \equiv \frac{z_A m_A}{z_A m_A + z_B m_B} \tag{5-68}$$

or, more generally, by

$$x_A \equiv \frac{z_A m_A}{\sum z_i m_i} \tag{5-69}$$

where the summation is carried out over all counter-ion species. The dependence of $\bar{x}_A$ on the total concentration of the solution can be shown in a three-dimensional representation in which the isotherm is a curved surface (see Fig. 5-37). Alternatively, a two-dimensional diagram of $\bar{x}_A$ versus x_A with a series of curves corresponding to different total concentrations of the solution may be used (see Fig. 5-25).

In a hypothetical system in which the ion exchanger shows no preference for A or B, the equivalent ionic fractions in the ion exchanger are the same as those in the solution. Here, the ion-exchange isotherm is linear and is the diagonal in the diagram $\bar{x}_A$ versus $\bar{x}_A$ (see Fig. 5-24). Actual ion exchangers in general select one counter ion in preference to the other. If the ion A is preferred throughout, the isotherm is negatively curved and lies above the diagonal, and if B is preferred, the isotherm is positively curved and falls below the diagonal. S-shaped isotherms are exceptions (see, for example, Figs. 5-32 and 5-33).

---

* For competing ions of equal valence, the term "mole fraction" instead of ionic fraction is frequently found in the literature. This notation dates back from earlier theories in which the (swollen) resinates are taken as the components of the ion-exchanger phase (see p. 195). However, this notation is misleading when applied to theories in which the solvent is an additional component of the ion-exchanger phase.

The origin and the end point of any isotherm must lie in the lower left and upper right corners of the diagram, respectively, since in equilibrium, absence of one counter ion in the solution requires absence of this ion in the ion exchanger also. On the other hand, selectivity of the ion exchanger requires deviation of the isotherm from the diagonal. Selectivity thus necessitates a *nonlinear* isotherm. Unfortunately this fact has been occasionally overlooked in theories of ion-exchange column performance.

Separation Factor. The preference of the ion exchanger for one of the two counter ions is often expressed by the *separation factor.** This quantity is particularly convenient for practical applications, for example, for calculations of column performance. The separation factor α_B^A is defined by

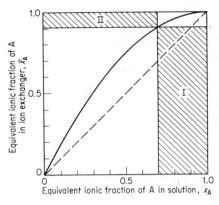

FIG. 5-24. Ion-exchange isotherm and separation factor (*schematic*). The isotherm is shown as a heavy line. For any ionic composition, the separation factor equals the ratio of the two rectangular areas I and II touching one another in the corresponding point on the isotherm. The broken line is the isotherm of a fictitious ion exchanger which has no preference for either counter ion.

$$\alpha_B^A \equiv \frac{\bar{m}_A m_B}{\bar{m}_B m_A} = \frac{\bar{C}_A C_B}{\bar{C}_B C_A} = \frac{\bar{x}_A x_B}{\bar{x}_B x_A} \qquad (5\text{-}70)$$

The separation factor is the quotient of the concentration ratios of the two counter ions in the ion exchanger and the solution. If the ion A is preferred, the factor α_B^A is larger than unity, and if B is preferred, the factor is smaller than unity. The numerical value of the (dimensionless) separation factor is not affected by the choice of the concentration units.

There is a simple relation between the separation factor and the ion-exchange isotherm. Equation (5-70) and Fig. 5-24 show that the separation factor is given by the ratio of the two rectangular areas which lie above and below the isotherm and touch the latter at the point which corresponds to the experimental conditions.

Of course, the separation factor is usually not constant, but depends on the total concentration of the solution, the temperature, and the equivalent fraction x_A.

Selectivity Coefficient. Instead of the separation factor, the so-called *selectivity coefficient** can be used for describing ion-exchange equilibria. This coefficient is more convenient for theoretical studies. The molal selectivity coefficient is defined by †

$$K_B^A \equiv \frac{\bar{m}_A^{|z_B|} m_B^{|z_A|}}{\bar{m}_B^{|z_A|} m_A^{|z_B|}} \qquad (5\text{-}71)$$

* Unfortunately, the uniformity of notation in the literature still leaves very much to be desired. Frequently the term "equilibrium constant" is found for the selectivity coefficient and even for the separation factor. These and similar names are also used for quantities which are differently defined (see survey, Ref. 118). Consequently, numerical data can only be evaluated when the definition of the coefficient is given. The notation used in this book is used by many authors, but is not yet generally accepted.

† It is preferable to use the absolute values $|z_i|$ of the ionic valences, so that $K_B^A > 1$ corresponds to preference for A in the case of anion exchangers also.

Molarities or equivalent ionic fractions may be used instead of molalities:

$$K'^{A}_{B} \equiv \frac{\bar{C}^{|z_B|}_{A} C^{|z_A|}_{B}}{\bar{C}^{|z_A|}_{B} C^{|z_B|}_{A}} \tag{5-72}$$

$$^{N}K^{A}_{B} \equiv \frac{\bar{x}^{|z_B|}_{A} x^{|z_A|}_{B}}{\bar{x}^{|z_A|}_{B} x^{|z_B|}_{A}} \tag{5-73}$$

The quantities K'^{A}_{B} and $^{N}K^{A}_{B}$ are the molar and the rational selectivity coefficients, respectively.

Equations of the form of Eqs. (5-71) to (5-73) are obtained when the mass-action law (without activity corrections) is applied to the ion exchange (5-67). However, the selectivity coefficients are *not* constants, but depend on the experimental conditions. To be sure, the relations (5-71) to (5-73) do not express the constancy of the quotient on the right-hand side, but are merely definitions of the quantities K^{A}_{B}, K'^{A}_{B}, and $^{N}K^{A}_{B}$.

For counter ions of equal valence ($z_A = z_B$), the numerical values of the molal, the molar, and the rational selectivity coefficients are identical and are related to the separation factor by

$$K^{A}_{B} = K'^{A}_{B} = {}^{N}K^{A}_{B} = (\alpha^{A}_{B})^{|z_A|} \qquad (z_A = z_B) \tag{5-74}$$

For counter ions of different valences, the numerical value of the selectivity coefficient depends on the choice of the concentration scale. The general relation is

$$(\alpha^{A}_{B})^{|z_A|} = K^{A}_{B}\left(\frac{\bar{m}_A}{m_A}\right)^{|z_A|-|z_B|} = K'^{A}_{B}\left(\frac{\bar{C}_A}{C_A}\right)^{|z_A|-|z_B|} = {}^{N}K^{A}_{B}\left(\frac{\bar{x}_A}{x_A}\right)^{|z_A|-|z_B|} \tag{5-75}$$

The coefficients K^{A}_{B} and K'^{A}_{B} can be converted into one another by use of Eqs. (5-69), (5-70), (5-30), and (5-31):

$$K'^{A}_{B} = K^{A}_{B}\left(\frac{\bar{m}C}{m\bar{C}}\right)^{|z_A|-|z_B|} = K^{A}_{B}\left[\frac{100\rho}{W\bar{\rho}\left(1 + \sum_i m_i M_i/1000\right)}\right]^{|z_A|-|z_B|} \tag{5-76}$$

where m and C are the total equivalent molality and molarity, respectively; W = solvent content in weight per cent; ρ = density; M_i = molecular weight of species i.

For certain purposes, the use of a "corrected" selectivity coefficient is more convenient. This quantity includes a correction for the activity coefficients in the solution. The corrected molal selectivity coefficient is defined by

$$K^{A}_{aB} \equiv \frac{\bar{m}^{|z_B|}_{A} a^{|z_A|}_{B}}{\bar{m}^{|z_A|}_{B} a^{|z_B|}_{A}} = K^{A}_{B}\frac{\gamma^{|z_A|}_{B}}{\gamma^{|z_B|}_{A}} \tag{5-77}$$

where γ_i = molal activity coefficient of species i.

The essential difference between the separation factor and the selectivity coefficient is that the latter contains the ionic valences as exponents. Thus the separation factor is usually quite different from the selectivity coefficient if the valences of the competing counter ions are not equal. In such cases, the selectivity coefficient remains more nearly constant when the experimental conditions, particularly the total solution concentration, are varied.

Distribution Coefficient. In certain practical applications, equilibrium is most conveniently expressed in terms of the *distribution coefficients* of the counter ions. The molal and molar distribution coefficients are defined by

$$\lambda_i \equiv \frac{\bar{m}_i}{m_i} = \frac{\bar{x}_i}{x_i}\frac{\bar{m}}{m} \tag{5-78}$$

and

$$\lambda_i' \equiv \frac{\bar{C}_i}{C_i} = \frac{\bar{x}_i}{x_i}\frac{\bar{C}}{C} \tag{5-79}$$

respectively [see Eqs. (5-28) and (5-29)]. The coefficients increase with dilution of the solution (decrease in m and C). Furthermore, if the ion exchanger shows selectivity (nonlinear isotherm and, hence, $\bar{x}_i/x_i \neq$ const.), the coefficients depend on the equivalent fraction x_i. For any given conditions, the distribution coefficient can be calculated from the selectivity coefficient. However, there is no simple explicit relationship between these two quantities.

The use of the distribution coefficient is particularly advantageous if the species is only a trace component (for example, $m_A \ll m$, $\bar{m}_A \ll \bar{m}$, and consequently $\bar{m}_B/m_B \cong \bar{m}/m$). In such cases, the exchange extends only over a short section of the isotherm near the origin. Usually this short section is practically linear so that, in the range under consideration, the distribution coefficient is independent of x_A. With Eqs. (5-78) and (5-71) or (5-79) and (5-72) one obtains

$$\lambda_A \cong (K_B^A)^{1/|z_B|}\left(\frac{\bar{m}}{m}\right)^{\frac{z_A}{z_B}} \tag{5-80}$$

$$(m_A \ll m;\ \bar{m}_A \ll \bar{m})$$

$$\lambda_A' \cong (K_B'^A)^{1/|z_B|}\left(\frac{\bar{C}}{C}\right)^{\frac{z_A}{z_B}} \tag{5-81}$$

However, even the short section of the isotherm may be strongly non-linear if the ion exchanger contains a small number of groups which interact specifically with the trace ion [97]. In such cases, the heterofunctional character of the ion exchanger and the resulting S shape of the isotherm (see page 184) are apparent just in the short isotherm section near the origin.

The Thermodynamic Equilibrium Constant. In theoretical studies, the *thermodynamic equilibrium constant* is occasionally used. This quantity is defined by the thermodynamic relation

$$\Delta G^0 = -RT \ln \mathcal{K}_B^A \tag{5-82}$$

where ΔG^0 is the standard free-energy change of the ion exchange (5-67) and the sorption and desorption of solvent and electrolytes by which this process is necessarily accompanied, and where $\mathcal{K}_B^A$ is the equilibrium constant. In contrast to the separation factor, the selectivity coefficient, and the distribution coefficient, which all refer to a given set of experimental conditions and thus correspond to one specific point on the isotherm surface, the equilibrium constant is an integral quantity characteristic of the whole isotherm surface and is a true constant depending on temperature only. Accordingly, the equilibrium constant gives no information about the exact counter-ion distribution under any particular experimental conditions.

The relationship between the equilibrium constant and the activities of the counter ions in the ion exchanger and the solution depends inherently on the definition of the activities and, hence, on the model on which the treatment is based. This point will be discussed in more detail in the course of the thermodynamic treatment (see pages 176 and 195). A simple relation exists only if electrolyte sorption and changes in swelling can be neglected. In this case, the equilibrium constant is

$$\mathcal{K}_{B}^{A} = \frac{\bar{a}_{A}^{|z_B|} a_{B}^{|z_A|}}{\bar{a}_{B}^{|z_A|} a_{A}^{|z_B|}}$$

(5-83)

The relations (5-82) and (5-83) show at first glance that the numerical value of the equilibrium constant depends on the choice of the standard states. Much confusion stems from the fact that this has been occasionally overlooked. The following difference in definitions should be kept in mind. Most authors use the *molal* scale for both the ion exchanger and the external solution. Here, the reference state (activity coefficients equal to unity) is a solution or a (fictitious) pore liquid of infinite dilution, and the standard state (activity equal to unity) is an approximately one molal solution or pore liquid (the deviation from 1 M is given by the activity coefficient, which is defined by the choice of the reference state). The equilibrium constant obtained by this choice of the standard and reference states will be called the *molal equilibrium constant*. In contrast, other authors use the *rational* scale for the ion exchanger while retaining the molal scale for the solution. Here, the ion exchanger is treated as a solid solution of the swollen resinates AR and BR, and both the standard and reference states of AR and BR are taken to be the respective monoionic forms of the ion exchanger in equilibrium with water. The equilibrium constant obtained with this choice of the standard and reference states will be called the *rational equilibrium constant*.

The two constants differ not only in their definition but also in their physical significance. If the same standard and reference states are chosen for both the ion exchanger and the external solution, as in the definition of the *molal* constant,* then the constant is close to unity, and *the selectivity of the ion exchanger is chiefly reflected in the activity coefficients*. In contrast, if the *rational* constant as defined above is used, *the selectivity of the ion exchanger is reflected in the equilibrium constant*, and the activity coefficients become merely correction factors which take care of the variation in selectivity with experimental conditions. Therefore it is important to distinguish clearly between the two equilibrium constants. Of course, the same is true for the activity coefficients, standard free-energy, enthalpy, and entropy changes, etc., which all depend on the choice of the standard and reference states. Several controversies, even in the most recent literature, have arisen merely from differences in the choice of the standard and reference states.

b. Selectivity and Its Causes

The *selectivity* of ion exchangers, i.e., the selection by the ion exchanger of one counter ion in preference to the other, may have various physical causes which are, in general, well understood. With the use of the models described in Sec. 5-1, the most important rules can be deduced by simple qualitative reasoning. In the following, the various factors which determine the selectivity are discussed in a qualitative way. Quantitative approaches are outlined in later parts of this section.

Effect of counter-ion valences; "electroselectivity." The valences of the counter ions have a strong effect on ion-exchange equilibria. This effect

---

* This is also true for the equilibrium constant defined by Dickel [76b] who uses, for both the ion exchanger and the external solution, a rational rather than molal concentration scale and infinite dilution as the reference state.

is purely electrostatic and arises even in ideal systems, i.e., in the absence of specific interactions, swelling-pressure effects, etc.   As a rule, *the ion exchanger prefers the counter ion of higher valence* [54,74,118,180,189,210,251a, 283,301,305,306].   *The preference increases with dilution of the solution and is strongest with ion exchangers of high internal molality* (see Fig. 5-25).

This effect is readily explained in terms of the Donnan potential.   The Donnan potential attracts counter ions into the ion exchanger and thus balances their tendency to diffuse out into the solution (see page 134).

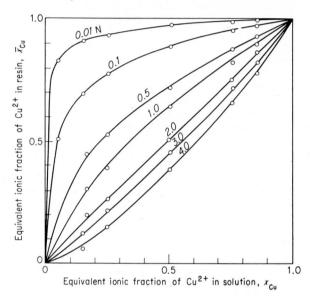

FIG. 5-25. Electroselectivity of a cation exchanger.   The diagram shows experimental isotherms for the Cu^{2+}/Na^+ exchange on Dowex 50-X8 at various total normalities of the external solution ($CuCl_2 + NaCl$).   The preference for the ion of higher valence increases with dilution of the solution.   *From H. C. Subba Rao and M. M. David* [283].

The force with which the Donnan potential acts on an ion is proportional to the ionic charge.   Hence the counter ion of higher charge is more strongly attracted and is preferred by the ion exchanger.   The absolute value of the Donnan potential increases with dilution of the solution and with increasing molality of the fixed ionic groups (see page 136).   Consequently, the same holds for the preference for the counter ion of higher valence.

The effect can also be explained in a more formal way.   In ideal systems, the *selectivity coefficient* (which corresponds to the mass-action-law coefficient) is unity [see also page 171 and Eq. (5-92)].   This coefficient, however, contains the ionic valences as exponents. The actual preference of the ion exchanger is expressed by the *separation factor* which does not involve the ionic valences [compare Eqs. (5-70) and (5-71)].   The two quantities are interrelated by

$$(\alpha_B^A)^{|z_A|} = K_B^A \left(\frac{\bar{m}_A}{m_A} \right)^{|z_A|-|z_B|} \tag{5-75}$$

As a rule, the counter-ion concentration in the ion exchanger is considerably higher than in the solution, particularly if the latter is dilute. Equation (5-75) shows that, in this case, α_B^A becomes larger than K_B^A if A is the ion of higher valence. Thus, even in ideal systems ($K_B^A = 1$), the ion of higher valence is preferred.

Usually this preference is not called "selectivity." Most (but unfortunately not all) authors use the term selectivity if the selectivity coefficient —rather than the separation factor—differs from unity. The electrostatic preference for the ion of higher valence is reflected only in the separation factor and can be called "electroselectivity," as suggested by Bonhoeffer.

The importance of electroselectivity is readily demonstrated by a simple numerical example. A cation exchanger with 8 meq/g H_2O molality of fixed ionic groups is equilibrated with a solution of total molality $m = 0.01$ meq/g H_2O containing equal amounts (in equivalents) of $CaCl_2$ and $NaCl$. The ionic composition of the ion exchanger is calculated. From Eqs. (5-68) and (5-71) one obtains the general relation

$$\frac{\bar{x}_A^{z_B/z_A}}{1 - \bar{x}_A} = (K_B^A)^{1/|z_A|} \left(\frac{\bar{m}}{m}\right)^{1 - z_B/z_A} \frac{x_A^{z_B/z_A}}{1 - x_A} \tag{5-84}$$

For the sake of simplicity it is assumed that the selectivity coefficient is unity and that electrolyte sorption is negligible. Thus:

$$\bar{m} = \bar{m}_R = 8 \text{ meq/g } H_2O \qquad z_{Ca} = 2 \qquad x_{Ca} = 0.5$$
$$m = 0.01 \text{ meq/g } H_2O \qquad z_{Na} = 1 \qquad x_{Na} = 0.5$$
$$K_{Na}^{Ca} = 1$$

Introducing these values in Eq. (5-84),

$$\frac{\bar{x}_{Na}^2}{1 - \bar{x}_{Na}} = \left(\frac{8}{0.01}\right)^{1-2} \frac{(0.5)^2}{1 - 0.5}$$

and solving for $\bar{x}_{Na}$, one obtains

$$\bar{x}_{Na} = 0.0244 \qquad \bar{x}_{Ca} = 1 - \bar{x}_{Na} = 0.9756$$

Thus the ratio of the equivalent fractions of Ca^{2+} and Na^+ in the ion exchanger is 40:1, while the equivalent fractions in the solution are equal. In actual systems, of course, the ionic composition of the ion exchanger will also be influenced by other effects which are reflected in the selectivity coefficient.

Ionic solvation and swelling pressure. Other factors which affect ion-exchange equilibria are the swelling pressure of the ion exchanger and the sizes of the (solvated) counter ions. The discussion of swelling equilibria has shown that large solvated counter ions in ion exchangers cause stronger swelling and higher swelling pressures than small ones (see Sec. 5-2a). When the resin swells, its elastic matrix is stretched. Because of its elasticity the matrix tends to relax, i.e., to contract. It can do so by exchanging a large counter ion for a small one (on a solvated equivalent volume basis) which causes less swelling. Thus *the ion exchanger prefers the counter ion with the smaller solvated equivalent volume* [109,112,116,230]. This tendency is a consequence of the elastic properties of the matrix and, hence, is most pronounced when the matrix is highly strained, i.e., when the swelling pressure is high. Consequently, the selectivity should increase, as does the swelling pressure, with dilution of the solution, with decreasing equivalent fraction of the smaller ion, and with increasing degree of crosslinking of the resin (see Sec. 5-2a). Of course, the selectivity should also increase with increasing difference in the equivalent volumes of the competing counter ions.

In practice, these rules are indeed observed in most systems in which specific interactions are absent. The exchange of alkali ions by strongly

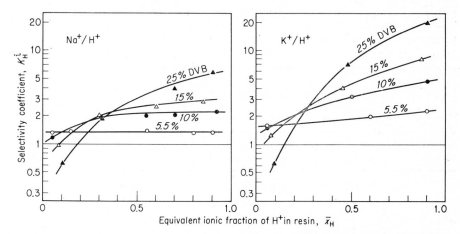

Fig. 5-26. Dependence of the selectivity on ionic composition and crosslinking. The selectivity coefficient of the exchanges Na^+/H^+ *(left)* and K^+/H^+ *(right)* on styrene-type cation exchangers of various DVB contents is shown as a function of the ionic composition of the resin. Selectivity for the alkali ion increases with decreasing equivalent fraction of this ion and with increasing degree of crosslinking. Note the selectivity reversal in highly crosslinked resins. *From experimental data by D. Reichenberg* [236,238].

acidic cation exchangers in aqueous media provides typical examples. Here, the selectivity sequence of the alkali ions is [40,109,112,116,179,218, 230,238,305,306].

$$Li^+ < Na^+ < K^+ < Rb^+ \leq Cs^+$$

(see also Fig. 5-29). This sequence is the same as that of the decreasing radii of the hydrated ions. The effects of solution concentration, equivalent ionic fractions, and degree of crosslinking are usually as predicted (Fig. 5-26) [112,218,230,236,238,298]. However, the "selectivity reversal" in the exchanges of alkali ions for H^+ in highly crosslinked resins (see Fig. 5-26) remains unexplained. In many other systems, the effect of swelling pressure and ionic size is outweighed by specific interactions. Particularly in anion exchange, swelling pressure and ionic size seem to be less important, probably because of the much weaker hydration and greater polarizability of the anions.

Sieve action.   So far, it has been tacitly implied that the larger counter ion is able to displace the smaller one completely from the resin.   In ion-exchange resins this is usually true for inorganic ions and for small organic ions.   However, very large organic ions and inorganic complexes may be mechanically excluded by *sieve action*.   Such an exclusion occurs if the meshes of the matrix are too narrow for accommodating the ion.   Sieve action is most dramatically displayed by the zeolites which have a regular and rather rigid lattice.   Certain zeolites even exclude inorganic ions such as Cs^+.   These conditions are discussed in more detail in Sec. 5-4f.   In ion-exchange resins, sieve action is much less pronounced because the pore width is not uniform, and is not so readily distinguished from swelling-pressure effects which also discourage uptake of large ions.   Sieve action is, of course, strongest in highly crosslinked resins.   Partial exclusion of the larger ion may occur if only the narrower pores are inaccessible.   The unique feature which distinguishes sieve action from swelling-pressure effects is that the smaller counter ion cannot be completely displaced by the larger one [72,73,100a,129,158,181,186]; see Table 5-6.

Table 5-6. Relative capacities of styrene-type cation exchangers of different degrees of crosslinking for various organic cations*

Counter ion	Degree of crosslinking			
	2% DVB, %	5% DVB, %	10% DVB, %	15% DVB, %
Tetramethylammonium	100	90	69	63
Tetraethylammonium	100	87	63	48
Benzyl-trimethylammonium	100	94	80	58
Trimethyl-*n*-octylammonium	100	100	71	38
Dibenzyldimethylammonium	100	94	43	15
Cetyltrimethylammonium	74	48	10	—

* Apparent capacities for ion exchange of H^+-form resins with chloride solutions, given in per cent of the capacity for NH_4^+.
From D. K. Hale, D. I. Packham, and K. W. Pepper [129].

Note that ion exchange is affected only by exclusion of a counter ion; the size of the co-ion is irrelevant.   Ion exchangers can freely exchange small counter ions with polyelectrolytes and ionic colloids ("contact exchange") [73].   The small counter ions of the polyelectrolyte or colloid have no difficulty in entering the ion exchanger, and the exclusion of the poly-co-ion or co-ionic colloid particle does not prevent the exchange.   On the other hand, no ion exchange can occur if the counter ion in the solution is a polyion [72].

Counter-ion exclusion by sieve action provides a convenient basis for testing pore sizes of ion exchangers [100a,122,181,186].   In a series of measurements, the ion exchanger is equilibrated with solutions containing successively larger counter ions. Failure to attain complete conversion indicates that the ionic size has exceeded the width of the narrower pores. Table 5-7 gives the (largest) diameters of a number of suitable ions. The test ions should be approximately spherical and should not form aggregates by association.

Sieve action can be used for separating large ions from small ones. A very simple separation is that of dyes such as Chicago blue, chlorazol red, benzopurine-4B, etc., from accompanying inorganic electrolytes. In an ion-exchange column, the small inorganic ions are readily removed whereas the large dye anions remain in the solution and pass through the column without hindrance [242]. The separation of dye anions of different sizes is more delicate, but equally feasible [182].

Table 5-7. Largest diameters of various ions which may be used for determining the pore width of ion exchangers

$N(CH_3)_4^+$	4.5 A
m-Phenylenediamine	5.5
Piperidine	6.5
β-Naphthylamine	6.5
$N(C_2H_5)_4^+$	7
Phenyldimethylethylammonium ion	8.5
Codeine	9
Trimethylamylammonium ion	9.5
Brucine	10
Phenylbenzyldimethylammonium ion	11
Laurylpyridinium ion	13
Resorcinol yellow (C.I. 148)	15
Carmoisine (C.I. 179)	20
Chicago blue (C.I. 518)	30

From R. Griessbach [122].

Specific interactions in the ion exchanger. Deviations from ideality are usually due to interactions between the various components of the system. One such phenomenon is solvation which results from charge-dipole interaction between the ions and the solvent molecules. Solvation, which has already been discussed, is by no means the only effect of this kind in ion-exchange equilibria. In many systems the selectivity results chiefly from other, usually more specific interactions. They may occur in the ion exchanger and in the solution. Interactions in the ion exchanger will be examined first.

Ion-pair Formation and Association. The most important specific interactions are those between the counter ions and the fixed ionic groups. Ion pairs and even covalent bonds can be formed. *The ion exchanger prefers the counter ion which forms the stronger ion pairs or bonds with the fixed ionic groups.* This rule is readily explained with the Le Châtelier principle; in the ion-exchange equilibrium

$$\bar{A} + B \rightleftharpoons \bar{B} + A \qquad (5\text{-}67)$$

the reverse process (right to left, uptake of A in exchange for B) is favored if A is sequestered in the ion exchanger by the fixed ionic groups. The situation is similar to that in other reversible chemical systems in which a reaction is favored if one of the products is removed by, say, evaporation or precipitation.

Interactions of this kind are likely to occur if the fixed ionic groups are similar in structure to precipitating or complexing agents which react with the counter ion [74,130,157,159,274]. Bond formation between carboxylic-acid anions and H^+ ions is an almost trivial example. The preference of weak-acid resins for H^+ ions [189,251a,305,306] which, by definition, associate with the weak-acid fixed groups results from such effects. Resins with groups resembling dipicrylamine (precipitating agent for K^+) are highly selective for K^+; see synthesis (3-21) [274]. Many resins with chelating groups show pronounced selectivities for various transition-group metal ions. To make use of the effect of interactions with the fixed ionic groups has been the leading idea in the attempts to prepare specific ion exchangers with outstanding selectivities for one or a few given counter ions (see Sec. 3-2c).

Electrostatic Attraction. Interactions between counter ions and fixed ionic groups do not necessarily involve the formation of chemical bonds or other specific chemical effects. The counter ions may be merely localized in the neighborhood of the fixed ionic groups by the electrostatic attraction between charges of opposite sign. Whether or not such purely electrostatic localization is described as a formation of incompletely dissociated ion pairs is essentially a matter of definition.

The strength of the electrostatic attraction depends chiefly on the ionic charge and the distance of closest approach between the counter ion and the fixed ionic group, i.e., on the value of the Debye-Hückel parameter a^0. Counter ions with higher valence and smaller a^0 value are more strongly held [39,179,228] because the electrostatic attraction is proportional to the ionic charge and inversely proportional to the square of the distance between the charges. The electrostatic effect thus favors *preference for the counter ion of higher valence* (as does the Donnan potential) and, in many cases, *preference for the smaller counter ion* (as does the swelling pressure).

It has already been mentioned that, in the case of the alkali ions, most cation-exchange resins do indeed prefer the smaller (solvated) ion to the larger one. This fact can be explained in terms of swelling pressure as well as of electrostatic attraction. However, even deviations from the simple ionic-size rule can be explained by the electrostatic effect. This is illustrated by two examples. Resins with sulfonic acid groups prefer Ag^+ and Tl^+ strongly to alkali ions, though there is little difference in the volumes of the hydrated ions. In spite of their almost identical size, Ag^+ and Tl^+ are more strongly attracted because their *polarizability* is greater and, hence, their a^0 values are smaller. This phenomenon is even more pronounced in resins with phosphonic acid groups which are excellent proton acceptors and rank even higher than water in the polarization sequence. As a result of the stronger polarization, resins with phosphonic acid groups prefer the larger, more strongly hydrated, and more polarizable cation even in the case of the alkali ions [43]. Resins with carboxylic acid groups behave in a similar manner though, here, the effect is less pronounced [120].

In certain cases, it is difficult to decide whether a counter ion forms a chemical bond with the fixed ionic group or whether its localization is

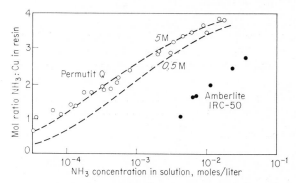

Fig. 5-27. Formation of ammonia complexes in cation exchangers. The circles give experimental values for the mole ratio NH_3:Cu in the cation-exchange resin Permutit Q (sulfonated polystyrene of 10 per cent DVB) and Amberlite IRC-50 (crosslinked polyacrylic acid) in Cu^{2+} form in equilibrium with solutions containing $CuCl_2$, NH_4Cl, and NH_3. The values are given as a function of the NH_3 concentration in the solution. The two broken lines give the average ligand numbers of copper ammonia complexes in 5 M and 0.5 M NH_4NO_3, as calculated by Bjerrum. The mole ratios in the strong-acid resin agree remarkably well with the average ligand numbers in the solution. In the weak-acid resin the mole ratios are considerably smaller. *From R. H. Stokes and H. F. Walton* [282].

merely electrostatic. Especially the behavior of silver and cupric ions has received much attention in this respect. It seems that bond formation between these ions and sulfonic acid groups can be ruled out. This view is strongly supported by experiments which show that, in the resin, Ag^+ and Cu^{2+} form amine complexes to the same extent as in aqueous solutions (see Fig. 5-27). Thus the sulfonic acid groups do not compete with ammonia and amines in occupying coordinative valences of the cations [282]. In resins with carboxylic acid groups, however, there is such a competition, indicating that bond formation with the fixed ionic groups does occur [282]. Other cases are still controversial.

London Interactions. Interactions in the ion exchanger do not necessarily involve the fixed ionic groups. In certain cases, selectivity may arise from *London forces* between the counter ion and the matrix and from *interactions of the solvent molecules with one another.* The action of these forces has been discussed in detail in Sec. 5-3b. Ion-exchange equilibria are likely to be affected by such interactions if one or both competing species are organic ions. *The ion exchanger prefers counter ions with organic groups which resemble the components of the matrix.* For example, styrene-type resins usually prefer counter ions with aromatic groups to those with aliphatic groups [181]. The strength of the interactions increases with increasing size of the organic groups of the counter ion, so that the ion exchanger may prefer the larger counter ion to the smaller one [181]; see Table 5-8. However, this effect is often outweighed by the swelling-pressure effect or by sieve action.

Table 5-8. Selectivity coefficients for the exchange of large organic counter ions for NH_4^+ on a weakly crosslinked cation exchanger (condensation product of phenolsulfonic acid and formaldehyde)

Counter ion	$K_{NH_4}^i$
Tetramethylammonium	3.67
Tetraethylammonium	5.0
Trimethyl-*n*-amylammonium	8.24
Phenyl-dimethylethylammonium	25.2
Phenyl-benzyldimethylammonium	44.4

From T. R. E. Kressman and J. A. Kitchener [181].

In certain cases, London interactions of organic counter ions with one another can occur. Ion exchangers in "soap form" are an interesting example. The soap form is obtained by exchanging the counter ions of a high-capacity resin for long-chain soap ions such as cetyltrimethylammonium ions. The high soap-ion concentration in the resin results in micelle formation. This internal interaction is so strong that the resin remains completely in the soap form when being equilibrated with electrolyte solutions, provided the latter contain a trace of the soap [243].

Association and complex formation in the solution. Ion-exchange equilibria are strongly affected by interactions of the counter ions with other components in the external solution. Interactions with the co-ion are particularly important because the co-ion is rather efficiently excluded from the resin phase, so that the effect of interactions in the solution is not compensated by that of similar interactions in the ion exchanger. The counter ions may form weakly dissociated aggregates or complex ions with the co-ions. Application of the Le Châtelier principle to the ion-exchange equilibrium

$$\bar{A} + B \rightleftharpoons \bar{B} + A \qquad (5\text{-}67)$$

shows that the reverse exchange (right to left, uptake of A in exchange for B) is favored when the species B is sequestered in the solution by reaction with the co-ion. Thus *the ion exchanger prefers the counter ion which associates less strongly with the co-ion.* This rule is illustrated by two typical examples. Strong-acid resins prefer other univalent cations to H^+ if the anion in the solution is that of a weak acid. Cation exchangers prefer other cations to Hg^{2+} if the solution contains Cl^- [180].

Cations can form positive, neutral, and even negative complexes with anionic ligands. Not only the strength, but also the effective charge of these complexes affects ion-exchange equilibria. Cation exchangers prefer cations of higher charge and exclude anions; the higher the negative charge of the anion, the stronger is the exclusion. Thus, *cation exchangers prefer the cation which forms, with the anion, the complex with the smaller average ligand number.* Of course, this rule holds only if the effect of complex formation is not outweighed by other factors.

Anionic complexes of metal ions behave like anions and can be taken up by anion exchangers in exchange for other anions. Such anion-exchange equilibria depend equally on complex formation. From considerations analogous to those immediately above it follows that, here, the situation is reversed: *anion exchangers prefer the cation which forms, with the anion, the stronger complex or the complex with the greater average ligand number.* Of course, this effect may be outweighed by other factors.

The discussion of interactions with fixed ionic groups (page 161) has shown that selectivity can be obtained by using specially prepared resins with particular ionic groups. In contrast, formation of complexes with anions in the solution provides a means of enhancing the selectivity of given ion exchangers. Under ordinary conditions, ion exchangers can hardly discriminate between very similar cations. However, complex formation is a highly specific interaction; with a suitable anion, even cations with very similar properties can form complexes which differ considerably in their strength and effective charge. Ion-exchange selectivities obtained by complex formation have been exploited for the most delicate separations of cations. An outstanding example is the separation of the rare earths by cation-exchange chromatography (see also Sec. 9-7d). Many analytical metal-ion separations, developed chiefly by K. A. Kraus and collaborators [174], are based on exchange of anionic complexes by anion exchangers (see also Sec. 9-6).

The formation of complexes with *nonionic ligands* such as ammonia, amines, polyalcohols, etc., has relatively little effect on ion-exchange equilibria since the effective charge of the counter ion remains unchanged and merely solvent molecules in the solvation shell are replaced by molecules of the ligand.

In view of their particular importance, ion-exchange and sorption equilibria in the presence of ionic complexing agents are discussed in more detail in a separate section (Sec. 5-6).

Formation of precipitates. The uptake of a counter ion by the ion exchanger can be enhanced by removing the competing counter ion from the solution by precipitation. The mechanism is obvious; precipitation reduces the concentration of the competing species in the solution, thus causing the ion exchanger to release this species.

In practice, precipitation is usually avoided because it may clog the pores at the surface of the ion exchanger.

One of the few applications which this effect has found is the use of briquettes consisting of Ag_2O, $Ba(OH)_2 \cdot 8H_2O$, and a cationic zeolite in Ag^+ form for desalting sea water in emergency situations (on life rafts, etc.) [50,287]. The precipitation of Ag^+ by Cl^- favors the uptake of the sea-water cations by the zeolite:

$$\overline{Ag^+} + Na^+ + Cl^- \to \overline{Na^+} + \underline{AgCl} \qquad (5\text{-}85)$$

Barium hydroxide is added for precipitating SO_4^{2-}.

A reversal of this phenomenon is the dissolution of slightly soluble electrolytes by ion exchangers (see Sec. 5-8).

Temperature and pressure. The *temperature dependence* of equilibria in general is related to the standard enthalpy change which accompanies the reaction. High temperature discourages the reaction which occurs with evolution of heat. The temperature dependence of ion-exchange equilibria is given by the thermodynamic relation

$$\left(\frac{d \ln {}^N\mathcal{K}_B^A}{dT} \right)_P = \frac{\Delta H^0}{RT^2} \qquad (5\text{-}86)$$

where ${}^N\mathcal{K}_B^A$ is the rational thermodynamic equilibrium constant and ΔH^0 is the standard enthalpy change of the ion exchange $A + \bar{B} \to B + \bar{A}$.

Ion exchange is not a chemical reaction and occurs, as a rule, with little evolution or uptake of heat. Standard enthalpy changes are usually smaller than 2 kcal/mole, though values of up to 10 kcal/mole have been observed in exceptional cases. Accordingly, the temperature dependence of ion-exchange equilibria is usually minor. However, ion exchange may be followed by other processes with considerable enthalpy changes. Cation exchange of a resin in H^+ form with a base such as NaOH is a typical example [53,195,275]:

$$\overline{H^+} + Na^+ \to \overline{Na^+} + H^+ \qquad (5\text{-}87)$$
$$H^+ + OH^- \to H_2O \qquad (5\text{-}88)$$

Here, the heat of neutralization (13.7 kcal/mole) is liberated in the consecutive reaction (5-88). Such systems are more likely to be affected by temperature changes.

In most cases, selectivity results from association or aggregation processes such as complex formation in the ion exchanger or the solution, ion-pair formation, solvation, etc. These processes are usually discouraged by an increase in temperature. Hence, the selectivity should be expected to decrease with increasing temperature. This is often, but not always, the case (see Fig. 5-28) [37,38,53,75,177,178,205]. Exceptions are found in systems involving counter ions of different valences.* No interpretation for this behavior has as yet been advanced.

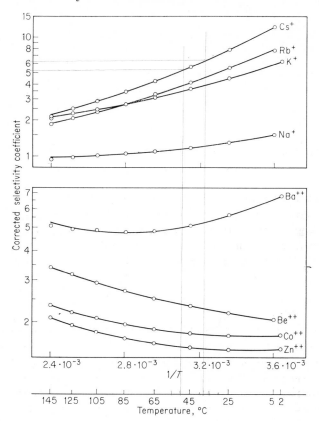

FIG. 5-28. Temperature dependence of ion-exchange equilibria. The curves show corrected selectivity coefficients for the exchange of traces of various univalent cations (upper diagram) and bivalent cations (lower diagram) on a logarithmic scale as a function of reciprocal temperature. The concentration scale for the resin phase is millimoles per gram of dry resin. The curves are not linear, indicating that ΔH^0 is not constant. *From K. A. Kraus and R. J. Raridon* [177].

The *pressure dependence* of equilibria is related to the standard volume change which accompanies the reaction. High pressure favors the reaction which results in contraction of the system. The pressure dependence of

---

* Note, however, that the selectivity coefficients in Fig. 5-28 are not the molal or rational coefficients. Rather, the internal concentrations refer to unit weight of dry resin. It is likely that, in the uni-bivalent exchanges, the temperature dependence becomes less pronounced when the molal coefficients are plotted. Furthermore, the experiments at over 100°C were carried out under pressure. It is tacitly (and probably correctly) assumed that the pressure dependence is insignificant.

ion-exchange equilibria is given by the thermodynamic relation

$$\left(\frac{d \ln {}^N \mathcal{K}_B^A}{dP}\right)_T = -\frac{\Delta V^0}{RT} \tag{5-89}$$

where ΔV^0 is the standard volume change of the total system (ion exchanger plus solution) in the course of the ion exchange $A + \bar{B} \to B + \bar{A}$. In ion exchange, there is hardly any change in the total volume of the system (ion exchanger plus solution) even though the resin may swell or shrink. Thus changes in pressure should have little, if any, effect on ion-exchange equilibria. No experimental measurements have so far been made.

Survey. The effects of the various factors can be briefly summarized as follows. *The ion exchanger tends to prefer:*

The counter ion of higher valence
The counter ion with the smaller (solvated) equivalent volume
The counter ion with the greater polarizability
The counter ion which interacts more strongly with the fixed ionic groups or with the matrix
The counter ion which participates least in complex formation with the co-ion

As a rule, the selectivity of an ion exchanger is enhanced by increasing its degree of crosslinking and by decreasing the solution concentration and the temperature. A fairly universal rule of thumb is that the ion causing less swelling is preferred.

There are, of course, exceptions to these rules, especially since some of the effects may counteract one another.

In the usual general-purpose cation exchangers the selectivity sequence of the most common cations is [32,34,36,251a,305,306]

$$Ba^{2+} > Pb^{2+} > Sr^{2+} > Ca^{2+} > Ni^{2+} > Cd^{2+} > Cu^{2+} > Co^{2+} > Zn^{2+} >$$
$$Mg^{2+} > UO_2^{2+}$$
$$Tl^+ > Ag^+ > Cs^+ > Rb^+ > K^+ > NH_4^+ > Na^+ > Li^+$$

(see also Table 5-9). The sequences of the univalent and bivalent cations overlap in resins of high capacity and moderate and high degree of crosslinking. For strong-acid resins, H^+ usually falls between Na^+ and Li^+. For weak-acid resins, the position of H^+ depends on the acid strength of the fixed anionic groups. Resins with groups of very low acid strength may prefer H^+ even to Tl^+.

The selectivity sequence of the usual general-purpose anion-exchange resins is [187,194,251a,305,306]

$$Citrate > SO_4^{2-} > oxalate > I^- > NO_3^- > CrO_4^{2-} > Br^- > SCN^- > Cl^-$$
$$> formate > acetate > F^-$$

For strong-base resins, OH^- usually falls between acetate and fluoride. For weak-base resins, the position of OH^- is farther to the left and depends on the base strength of the fixed ionogenic groups.

Of course, the sequences do not apply without exceptions.

Experimental evidence is generally in good agreement with the theoretical picture outlined in this section. This is illustrated by the numerous practical examples in the text.

Table 5-9. Rational thermodynamic equilibrium constants $^N\mathcal{K}_B^A$ for the exchange of various cations for Li^+ on sulfonated polystyrenes (Dowex 50) of different crosslinking*

Counter ion	Degree of crosslinking			Counter ion	Degree of crosslinking		
	4% DVB	8% DVB	16% DVB		4% DVB	8% DVB	16% DVB
Li^+	1.00	1.00	1.00	Mg^{2+}	2.95	3.29	3.51
H^+	1.32	1.27	1.47	Zn^{2+}	3.13	3.47	3.78
Na^+	1.58	1.98	2.37	Co^{2+}	3.23	3.74	3.81
NH_4^+	1.90	2.55	3.34	Cu^{2+}	3.29	3.85	4.46
K^+	2.27	2.90	4.50	Cd^{2+}	3.37	3.88	4.95
Rb^+	2.46	3.16	4.62	Ni^{2+}	3.45	3.93	4.06
Cs^+	2.67	3.25	4.66	Ca^{2+}	4.15	5.16	7.27
Ag^+	4.73	8.51	22.9	Sr^{2+}	4.70	6.51	10.1
Tl^+	6.71	12.4	28.5	Pb^{2+}	6.56	9.91	18.0
UO_2^{2+}	2.36	2.45	3.34	Ba^{2+}	7.47	11.5	20.8

* The choice of Li^+ as the reference ion is arbitrary. For the standard and reference states, see pages 156 and 195.

From O. D. Bonner and L. L. Smith [36].

c. Quantitative Treatment

In the simplest and most clear-cut quantitative treatment of ion-exchange equilibria, the model of the elastic matrix (Fig. 5-1) is used. This model leads to the relation

$$E_{\text{Don}} = \frac{1}{z_i \mathcal{F}} \left(RT \ln \frac{a_i}{\bar{a}_i} - \Pi v_i \right) \tag{5-39}$$

where E_{Don} = Donnan potential; z_i = electrochemical valence of species i; $\mathcal{F}$ = Faraday constant; a_i = activity of species i; Π = swelling pressure; v_i = partial molar volume of species i,

which has previously been derived and applied to electrolyte sorption (see Sec. 5-3c). Equation (5-39) holds for any mobile ionic species, irrespective of the number of species present in the system. Combination of the two Eqs. (5-39) for the two competing counter ions A and B gives

$$RT \ln \left[\left(\frac{\bar{a}_A}{a_A} \right)^{z_B} \left(\frac{a_B}{\bar{a}_B} \right)^{z_A} \right] = \Pi(z_A v_B - z_B v_A) \tag{5-90}*$$

* Note that the molar volumes have been assumed to be independent of pressure; see footnote to p. 110 for pressure dependence,

Substituting the activities by molalities m_i according to

$$a_i = m_i \gamma_i \tag{5-91}$$

γ_i = molal activity coefficient of species i,

and using Eq. (5-71) one obtains the following relation for the molal selectivity coefficient [40,104]:

$$\ln K_B^A = \ln \frac{\bar{\gamma}_B^{|z_A|}}{\bar{\gamma}_A^{|z_B|}} + \ln \frac{\gamma_A^{|z_B|}}{\gamma_B^{|z_A|}} + \frac{\Pi}{RT} \left(|z_A| v_B - |z_B| v_A \right) \tag{5-92}$$

Equation (5-92) contains only thermodynamically defined quantities. It is true that the relation involves single activity coefficients and partial molar volumes of ions. However, the former appear only as ratios (which are thermodynamically defined), and the latter can be expressed in terms of the partial molar volumes of electrolytes AY and BY:

$$z_A v_B - z_B v_A = \frac{z_A}{v_B} v_{BY} - \frac{z_B}{v_A} v_{AY} \tag{5-93}$$

Equation (5-92) describes ion-exchange equilibrium in terms of the selectivity coefficient from which the concentration ratio of the competing counter ions in the ion exchanger can be calculated for a given concentration ratio in the solution. For most practical purposes, the knowledge of this concentration ratio in the ion exchanger is sufficient since the total counter-ion content of the ion exchanger is approximately stoichiometrically equivalent to the ion-exchange capacity of the latter. For an accurate calculation of the absolute counter-ion concentrations in the ion exchanger, electrolyte sorption and swelling must be known in addition to the selectivity coefficient, and Eq. (5-92) must be combined with the relations derived for these equilibria (see Secs. 5-2d and 5-3c, respectively).

The relation (5-92) reflects the effects of the various factors which have been qualitatively discussed in the previous section. According to the definition (5-71), a selectivity coefficient larger than unity ($\ln K_B^A > 0$) indicates selectivity for the ion A. In Eq. (5-92), *swelling-pressure effects* appear in the third term which becomes positive when A has the smaller partial molar volume. This term is more important when the swelling pressure is high. *Specific interactions* in the ion exchanger appear in the first term which becomes positive when A has the smaller activity coefficient in the ion exchanger. The activity coefficient of an ion is reduced by *ion-pair formation, association,* or similar interactions. *Interactions with the co-ion in the solution* appear in the second term which becomes positive when B has the smaller activity coefficient in the solution. *Ionic solvation* affects both the second and the third term and will be discussed later. *Pre-*

cipitation of one of the competing counter ions from the solution does not affect the selectivity coefficient; ion-exchange equilibrium is merely shifted by the decrease in concentration of this ion in the solution. In the absence of all these effects, the selectivity coefficient is unity, and the ion exchanger shows no selectivity. However, *electroselectivity* for the counter ion of higher valence is still operative.

The selectivity coefficient can be calculated from Eq. (5-92) when the activity coefficients, the swelling pressure, and the partial molar volumes are known. Activity coefficients and partial molar volumes of electrolytes in aqueous solutions are readily available, and the swelling pressure can be computed from the equations in Sec. 5-2d. Unfortunately, the calculation of the activity coefficients in the ion exchanger poses a problem. By means of rigorous thermodynamics, these coefficients can only be obtained from measurements of just those equilibria to which they are to be applied (see page 197). A rigorous method for predicting the coefficients from fundamental data has so far not been developed. This is, as in sorption and swelling, the missing link in the theory. However, as in sorption and swelling, this gap has been partly bridged by empirical and semiempirical approaches which will be discussed in Sec. 5-4d.

The activity coefficients are, by nature, the quantities which reflect all those effects which are not included in the model. This point is well illustrated by a comparison of Eq. (5-92) with the corresponding relation derived from a model which does not include swelling-pressure effects. In this model, the appropriate definition of the activities is Eq. (5-54) rather than Eq. (5-8). One obtains [30,201]

$$\left(\frac{\bar{a}_A}{a_A}\right)^{z_B} = \left(\frac{\bar{a}_B}{a_B}\right)^{z_A} \tag{5-94}$$

instead of Eq. (5-90). The relation for the selectivity coefficient differs from Eq. (5-92) in that the swelling-pressure term is missing. With activities defined according to this model, the swelling-pressure effect—which appears explicitly in Eq. (5-92)—is disguised in the activity coefficients. The relations derived from the simpler model without swelling pressure are not less exact thermodynamically. In this book they will be used in the study of kinetic problems in which swelling-pressure effects are less relevant.

The only particular property of the model which leads to Eq. (5-92) is the elasticity of the matrix. By equipping the model with further properties, further effects can be made susceptible to quantitative or semiquantitative treatment, and the relative importance of the (accordingly redefined) activity coefficients can be decreased. The activity coefficients become superfluous when all relevant effects are accounted for in the model. In this way, progress is made toward the aim of predicting ion-exchange equilibria from fundamental data, and valuable insight into the action of the various physical forces is obtained. However, such approaches which bypass the introduction of activity coefficients are, of course, not rigorous since it is virtually impossible to include all conceivable effects in a model. The proper choice of the model thus is of vital importance and requires considerable experience. Several simple examples of approaches of this kind follow.

Ionic solvation and swelling pressure. Equation (5-92) is derived from the model with the elastic matrix and thus includes swelling-pressure effects explicitly. These effects appear in the third term of the equation. However, the relative importance of this term is usually small and is insufficient for explaining the selectivities of resins. The differences in the partial equivalent volumes of ions are, as a rule, of the order of only a few milliliters. A simple calculation shows that, with $R = 0.082$ liter atm mole^{-1} deg^{-1} and $T \approx 300°$, the swelling-pressure term rarely exceeds 0.01, even if the swelling pressure is several hundred atmospheres. In comparison, experimental values of $\ln K_B^A$ are quite often higher by one order of magnitude or more.

The picture becomes quite different when the solvation of the ions is explicitly taken into account. This was done by Gregor [109,112,116] who, in his first model, chose the components of the system to be the *solvated* ions, the *free* solvent, and the matrix with *solvated* fixed ionic groups (see also page 117). With the assumption that the system behaves ideally except for solvation, i.e., that the activity-coefficient ratios in Eq. (5-92) are determined by solvation alone, one obtains

$$\ln K^{*A}_{B} \equiv \ln \left[\left(\frac{\bar{m}_A^*}{m_A^*} \right)^{|z_B|} \left(\frac{m_B^*}{\bar{m}_B^*} \right)^{|z_A|} \right] = \frac{\Pi}{RT} \left(|z_A| v_B^* - |z_B| v_A^* \right) \qquad (5\text{-}95)$$

instead of Eq. (5-92). The molalities m_i^* refer to free solvent, and the quantities v_i^* are the molar volumes of the solvated ions. Only for counter ions of equal valence is K^{*A}_{B} equal to K_B^A. The molar volumes v_i^* of the solvated counter ions are considerably larger than the partial molar volumes v_i. Therefore swelling pressure and ionic size are much more important in Eq. (5-95) than in Eq. (5-92).

The solvation of the ions is thermodynamically not well defined, so that the distinction between free solvent and solvation shells is, to a certain extent, arbitrary. Thus Eq. (5-95) is not thermodynamically rigorous, even if activity coefficients are introduced as correction factors for effects other than solvation. Nevertheless, the relation is a very useful approximation for systems in which, indeed, solvation is the most important factor. The dependence of the selectivity on ionic size, degree of crosslinking and ionic composition of the ion exchanger, and concentration of the solution (see Figs. 5-26 and 5-29) is reflected in a semiquantitative way. Of course, quantitative agreement with experimental results cannot be expected.

The comparison of the conclusions drawn from Eqs. (5-92) and (5-95) shows that the choice of the components of the system determines whether or not swelling pressure and ionic size should be considered as decisive factors in ion-exchange equilibria. In Eq. (5-92), solvation effects are reflected in the activity coefficients, and the swelling pressure term usually remains unimportant. In Eq. (5-95), solvation is reflected in the ionic volumes, and the swelling pressure becomes an essential factor. Thus the historical controversy about the importance of the swelling pressure proves to be only a matter of definition.

Ion-pair formation and association.

In the thermodynamic treatment based on the simple model of the elastic matrix, ion-pair formation and association are not included explicitly. In Eq. (5-92) and its derivation, no distinction is made between associated and "free" counter ions. The interaction between counter ions and fixed ionic groups is reflected only in a lowering of the activity coefficient of the counter ion involved. The distinction between associated and free counter ions is thermodynamically as undefined as that between solvation shells and free solvent (see page 172). However, the use of (thermodynamically less rigorous) models in which such distinctions are

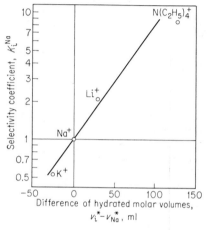

Fig. 5-29. Correlation between selectivity coefficients and molar volumes of hydrated counter ions. The diagram shows the (average) selectivity coefficients of Dowex 50-X10 for the exchanges of various univalent counter ions i for Na^+ in 0.001 M solutions. The coefficients are given as a function of the difference $v_i^* - v_{Na}^*$ of the hydrated molar volumes. There is an approximately linear relation between $\log K_i^{Na}$ and the molar-volume difference. *From data by H. P. Gregor* [109].

made, contributes considerably to a better qualitative understanding of the physical factors and mechanisms involved.

Two simple approaches which include ion-pair formation and association are briefly outlined in the following. For the sake of simplicity, the discussion is restricted to univalent counter ions, and it is assumed that electrolyte sorption is negligible and that the system behaves ideally except for association effects.

In such ideal systems in which selectivity results from association alone, the concentration ratio of the *free* counter ions in the ion exchanger should be the same as in the solution. The selectivity coefficient can thus be calculated when the extent of association of the counter ions is known.

Gregor [119] has applied the mass-action law for *homogeneous* reactions to the association or ion-pair formation in the ion exchanger:

$$A + R \rightleftharpoons AR \qquad \frac{\bar{m}_A^0 \bar{m}_R^0}{\bar{m}_{AR}} = K_{AR} \qquad (5\text{-}96)$$

$$B + R \rightleftharpoons BR \qquad \frac{\bar{m}_B^0 \bar{m}_R^0}{\bar{m}_{BR}} = K_{BR} \qquad (5\text{-}97)$$

Superscripts 0 denote unassociated ions or fixed ionic groups,

where K_{AR} and K_{BR} are the dissociation constants of the ion pairs. Calculations with arbitrary values for these constants lead to a *decrease* in selectivity with increasing equivalent fraction of the preferred ion (see Fig. 5-30, curve I). This dependence on ionic composition is qualitatively the same as in cases in which the smaller counter ion is preferred because of the swelling-pressure effect. Many actual systems behave in this manner. Gregor invokes ion-pair formation in anion exchange where the selectivity cannot be explained by a swelling-pressure effect [119]; see also Fig. 5-31.

The mentioned dependence of the selectivity on ionic composition is not universal. In anion-exchange systems involving perchlorate, thiocyanate, and trichloroacetate ions, Gregor found an *increase* in selectivity with increasing equivalent fraction of the preferred ion [114,119]; see Fig. 5-31. He explains these results with a slightly different model in which the mass-action law for a *heterogeneous* instead of a homogeneous reaction is used. Here, the fixed ionic groups and ion pairs are treated as solid phases in equilibrium with the pore liquid. According to Gregor, Eqs. (5-96) and (5-97) (homogeneous reaction) apply if an ion pair has no effect on the behavior of the neighboring fixed ionic groups, so that the pairs are distributed statistically. He assumes formation of "clusters" of ion pairs in those cases in which the homogeneous-phase treatment fails.

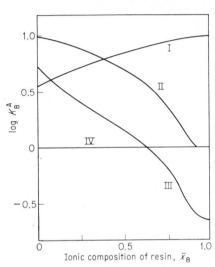

FIG. 5-30. Theoretical selectivity coefficients as a function of the ionic composition in systems involving ion-pair formation:
I: Pairs AR are statistically distributed, $K_{AR} = 0.1$; B forms no ion pairs.
II: Pairs AR form clusters, $K_A = 0.1$; B forms no pairs.
III: Pairs AR form clusters, $K_A = 0.1$; pairs BR are statistically distributed, $K_{BR} = 0.1$.
IV: Pairs AR and BR form common solid cluster phase; $K_A = K_B$. *From H. P. Gregor, J. Belle, and R. A. Marcus* [119].

Systems with cluster formation are treated by Gregor in the following way. If only the pairs AR form clusters, the mass-action law for a heterogeneous reaction (solid phases are underscored)

$$\underline{A} + R \rightleftharpoons \underline{AR} \qquad \bar{m}_A^0 \leq K_A \qquad (5\text{-}98)$$

is used instead of Eq. (5-96). The constant K_A resembles the solubility constant of a slightly soluble substance, indicating the maximum possible concentration of the free species A. In equilibrium with the solid phase AR, the concentration of the free ions A is equal to K_A (saturated solution), and with $\bar{m}_A < K_A$ the solid phase disappears. Calculations with Eq. (5-98) lead to an increase in the preference for A with increasing equivalent fraction of A (see Fig. 5-30, curve II). In systems in which both AR and BR

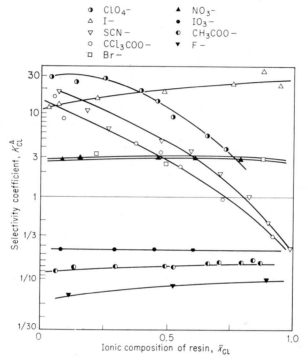

FIG. 5-31. Experimental selectivity coefficients of the exchanges of various univalent anions for Cl^- on Dowex 2-X8, shown as a function of ionic composition. *From H. P. Gregor, J. Belle, and R. A. Marcus* [119].

form clusters, Gregor assumes that an ideal solid solution of the ion pairs is formed. Thus he obtains

$$\frac{\bar{m}_A^0}{\tilde{N}_{AR}} = K_A \qquad \frac{\bar{m}_B^0}{\tilde{N}_{BR}} = K_B \qquad (5\text{-}99)$$

where

$$\tilde{N}_{AR} \equiv \frac{\bar{m}_{AR}}{\bar{m}_{AR} + \bar{m}_{BR}} \qquad \tilde{N}_{BR} \equiv \frac{\bar{m}_{BR}}{\bar{m}_{AR} + \bar{m}_{BR}} \qquad (5\text{-}100)$$

are the mole fractions of the ion pairs in the solid cluster phase. The selectivity in this model depends little on ionic composition (see Fig. 5-30, curve IV).

The theory of cluster formation in ion exchange resins is interesting, but is still rather controversial. The ion-pair formation constants are purely empirical, and the fact that such constants can be fitted to experimental ion-exchange isotherms is not a sufficient proof of the theory. Direct evidence of cluster formation in resins has so far not been

found.   Also, later investigators have failed to find the characteristic dependence of the
selectivity on ionic composition which Gregor explained with cluster formation [56].

Various other approaches which are based on fundamentally different
models are briefly discussed in Sec. 5-4g.

Thermodynamic functions.   The thermodynamic equilibrium constant and the free-
energy, enthalpy, and entropy changes which accompany ion exchange are interrelated
in the following way.

Suppose that the exchange of $|z_A|$ moles of counter ions B for $|z_B|$ moles of counter ions
A, occurring between infinite amounts of the ion exchanger and the solution (no noticeable concentration changes) is accompanied by desorption of f moles of BY and sorption
of g moles of AY and h moles of solvent (h may be positive or negative).   The *free-energy
change* of the total system (ion exchanger plus solution) then is

$$\Delta G = \Delta G^0 - RT \ln \left[\left(\frac{a_A}{\bar{a}_A} \right)^{|z_B|} \left(\frac{\bar{a}_B}{a_B} \right)^{|z_A|} \right] - RT \ln \left(\frac{\bar{a}_{BY}}{a_{BY}} \right)^f$$

$$+ RT \ln \left(\frac{\bar{a}_{AY}}{a_{AY}} \right)^g + RT \ln \left(\frac{\bar{a}_w}{a_w} \right)^h \quad (5\text{-}101)$$

where ΔG^0 = standard free-energy change.

The activities and the values of f, g, and h are those for the momentary state of the system which is not necessarily in equilibrium.   In the special case of equilibrium, ΔG
becomes zero.   Thus one obtains

$$\Delta G^0 = -RT \ln \left[\left(\frac{\bar{a}_A}{a_A} \right)^{|z_B|} \left(\frac{a_B}{\bar{a}_B} \right)^{|z_A|} \left(\frac{\bar{a}_w}{a_w} \right)^h \left(\frac{\bar{a}_{AY}}{a_{AY}} \right)^g \left(\frac{a_{BY}}{\bar{a}_{BY}} \right)^f \right] \quad (5\text{-}102)$$

In this relation, the expression in square brackets is the *thermodynamic equilibrium constant*, $\mathcal{K}_B^A$, defined by

$$\Delta G^0 = -RT \ln \mathcal{K}_B^A \quad (5\text{-}82)$$

Comparison with Eq. (5-71) shows that the equilibrium constant and the selectivity
coefficient are interrelated by

$$\mathcal{K}_B^A = K_B^A \left(\frac{\bar{\gamma}_A}{\gamma_A} \right)^{|z_B|} \left(\frac{\gamma_B}{\bar{\gamma}_B} \right)^{|z_A|} \left(\frac{\bar{a}_w}{a_w} \right)^h \left(\frac{\bar{a}_{AY}}{a_{AY}} \right)^g \left(\frac{a_{BY}}{\bar{a}_{BY}} \right)^f \quad (5\text{-}103)$$

Combination of these relations with Eqs. (5-90), (5-16), and (5-53) shows the dependence
of the *molal* equilibrium constant on the swelling pressure and the partial molar volumes:

$$\ln \mathcal{K}_B^A = \frac{\Pi}{RT} \left(|z_A| v_B - |z_B| v_A - h v_w - g v_{AY} + f v_{BY} \right) \quad (5\text{-}104)$$

In many cases, the correction terms for electrolyte and solvent sorption and desorption
in Eqs. (5-101) to (5-104) are rather small and can often be neglected.

The free-energy, enthalpy, and entropy changes are interrelated by the general thermodynamic expression

$$\Delta G = \Delta H - T \Delta S \quad (5\text{-}23)$$

The *enthalpy* term ΔH is usually rather small.   The more important contribution to the
"driving force" of ion exchange—i.e., to the free-energy change—stems from the *entropy*
increase given by the second term in Eq. (5-23).   This term arises mainly from the
entropy of mixing.   In addition, it includes the configurational entropy change of the
matrix and contributions from changes in the state of order of solvent molecules resulting
from the formation and degradation of aggregates and solvation shells.   If the activities
in the ion exchanger and the equilibrium constant are known, Eqs. (5-101) and (5-23)

can be used for calculating the *entropy change* from calorimetric measurements of the heat of ion exchange, $-\Delta H$ [59,60]. Alternatively, the standard enthalpy change $-\Delta H^0$ and standard entropy change ΔS^0 can be calculated from the temperature dependence of the equilibrium constant by use of Eq. (5-86) [38,83]. The interpretation of the entropy change, however, is somewhat speculative.

d. Prediction of Ion-exchange Equilibria

The prediction of ion-exchange equilibria is a very important problem to which much work has been devoted. In essence, two somewhat different lines of approach have been followed.

In the studies of the first type, attempts have been made to design more and more elaborate models which include more and more effects and thus behave more nearly like actual ion exchangers. Simple examples of models which account for ionic solvation, ion-pair formation, etc., have been given in the previous section. Other examples are found in Secs. 5-4g and 5-6. The final goal of such attempts is to arrive at an adequate description of ion-exchange equilibria in terms of physical forces and, in this way, to provide means of predicting equilibria from fundamental data. Approaches of this kind appeal primarily to the practical chemist who is interested in understanding the mechanism and the physical causes of the phenomena and is satisfied with a semiquantitative picture. However, these approaches are not rigorous* and are often based on concepts or quantities which are thermodynamically ill-defined; thus they are less likely to satisfy the theoretical chemist who is used to thinking in terms of rigorous thermodynamics.

The approaches of the second type have originated from just this desire for greater thermodynamic rigor. In essence, they consist in attempts to correlate the activity coefficients in thermodynamically rigorous equations such as (5-92) or (5-94) with other quantities which are accessible by independent measurements. Theories of this type, in turn, have less appeal for those who are interested in understanding mechanisms since they give less information about the action of the various physical forces in the system.

In predictions of ion-exchange equilibria by use of theories of the first type, the choice of the model is crucial. Significant answers can only be obtained if all relevant properties of the system are adequately represented in the model. Otherwise the application is straightforward and requires no further comment. Various theories of the second type are outlined in the following.

Glueckauf [104] predicts ion-exchange equilibria merely from measurements of water-vapor sorption by the monoionic A form and B form of the

---

* Of course, they can be made rigorous by introducing activity coefficients as correction factors; this, however, is of little help since the factors cannot be predicted.

resin. These measurements yield the osmotic coefficients ϕ_{AR} and ϕ_{BR}, as defined by Eq. (5-15). From these osmotic coefficients he calculates the activity coefficients of the monoionic "resinates," AR and BR, by use of the semiempirical relation

$$\ln \frac{\bar{\gamma}^0_{\pm AR}}{\bar{\gamma}^0_{\pm BR}} = 2(\phi_{AR} - \phi_{BR}) \tag{5-105}$$

Activity coefficients of the monoionic forms are denoted by superscripts 0.

For calculating the activity coefficients of the resinates in the heteroionic forms of the resin (containing both A and B), Harned's rule [131] is used. According to this empirical rule, the mean activity coefficient of an electrolyte j in a mixture of the electrolytes j, k, l, . . . is given by

$$\ln \gamma_{\pm j} = \ln \gamma^0_{\pm j} + \sum_{i \neq j} \alpha_{ji} m_i \tag{5-106}$$

where $\gamma^0_{\pm j}$ = mean activity coefficient of the pure electrolyte j.

In a mixture of univalent electrolytes, the interaction coefficients α_{jk} are interrelated by

$$\alpha_{jk} - \alpha_{kj} = \frac{\nu_j \ln \gamma^0_{\pm j} - \nu_k \ln \gamma^0_{\pm k}}{m} \tag{5-107}$$

where m = total molality; a correction term is omitted.

The ion-exchanger phase is treated as a mixture of the resinates AR and BR and the electrolytes AY and BY. Application of Eqs. (5-106) and (5-107) to the ion exchanger and the solution and combination with Eqs. (5-105) and (5-92) leads to the following relation for the selectivity coefficient in uni-univalent ion-exchange equilibria

$$\ln K^A_B = \phi_{BR} - \phi_{AR} + \ln \frac{\gamma^0_{\pm AY}}{\gamma^0_{\pm BY}} + \frac{\Pi}{RT}(v_{BY} - v_{AY}) \tag{5-108}$$

This relation, in contrast to Eq. (5-92), contains only quantities which are readily accessible.

Harned's rule in this or similar forms has been repeatedly applied to ion-exchange equilibria [64,82,104]. However, without further empirical corrections the agreement with experimental results is only fair. Note that Eq. (5-108) fails to reflect the dependence of the selectivity coefficient on the ionic composition of the resin (i.e., on the equivalent ionic fraction $\bar{x}_A$).

Another approximation which has been occasionally used is the replacement of the quotient $\bar{\gamma}_A \gamma_B / \bar{\gamma}_B \gamma_A$ (for univalent ions) in Eq. (5-94) by the quotient $\bar{\gamma}^0_{\pm AY} \gamma^0_{\pm BY} / \bar{\gamma}^0_{\pm BY} \gamma^0_{\pm AY}$ [30,201]. The latter is directly obtained from measurements of sorption of the electrolytes AY and BY by the monoionic A form and B form, respectively, of the resin [see Eq. (5-57)]. This approach, like the previous one, fails to give the dependence of the selectivity coefficient on ionic composition.

Recently, Glueckauf's method has been refined by Soldano [276–78]. This author uses the semiempirical Scatchard-Breckenridge relation [258]

$$\bar{\phi} = \frac{a\bar{m}}{1 + b\bar{m}} + f(\bar{m}) \tag{5-109}$$

where a and b are constants; $f(\bar{m})$ is a correction term for the initial part of the function $\bar{\phi}(\bar{m})$

for the osmotic coefficient $\bar{\phi}$ in the resin, defined by

$$\ln \bar{a}_w = -\frac{M_w}{1,000}\left(\bar{\phi}\bar{m} + \frac{\Pi}{RT}\right) \tag{5-110}$$

Application of the Gibbs-Duhem equation leads to

$$\ln \bar{\gamma}^0_{\pm AR} = \frac{a_{AR}}{b_{AR}}\left[\ln\,(1 + b_{AR}\bar{m}) + \frac{b_{AR}\bar{m}}{1 + b_{AR}\bar{m}}\right] + F(\bar{m}) \tag{5-111}$$

where a_{AR} and b_{AR} are the constants in Eq. (5-109), and $F(\bar{m})$ results from the application of the Gibbs-Duhem equation to $f(\bar{m})$. The derivation of Eq. (5-111) implies that the term $F(\bar{m})$ is the same for all ionic forms of a given ion exchanger. The activity coefficients in the heteroionic forms of the resin—treated as mixtures of the resinates AR and BR only—are calculated by a modified Harned rule:

$$\ln \frac{\bar{\gamma}_{\pm AR}}{\bar{\gamma}_{\pm BR}} = \ln \frac{\bar{\gamma}^0_{\pm AR}}{\bar{\gamma}^0_{\pm BR}} + \alpha_{21}\bar{m}_{AR} - \alpha_{12}\bar{m}_{BR} \tag{5-112}$$

For strong-base styrene-type anion exchangers, Soldano finds that the interaction coefficients α_{ij} can be approximated by the empirical relations [277]

$$\alpha_{12} = \frac{\alpha^0_{12}}{R_1(\bar{m})} \qquad R_1(\bar{m}) \equiv \ln\,(1 + b_{AR}\bar{m}) + b_{AR}\bar{m}(1 + b_{AR}\bar{m})$$
$$\alpha_{21} = \frac{\alpha^0_{21}}{R_2(\bar{m})} \qquad R_2(\bar{m}) \equiv \ln\,(1 + b_{BR}\bar{m}) + b_{BR}m(1 + b_{BR}\bar{m}) \tag{5-113}$$

The quantities α^0_{12} and α^0_{21} are constants and can be calculated from two equlibrium measurements, one with species A and one with species B as a trace component, so that either the second or the third term in Eq. (5-112) vanishes. For strong-acid styrene-type resins, the relation (5-113) fails, and further empirical constants must be introduced [278]:

$$\ln \frac{\bar{\gamma}_{\pm AR}}{\bar{\gamma}_{\pm BR}} = \ln \frac{\bar{\gamma}^0_{\pm AR}}{\bar{\gamma}^0_{\pm BR}} + \alpha_{21}\bar{m}_{AR} - \alpha_{12}\bar{m}_{BR} + \beta_{12}\bar{m}^2_{BR} + c$$
$$\alpha_{12} = \frac{\alpha^0_{12}}{R^2_1} \qquad \alpha_{21} = \frac{\alpha^0_{21}}{R^2_2} \tag{5-114}$$

By use of Eqs. (5-109) and (5-111) to (5-114), the whole ion-exchange isotherm can be predicted from the water-vapor sorption isotherms of the monoionic forms and two equilibrium measurements on a trace level. Cation-exchange equilibria require in addition a knowledge of the empirical constants β_{12} and c. So far it has not yet been established whether the relations are valid for other than the two types of resins mentioned.

In the treatment given by Myers and Boyd [218], the use of empirical relations is completely avoided. The resin phase is treated as a ternary electrolyte with the species R^-, A^+, and B^+ (for the sake of simplicity, the calculations are made with univalent cations). Thus the treatment is not applicable if electrolyte sorption is strong and, hence, the co-ion is an additional species in the resin, and if the resin contains fixed ionic groups of more than one type. On this basis, the activity-coefficient ratio in the resin and the partial molar volume difference in the resin are calculated by thermodynamic methods and used in Eq. (5-92) for computing the selectivity coefficient (however, see footnote to page 110 regarding nonconstant partial molar volumes).

The partial molar volume difference in the ion exchanger is calculated in the following way. The equivalent volume of the resin can be written as

$$\bar{V}_e = \bar{q}_A \bar{v}_A + \bar{q}_B \bar{v}_B + \bar{q}_w \bar{v}_w + \text{const.} \tag{5-115}$$

where $\bar{q}_i$ = number of moles of species i per equivalent of resin; $\bar{v}_i$ = partial molar volume of species i in the resin.

Differentiation of this equation gives

$$d\bar{V}_e = (\bar{v}_A - \bar{v}_B)\, d\bar{q}_A + \bar{v}_w\, d\bar{q}_w \tag{5-116}$$

Application of the cross-differentiation identity, which holds since $d\bar{V}_e$ is an exact differential, gives

$$\left[\frac{\partial(\bar{v}_A - \bar{v}_B)}{\partial \bar{q}_w}\right]_{\bar{q}_A} = \left(\frac{\partial \bar{v}_w}{\partial \bar{q}_A}\right)_{\bar{q}_w} = -\left(\frac{\partial \bar{v}_w}{\partial \bar{q}_B}\right)_{\bar{q}_w} \tag{5-117}$$

The partial molar volume difference for a particular ionic composition (i.e., a particular value of $\bar{q}_A$) is found by integration:

$$\left[(\bar{v}_A - \bar{v}_B) = (\bar{V}_A - \bar{V}_B) - \int_0^{\bar{q}_w} \left(\frac{\partial \bar{v}_w}{\partial \bar{q}_B}\right)_{\bar{q}_w} d\bar{q}_w\right]_{\bar{q}_A} \tag{5-118}$$

where $\bar{V}_i$ = equivalent volume of monoionic i form.

The integral in Eq. (5-118) is evaluated in the following way. The equivalent volume $\bar{V}_e$ is measured as a function of the solvent content for a series of different ionic compositions $\bar{q}_A$. From these data, the partial molar volume of the solvent, defined by

$$\bar{v}_w \equiv \left(\frac{\partial \bar{V}_e}{\partial \bar{q}_w}\right)_{\bar{q}_A} \tag{5-119}$$

is calculated. Its dependence on ionic composition gives the differential quotient $(\partial \bar{v}_w/\partial \bar{q}_B)_{\bar{q}_w}$. In Eq. (5-118), this quotient is integrated from zero to the solvent content of the completely swollen resin of the respective ionic composition. After evaluation of the integral, Eq. (5-118) can be used for calculating the partial molar volume difference as a function of the ionic composition $\bar{q}_A$.

For calculating the activity-coefficient ratio in the resin, the relation

$$d\bar{G} = RT(\ln \bar{a}_A \, d\bar{n}_A + \ln \bar{a}_B \, d\bar{n}_B + \ln \bar{a}_w \, d\bar{n}_w) \qquad (5\text{-}120)$$

where $\bar{n}_i$ = number of moles of species i in the resin,

is used. The cross-differentiation identity gives

$$\left(\frac{\partial \ln \bar{a}_A}{\partial \bar{n}_w}\right)_{\bar{n}_A, \bar{n}_B} = \left(\frac{\partial \ln \bar{a}_B}{\partial \bar{n}_w}\right)_{\bar{n}_A, \bar{n}_B} = \left(\frac{\partial \ln \bar{a}_w}{\partial \bar{n}_A}\right)_{\bar{n}_B, \bar{n}_w} \qquad (5\text{-}121)$$

Introducing molalities and rearranging, one obtains

$$\frac{M_w}{1,000} \left[\frac{\partial \ln (\tilde{\gamma}_A/\tilde{\gamma}_B)}{\partial \ln \bar{a}_w}\right]_{\bar{q}_A} = -\left[\frac{\partial(1/\bar{m}_R)}{\partial \bar{q}_B}\right]_{\bar{a}_w} \qquad (5\text{-}122)$$

M_w = molecular weight of the solvent,

and after integration

$$\ln \frac{\tilde{\gamma}_A}{\tilde{\gamma}_B} = \ln \frac{\tilde{\gamma}'_A}{\tilde{\gamma}'_B} - \frac{1,000}{M_w} \int_0^{\ln \bar{a}_w} \left[\frac{\partial(1/\bar{m}_R)}{\partial \bar{q}_B}\right]_{\bar{a}_w} d \ln \bar{a}_w \qquad (5\text{-}123)$$

The activity coefficients $\tilde{\gamma}'_i$ are introduced for the following reason. In the evaluation of Eq. (5-123), the sorption measurements cannot be performed in practice with resins containing ions at infinite dilution [here, $\ln (\tilde{\gamma}'_A/\tilde{\gamma}'_B)$ would be zero]. This limitation is overcome by introducing the activity coefficients $\tilde{\gamma}'_i$ which refer to a weakly crosslinked resin (say, 0.5 per cent DVB) of otherwise identical structure. The swelling pressure in such a resin is negligible, so that the activity-coefficient ratio can be calculated from the experimental selectivity coefficient by use of Eq. (5-92).

The integral in Eq. (5-123) is evaluated by measuring the solvent content at various known solvent activities for a series of ionic compositions. From these data, the differential quotient $[\partial(1/\bar{m}_R)/\partial \bar{q}_B]_{\bar{a}_w}$ is calculated. This quotient is integrated (at constant ionic composition) with respect to $\ln \bar{a}_w$ between the limits zero and the value of $\ln \bar{a}_w$ in the completely swollen resin. After evaluation of the integral, Eq. (5-123) can be used for calculating the activity-coefficient ratio as a function of ionic composition.

The partial molar volume difference and the activity-coefficient ratio are then used in Eq. (5-92) to obtain the selectivity coefficient.

The great advantage of this approach is that empirical relations are avoided. However, the evaluation of the equations requires a large number of measurements with the resin in various heteroionic compositions. Therefore the treatment is more a valuable theoretical contribution than a practical aid for predicting ion exchange equilibria.

Table 5-10 shows a comparison of calculated and observed selectivity coefficients in various systems. In most cases, the agreement is reasonable, but it leaves much to be desired at high degrees of crosslinking. The authors attribute these deviations tentatively to nonuniform behavior of the fixed ionic groups.

Table 5-10. Comparison of observed selectivity coefficients with values calculated by Myers and Boyd[*]

Ion exchange	Degree of crosslinking, % DVB	Ionic composition, % Na$^+$	Selectivity coefficient	
			Calculated	Observed
Na$^+$/Li$^+$	2	0	1.28	1.12 ± 0.03
		50	1.24	1.10 ± 0.03
		100	1.21	1.08 ± 0.02
	8	0	2.00	1.72 ± 0.03
		50	1.88	1.80 ± 0.04
		100	1.72	1.89 ± 0.04
	24	0	3.34	3.25 ± 0.07
		50	2.92	2.40 ± 0.05
		100	2.80	1.80 ± 0.04
Na$^+$/H$^+$	2	0	0.99	1.02 ± 0.02
		50	1.08	1.07 ± 0.02
		100	1.25	1.12 ± 0.03
	8	0	1.35	1.38 ± 0.03
		50	1.66	1.52 ± 0.03
		100	2.24	1.20 ± 0.03
	24	0	9.36	6.38 ± 0.13
		50	3.79	2.32 ± 0.05
		100	3.06	0.69 ± 0.02

[*] Ion exchangers: sulfonated polystyrenes of various degrees of crosslinking.
From G. E. Myers and G. E. Boyd [218].

It is interesting to note that, with strong-acid cation exchangers and alkali and H$^+$ ions, the ratio $\bar{\gamma}'_A/\bar{\gamma}'_B$ in Eq. (5-123) is close to unity [218] whereas, with strong-base anion exchangers and halogen and OH$^-$ ions, this ratio differs considerably from unity and contributes substantially to the selectivity [42a]. In other words, at least in the mentioned cases, cation-exchange selectivities arise mainly from interactions that are absent in very highly swollen gels of low crosslinking, whereas anion-exchange selectivities are largely due to interactions that occur even in such highly swollen gels.

e. Calculation of Activity Coefficients in Solutions

Ion exchange has repeatedly been used for determining activity coefficients in mixed electrolyte solutions. This method was first suggested by Vanselow [291]. In earlier investigations, the activities of the competing counter-ion species in the ion exchanger were assumed to be proportional to the mole fractions of the respective (swollen) resinates. With this assumption, activity ratios of counter ions and mean activity coefficients of trace electrolytes in a supporting electrolyte can be calculated from ion-exchange equilibrium measurements [262,268,291]. Unfortunately the assumption is incorrect. The thermodynamic treatment outlined above permits the activity coefficients in the ion exchanger to be calculated and thus provides a sounder basis for the determination of activity coefficients in the solution from measurements of ion-exchange equilibria.

f. Ion Exchangers of Particular Structure and Composition

In the previous sections, general rules for the selectivities of ordinary general-purpose ion exchangers have been given. Ion exchangers with particular properties may differ from the usual pattern. Various characteristic features of such materials are briefly discussed in this section.

Polyfunctional ion exchangers. In the derivations in the previous sections, it was tacitly implied that the ion exchanger is homogeneous and that all its fixed ionic groups are identical in their behavior. For monofunctional addition polymers, especially styrene-type ion exchangers, this assumption usually holds quite well. However, it is by no means generally valid.

A characteristic selectivity behavior is shown, for example, by polyfunctional ion exchangers, i.e., resins containing different types of ionogenic groups. Each individual group behaves essentially in accordance with the rules derived, but the different types of groups may well counteract one another. In such cases, phenomena are observed which are absent or at least exceptional in monofunctional resins.

The behavior of a polyfunctional resin is similar to that of a mixture of different monofunctional resins containing, in total, the same amounts of the various ionogenic groups [55]. Of course, there is no quantitative agreement since the environment of the groups is quite different in the two systems.

A bifunctional cation exchanger with sulfonic and carboxylic acid groups may serve as a characteristic example. The weak-acid carboxylic group prefers H^+ to most other cations, whereas the strong-acid sulfonic group does not. In the exchange of H^+ for a cation A which is preferred to H^+ by the sulfonic but not by the carboxylic acid group, the selectivities of the two groups counteract one another. At low ionic fractions of H^+, the carboxylic groups sequester H^+. The result is a preference of the resin for H^+. The sulfonic groups are still occupied by A and do not participate in the uptake of H^+. When the ionic fraction of H^+ in the solution is increased beyond the saturation of the carboxylic groups, the selectivity of the resin is reversed because the sulfonic groups prefer species A. *The ion exchanger prefers the counter ion which is present in lower concentration.* The ion-exchange isotherm has a characteristic S shape [55]; see Fig. 5-32. Of course, selectivity reversal does not occur if both types of active groups prefer the same counter ion. Figure 5-32 shows ion-exchange isotherms for the pairs H^+/Na^+, H^+/Ca^{2+}, and H^+/Cu^{2+} on the bifunctional resin Lewatit H-236 (sulfonic and carboxylic acid groups), where selectivity reversal is found. The isotherms of a mixture of corresponding amounts of the monofunctional resins Dowex 50 (sulfonic acid groups) and Amberlite IRC-50

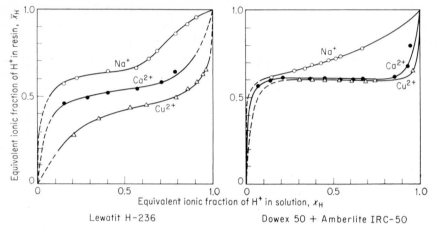

Lewatit H-236   Dowex 50 + Amberlite IRC-50

FIG. 5-32. Ion-exchange isotherms of a bifunctional cation exchanger and of a cation-exchanger mixture. The isotherms for the exchanges Na^+/H^+, Ca^{2+}/H^+, and Cu^{2+}/H^+ on Lewatit H-236 (sulfonic and carboxylic acid groups) at 0.0001 N solution concentration are shown on the left. For comparison, the isotherms for a mixture of Dowex 50 (sulfonic acid groups) and Amberlite IRC-50 (carboxylic acid groups) with equal ratio of sulfonic to carboxylic groups are shown on the right. *From J. P. Cornaz and H. Deuel* [55].

(carboxylic acid groups) are shown for comparison. In the case of the mixture, the isotherms of the individual resins are strictly additive, and the S shape of the curves is more pronounced.

Selectivity reversal may also occur in very highly crosslinked sulfonated polystyrene resins (cf. the exchange H^+/Na^+, Fig. 5-26). This has been tentatively explained by postulating the presence of a few carboxylic acid groups which may have been formed by oxidation in the course of sulfonation [218,236]. However, the reversal may have other, more fundamental causes. Evidence pointing in this direction is a similar reversal, with change in concentration, of the order of the activity coefficients of monomeric dissolved sulfonic acids and their salts [33,35].

Ion exchangers with inhomogeneous structure. Similar effects—though usually much less pronounced—may be found even with monofunctional resins, i.e., with materials containing a single kind of fixed ionic group. The behavior of a fixed ionic group depends not only on its chemical nature but also on its environment. Many ion-exchange resins, particularly the condensation polymers, are inhomogeneous in colloidal dimensions. They consist of "islands" of high crosslinking and fixed-charge molality embedded in regions of much lower crosslinking and fixed-charge molality (see page 121). The resin behaves like a mixture of a strongly and a weakly crosslinked resin. The degree of crosslinking can affect the selectivity. For example, large ions have a lower relative affinity for the highly crosslinked regions. This effect has been offered as an alternative explanation for the selectivity reversal in very highly crosslinked resins [238] (see page 184 and Fig. 5-26). Also, the electroselectivity for the counter ion of higher valence is stronger in the islands which have the higher internal molality. Several other effects are conceivable and have occasionally been offered as explanations for irregular behavior, but none of them has so far been firmly established.

Zeolites. Natural and synthetic zeolites have a regular, three-dimensional, and rather rigid lattice structure. Thus the model of the elastic matrix, used in the previous sections for ion-exchange resins, is inadequate for zeolites. The selectivities—which are usually much greater than those of resins—are primarily determined by lattice forces and steric effects such as sieve action and space requirements. The various selectivity patterns are discussed below.

"Regular" Systems. Ion exchange with certain zeolites obeys very simple rules. A representative example for systems with such "regular" behavior is the exchange of Na^+ for K^+, Li^+, or Ag^+ in basic sodalite (see Fig. 5-33, upper diagrams). Except for a deviation at high equivalent fractions of K^+ (see below) the systems obey the mass-action law in its simplest form, i.e., without activity coefficients [14];

$$\frac{\bar{m}_A m_B}{\bar{m}_B m_A} \equiv K_B^A = \text{const.} \tag{5-124}$$

The selectivity coefficient is constant, i.e., independent of the relative amounts of the competing species A and B. Furthermore, the selectivity coefficients of different equilibria with common counter ions obey the simple "triangle rule" [14]:

$$K_B^A = K_C^A K_B^C \tag{5-125}$$

The sequence of selectivity and the selectivity coefficients for basic sodalite are [14]

$$Ag^+ \gg Na^+ > Li^+ > K^+$$
$$K_{Na}^{Ag} = 335 \qquad K_{Na}^{Li} = 0.46 \qquad K_{Na}^{K} = 0.063 \tag{5-126}$$

The regular behavior of the systems shows that the interaction between the lattice and the counter ions is independent of ionic composition; the affinity of an exchange site for a given counter ion is always the same, regardless of the mode of occupancy of the neighboring sites.

In view of these seemingly simple conditions, the strong selectivity is quite astonishing. It cannot be explained with preference for the smaller ion or distortion of the lattice by ion exchange. The changes in the dimensions of the unit cell of the lattice are minor, and when the counter ions are arranged according to the lattice expansion they cause, the sequence $(Li^+ < Na^+ < Ag^+ < K^+)$ does not coincide with the selectivity sequence. Also, the various zeolites show quite different selectivities. Ultramarine, for example, has a high selectivity for Na^+ ($K_{Na}^{Li} = 0.005$) [10], while chabazite differs from sodalite in preferring K^+ to Na^+ [11]. On the other hand, the selectivity for the heavy-metal ions Ag^+ and Tl^+ is common to all zeolites [14]. It is evident that selectivity is caused by lattice forces. Reasonable explanations can be given, for example, in terms of the Born lattice theory.

Ionic-size Effects. Because of their regular and rigid crystal structure, the zeolites show a remarkably sharp *sieve action.* Counter ions which are larger than the channels in the lattice are excluded. For example, analcite can exchange its Na^+ ions for Li^+, K^+, and Ag^+, but not for Cs^+ [14]. With zeolites, in contrast to ion-exchanger gels, exclusion depends on the size of the *nonsolvated* ion since the lattice forces are strong enough to overcome solvation.

In addition to straightforward screening by sieve action, other ionic-size effects are found which cannot be explained in such a simple way. For example, Cs^+ is completely excluded by basic cancrinite even though the Cs^+ ion is considerably smaller than the channels of this zeolite [13]. The most probable explanation for this effect is the following. Ion exchange requires inherently a "two-way traffic" and cannot take place in a "one-way street." The channels in basic cancrinite are not interconnected and are too narrow for a Cs^+ ion to pass another ion. Thus Cs^+, though small enough to fit into the channels, is nevertheless excluded.

A peculiar effect is observed even in certain otherwise completely regular systems. For example, the exchange of Na^+ for the larger ion K^+ in basic sodalite is completely regular until about 60 per cent conversion is attained. However, the conversion cannot be carried beyond this point [14]; see Fig. 5-33, upper right. Similarly, in synthetic faujasite, only about 20 per cent of the Na^+ ions can be replaced by $N(CH_3)_4^+$ [15]. It is obvious that such effects are not caused by sieve action. They can be explained in terms of the *space requirement* of the ions, as shown by Barrer. Two examples are given. In faujasite, conversion to the $N(CH_3)_4^+$ form must remain incomplete because the total available intracrystalline void volume is too

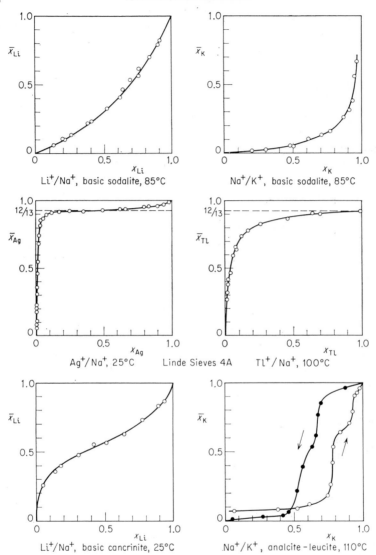

Fig. 5-33. Six characteristic ion-exchange isotherms of zeolites. *Upper left:* a "regular" system with constant selectivity coefficient (symmetrical isotherm). *Upper right:* a "regular" system with limited convertibility. *Middle left:* a system with two types of "regular" sites of opposite selectivity. *Middle right:* the same zeolite in an exchange in which one type of sites remains inaccessible for the exchanging ion. *Lower left:* an "irregular" system with selectivity reversal. *Lower right:* a system with discontinuous lattice rearrangement and hysteresis. *From experimental data by R. M. Barrer et al.* [8,14,18].

small for accommodating the stoichiometric amount of the large organic ion [15]. In silicaceous chabazites, the interconnected cavities in the crystals are rather small. Electroneutrality requires the presence of (on the average) 3.3 to 4 univalent ions per cavity, depending on the $Al_2O_3:SiO_2$ ratio of the chabazite. The cavities may have sufficient room for, say, one small and three large ions, but not for four large ions.* In such cases, conversion is attained when every cavity contains three large ions, even though the intracrystalline void volume is not completely used up [14].

Systems with Two Types of Exchange Sites. Certain zeolites contain exchange sites of different types. The synthetic Linde molecular sieves 4A, studied by Barrer, are a characteristic example [18]. The composition is $Na_{12}[(AlO_2)_{12}(SiO_2)_{12}]\cdot NaAlO_2\cdot xH_2O$. The structural unit contains $13Na^+$ ions, but one of these occupies a structurally different site. All 13 sites are accessible for Ag^+, but only 12 for larger ions such as Tl^+. In ion exchanges involving Na^+, Ag^+, and Tl^+, each type of site behaves in a completely regular manner. The resulting ion-exchange isotherms of the bifunctional zeolite are superpositions of the two regular isotherms of the two types of sites. The zeolite behaves exactly like a mixture of two ion exchangers with different, but constant, selectivity coefficients. The isotherm for Na^+/Ag^+ (Fig. 5-33, middle left) is S-shaped because the thirteenth site prefers Na^+ ($K_{Na}^{Ag} = 0.135$), whereas the other 12 sites prefer Ag^+ ($K_{Na}^{Ag} = 535$). The isotherms for Na^+/Tl^+ (Fig. 5-33, middle right) and Ag^+/Tl^+ are regular isotherms reduced in height by the factor $12/13$, since the Ag^+ or Na^+ ion on the thirteenth site cannot be exchanged. The selectivity coefficients K_{Na}^{Ag}, K_{Na}^{Tl}, and K_{Tl}^{Ag} of the 12 universally accessible sites obey the triangle rule (5-125).

"Irregular" Systems without Phase Transition. The regular behavior of exchange sites in zeolites is an exception rather than the rule. Most systems behave in an "irregular" manner, i.e., the selectivity coefficient varies strongly with ionic composition. In certain cases, irregularities arise from a discontinuous rearrangement (phase transition) of the lattice in the course of ion exchange. Such systems are discussed later. However, deviations from the regular pattern are also found in many systems in which no phase transition occurs.

In the great majority of the latter systems, the relative affinity for a counter ion decreases with increasing equivalent fraction of this ion. Often the isotherms are S-shaped, i.e., the selectivity is reversed in the course of conversion (see Fig. 5-33, lower left). This is particularly true for exchanges of ions of different valences [11,14].

---

* Barrer's original estimate of 1.65 univalent ions per cavity in his chabazite was based on a crystal structure which has meanwhile been revised [71]. However, his argument probably still stands since it may be impossible to accomodate four Cs^+ ions in the larger cavity of the revised structure.

It has been shown above that irregular or S-shaped isotherms may arise from the presence of two or more different types of exchange sites which, individually, behave in a regular manner. In many cases, however, this explanation can be ruled out. In Linde sieves 4A, for example, the 12 readily accessible sites are identical and behave regularly in exchanges of univalent ions (see page 188), but the exchange Na^+/Ca^{2+} on these sites is nevertheless irregular [18]. The most probable explanation for such irregular behavior is the following. When a small counter ion is replaced by a larger one, the accommodation of the latter becomes more and more difficult as conversion progresses. It was pointed out above that, for lack of space, conversion in certain otherwise regular systems may remain incomplete (see page 186). In other systems, however, there may be sufficient room for the stoichiometric amount of the larger counter ion, provided that the late-comers content themselves with energetically less and less favorable places or that the lattice can be slightly distorted. In either case, the relative affinity of the zeolite for the larger ion decreases with increasing equivalent fraction of this ion, so that the isotherm is "irregular." Selectivity reversal (S-shaped isotherms) may occur if, in the absence of steric hindrance, the exchange sites prefer the larger ion.

A quantitative theory of irregular systems is given farther below (see page 191).

Systems with Phase Transition. In certain zeolites, ion exchange can be accompanied by a discontinuous change in lattice structure. A characteristic example is

$$\overline{Na^+}(analcite) + K^+ \rightleftharpoons \overline{K^+}(leucite) + Na^+ \tag{5-127}$$

Analcite, containing Na^+ ions, undergoes a structural change and forms leucite when being converted to the K^+ form. Analcite prefers Na^+ to K^+ and can accommodate a limited amount of K^+ ions. As soon as the uptake of K^+ exceeds a certain critical value (about 20 per cent conversion), the crystal lattice adapts itself to the new counter ion by rearrangement, forming the leucite lattice. Leucite, in turn, prefers K^+ to Na^+ and can accommodate a limited amount of Na^+ ions (again, about 20 per cent) without structural change. During the lattice rearrangement the zeolite consists of two coexisting solid phases, one with the analcite and the other with the leucite lattice. The ion-exchange isotherm rises almost vertically during the lattice rearrangement and is rather flat on both sides of this step [8]; see Fig. 5-33, lower right.

The ion exchange (5-127) is reversible in so far as leucite can be reconverted to analcite by exchange of K^+ for Na^+. However, a very distinct *hysteresis* is observed, i.e., lattice rearrangement in conversion and reconversion occurs at different compositions of the solution, so that the isotherms of the conversions analcite $\rightarrow$ leucite and leucite $\rightarrow$ analcite do not coincide.

To be sure, the isotherm of the reconversion also shows the characteristic, almost vertical step, but at a different place in the diagram.

According to the phase rule, the two coexisting solid phases should be in thermodynamic equilibrium with the solution at only one distinct composition of the latter. Thus hysteresis should not occur, and the isotherm should be exactly vertical during the lattice rearrangement. In reality, the rearrangement is delayed by a potential-energy barrier and occurs only after the original solid phase has been supersaturated with the foreign counter ion up to a critical concentration. Hence the portions of the isotherms on the hysteresis loop correspond to a partially hindered (metastable) rather than to the true thermodynamic equilibrium. Furthermore, the experimental isotherms are not exactly vertical during the rearrangement. This is not astonishing since even with the greatest care it is hardly possible to avoid exceeding the critical concentration of the foreign counter ion in the surface layers of the crystal before attaining it in the center.

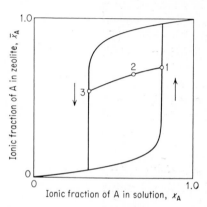

FIG. 5-34. Ion-exchange isotherm in a system with discontinuous lattice rearrangement (*schematic*). The arbitrary point 2 within the hysteresis loop can be reached as indicated.

A solution of a composition which falls within the range of the hysteresis loop is in (metastable) equilibrium with both a solid "solution" of K^+ analcite in Na^+ analcite and a solid "solution" of Na^+ leucite in K^+ leucite. Both solid phases differ widely in their ionic compositions. Either phase may be present, depending on whether the initial solid phase was pure analcite or pure leucite. Note that any point within the hysteresis loop can be reached [8]. This is illustrated in the schematic diagram 5-34. Point 2 can be reached by starting from the zeolite in pure A form, converting partially to B form up to point 3, and then reconverting partially by decreasing the equivalent fraction of B in the solution to the value corresponding to point 2. Alternatively, point 2 can be reached by starting from the zeolite in pure B form, converting partially to A form up to point 1, and then reconverting partially to point 2. At any point within the hysteresis loop, the zeolite consists of two coexisting solid phases.

Similar hysteresis loops are found in many other systems. Ion exchange of Rb^+ for K^+ in analcite and of Ag^+ for Na^+ or Li^+ in basic cancrinite [14] are examples.

The discontinuity of the lattice rearrangement and the coexistence of two solid phases has been directly verified by fractionation and analysis of small crystals and by X-ray diffraction [8]; see Fig. 5-35.

It is interesting to note that, in the course of its rearrangement, the lattice may take up ions which are otherwise excluded because of their size. It has been observed that Cs^+ can penetrate into the crystal during the transition from Ag^+ analcite to K^+ leucite, whereas this ion is excluded from both individual solid phases [13].

Theory. By the use of statistical thermodynamics, Barrer [6,14] has derived an equation which is remarkably successful in describing the behavior of most regular and irregular systems with and without phase transition. Barrer's approach is based on the following idea. Irregular behavior results from the fact that occupancy of an exchange site by an ion A or B affects the relative affinities of the adjacent sites for these ions. In

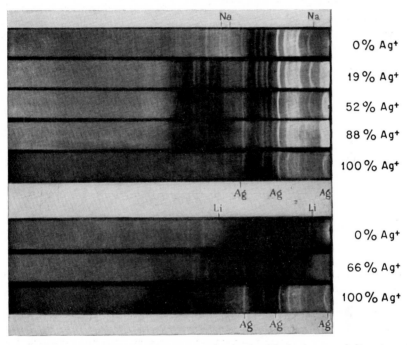

Fig. 5-35. Debye-Scherrer X-ray exposures obtained with basic cancrinite at various degrees of conversion from the Na^+ form (*upper part*) and Li^+ form (*lower part*) to the Ag^+ form. The characteristic lines marked "Na" and "Li" vanish in the course of the conversion, and new lines marked "Ag" appear. The exposures are evidence for discontinuous lattice rearrangement and coexistence of both solid phases in the region in which both sets of lines are visible. *From R. M. Barrer and J. D. Falconer* [14].

irregular systems in which accommodation of the larger counter ions becomes more and more difficult as conversion progresses (see page 189), occupancy of two neighboring sites by two large ions is evidently energetically less favorable than occupancy by one large and one small or by two small ions. In contrast, in systems with phase transition, the incomplete miscibility of the two solid phases shows that occupancy of neighboring sites by ions of the same kind is energetically more favorable.

Barrer's equation is derived with the following assumptions. At constant over-all ionic composition of the zeolite, there is a characteristic difference in energy between the occupancy of two neighboring sites by two ions B and by two ions A and B or two ions A. This energy may be written as $2E_w/z$, where E_w is a (positive or negative) interaction energy and z is the coordination number of the lattice. A statistical distribution of the pairs of exchange sites occupied by two ions B is assumed. The number of these pairs is $z\bar{n}_B/2\bar{n}_Z$ ($\bar{n}_B$ = number of counter ions B in the zeolite; $\bar{n}_Z$ = number of exchange sites). Changes in solvent content and in the partition functions of the counter ions in the course of ion exchange are disregarded. The counter ions are assumed to be univalent. In this way, a simple expression giving the total partition function of the zeolite can be obtained. By differentiation of this expression and use of the equilibrium condition, the following relation is found

$$\ln \frac{\bar{n}_A a_B}{\bar{n}_B a_A} = \ln \frac{\bar{j}_A(T)}{\bar{j}_B(T)} + \frac{\mu_A^0 - \mu_B^0}{kT} + \frac{\bar{E}_A - \bar{E}_B}{kT} + \frac{2\bar{n}_B}{\bar{n}_Z}\frac{E_w}{kT} \qquad (5\text{-}128)$$

where $\bar{j}_i$ = partition function of species i in the zeolite; $\bar{E}_i$ = energy of species i in the zeolite; μ_i^0 = standard chemical potential of species i.

After substituting equivalent ionic fractions $\bar{x}_i \equiv \bar{n}_i(\bar{n}_A + \bar{n}_B)$, one can write Eq. (5-128) in the form

$$\ln \mathcal{K}_{aB}^A \equiv \ln \frac{\bar{x}_A a_B}{\bar{x}_B a_A} = \ln {}^N\mathcal{K}_B^A + c(1 - 2\bar{x}_B) \qquad (5\text{-}129)$$

The quantity ${}^N\mathcal{K}_B^A$ is the rational thermodynamic equilibrium constant.

Comparison with Eq. (5-128) shows that

$$\ln {}^N\mathcal{K}_B^A = \ln \frac{\bar{j}_A(T)}{\bar{j}_B(T)} + \frac{\mu_A^0 - \mu_B^0}{kT} + \frac{\bar{E}_A - \bar{E}_B}{kT} + \frac{(\bar{n}_A + \bar{n}_B)}{\bar{n}_Z}\frac{E_w}{kT} = \text{const.}$$

and that the constant c is

$$c = -\frac{\bar{n}_A + \bar{n}_B}{\bar{n}_Z}\frac{E_w}{kT}$$

($\bar{n}_A + \bar{n}_B$ is not necessarily equal to $\bar{n}_Z$ because substitutions such as $NaAl \rightarrow Si$ may occur.) Since $\bar{x}_A + \bar{x}_B = 1$, it follows that $(1 - 2\bar{x}_B) = (\bar{x}_A^2 - \bar{x}_B^2)$. The equivalent ionic fractions $\bar{x}_A$ and $\bar{x}_B$ can be replaced by the mole fractions, $\bar{N}_{AZ}$ and $\bar{N}_{BZ}$, of the solid components. Then Eq. (5-129) becomes identical to Kielland's semiempirical relation (5-136); see page 195.

The second term on the right-hand side of Eq. (5-129) arises from the gain or loss in free energy resulting from interaction between neighboring sites occupied by ions B. In "regular" systems this term is *zero* since no interaction occurs. Accordingly, the (corrected) selectivity coefficient is constant. In irregular systems in which occupancy of two neighboring sites by two ions B is *unfavorable*, the constant c is *negative*. For $|c| < |\ln {}^N\mathcal{K}_B^A|$, the ion-exchange isotherms are asymmetrical, but no selectivity reversal occurs. For $|c| > |\ln {}^N\mathcal{K}_B^A|$, the isotherms are S-shaped and have steep flanks and a flat middle portion, and selectivity reversal occurs (compare Fig. 5-33, lower left). In both cases the selectivity for the preferred counter ion decreases with increasing equivalent fraction of this ion. There is always an unambiguous correlation between x_A and $\bar{x}_A$, no matter how large $-c$ becomes. In irregular systems (with or without phase transition) in which occupancy of two neighboring sites by two ions B is *favorable*, the constant c is *positive*. The ion-exchange isotherms are S-shaped and have a steep middle section. For $c > 2$, the correlation between x_A and $\bar{x}_A$ is no longer unambiguous; x_A as a function of $\bar{x}_A$ has a maximum and a minimum at $\bar{x}_A = \frac{1}{2} \pm \sqrt{\frac{1}{4} - 1/2c}$. The descending part of this function between the maximum and the minimum is thermodynamically unstable and cannot be realized (in the schematic diagram 5-36, this part is given as a dotted line; note that the diagram shows $\bar{x}_A$ versus x_A rather than x_A versus $\bar{x}_A$). Instead, a separation into two solid phases occurs. The situation is much the same as in the condensation of a gas where the van der Waals equation of state describes a thermodynamically unstable S curve in the volume versus pressure diagram, whereas, actually, a gaseous and a condensed phase coexist. Thus the theoretical approach leading to Eq. (5-129) explains the incomplete miscibility and the resulting coexistence of two solid phases. As an illustration, Fig. 5-36 shows ion-exchange isotherms calculated from Eq. (5-129) for various values of the constant c; here, it was arbitrarily assumed that $^N\mathcal{K}_B^A = 1$, and that $K_{aB}^A = K_B^A$ (only under these conditions are the curves symmetrical to the center of the diagram). In systems with incomplete miscibility ($c > 2$), hysteresis may occur because of supersaturation of the initial solid phase; in this case, the experimental isotherms will fall partly on the metastable sections of the calculated curve (given as broken lines in Fig. 5-36; compare also Fig. 5-34).

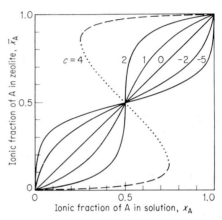

FIG. 5-36. Theoretical ion-exchange isotherms calculated from the Kielland equation with different values of the constant c. In the calculation it was arbitrarily assumed that $\ln{}^N\mathcal{K}_B^A = 0$, and $\ln{(\gamma_A/\gamma_B)} = 0$; only in this case are the curves symmetrical with respect to the center of the diagram. For $c > 2$, the S-shaped middle section of the isotherm is thermodynamically unstable (*broken and dotted line*). The experimental isotherm may follow the broken line (supersaturation, metastable equilibrium). However, phase separation must occur at or before the point where the dotted line starts.

Crystalline ion exchangers with layer structure. Mineral ion exchangers with layer structure, montmorillonite [88], attapulgite [213], etc., are able to swell by increasing the interlayer distance. Their selectivity behavior resembles that of gels rather than that of zeolites. No sharp sieve action is observed. In contrast to the zeolites, these materials are able to take up large organic counter ions [107,139] and even proteins [149].

g. Other Theoretical Approaches and Models

Earlier Approaches. In most earlier theoretical studies of ion-exchange equilibria, attempts were made to fit empirical or semi-empirical equations to experimental results. The equations used were modifications of either the mass-action law or adsorption isotherms of the Langmuir or Freundlich type. Today, these approaches are but of historical interest. Only a brief review of the most widely used equations will be given.*

Probably the first attempt to give a quantitative formulation of ion-exchange equilibria was made by Gans [100]. He used the mass-action law in its simplest form (i.e., without activity coefficients) and obtained a relation identical to Eq. (5-124). This equation holds for zeolites with "regular" behavior (see page 185). For "irregular" systems and ion-exchanger gels this simple approach is inadequate.

---

* More detailed and critical discussions of the earlier approaches have been given in reviews by Weisz [296] in 1932, Møller [215] in 1937, Walton [294] in 1943, Högfeldt [147] in 1955, and Griessbach [122] in 1957.

The Wiegner-Jenny equation [160,299,300]

$$y = k \left(\frac{C}{C_0 - C} \right)^{1/p} \tag{5-130}$$

where y = counter ions exchanged per unit weight of ion exchanger; C = equilibrium concentration of exchanging ion in solution; C_0 = initial concentration of exchanging ion in solution; k and p are empirical constants,

contains two empirical constants and is closely related to the Freundlich adsorption isotherm

$$y = kC^{1/p} \tag{5-131}$$

The more convenient equation (5-132) suggested by Vageler [290] resembles the Langmuir adsorption isotherm.

$$y = \bar{Q} \frac{Q}{Q + c} \tag{5-132}$$

where Q = amount of exchangeable counter ions in solution; $\bar{Q}$ = weight capacity of the ion exchanger; c is an empirical constant.

The equation used by Rothmund and Kornfeld [248], in terms of the quantities used in this chapter,

$$\frac{\bar{C}_A^{z_B}}{\bar{C}_B^{z_A}} = k \left(\frac{C_A^{z_B}}{C_B^{z_A}} \right)^{1/p} \tag{5-133}$$

may be considered as a crossbreed between the simple form of the mass-action law to which it reduces for $p = 1$, and the Freundlich adsorption isotherm with which it shares the exponent $1/p$.

All these equations can be fairly well fitted to experimental results by suitable choice of the empirical constants. In view of the rather different forms of the various equations, this may seem astonishing. Actually the equations are more similar to one another than they appear at first sight since there are theoretical relations between the mass-action law and the adsorption isotherms.* Thus the earlier and rather acrid controversy as to whether ion exchange obeys a (refined) mass-action law or an (also refined) adsorption isotherm was beside the point.

Kielland's Equation. The first attempt to describe ion-exchange equilibria by a theoretical equation which accounts for deviations from the "regular" pattern was made by Kielland [167]. This author introduced the use of solid-phase activity coefficients. Kielland followed Vanselow [291] in treating the heteroionic form of the ion exchanger (containing both competing species A and B) as a *solid solution* of the components AZ and BZ (Z symbolizes a structural unit of the zeolite). He neglected changes in water content and electrolyte sorption, two simplifying assumptions which hold fairly well for the zeolites then in use. For the exchange of univalent ions

$$AZ + B \rightleftharpoons BZ + A \tag{5-134}$$

the mass-action law in its general form is, under the assumptions mentioned (see also page 155)

$$\frac{\bar{a}_{AZ} a_B}{\bar{a}_{BZ} a_A} = \mathcal{K}_B^A = \text{const.} \tag{5-83}$$

where $\mathcal{K}_B^A$ is the thermodynamic equilibrium constant. In contrast to Vanselow who equated the activities of the solid components AZ and BZ to their mole fractions in the

---

* Compare for instance, the studies by Dunken [84], Schwab [269a], and Boyd [39].

solid, Kielland assumed a van der Waals type of equation of state and obtained the following relations for the rational activity coefficients* in the solid (the relations hold only for univalent ions):

$$\ln \bar{f}_{AZ} = c\bar{N}_{BZ}^2 \qquad \ln \bar{f}_{BZ} = c\bar{N}_{AZ}^2 \qquad (5\text{-}135)$$

$\bar{f}_{iZ}$ = rational activity coefficient of the component iZ; $\bar{N}{IZ} \equiv \bar{n}_{iZ}/(\bar{n}_{AZ} + \bar{n}_{BZ})$ = mole fraction of the component iZ in the solid; c is an empirical constant.

The selectivity coefficient K_B^A, obtained from Eqs. (5-83), (5-135), and (5-71), is

$$\ln K_B^A = \ln {}^N\mathcal{K}_B^A + c(\bar{N}_{AZ}^2 - \bar{N}_{BZ}^2) + \ln \frac{\gamma_A}{\gamma_B} \qquad (5\text{-}136)$$

Recently this equation has been given a sounder theoretical foundation by Barrer [see page 192 and Eq. (5-129)]. The relation is able to represent most experimental results obtained with zeolites. For ion-exchanger gels, however, it proves inadequate because here, as a rule, the assumptions leading to Eq. (5-135) do not hold.

Abstract Thermodynamic Treatment. The abstract thermodynamic treatment of ion-exchange equilibria has a certain resemblance to Kielland's approach except that no assumptions are made; thus Eq. (5-135) is not used. This treatment was developed initially by Argersinger, Davidson, and Bonner [4,31,32,197] and by Högfeldt, Ekedahl, and Sillén [85,142,144] and was presented in its most complete form by Gaines and Thomas [99]. It requires no model with particular properties and uses only thermodynamic relations.

Ion exchange is pictured as a heterogeneous reaction involving the electrolytes AY and BY and the resinates AR and BR (corresponding to the solid components AZ and BZ in Kielland's approach). Thus the components of the system are the resinates, the electrolytes, and the solvent. The treatment consists essentially in the calculation of the thermodynamic equilibrium constant and the activity coefficients in the ion exchanger from experimental measurements of the selectivity coefficient under various conditions. To this aim, the Gibbs-Duhem equation is used. For the sake of simplicity, the procedure will be explained in terms of the less elaborate and more common approach in which solvent and electrolyte sorption effects are disregarded. Furthermore, it will be assumed that the counter ions are univalent. The rigorous and more general treatment given by Gaines and Thomas is outlined subsequently.

The ion-exchanger phase is treated as a solid solution of the (swollen) resinates AR and BR. The mole fractions of the latter in the solid are defined by

$$\bar{N}_{AR} \equiv \frac{\bar{n}_{AR}}{\bar{n}_{AR} + \bar{n}_{BR}} \qquad \bar{N}_{BR} \equiv \frac{\bar{n}_{BR}}{\bar{n}_{AR} + \bar{n}_{BR}} \qquad (5\text{-}137)$$

where n_i = number of moles of species i in the ion exchanger.

The thermodynamic equilibrium constant $\mathcal{K}_B^A$ of the ion-exchange process is given by

$$\frac{\bar{a}_{AR}a_{BY}}{\bar{a}_{BR}a_{AY}} = \mathcal{K}_B^A \qquad (5\text{-}138)$$

---

* In the definition of the rational activities in the zeolite, standard and reference states for the components AZ and BZ are the monoionic A and B forms, respectively. In Eq. (5-136), the activity definition (5-8) used previously (molar activity) has been retained for the solution phase; the numerical value of the equilibrium constant ${}^N\mathcal{K}_B^A$ corresponds to this choice of the standard and reference states. Compare also page 156.

As the standard and reference states for AR and BR, the mono-ionic A form and B form, respectively, of the ion exchanger are chosen, so that

$$\bar{N}_{AR} = 1,\ \bar{a}_{AR} = 1,\ \bar{f}_{AR} = 1 \qquad \bar{N}_{BR} = 1,\ \bar{a}_{BR} = 1,\ \bar{f}_{BR} = 1 \qquad (5\text{-}139)$$

The rational equilibrium constant $^N\mathcal{K}_B^A$ * and the corrected selectivity coefficient K_{aB}^A are interrelated by

$$K_{aB}^A \equiv \frac{\bar{N}_{AR} a_{BY}}{\bar{N}_{BR} a_{AY}} = {}^N\mathcal{K}_B^A \frac{\bar{f}_{BR}}{\bar{f}_{AR}} \qquad (5\text{-}140)$$

Differentiation of Eq. (5-140) yields

$$d \ln K_{aB}^A = d \ln \bar{f}_{BR} - d \ln \bar{f}_{AR} \qquad (5\text{-}141)$$

The application of the Gibbs-Duhem equation to the ion-exchanger phase gives

$$\bar{N}_{AR}\, d \ln \bar{f}_{AR} + \bar{N}_{BR}d \ln \bar{f}_{BR} = 0 \qquad (5\text{-}142)$$

By combination of these equations, use of $\bar{N}_{AR} + \bar{N}_{BR} = 1$ and $d\bar{N}_{AR} + d\bar{N}_{BR} = 0$, and partial integration under the restriction (5-139) one obtains

$$\ln \bar{f}_{AR} = -\bar{N}_{BR} \ln K_{aB}^A + \int_{\bar{N}_{AR}}^{1} \ln K_{aB}^A\, d\bar{N}_{AR} \qquad (5\text{-}143)$$

and

$$\ln {}^N\mathcal{K}_B^A = \int_0^1 \ln K_{aB}^A\, d\bar{N}_{AR} \qquad (5\text{-}144)$$

The activity coefficients and the rational thermodynamic equilibrium constant can be calculated by graphical integration according to Eqs. (5-143) and (5-144).† The numerical values of these rational quantities *cannot be compared directly* with those of the corresponding molal quantities used in the previous sections. Rational and molal quantities differ in their numerical values because of the different choice of the standard and reference states. It should be emphasized once more that the rational equilibrium constant, in contrast to the molal equilibrium constant, is characteristic of the selectivity of the ion exchanger (see page 156).

The general treatment given by Gaines and Thomas [99] differs from the simple approach given above in that electrolyte sorption and changes in solvent content are taken into account. This necessitates a sharper definition of the standard and reference states of the resinates since the chemical potentials of the latter depend also on the solvent content and the extent of electrolyte sorption. A suitable choice is the respective monoionic resinate in equilibrium with a solution of infinite dilution. Calculation of the thermodynamic equilibrium constant requires three integration steps: (1) from the B form in the standard state (point a in Fig. 5-37) to the B form in equilibrium with a solution BY of finite concentration (point a'), (2) from this point across the isotherm surface to the A form in equilibrium with a solution AY of finite concentration (point b'), and (3) from this point to the A form in the standard state (point b). The path across the isotherm and the location of the points a' and b' can be arbitrarily chosen, but the integration becomes simpler if one variable is kept constant between a' and b'. Gaines

---

* See footnote to p. 195.

† Recently, Freeman [91a] has given a procedure in which graphical integration is avoided. Instead, a relation involving the excess free energy is derived, and the equilibrium constant and the activity coefficients are obtained by fitting the coefficients in the equation to experimental values of the selectivity coefficient.

and Thomas integrate at constant co-ion content of the ion exchanger and obtain

$$\ln {}^N\mathfrak{K}_B^A = (|z_B| - |z_A|)(1 + \bar{Q}_Y) + \ln \frac{\bar{\mathscr{F}}_A^{|z_B|}(a')}{\bar{\mathscr{F}}_B^{|z_A|}(b')} - \bar{Q}_Y \frac{K_A^{|z_B|}(a')}{K_B^{|z_A|}(b')}$$

$$+ \int_{a'}^{b'} \ln K_{aB}^A \, d\bar{Q}_B - z_A z_B \int_{a'}^{b'} \bar{q}_w \, d\ln \bar{a}_w \quad (5\text{-}145)$$

where

$$K_A \equiv \left(\frac{\bar{Q}_A^{|z_Y|} \bar{Q}_Y^{|z_A|}}{m_A^{|z_Y|} m_Y^{|z_A|} \bar{\mathscr{F}}_A^{|z_Y|} \bar{\mathscr{F}}_Y^{|z_A|}} \right)^{1/|z_Y|} \qquad K_B \equiv \left(\frac{\bar{Q}_B^{|z_Y|} \bar{Q}_Y^{|z_B|}}{m_B^{|z_Y|} m_Y^{|z_B|} \bar{\mathscr{F}}_B^{|z_Y|} \bar{\mathscr{F}}_Y^{|z_B|}} \right)^{1/|z_Y|}$$

where $\bar{q}_i$ = number of moles of species i in the ion exchanger per equivalent of fixed ionic groups; $\bar{Q}_i \equiv z_i \bar{q}_i$.

The activity coefficients at the points a' and b' are given by

$$\ln [\bar{Q}_A(a') \bar{\mathscr{F}}_A(a')]^{|z_B|} = -z_A z_B \int_0^{a'} \left(\bar{q}_w + \frac{1{,}000 \bar{q}_Y}{M_w m_Y} \right) d\ln \bar{a}_w \quad (5\text{-}146)$$

and an analogous relation for $\bar{\mathscr{F}}_B(b')$. Instead of the co-ion content, the total concentration of the solution can be kept constant between a' and b'. The corresponding equations have been given by Baumann and Argersinger [23].

This treatment is thermodynamically exact, requires no assumptions and no model with particular properties, and is universally applicable to ion exchangers of any conceivable structure. In this respect, the treatment is superior to any other. For practical applications, however, its value is limited. The activity coefficients and the thermodynamic equilibrium constant can be calculated only from a considerable number of ion-exchange equilibrium measurements, so that prediction of equilibria is not possible. It is true that the rational thermodynamic equilibrium constant ${}^N\mathfrak{K}_B^A$ of the exchange A/B can be calculated from the constants ${}^N\mathfrak{K}_C^A$ and ${}^N\mathfrak{K}_C^B$ of the exchanges A/C and B/C, respectively, by use of the so-called "triangle rule"

$$^N\mathfrak{K}_B^A = \frac{{}^N\mathfrak{K}_C^A}{{}^N\mathfrak{K}_C^B} \quad (5\text{-}147)$$

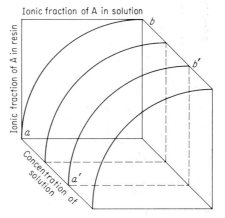

FIG. 5-37. Path of integration over the isotherm surface in the calculation of the thermodynamic equilibrium constant. The path leads from a via a' and b' to b.

but even this result provides only a general idea about the selectivity in the exchange A/B because the equilibrium constant is an integral quantity and does not give the selectivity under any particular conditions. Also, the dependence of the selectivity on the ionic composition and the concentration of the solution cannot be predicted. Thus the abstract thermodynamic treatment gives a rigorous description of ion-exchange equilibrium, but it provides less insight into the physical causes for the behavior of the systems than the approach adopted in Sec. 5-4c.

Pauley's Model. Pauley [228] has interpreted selectivities in ion-exchange equilibria in terms of a very simple model. Its essential feature is the *electrostatic attraction* between the counter ions and the fixed ionic groups.

It is assumed that all counter ions in the ion exchanger are found at their distance of closest approach to the fixed ionic groups. Writing AR and BR for the pairs of fixed ionic groups and counter ions at the distance of closest approach, one can split the exchange of A for B into the two processes

$$AR \rightarrow A + R \tag{5-148}$$
$$R + B \rightarrow BR \tag{5-149}$$

Using Coulomb's law without any corrections, one obtains for the free energy changes ΔG_1^0 and ΔG_2^0 accompanying the processes (5-148) and (5-149), respectively,

$$\Delta G_1^0 = \int_{a_A^0}^{\infty} \frac{e^2}{r^2 \epsilon}\, dr = \frac{e^2}{a_A^0 \epsilon} \tag{5-150}$$

and

$$\Delta G_2^0 = \int_{\infty}^{a_B^0} \frac{e^2}{r^2 \epsilon}\, dr = -\frac{e^2}{a_B^0 \epsilon} \tag{5-151}$$

where e = electronic charge; ϵ = dielectric constant; r = distance from center of fixed charge; a_i^0 = distance of closest approach between counter ion i and fixed ionic group.

Hence the over-all free-energy change is

$$\Delta G^0 = \Delta G_1^0 + \Delta G_2^0 = \frac{e^2}{\epsilon}\left(\frac{1}{a_A^0} - \frac{1}{a_B^0}\right) \tag{5-152}$$

and the thermodynamic equilibrium constant $\mathcal{K}_A^B$ is

$$\ln \mathcal{K}_A^B = -\frac{\Delta G^0}{kT} = \frac{e^2}{kT\epsilon}\left(\frac{1}{a_B^0} - \frac{1}{a_A^0}\right) \tag{5-153}$$

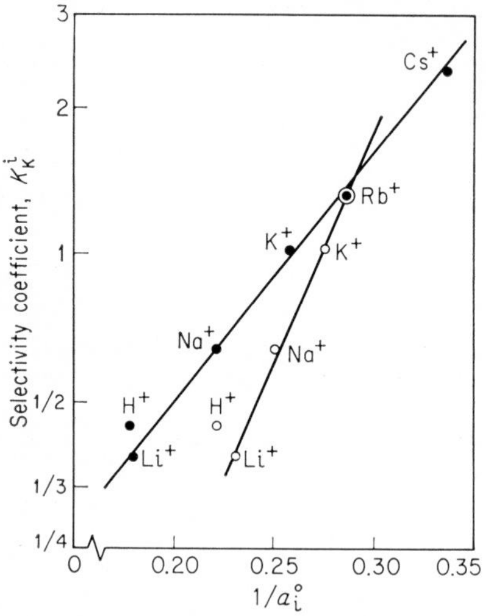

FIG. 5-38. Correlation between selectivity coefficients and Debye-Hückel parameter a^0. Experimental selectivity coefficients for the exchanges of H$^+$, Li$^+$, Na$^+$, and Cs$^+$ for K$^+$ obtained with a phenolsulfonic-acid resin are shown on a logarithmic scale as a function of $1/a^0$. The relation between $\ln K_K^i$ and $1/a_i^0$ is approximately linear. The two curves are for a^0 values according to *Harned and Owen* [131] (●) and to *Stokes and Robinson* [281] (○). *From T. R. E. Kressman and J. A. Kitchener* [179].

According to Eq. (5-153), the counter ion with the smaller a^0 value is preferred. In the exchanges of various univalent counter ions i for an arbitrary univalent reference ion A, a linear relationship should exist between $\ln \mathcal{K}_A^i$ and $1/a_i^0$. In several systems, such a rule does indeed hold [39,179]; see Fig. 5-38. However, there is no doubt that the situation in actual systems is much more complex. Certainly interactions will at least occur between neighboring Coulomb fields. For multivalent ions, the calculation is not quite as simple because assumptions must be made as to how the (univalent) fixed ionic groups and the polyvalent counter ions are paired. The model leads qualitatively to preference of the ion exchanger for counter ions of higher valences.

Statistical Thermodynamics. Statistical thermodynamics has repeatedly been used to derive theoretical equations for ion-exchange equilibria. Most of these approaches are based on a model first developed by Jenny [161] for ion exchange with colloidal alumosilicates. Jenny assumed that the counter ions compensating the framework surplus charge are located in a diffuse double layer at the colloid surface. Every counter ion is coordinated to an exchange site and oscillates within a certain volume character-istic of the ion and its interaction with the colloid particle.   Other counter ions from the solution are able to penetrate into this oscillation volume.   The probability of ion exchange occurring at a given site is calculated from the probability that a competing counter ion will enter the oscillation volume.   Multivalent counter ions occupy several neighboring sites.   By adaptation of the Fowler-Guggenheim theory of adsorption in a monomolecular layer [90,125] to this model, Davis [67,68] obtained the relation

$$\ln \frac{\bar{n}_A^{|z_B|} a_B^{|z_A|}}{\bar{n}_B^{|z_A|} a_A^{|z_B|}} = \ln K + (|z_B| - |z_A|) \ln (g_A \bar{n}_A + g_B \bar{n}_B) \tag{5-154}$$

where $\bar{n}_i$ = number of adsorbed ions of species i.

In Eq. (5-154) K is a constant and g_i is a function of the ionic valence $|z_i|$ and the coordi-nation number z of the (two-dimensional) lattice:*

$$g_i = \frac{z|z_i| - 2|z_i| + 2}{z} \tag{5-155}$$

For exchange of counter ions of equal valences, the second term in Eq. (5-154) vanishes and the (corrected) selectivity coefficient becomes constant.   In the exchange of counter ions of different valences, the selectivity coefficient depends on ionic composition.   It has been claimed that Eq. (5-154) adequately describes ion-exchange processes with colloids in soils [183].

Later, Davis's statistical treatment was extended by Sakai [249].   The equation derived by this author is

$$\ln \frac{\bar{m}_A^{|z_B|} a_B^{|z_A|}}{\bar{m}_B^{|z_A|} a_A^{|z_B|}} = \ln K + \frac{z}{2} \ln \left(\frac{\beta - 1 + 2\theta}{\theta} \right)^{g_A|z_B|} \left(\frac{1 - \theta}{\beta + 1 - 2\theta} \right)^{g_B|z_A|}$$
$$+ (|z_A| - |z_B|) \ln (\beta + 1) \tag{5-156}$$

where g_i is defined as above, and

$$\beta \equiv \left[(1 - 2\theta)^2 + 4\theta(1 - \theta) \exp \left(\frac{E_w}{kT} \right) \right]^{1/2}$$

$$\theta \equiv \frac{g_A \bar{x}_A}{g_A \bar{x}_A + g_B \bar{x}_B}$$

Here, E_w is an interaction energy characteristic of differences in the mode of occupancy of neighboring sites.   Sakai claims success in applying his equation to ion-exchanger gels also.

The Model of Harris and Rice.   The molecular model of Harris and Rice [132,241,241a], briefly discussed in Secs. 5-1 and 5-2e, leads to rather interesting conclusions about ion-exchange equilibria.

The two most important particular features of the model are the assumed ion-pair formation between counter ions and fixed ionic groups and the electrostatic repulsion between neighboring fixed charges.   The authors assume in their treatment that the concentration ratio of the "free" counter ions A and B in the ion exchanger is the same as in the external solution.   Accordingly, a greater extent of ion-pair formation by one

---

* Compare, however, the criticism by Bloksma [29].

counter-ion species is the only possible cause for selectivity for this species. This premise is reflected in the relation for the selectivity coefficient*

$$K_B^A = \frac{K_{BR}/K_{AR} + [n_R/(N + n_R)][(K_{BR}C_A/K_{AR}C_B + 1)/(C_A/C_B + 1)]}{1 + [n_R/(N + n_R)][(K_{BR}C_A/K_{AR}C_B + 1)/(C_A/C_B + 1)]} \quad (5\text{-}157)$$

where K_{iR} = "intrinsic" dissociation constant of the ion pair iR; C_i = concentration of species i in the external solution; N = total number of fixed ionogenic groups; n_R = number of nonpaired fixed ionogenic groups,

which shows that the ion forming the stronger ion pair (smaller value of K_{iR}) is always preferred. The extent of ion-pair formation depends not only on the intrinsic constants K_{iR}, but also in a complex manner on the electrostatic interactions between neighboring fixed ionic groups (see page 119).

In essence, application of the model leads to the following conclusions. The selectivity should increase with increasing capacity and degree of crosslinking of the resin, with decreasing equivalent fraction of the preferred ion, and with dilution of the external solution. These rules, except for the capacity dependence [42,193], are in agreement with experimental observations.

It is interesting to see that the model attributes the dependence of the selectivity on the various variables to other physical causes than the models discussed in Sec. 5-4c.

Note that the calculations of Harris and Rice are restricted to univalent ions, that electrolyte sorption is disregarded, and that the model is not applicable to weakly cross-linked gels (see also page 120).

5-5. SYSTEMS WITH MORE THAN TWO COUNTER-ION SPECIES

In practical applications, ion exchangers are usually exposed to more than two counter-ion species. Here, the theoretical treatment in Sec. 5-4, which was restricted to two counter-ion species, is insufficient. However, it can be extended without much difficulty.

The basic equation

$$\bar{\eta}_i = \eta_i \quad (5\text{-}37)$$

describing the equilibrium distribution of an arbitrary species i between the ion exchanger and the external solution is a quite general thermodynamic relation which holds regardless of how many species are present. The same is true for

$$E_{Don} = \frac{1}{z_i \mathfrak{F}} \left(RT \ln \frac{a_i}{\bar{a}_i} - \Pi v_i \right) \quad (5\text{-}39)$$

and

$$\ln K_B^A = \ln \frac{\bar{\gamma}_B^{|z_A|}}{\bar{\gamma}_A^{|z_B|}} + \ln \frac{\gamma_A^{|z_B|}}{\gamma_B^{|z_A|}} + \frac{\Pi}{RT} (|z_A|v_B - |z_B|v_A) \quad (5\text{-}92)$$

---

* The relation is derived for univalent counter ions. Quantitative evaluation requires calculation of n_R which can be obtained from other, more complex relations. For details, the reader is referred to the original publication [241,241a].

which follow from Eq. (5-37) and give the Donnan potential and the selectivity coefficient for a pair of arbitrary counter ions, A and B (see Sec. 5-4c). Of course, the activity coefficients and the swelling pressure in Eq. (5-92) are now those in the multicomponent system and not the same as in systems with only A and B as counter ions.

The coefficient K_B^A gives only the concentration *ratio* of the counter ions A and B in the ion exchanger; their *absolute* concentrations cannot be estimated from this coefficient alone since the latter does not indicate how large a fraction of the ion-exchange capacity is taken up by other competing counter ions. The distribution of all species is completely described by the following set of equations:

$$\frac{1}{z_A}\left(\ln\frac{a_A}{\bar{a}_A} - \frac{\Pi v_A}{RT}\right) = \frac{1}{z_B}\left(\ln\frac{a_B}{\bar{a}_B} - \frac{\Pi v_B}{RT}\right) = \cdots \qquad (5\text{-}158)$$

for all ionic species A,B, . . . ,Y, . . . , including co-ions [obtained from Eq. (5-39)], the appropriate relations for swelling equilibrium (as derived in Sec. 5-2d), and the electroneutrality condition

$$\sum_i z_i\bar{m}_i + \omega\bar{m}_R = 0 \qquad (5\text{-}159)$$

where ω = sign of fixed charges; the summation is carried out over all species including co-ions.

The difficulties encountered in the evaluation of activity coefficients and osmotic coefficients are the same as in simpler systems.

The general qualitative rules for the selectivity of ion exchangers (see Sec. 5-4b) are essentially valid also in systems with more than two counter-ion species. Of course, the ability of the ion exchanger to discriminate between two species is affected by the presence of others which alter the Donnan potential and the swelling pressure and partially compensate the fixed charges. In addition, direct interactions between the different counter ions may occur. Nevertheless, the knowledge of the factors which are important in two-component systems is usually quite sufficient for qualitative purposes.

When equilibrating an ion exchanger with a multicomponent solution, it should be kept in mind that the rates of exchange may be rather different for the various counter ions. It is possible that the concentrations of certain species in either the ion exchanger or the solution go through a maximum or minimum before attaining the equilibrium value (see Sec. 6-5).

Ion-exchange equilibria in systems with three counter-ion species are conveniently represented by a triangular diagram in which any point corresponds to a certain ratio of the three counter ions present (see Fig. 5-39). In such a diagram, a series of compositions of ion exchanger and solution in equilibrium with one another are connected by arrows; the arrowhead gives the ionic composition of the ion exchanger, the arrow base the composition of the solution. Separate graphs are required to give the variation with temperature and total concentration of the solution.

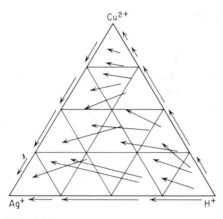

FIG. 5-39. Triangular representation of equilibria in systems with three counter ion species. The arrows connect ionic compositions of the solution (*arrow base*) and the ion exchanger (*arrow head*) in equilibrium with one another. (Resin: Amberlite IR-120; total solution concentration: 0.4 N.) *From W. A. Selke* [271].

A comparatively simple situation is encountered if one counter-ion species predominates and the others are present as traces only. The presence of mere traces of other species has, as a rule, no significant effect on the distribution of a given species. Hence the distribution of a trace component can be calculated considering only the binary equilibrium of this component and the macrocomponent [271,292]. Furthermore, the trace exchange is covered by only a short section of the binary ion-exchange isotherm near the origin. This section is usually practically linear, so that the distribution coefficient of the trace component is approximately constant within the trace concentration range (see also page 155). The constancy of the distribution coefficients of the trace components greatly facilitates calculations of column performance in ion-exchange chromatography (see Sec. 9-9).

Experimental evidence [69,70,80,271,292,302] on systems with three or more counter ions is still rather scanty, but it is at least qualitatively in good agreement with the theory.

5-6. ION-EXCHANGE EQUILIBRIA INVOLVING COMPLEXING AGENTS

Ion-exchange and sorption equilibria are strongly affected by complex formation of the various mobile species—counter ions, co-ions, and neutral molecules—with one another. Complex formation is a highly specific interaction and may greatly enhance the selectivities of ion exchangers. For example, the separation of the rare earths by ion-exchange chromatography was made possible by the use of complexing agents (see Sec. 9-7d).

Three cases, in particular, are of great practical importance:

1. Cation-exchange equilibria with cation exchangers in the presence of a complexing anion
2. Cation-exchange equilibria with anion exchangers in the presence of a complexing anion
3. Sorption equilibria of neutral molecules or co-ions which form complexes with the counter ion

The behavior of such systems has been briefly outlined in a qualitative way in Secs. 5-4b and 5-3b. The first two cases are discussed in detail in this section, the third one in Sec. 5-7. Other cases are of less general interest* and can be treated in a similar manner.

The general thermodynamic treatment of ion-exchange and sorption equilibria, given in Secs. 5-4c and 5-3c, is valid, no matter whether or not complexes are formed. In the equations in these sections, the effect of complex formation is reflected in the behavior of the activity coefficients. Alternatively, complex ions can be treated as additional, distinct species. This approach is adopted in the present section. Such a treatment requires the use of quantities which cannot be determined by purely thermodynamical means and, thus, leads one step farther away from the generally valid formulations of rigorous thermodynamics. On the other hand, as in many other cases discussed previously, more insight into the action of the physical forces is gained. In particular, the treatment can serve two specific purposes, namely, the semiquantitative prediction of ion-exchange and sorption equilibria from known complex-stability constants, and the calculation of complex-stability constants in solutions from ion-exchange equilibrium measurements.

The quantitative treatment of complex-ion exchange equilibria is based on the well-known relations for the equilibria of the various complex species in solutions. These relations are reviewed first. Since the equations for the general case may seem difficult to the inexperienced, they will be illustrated by a simple example, namely, the equilibria of the chloro complexes of zinc and their effect on the Zn^{2+}/H^+ ion exchange.

a. Complex-ion Equilibria in Solutions

The equilibria of the ions Zn^{2+} and Cl^- and their various complexes in the solution are the following:

---

* The effect of nonionic ligands on ion-exchange equilibria is relatively small. Here, complex formation essentially amounts to a replacement of solvent molecules in the solvation shells of the ions by ligand molecules; the effective charge of the ion is not altered. It is mainly through the change in effective ionic charge that anionic ligands produce their striking effects on cation-exchange equilibria.

$$\text{Zn}^{2+} + \text{Cl}^- \rightleftharpoons [\text{ZnCl}]^+ \qquad \frac{m_{\text{ZnCl}}}{m_{\text{Zn}} m_{\text{Cl}}} = K_1$$

$$\text{Zn}^{2+} + 2\text{Cl}^- \rightleftharpoons [\text{ZnCl}_2] \qquad \frac{m_{\text{ZnCl}_2}}{m_{\text{Zn}} m_{\text{Cl}}^2} = K_2$$

$$\text{Zn}^{2+} + 3\text{Cl}^- \rightleftharpoons [\text{ZnCl}_3]^- \qquad \frac{m_{\text{ZnCl}_3}}{m_{\text{Zn}} m_{\text{Cl}}^3} = K_3 \tag{5-160}$$

$$\text{Zn}^{2+} + 4\text{Cl}^- \rightleftharpoons [\text{ZnCl}_4]^{2-} \qquad \frac{m_{\text{ZnCl}_4}}{m_{\text{Zn}} m_{\text{Cl}}^4} = K_4$$

The quantities K_n are the (cumulative) molal Bjerrum stability constants of the various complexes [27,28]. For the time being it will be assumed that they are really constant.* Equation (5-160) can be written in the general form

$$\text{A}^a + n\text{Y}^{-y} = [\text{AY}_n]^{a-ny} \qquad \frac{m_{\text{AY}_n}}{m_{\text{A}} m_{\text{Y}}^n} = K_n \tag{5-161}$$

where $a \equiv z_{\text{A}}$ and $y \equiv -z_{\text{Y}}$ are the valences of the cation and the anion, and where n is the number of ligands (coordination number); n is an integer and can assume any positive value not exceeding the maximum coordination number N of the complex formed by A and Y. For the chloro complexes of zinc, the maximum coordination number is 4. Equations (5-160) and (5-161) imply tacitly that no polynuclear complexes (i.e., containing more than one atom A) are formed.

The over-all concentration M_{Zn} of zinc in the solution is equal to the sum of the concentrations of all species containing Zn. According to Eqs. (5-160) one obtains

$$M_{\text{Zn}} = m_{\text{Zn}} + m_{\text{ZnCl}} + m_{\text{ZnCl}_2} + m_{\text{ZnCl}_3} + m_{\text{ZnCl}_4}$$

$$= m_{\text{Zn}}(1 + m_{\text{Cl}}K_1 + m_{\text{Cl}}^2 K_2 + m_{\text{Cl}}^3 K_3 + m_{\text{Cl}}^4 K_4) \tag{5-162}$$

or, for the general case,

$$M_{\text{A}} = m_{\text{A}} \sum_{n=0}^{N} (m_{\text{Y}}^n K_n) \tag{5-163}$$

(Here and in all subsequent equations, K_0 is defined as being unity.)

The fraction x_j of A present in the form of the complex $[\text{AY}_j]^{a-jy}$ with j ligands—for example $[\text{ZnCl}_3]^-$ for $j = 3$—as obtained from Eqs. (5-161) and (5-163) is

$$x_j \equiv \frac{m_{\text{AY}_j}}{M_{\text{A}}} = \frac{(m_{\text{Y}})^j K_j}{\displaystyle\sum_{n=0}^{N} (m_{\text{Y}}^n K_n)} \tag{5-164}$$

This fraction is a function of the concentration m_{Y} of the complexing agent. If m_{Y} is small, the terms with powers of m_{Y} lower than j are predominant

---

* For nonconstant K_n, see footnotes to pp. 207 and 216.

in the denominator of Eq. (5-186); here, an increase in concentration of the complexing anion increases the fraction x_j (of course, this reasoning does not apply to $j = 0$). On the other hand, if m_Y is large, the terms with powers of m_Y higher than j predominate in the denominator; here, an increase in concentration of the complexing anion results in a decrease of x_j (this does not apply to the saturated complex with $j = N$). Thus, for any complex, except for the saturated one, there is a certain anion concentration at which the fraction x_j of the complex attains a maximum value. Usually only a few of the potential complexes coexist in significant concentrations. An increase in concentration of the complexing anion favors the formation of complexes with higher ligand numbers. The over-all cation concentration M_A has relatively little effect on the fractions x_j. The fractions depend on M_A only in so far as a variation in M_A may cause a change in m_Y [see below, Eq. (5-165)].

The relations (5-160) to (5-164) involve the concentration m_Y of the free complexing anion. At a given over-all anion concentration M_Y the free-anion concentration depends on the extent of complex formation and is given by the root of the equation

$$m_Y + \frac{M_A \sum\limits_{n=1}^{N} (n m_Y^n K_n)}{\sum\limits_{n=0}^{N} (m_Y^n K_n)} - M_Y = 0 \qquad (5\text{-}165)$$

One limiting case is particularly important: m_Y becomes practically equal to M_Y (and thus independent to M_A) when a "supporting electrolyte"— say, HCl—is present in large excess, so that $M_A \ll M_Y$.

The relations for complex equilibria in solutions hold, of course, regardless of whether or nor an ion exchanger is present.

b. Equilibria with Cation Exchangers in the Presence of a Complexing Anion

The systems which are studied in this section are of the following type. A cation exchanger is in equilibrium with a solution containing two or more cations and one complexing anion. First, the relatively simple case of binary equilibria with only one complex-forming cation will be studied. The more complicated behavior of systems with two or more complex-forming cations is subsequently outlined.

Ion-exchange equilibria with one complex-forming cation. In systems such as $ZnCl_2/HCl$/cation exchanger, only one cation (Zn^{2+}) forms complexes. Qualitatively, the effect of complex formation is obvious. The stronger the complexes and the higher the concentration of the free anion, the larger is the fraction of the complexing cation A present in the form of complexes of lower positive or even of negative charge. Thus the relative affinity of the ion exchanger for A is reduced since cation exchangers prefer ions of higher positive charge (electroselectivity, see page 156) and exclude ions of higher negative charge more efficiently (Donnan exclusion, see page 136). Hence, selectivity for the competing species B is high when A forms strong complexes with Y and when the concentration of BY is high.

Quantitative relations can be derived in the following way. The ion-exchange equilibria of the cation Zn^{2+} and the cationic complex $[ZnCl]^+$ with the competing counter ion H^+ are

$$Zn^{2+} + \overline{2H^+} \rightleftharpoons \overline{Zn^{2+}} + 2H^+ \qquad \bar{m}_{Zn} = K_H^{Zn} m_{Zn} \left(\frac{\bar{m}_H}{m_H}\right)^2$$

$$[ZnCl]^+ + \overline{H^+} \rightleftharpoons \overline{[ZnCl]^+} + H^+ \qquad \bar{m}_{ZnCl} = K_H^{ZnCl} m_{ZnCl} \frac{\bar{m}_H}{m_H} \tag{5-166}$$

and the sorption equilibria of the neutral complex $[ZnCl_2]$ and the electrolytes $H[ZnCl_3]$ and $H_2[ZnCl_4]$ with complex anions are

$$[ZnCl_2] \rightleftharpoons \overline{[ZnCl_2]} \qquad \bar{m}_{ZnCl_2} = \lambda_2 m_{ZnCl_2}$$

$$[ZnCl_3]^- + H^+ \rightleftharpoons \overline{[ZnCl_3]^-} + \overline{H^+} \qquad \bar{m}_{ZnCl_3} = \lambda_3 m_{ZnCl_3} \tag{5-167}$$

$$[ZnCl_4]^{2-} + 2H^+ \rightleftharpoons \overline{[ZnCl_4]^{2-}} + \overline{2H^+} \qquad \bar{m}_{ZnCl_4} = \lambda_4 m_{ZnCl_4}$$

The quantities K_H^{Zn} and K_H^{ZnCl} in Eqs. (5-166) are the molal selectivity coefficients [as defined by Eq. (5-71)] of the ion-exchange processes written on the left. The quantities λ_j in Eqs. (5-167) are the molal distribution coefficients [as defined by Eq. (5-28)] of the complexes. If the effect of swelling pressure is included in the activity coefficients by use of the activity definition (5-54), the selectivity and distribution coefficients, as calculated from Eqs. (5-94) and (5-56), are

$$K_H^{Zn} = \frac{\gamma_{Zn}}{\bar{\gamma}_{Zn}} \left(\frac{\bar{\gamma}_H}{\gamma_H}\right)^2 \qquad \lambda_2 = \frac{\gamma_{ZnCl_2}}{\bar{\gamma}_{ZnCl_2}}$$

$$K_H^{ZnCl} = \frac{\gamma_{ZnCl}}{\bar{\gamma}_{ZnCl}} \frac{\bar{\gamma}_H}{\gamma_H} \qquad \lambda_3 = \frac{\gamma_{ZnCl_3}}{\bar{\gamma}_{ZnCl_3}} \frac{\gamma_H}{\bar{\gamma}_H} \frac{m_H}{\bar{m}_H} \tag{5-168}$$

$$\gamma_4 = \frac{\gamma_{ZnCl_4}}{\bar{\gamma}_{ZnCl_4}} \left(\frac{\gamma_H}{\bar{\gamma}_H}\right)^2 \left(\frac{m_H}{\bar{m}_H}\right)^2$$

Quite generally the equilibria (5-166) and (5-167) can be written

$$b[AY_n]^{a-ny} + (a - ny)\overline{B^b} \rightleftharpoons b\overline{[AY_n]^{a-ny}} + (a - ny)B^b$$

$$(\bar{m}_{AY_n})^b = K_B^{AY_n}(m_{AY_n})^b \left(\frac{\bar{m}_B}{m_B}\right)^{a-ny} \tag{5-169}$$

where the coefficients $K_B^{AY_n}$ are defined by

$$K_B^{AY_n} \equiv \left(\frac{\gamma_{AY_n}}{\bar{\gamma}_{AY_n}}\right)^b \left(\frac{\bar{\gamma}_B}{\gamma_B}\right)^{a-ny} \tag{5-170}$$

and $b \equiv z_B$ is the valence of the competing cation (H^+ in our model case). It is easily verified that, with the definition (5-170), the formulation (5-169) holds for the ion exchange of the free and complex cations as well as for the sorption of the neutral and the anionic complexes. It is true, however, that only in the first cases ($ny < a$) the coefficients $K_B^{AY_n}$ have the physical meaning of selectivity coefficients of ion-exchange processes.

After substituting the quantities m_{AY_n} on the right-hand side of Eqs. (5-169) by use of Eq. (5-161) one obtains for the over-all concentration $\bar{M}_A$ of the species A (Zn in our model case) in the ion exchanger

$$\bar{M}_A = \sum_{n=0}^{N} \bar{m}_{AY_n} = m_A \sum_{n=0}^{N} \left[m_Y^n K_n (K_B^{AY_n})^{1/b} \left(\frac{\bar{m}_B}{m_B}\right)^{(a-ny)/b} \right] \quad (5\text{-}171)^*$$

The over-all distribution coefficient Λ_A of species A is obtained from Eqs. (5-171) and (5-163):

$$\Lambda_A \equiv \frac{\bar{M}_A}{M_A} = \frac{\displaystyle\sum_{n=0}^{N} [m_Y^n K_n (K_B^{AY_n})^{1/b} (\bar{m}_B/m_B)^{(a-ny)/b}]}{\displaystyle\sum_{n=0}^{N} (m_Y^n K_n)} \quad (5\text{-}172)^*$$

The separation factor α_B^A is accordingly

$$\alpha_B^A \equiv \frac{\bar{M}_A m_B}{M_A \bar{m}_B} = \frac{\displaystyle\sum_{n=0}^{N} [m_Y^n K_n (K_B^{AY_n})^{1/b} (\bar{m}_B/m_B)^{(a-ny-b)/b}]}{\displaystyle\sum_{n=0}^{N} (m_Y^n K_n)} \quad (5\text{-}173)^*$$

Equation (5-172) may also be written in the following somewhat more perspicuous form [92]

$$\Lambda_A = \frac{\lambda_0 + \lambda_1 K_1 m_Y + \cdots + \lambda_N K_N m_Y^N}{1 + K_1 m_Y + \cdots + K_N m_Y^N} = \frac{\displaystyle\sum_{n=0}^{N} (\lambda_n m_Y^n K_n)}{\displaystyle\sum_{n=0}^{N} (m_Y^n K_n)} \quad (5\text{-}174)$$

---

* Equations (5-171) to (5-173) and (5-179) can also be written in terms of the "true" thermodynamic stability constants $\mathcal{K}_n$ defined by

$$\frac{a_{AY_n}}{a_A a_Y^n} = \mathcal{K}_n$$

instead of the molal constants K_n defined by Eqs. (5-161). To this aim, the following substitutions are made:

$$K_n = \frac{\mathcal{K}_n \gamma_A \gamma_Y^n}{\gamma_{AY_n}}$$

and

$$K_n (K_B^{AY_n})^{1/b} = \mathcal{K}_n \frac{\gamma_A \gamma_Y^n}{\bar{\gamma}_{AY_n}} \left(\frac{\bar{\gamma}_B}{\gamma_B}\right)^{(a-ny)/b}$$

where the quantities

$$\lambda_n \equiv \frac{\bar{m}_{AY_n}}{m_{AY_n}} = (K_B^{AY_n})^{1/b} \left(\frac{\bar{m}_B}{m_B}\right)^{(a-ny)/b} \tag{5-175}$$

are the distribution coefficients of the complexes $[AY_n]^{a-ny}$. Equation (5-175) shows that these coefficients decrease rapidly with increasing ligand numbers n, particularly when the solution concentration is low and the capacity of the ion exchanger is high ($m_B \ll \bar{m}_B$). In other words, the cation exchanger prefers the complexes with lower ligand number. The result is that the average ligand number is smaller in the ion exchanger than in the solution.

Equations (5-171) to (5-173) are in a convenient form for systems in which the complexing agent BY is in large excess over AY. Here, $b\bar{m}_B$ is approximately equal to the concentration of the fixed ionic groups and is practically independent of M_A. If higher precision is required, $\bar{m}_B$ as a function of m_B can be obtained from sorption measurements with BY in the absence of AY. However, $\bar{m}_B$ depends in a more complex way on the other concentrations if AY and BY are present in comparable concentrations. In such cases, $\bar{m}_B$ can be calculated in the following way. A relation for $\bar{m}_B$ is obtained from the electroneutrality condition in the ion exchanger

$$b\bar{m}_B - \bar{m}_R - y\bar{m}_Y + \sum_{n=0}^{N}(a - ny)\bar{m}_{AY_n} = 0 \tag{5-176}$$

where $\bar{m}_R$ = concentration of fixed ionic groups,

in which the quantities $\bar{m}_{AY_n}$ and $\bar{m}_Y$ must be expressed in terms of $\bar{m}_B$ and known quantities. For $\bar{m}_{AY_n}$, the necessary relation is obtained from Eqs. (5-169) and (5-161)

$$\bar{m}_{AY_n} = \frac{(K_B^{AY_n})^{1/b} K_n m_A m_Y^n (\bar{m}_B/m_B)^{(a-ny)/b} \sum_{n=0}^{N}(m_Y^n K_n)}{M_A} \tag{5-177}$$

For $\bar{m}_Y$, a relation analogous to Eqs. (5-169) is obtained from the sorption equilibrium of BY:

$$\bar{m}_Y = m_Y \left(\frac{\bar{m}_B}{m_B}\right)^{y/b} \left(\frac{\bar{\gamma}_B}{\gamma_B}\right)^{y/b} \frac{\gamma_Y}{\bar{\gamma}_Y} \tag{5-178}$$

The general relations are rigorous, but rather complicated. The evaluation in practical cases can often be simplified since, under any given experimental conditions, usually only a few of the potential complexes coexist in significant concentrations, so that many terms can be omitted as unimportant. Difficulties in evaluating the activity-coefficient ratios are discussed later (see page 212).

Equations (5-171) to (5-173) also show the effect of concentration on the over-all distribution coefficient and the separation factor. At very low concentrations of the complexing agent BY (HCl in our model case) the terms of higher order in the sums are negligible. There is little complexing, and the system behaves like an ordinary ion-exchange equilibrium.

With increasing concentration of BY, complex formation becomes notice-able. The terms of higher order increase more rapidly in the denominator than in the numerator. Hence both the over-all distribution coefficient and the separation factor α_B^A fall more and more short of the corresponding values in an analogous system without complex formation: the affinity of the cation exchanger for the complexing cation is reduced. This result is as anticipated (see page 205). The concentration M_A of the complexing cation (Zn in the model case) is not involved explicitly. There is no effect on the distribution as long as species B (H$^+$) is present in large excess. How-ever, the distribution does depend on M_A if the concentrations of A and B are comparable; an increase in M_A (at con-stant M_Y) lowers m_Y [see Eq. (5-165)] and thus counteracts the effect of com-plex formation, i.e., increases the affin-ity of the ion exchanger for species A.

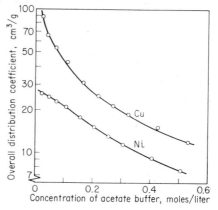

FIG. 5-40. Over-all distribution coeffi-cients of Cu and Ni in equilibria be-tween a cation exchanger (Amberlite IR-105) and 1:2 acetic acid–sodium acetate buffers. The ionic strength and the Na$^+$ concentration of the solution were kept constant by addi-tion of NaClO$_4$. The distribution co-efficients are shown as a function of the buffer concentration. (Concentration scale in the resin is millimoles per gram of dry resin.) *From experimental data by S. Fronaeus* [92,93].

Trace-component systems. Other systems of great practical importance are those in which several cationic species A, B, . . . are present in a large excess of a supporting electrolyte CY with complexing anion Y. This situation arises, for example, in elution-development chromatography where small quantities of cations are separated in a column by "development" with a large excess of an eluting agent (see Secs. 9-7b and 9-9).

As in systems without complex for-mation, the distribution coefficient of one trace component is not affected by the presence of other trace com-ponents (see page 202). Thus the over-all distribution coefficient Λ_i of an arbitrary trace cation i can be calculated from Eq. (5-172). (Of course, if the supporting electrolyte is CY, then B and b in Eq. (5-172) must be replaced by C and $c \equiv z_C$, respectively. If CY is a strong electrolyte, Eq. (5-172) can be further simplified since the equivalent concentrations of C and Y will then equal the over-all equivalent concentration.)

The over-all distribution coefficient of a species determines the rate with which the species travels down a chromatographic column. The sharpness of separation of a multicomponent mixture thus depends on the differences in the over-all distribution coefficients of the species. The ratios Λ_A/Λ_B, . . . , of the coefficients of the species, i.e., the *separation factors*, should differ from unity as much as possible.   The over-all distribution coefficients and, hence, the separation factors depend on the free-anion concentration m_Y [see Eq. (5-172)].   Optimum conditions for the separation can be attained by proper adjustment of this concentration.

This latter, very important point may be illustrated by the following qualitative argument.   Consider the separation of traces of two very similar cations having equal valence, almost equal affinity for the ion exchanger, and forming complexes with equal maximum coordination number but of different strengths.   If the development agent is very dilute, i.e., if the concentration of the complexing anion is very low, neither of the competing cations will form complexes to an appreciable extent.   Thus the separation factor is near unity.   On the other hand, if the development agent is very concentrated, i.e., the concentration of the complexing anion very high, both competing cations will be present almost exclusively in the form of the coordinatively saturated complexes.   Again the separation factor will be near unity because the ion exchanger can hardly discriminate between the complexes $[AY_N]$ and $[BY_N]$.   In between, there is a concentration range in which the average ligand number of the cation forming the stronger complexes is higher than that of the other cation.   Here, the latter is preferred by the cation exchanger.   With increasing concentration of the complexing anion, the separation factor thus goes through an optimum (maximum or minimum) value.   (Of course, if the complexes are rather weak, the corresponding concentration of the anion may be too high to be reached experimentally.)   Note that the free-anion concentration depends on the pH if the anion is that of a weak acid (see also page 211).

Macrocomponent systems with two complex-forming cations. Cases in which two complex-forming cations A and B are present in significant and comparable concentrations are slightly more complicated.   This situation occurs, for example, in separations of such cations by displacement-development chromatography (see Secs. 9-7a and d and 9-9).

Equation (5-172), which gives the over-all distribution coefficient of species A, remains unchanged even if the competing species B also forms complexes.   An exactly analogous relation, with A and B as well as a and b interchanged, holds for the over-all distribution coefficient of B.   The separation factor of the two species thus is

$$\alpha_B^A \equiv \frac{\bar{M}_A M_B}{M_A \bar{M}_B} = \frac{\Lambda_A}{\Lambda_B}$$

$$= \frac{\displaystyle\sum_{n=0}^{N} [m_Y^n K_n (K_B^{AY_n})^{1/b} (\bar{m}_B/m_B)^{(a-ny-b)/b}] \sum_{m=0}^{M} (m_Y^m K_m)}{\displaystyle\sum_{m=0}^{M} [m_Y^m K_m (K_A^{BY_m})^{1/a} (\bar{m}_A/m_A)^{(b-my-a)/a}] \sum_{n=0}^{N} (m_Y^n K_n)} \qquad (5\text{-}179)^*$$

where the K_m are the stability constants of the complexes $[BY_m]$ and M is the maximum

---

*For a relation in terms of "true" thermodynamic stability constants, see footnote to p. 207.

coordination number of these complexes. Evaluation of this expression requires relations for the unknown quantities m_Y, $\bar{m}_A$, and $\bar{m}_B$. The two latter concentrations can be expressed in terms of $\bar{m}_Y$ by Eq. (5-178) and an analogous relation from $\bar{m}_A$. The concentration $\bar{m}_Y$, in turn, is obtained by solving the electroneutrality condition in the ion exchanger

$$\bar{m}_R + y\bar{m}_Y - \sum_{n=0}^{N} [(a - ny)\bar{m}_{AY_n}] - \sum_{m=0}^{M} [(b - my)\bar{m}_{BY_m}] = 0 \qquad (5\text{-}180)$$

in which $\bar{m}_{AY_n}$ and $\bar{m}_{BY_n}$ are substituted as before (see page 208). The concentration m_Y is given by

$$m_Y + \frac{M_A \sum_{n=1}^{N} (nm_Y^n K_n)}{\sum_{n=0}^{N} (m_Y^n K_n)} + \frac{M_B \sum_{m=1}^{M} (mm_Y K_m)}{\sum_{m=0}^{M} (m_Y^m K_m)} - M_Y = 0 \qquad (5\text{-}181)$$

In chromatographic separations by displacement development, the separation factor determines the sharpness of the boundary between the "bands" of the species A and B and thus the sharpness of separation. Qualitatively, the dependence of this factor on the concentration of the free anion is the same as in trace-component systems (see page 210). As a rule, the separation factor attains an optimum (maximum or minimum) value at a certain concentration of the free complexing anion.

Weak acids and buffer solutions as complexing agents. Many excellent complexing agents are anions of *weak acids* such as citric acid, EDTA (ethylenediaminetetraacetic acid), etc. Here, the free-anion concentration, which determines the over-all distribution coefficients and separation factors, is, of course, not equal to the total acid concentration. The concentration of the free anion (citrate ion, EDTA anion, etc.) can be calculated from the dissociation constants of the acid; the dissociation equilibrium of the acid is given by a set of equations which is exactly analogous to Eqs. (5-160), the stability constants being the reciprocals of the dissociation constants. (Complexing by partially dissociated species such as $H\text{cit}^{2-}$ or $H_2\text{cit}^-$, etc., is discussed later.)

The optimum concentration of the free weak-acid anion—which gives the optimum separation factors—can be attained by proper adjustment of the pH. For this purpose, *buffer solutions* such as ammonium citrate–citric acid mixtures are often used. Raising the pH, for example by addition of ammonia, enhances the dissociation of the acid and thus increases the free-anion concentration. The latter can be calculated as before from the dissociation constants of the acid.

Polynuclear complexes and weak complex acids. It has been assumed so far that the complex species contain not more than one metal ion and no H^+ ions. These assumptions, however, are not necessarily valid. For example, in the case of zinc chloride, it is conceivable that polynuclear complexes such as $[Zn_2Cl_6]^{2-}$, etc., might be formed, and that the complex acid $H_2[ZnCl_4]$ might be incompletely dissociated.

The qualitative aspects of such effects are these: The formation of polynuclear complexes is obviously favored by a high over-all concentration of the metal species; if the latter is a trace component, polynuclear complexes are very unlikely to occur. The formation of undissociated complex acids is favored by low pH of the solution and a high concentration of the free anion. The formation of polynuclear complexes reduces the average ligand number per atom A, and the formation of complex weak acids reduces the negative charge of the anionic complexes. Thus both effects tend to raise the affinity of the ion exchanger for the cation involved and counteract the effect of complex formation. The situation is less clear-cut when complexes with ligands such as $Hcit^{2-}$ or H_2cit^- are formed, since the latter species may well be present in higher concentrations than the free anion cit^{3-}. Note that all these effects can be accounted for in the activity coefficients in Eqs. (5-171) to (5-173) and (5-179).

The derivation of quantitative relations which include polynuclear and weak-acid complexes explicitly is rather lengthy, but straightforward.

Deviations. It has recently been found that trace amounts of anionic chloro complexes of certain metals [Au(III), Fe(III), Ga(III), and, to a lesser degree, Sb(V) and Tl(III)] are strongly sorbed from concentrated chloride solutions by cation exchangers [176]. The over-all distribution coefficients—often of the order of 10^5—*increase* with increasing concentration (above 5 M) of the supporting electrolyte. No explanations for these unexpected deviations have so far been advanced.

Prediction of equilibria.

The relations (5-172), (5-173), and (5-179) for the distribution coefficients and separation factors involve the coefficients $K_B^{AY_n}$ defined by Eq. (5-170). Assumptions regarding the activity coefficients are required before these coefficients can be calculated. Without such assumptions no quantitative predictions of complex-ion exchange equilibria are possible. All interactions except for complex formation are reflected in the activity coefficients. Thus the treatment given here is not more "complete" than other approaches in previous sections where the effects of certain interactions (solvation, ion-pair formation, etc.) have been studied one at a time. Nevertheless, the equations contribute greatly to the general understanding of the phenomena and can be used efficiently for semiquantitative predictions in systems in which, indeed, complex formation is the most important interaction. In the absence of all other interactions, all activity coefficients and therefore all coefficients $K_B^{AY_n}$ are, of course, equal to unity.

Calculation of complex-stability constants.

Complex-stability constants can be calculated from ion-exchange equilibria by a method which has been developed by Fronaeus [92].* The constants K_n are determined from equilibrium measurements with solutions containing the complex-

---

* At first sight it may seem strange that stability constants can be calculated from ion-exchange equilibria, whereas a reversal of the procedure—the calculation of equilibria from the stability constants— requires additional assumptions. The reason is the following. The equilibria are measured under conditions which guarantee the constancy of the coefficients $K_B^{AY_n}$ as closely as possible. In the calculation of the stability constants, the constant coefficients are eliminated one at a time by repeated differentiation. A reversal of this procedure would amount to a series of integrations and would introduce, in each step, an unknown integration constant, namely, one of the coefficients.

forming species A as a trace component in a large excess of a supporting electrolyte BY. The supporting electrolyte must be completely dissociated. The evaluation requires m_Y to be varied but m_B to be kept constant. This can be achieved by addition of corresponding amounts of another electrolyte BZ with an anion which forms no complexes. Thus m_Y and m_B can be varied independently. For most purposes, the choice of Na^+ and ClO_4^- as species B and Z is quite adequate. The calculation of the stability constants implies that, under the conditions mentioned, the coefficients $K_B^{AY_n}$ [and hence also the distribution coefficients λ_n, see Eq. (5-175)] remain constant, i.e., independent of m_Y.

From equilibrium measurements the dependence of the over-all distribution coefficient Λ_A on m_Y is calculated. The numerator on the right-hand side of Eq. (5-174) contains the quantity m_Y^N as the highest power of m_Y. Hence

$$\frac{\partial^{N+1}\left[\Lambda_A \sum_{n=0}^{N} (m_Y^n K_n)\right]}{\partial m_Y^{N+1}} = 0 \tag{5-182}$$

Alternatively, this relation may be written in the form

$$\frac{\partial^{N+1}\Lambda_A}{\partial m_Y^{N+1}} + \sum_{n=0}^{N} (\alpha_n K_n) = 0 \tag{5-183}$$

where the coefficients α_n (which are functions of m_Y and $\partial^n \Lambda_A / \partial m_Y^n$) must be calculated from Eq. (5-182). The determination of all the differential coefficients at N values of m_Y in combination with Eq. (5-183) gives a set of N equations from which all stability constants K_n can be calculated.

In the numerator in Eq. (5-174), the terms with $n < ay$ (i.e., those stemming from the ions with positive charge) greatly exceed the others. In practice it is therefore usually sufficient to differentiate in Eq. (5-182) only ay times instead of $(N + 1)$ times [92] to obtain the stability constants of the cationic complexes.

An alternative way [92] of determining the stability constants of higher order, after the first one has been calculated by use of Eq. (5-183), is the following. According to Eq. (5-174)

$$\lim_{m_Y \to 0} \left(\frac{1}{\Lambda_A}\right) = \frac{1}{\lambda_0}$$

$$\lim_{m_Y \to 0} \frac{1/\Lambda_A - 1/\lambda_0}{m_Y} = \frac{K_1(\lambda_0 - \lambda_1)}{\lambda_0^2} \tag{5-184}$$

etc. Thus the distribution coefficients can be determined by extrapolation of the corresponding functions to $m_Y = 0$. Then, by use of Eq. (5-174), the stability constants are calculated from the distribution coefficients and N values of Λ_A at different values of m_Y.

In practice, these procedures yield reliable values for the stability constants of low order only. Stability constants of anionic complexes can be determined much more accurately from equilibria with anion exchangers (see page 221).

In many earlier publications [196,211,262–264,266–269,288], the stability constants were calculated by a much simpler procedure. However, this method involves rather drastic simplifications. It is assumed that, at any given value of m_Y, the solution contains only *one* complex $[AY_n]^{a-ny}$ which is in equilibrium with the free ions A and Y:

$$A^a + nY^{-y} \rightleftarrows [AY_n]^{a-ny} \qquad \frac{m_{AY_n}}{m_A m_Y^n} = K_n \qquad (5\text{-}185)$$

(Of course, the ligand number n is considered to be a function of m_Y.) Furthermore it is assumed that the cation exchanger takes up only the free ions A and B, but no complexes, so that

$$\bar{M}_A = \bar{m}_A = K_B^A m_A \left(\frac{\bar{m}_B}{m_B}\right)^a \qquad (5\text{-}186)$$

(for simplicity, B is assumed to be univalent). Under these conditions Eq. (5-172) reduces to

$$\Lambda_A = \frac{K_B^A (\bar{m}_B/m_B)^a}{1 + m_Y^n K_n} \qquad (5\text{-}187)$$

The ion-exchange equilibrium in the presence of the complexing anion Y is compared with another ion-exchange equilibrium where all conditions are identical, except that Z, a noncomplexing anion, is substituted for Y. The distribution coefficient Λ_A^0 in this system is

$$\Lambda_A^0 \equiv \frac{\bar{m}_A^0}{m_A^0} = K_B^{A^0} \left(\frac{\bar{m}_B^0}{m_B}\right)^a \qquad (5\text{-}188)$$

Superscript 0 refers to the system without complex formation.

If A is a trace component, then $\bar{m}_B^0 = \bar{m}_B$. Under the additional assumption that the replacement of the anion Y by Z has no effect on the selectivity coefficient of the free ions A and B ($K_B^{A^0} \cong K_B^A$), one obtains from Eqs. (5-187) and (5-188)

$$K_n = \frac{\Lambda_A^0/\Lambda_A - 1}{m_Y^n} \qquad (5\text{-}189)$$

or $$\log \left(\frac{\Lambda_A^0}{\Lambda_A} - 1\right) = \log K_n + n \log m_Y \qquad (5\text{-}190)$$

In a plot of $\log (\Lambda_A^0/\Lambda_A - 1)$ versus $\log m_Y$, the slope at any value of m_Y is equal to the ligand number n of the complex then existing. Having determined n, one can calculate the corresponding stability constant K_n from Eq. (5-189).

In view of the simplifications involved, this simple procedure cannot be expected to give accurate answers.

Stability constants calculated from ion-exchange equilibria are generally in very good agreement with those obtained by other methods such as polarographic or potentiometric measurements [92,93,94,96,153,206,233]. Ion exchange is now considered as a well-established technique for determining such constants. This fact lends additional support to the theoretical treatment in this chapter.

c. Equilibria with Anion Exchangers in the Presence of a Complexing Anion

The systems which are studied in this section are of the following type. An anion exchanger is in equilibrium with a solution containing one or more cations and one complexing anion. Systems with only one complexing cation are examined first.

Equilibria with one complex-forming cation. Anion exchangers in, say, Y form usually exclude electrolytes AY rather efficiently (Donnan exclusion, see Sec. 5-3c). However, the situation is quite different when the cation A forms anionic complexes with the anion Y. Zinc chloride may again serve as an example. The anionic complexes $[ZnCl_3]^-$ and $[ZnCl_4]^{2-}$ are not excluded by the Donnan effect and can be taken up by the anion exchanger in exchange for Cl^- ions. Complex formation thus *enhances* the uptake of the metal species by the anion exchanger. (Note that the opposite holds for the uptake by a cation exchanger; see previous section.)

Quantitative relations for such equilibria can be derived in a manner similar to that in the previous section. The complex-ion equilibria in the solution are given by Eqs. (5-160) or (5-161). In the case of zinc chloride, they are combined with the ion-exchange equilibria of the free and complex anions

$$[ZnCl_4]^{2-} + 2\overline{Cl^-} \rightleftharpoons \overline{[ZnCl_4]^{2-}} + 2Cl^- \qquad \bar{m}_{ZnCl_4} = K_{Cl}^{ZnCl_4} m_{ZnCl_4} \left(\frac{\bar{m}_{Cl}}{m_{Cl}}\right)^2$$

$$[ZnCl_3]^- + \overline{Cl^-} \rightleftharpoons \overline{[ZnCl_3]^-} + Cl^- \qquad \bar{m}_{ZnCl_3} = K_{Cl}^{ZnCl_3} m_{ZnCl_3} \frac{\bar{m}_{Cl}}{m_{Cl}}$$

$$(5\text{-}191)$$

and the sorption equilibria of the neutral complex $[ZnCl_2]$ and the electrolytes $[ZnCl]Cl$ and $ZnCl_2$

$$[ZnCl_2] \rightleftharpoons \overline{[ZnCl_2]} \qquad \bar{m}_{ZnCl_2} = \lambda_2 m_{ZnCl_2}$$

$$[ZnCl]^+ + Cl^- \rightleftharpoons \overline{[ZnCl]^+} + \overline{Cl^-} \qquad \bar{m}_{ZnCl} = \lambda_1 m_{ZnCl} \qquad (5\text{-}192)$$

$$Zn^{2+} + 2Cl^- \rightleftharpoons \overline{Zn^{2+}} + \overline{2Cl^-} \qquad \bar{m}_{Zn} = \lambda_0 m_{Zn}$$

The quantities $K_{Cl}^{ZnCl_n}$ in Eqs. (5-191) are the molal selectivity coefficients [as defined by Eq. (5-71)] of the ion-exchange processes indicated on the left. The quantities λ_n in Eqs. (5-192) are the molal distribution coefficients [as defined by Eq. (5-28)] of the electrolytes. As in Eqs. (5-168), the coefficients are given by

$$K_{Cl}^{ZnCl_4} = \frac{\gamma_{ZnCl_4}}{\bar{\gamma}_{ZnCl_4}} \left(\frac{\bar{\gamma}_{Cl}}{\gamma_{Cl}}\right)^2$$

$$\lambda_2 = \frac{\gamma_{ZnCl_2}}{\bar{\gamma}_{ZnCl_2}}$$

$$K_{Cl}^{ZnCl_3} = \frac{\gamma_{ZnCl_3}}{\bar{\gamma}_{ZnCl_3}} \frac{\bar{\gamma}_{Cl}}{\gamma_{Cl}}$$

$$\lambda_1 = \frac{\gamma_{ZnCl}}{\bar{\gamma}_{ZnCl}} \frac{\gamma_{Cl}}{\bar{\gamma}_{Cl}} \frac{m_{Cl}}{\bar{m}_{Cl}}$$

$$\lambda_0 = \frac{\gamma_{Zn}}{\bar{\gamma}_{Zn}} \left(\frac{\gamma_{Cl}}{\bar{\gamma}_{Cl}}\right)^2 \left(\frac{m_{Cl}}{\bar{m}_{Cl}}\right)^2$$

(5-193)

The ion-exchange and sorption equilibria can be written in the general form

$$y[AY_n]^{a-ny} + (ny - a)\overline{Y^{-y}} \rightleftharpoons y\overline{[AY_n]^{a-ny}} + (ny - a)Y^{-y}$$

$$(\bar{m}_{AY_n})^y = K_Y^{AY_n}(m_{AY_n})^y \left(\frac{\bar{m}_Y}{m_Y}\right)^{ny-a}$$

(5-194)

where the coefficients $K_Y^{AY_n}$ are defined, as in Eq. (5-170), by

$$K_Y^{AY_n} \equiv \left(\frac{\gamma_{AY_n}}{\bar{\gamma}_{AY_n}}\right)^y \left(\frac{\bar{\gamma}_Y}{\gamma_Y}\right)^{ny-a}$$

(5-195)

Again, it is easily verified that the formulation (5-194) holds for both ion-exchange and sorption equilibria.

After substituting the quantities m_{AY_n} on the right-hand side of Eqs. (5-194) by use of Eqs. (5-161), one obtains for the over-all concentration $\bar{M}_A$ of the species A (Zn in our model case) in the ion exchanger

$$\bar{M}_A = \sum_{n=0}^{N} \bar{m}_{AY_n} = m_A(m_Y)^{a/y} \sum_{n=0}^{N} [K_n(K_Y^{AY_n})^{1/y}(\bar{m}_Y)^{n-a/y}] \quad (5\text{-}196)^*$$

The over-all distribution coefficient Λ_A is, according to Eqs. (5-196) and (5-163),

$$\Lambda_A \equiv \frac{\bar{M}_A}{M_A} = \frac{(m_Y)^{a/y} \sum_{n=0}^{N} [K_n(K_Y^{AY_n})^{1/y}(\bar{m}_Y)^{n-a/y}]}{\sum_{n=0}^{N} (m_Y^n K_n)} \quad (5\text{-}197)^*$$

Comparison of Eq. (5-197) with Eq. (5-164) shows that the over-all distribution coefficient may be written as

$$\Lambda_A = \frac{x_{a/y} \sum_{n=0}^{N} [K_n(K_Y^{AY_n})^{1/y}(\bar{m}_Y)^{n-a/y}]}{K_{a/y}} \quad (5\text{-}198)^*$$

---

* Equations (5-196) to (5-198) can also be written in terms of the "true" thermodynamic equilibrium constants $\mathcal{K}_n$ instead of the molal constants K_n by substituting

$$K_n = \frac{\mathcal{K}_n \gamma_A \gamma_Y^n}{\gamma_{AY_n}}$$

and

$$K_n(K_Y^{AY_n})^{1/y} = \mathcal{K}_n \frac{\gamma_A \gamma_Y^n}{\bar{\gamma}_{AY_n}} \left(\frac{\bar{\gamma}_Y}{\gamma_Y}\right)^{(ny-a)/y}$$

(see also footnote to p. 207).

This relation is applicable only if a/y is an integer since otherwise the quantities $x_{a/y}$ and $K_{a/y}$ are not defined.   If a/y is an integer, the species A and Y can form a neutral complex—for example, $[ZnCl_2]$ or $[CuSO_4]$—and $x_{a/y}$ is the fraction of total A in the solution present in the form of the neutral complex, and $K_{a/y}$ is the formation constant of this complex.

The relations (5-196) to (5-198) hold, regardless of whether or not a supporting electrolyte BY is present.   The relations are in a convenient form for systems in which the *supporting electrolyte is in large excess*.   A simple example is the system $ZnCl_2$(traces)/HCl/anion exchanger.   Here, m_Y equals the (known) total anion concentration in the solution, and $y\bar{m}_Y$ is approximately equal to the concentration of the fixed ionic groups and is practically independent of M_A.   If higher accuracy is required, $\bar{m}_Y$ as a function of m_Y can be determined by sorption measurements with BY in the absence of AY.   The effect of the concentration of the supporting electrolyte on the uptake of the trace component A is readily derived from Eq. (5-197) or (5-198).   At low concentrations of the supporting electrolyte $(m_Y \ll \bar{m}_R)$, there is strong Donnan exclusion and, hence, little sorption of BY.   Thus $y\bar{m}_Y$, the equivalent concentration of free anions in the ion exchanger, is practically equal to the (constant) concentration of fixed ionic groups and almost independent of the solution concentration.   At the same time, the coefficients $K_B^{AY_n}$ also depend little on the solution concentration.   Thus all quantities on the right-hand side of Eq. (5-198), except $x_{a/y}$, are practically constant.   Hence, the over-all distribution coefficient Λ_A is proportional to $x_{a/y}$, and *the maximum uptake of* A *occurs when the ligand concentration is such that the neutral complex predominates in the solution* [95].   The explanation is straightforward.   At lower average ligand number, the species A is largely in cationic form.   The uptake increases with increasing concentration of the supporting electrolyte (increasing ligand number) because Donnan exclusion becomes less effective.   At higher average ligand number, the species A is largely in anionic form.   Here, the uptake decreases with increasing concentration of the supporting electrolyte because the higher complexes occupy more fixed ionic groups per atom A and have to compete with an increasing number of free anions Y.   Note, however, that these arguments no longer apply when the concentration of the supporting electrolyte becomes comparable to that of the fixed ionic groups.   In this concentration range, "invasion" takes place, i.e., the anion exchanger sorbs significant amounts of BY.   Thus $\bar{m}_Y$ increases with increasing m_Y, and so does the sum in the numerator on the right hand side of Eq. (5-198).   Consequently, if the maximum of $x_{a/y}$ occurs in this concentration range, the maximum of the over-all distribution coefficient is shifted to a higher concentration of the supporting electrolyte and may even disappear completely if the supporting electrolyte is strongly sorbed or if the complexes are weak [175,204].

Systems in which the *supporting electrolyte is not in large excess or is completely absent* require additional relations for the unknown quantities m_Y and $\bar{m}_Y$ in Eqs. (5-196) to (5-198). Here, m_Y is given by Eq. (5-165); $\bar{m}_Y$ can be calculated by solving the electroneutrality condition in the ion exchanger

$$y\bar{m}_Y - \bar{m}_R - b\bar{m}_B - \sum_{n=0}^{N} [(a - ny)\bar{m}_{AY_n}] = 0 \qquad (5\text{-}199)$$

after substituting $\bar{m}_B$ and $\bar{m}_{AY_n}$ according to Eq. (5-178) and Eqs. (5-194) and (5-161), respectively.

Simplifications. The concentration of the complexing anion in the anion exchanger is usually very large, particularly in high-capacity resins. Hence the average ligand number in the ion exchanger is high. If the complexes are strong, practically all atoms A in the ion exchanger will form the coordinatively saturated complex $[AY_N]^{a-ny}$

$$\bar{M}_A \cong \bar{m}_{AY_N} = m_A m_Y^{a/y} K_N (K_Y^{AY_N})^{1/y} (\bar{m}_Y)^{N-a/y} \qquad (5\text{-}200)$$

Now, if, at a given concentration of the free anion, one complex $[AY_j]^{a-jy}$ predominates in the solution, then

$$M_A \cong m_{AY_j} = m_A m_Y^j K_j \qquad (5\text{-}201)$$

and the relation (5-197) for the over-all distribution coefficient reduces to

$$\Lambda_A \cong m_Y^{a/y-j} \left(\frac{K_N}{K_j}\right) (K_Y^{AY_n})^{1/y} (\bar{m}_Y)^{N-a/y} \qquad (5\text{-}202)$$

or

$$\log \Lambda_A \cong \log \frac{K_N (K_Y^{AY_N})^{1/y}}{K_j} + \left(N - \frac{a}{y}\right) \log \bar{m}_Y - \left(j - \frac{a}{y}\right) \log m_Y \qquad (5\text{-}203)$$

Provided that the stability constants, the selectivity coefficients, and $\bar{m}_Y$ are practically independent of m_Y, the ligand number j of the complex which prevails in the solution can be determined from Eq. (5-203); in a plot of $\log \Lambda_A$ versus $\log m_Y$, the slope of the curve at any point is $j - a/y$ [170].

Other systems. The behavior of other systems is only briefly outlined since most of the arguments are analogous to those which apply to equilibria with cation exchangers (see pages 209 to 212).

Trace-component Systems. Systems in which small quantities or traces of several complex-forming cations and a large excess of a supporting electrolyte are present are of considerable practical importance for analytical separations. Equations (5-196) to (5-198) hold for all trace components. The over-all distribution coefficients of the complex-forming cations usually vary over several orders of magnitude and have their maxima, if any, at different concentrations of the supporting electrolyte (see, for example, Fig. 5-41). These differences provide an excellent basis for analytical and preparative separations (see also Sec. 9-6). Optimum separation factors can be attained by proper adjustment of the free-anion concentration.

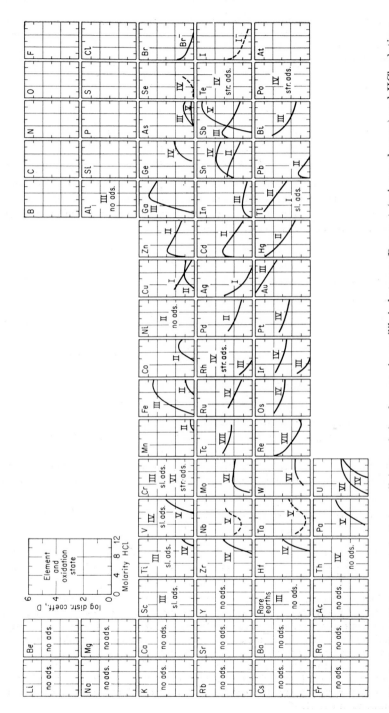

Fig. 5-41. Over-all trace distribution coefficients of the elements in equilibria between Dowex 1 (anion exchanger) and HCl solutions. The coefficients are shown as a function of the HCl molarity. (Concentration scale in the ion exchanger: millimoles per gram dry resin.) *From K. A. Kraus and F. Nelson [174].* (An analogous table has been published for sorption from HF solutions [86].)

Macrocomponent Systems with Two or More Complex-forming Cations. Equations (5-196) to (5-198) can also be used when two or more complexing cations are present in significant concentrations. Here, however, the quantities m_Y and $\bar{m}_Y$ are unknown and must be calculated from an equation analogous to (5-165) and the electroneutrality condition in the ion exchanger, respectively.

Weak Acids and Buffer Solutions as Complexing Agents. Here, exactly the same considerations as for equilibria with cation exchangers apply (see page 211).

Formation of Polynuclear Complexes and Weak Complex Acids. Formation of polynuclear complexes and of weak complex acids leads to complexes which carry, on the average, less negative charge per metal atom in the complexes. Hence such interactions may give rise to a higher over-all distribution coefficient at high concentrations of the supporting electrolyte. Note that formation of weak complex acids such as $H_2[ZnCl_4]$, if occurring at all, should become more noticeable at high concentrations of the free anion or the supporting electrolyte, and should lower the over-all distribution coefficient of the metal primarily in this concentration range [204].

The interested reader will have no difficulty in deriving quantitative relations for the various systems by methods analogous to those which were used in the previous section for equilibria with cation exchangers.

Prediction of equilibria, experimental evidence, and interpretation of experimental results.

The relations for equilibria with anion exchangers—like those for cation exchangers—contain activity coefficients and cannot be evaluated quantitatively without assumptions about these coefficients (see also page 212). However, the general qualitative picture is quite clear and in good agreement with experimental evidence, though the interpretation of certain secondary effects is still somewhat controversial.

This latter point may be illustrated by a typical example. The uptake of traces of zinc from supporting chloride solutions has been studied rather thoroughly. The uptake depends strongly on the nature of the supporting cation. Figure 5-42 (left) shows the experimental over-all distribution coefficients of zinc (as a trace component) in the presence of the supporting electrolytes LiCl, HCl, and CsCl as a function of the chloride activity in the solution. The curve for LiCl has no maximum; this can be readily explained by "invasion" (sorption of the supporting electrolyte) [204]. However, it was found that sorption of HCl is about the same as that of LiCl; yet, the curve for HCl has a maximum and falls far short of that for LiCl at high chloride concentrations. Marcus and Coryell [204] attribute this fact to incomplete dissociation of the complex acid $H_2[ZnCl_4]$. This interpretation, however, helps little in understanding the curve with CsCl as the supporting electrolyte. Here, the zinc uptake at high chloride concentrations is still lower than with HCl, though it is very unlikely that $Cs_2[ZnCl_4]$ is less dissociated than $H_2[ZnCl_4]$. Moreover, the general shape of the three curves seems to depend little on the nature of the ion exchanger. Almost identical curves were obtained with a liquid anion exchanger, a material of basically different structure (Fig. 5-42, right) [260]. Invasion of the liquid anion exchanger was too small to be detected, except in the case of HCl which behaves anomalously. Thus it seems that the effect of the supporting cation is due primarily to interactions *in the solution* (affecting the activity coefficients of the complexes) rather than to invasion of the ion exchanger. In view of these facts, the interpretation of the curves and the complex-stability constants calculated therefrom are still somewhat in doubt.

Considerable experimental evidence has been obtained for most poly-valent metals with HCl [174], HBr [140], HF [86], HCl-HF mixtures [170, 221], EDTA [222], and various other complexing agents [95,98,150,152,152a, 175,192,203,223,251,278a]. The results constitute an excellent basis for the design of chromatographic separations of metals (see also Secs. 9-6 and 9-7).

Calculation of complex-stability constants. Stability constants of complexes can be calculated from equilibrium measurements with anion exchangers [95,98,152,175,204,222,278a]. The experimental and mathe-matical procedures are analogous to those for the evaluation of equilibria

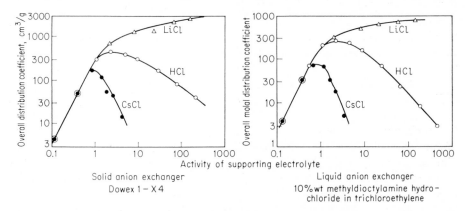

Solid anion exchanger
Dowex 1 – X 4

Liquid anion exchanger
10%wt methyldioctylamine hydro–
chloride in trichloroethylene

FIG. 5-42. Effect of the supporting cation on the over-all distribution coefficient of a trace component. The distribution coefficient of Zn with LiCl, HCl, and CsCl as sup-porting electrolytes is shown as a function of the activity of the solution. *Left:* equilibria with anion-exchange resin Dowex 1-X4. *Right:* equilibria with a liquid anion exchanger. Note the strong effect of the supporting cation and the similar behavior of the two struc-turally quite different anion exchangers. *From U. Schindewolf [260], and experimental data by K. A. Kraus [173] and R. A. Horne [152].*

with cation exchangers (see page 212) and require the same simplifying assumptions. For details, the reader is referred to the work of Fronaeus [95], Marcus and Coryell [204], and K. A. Kraus [175].

Anion exchangers take up the anionic complexes, i.e., the complexes with *high* ligand number, in preference to the other species, whereas cation exchangers prefer the complexes with *low* ligand number. Hence, high-order stability constants are more accurately determined with anion exchangers. Thus the two techniques supplement one another in a for-tunate way [150,153,203,223,251].

One qualitative conclusion can be drawn from experimental results without calculation. The occurrence of a maximum of the over-all distribution coefficient (when plotted as a function of the concentration of the supporting electrolyte) proves the formation of anionic complexes [95,98]. However, the absence of a maximum is no proof for the absence of anionic complexes (see, for example, the curve for LiCl as the supporting electrolyte in Fig. 5-42).

d. Nonequilibrium in the Solution

In the preceding sections, equilibrium throughout the system was assumed. The equations are based on equilibrium between the ion exchanger and the solution and on equilibrium of the complexes with one another. When an ion exchanger is added to a solution, the dissociation equilibrium of the complexes is at first disturbed. Usually, however, this equilibrium is rapidly reestablished. In most cases, the rates of complex formation and dissociation are much higher than those of ion exchange and sorption. A few exceptions should be noted. For example, the rearrangement of chromium complexes is well known to occur at such a low rate that any one species can be determined in the presence of others by the usual analytical methods (titration, etc.). If the determination is carried out fast enough, the various coexisting complexes behave as independent species. During the determination, a complex removed from the solution is not formed anew by rearrangement of other complexes. Thus it is possible to separate the individual complexes from one another. Ion exchange is a very convenient means for such separations since the various complexes differ in their charges [48,126–128,168,184,235a,252]. For example, neutral and anionic complexes pass through a cation-exchange column without much hindrance, while the free cations and cationic complexes are held by ion exchange with the counter ion in the column. By ion-exchange chromatography, even complexes having charges of the same sign can be separated [48,168,235a]. If the rate of rearrangement is sufficiently low, separation and direct analysis can be used for determining the concentrations of the various complex species in a solution in which equilibrium was previously attained. From these concentrations, the stability constants can be calculated by use of Eq. (5-161). Such methods were used by Gustavson [126] as early as 1925.

Slow complex rearrangement and, consequently, unintended chromatographic separation of individual complexes is the most likely explanation for an unpleasant disturbance which is occasionally encountered in chromatographic separations of metals by ion exchange in the presence of a complexing agent; one metal may form several bands [156]. (See also page 480.)

5-7. "LIGAND EXCHANGE"

The previous section has dealt with the effect of complex-forming anionic ligands on the distribution of cations between ion exchangers and solutions. In the present section, the effect of complex-forming cations in ion exchangers on the distribution of non-ionic and anionic ligands will be discussed.

Ion exchangers containing complexing cations such as Cu^{2+}, Ni^{2+}, Ag^+, etc., can be used as highly selective sorbents for molecules or anions which can act as ligands. Potential ligands are, among others, ammonia [135,282], aliphatic amines [135,282], polyhydric alcohols [101], and anions of car-

boxylic and amino acids [135].* The complexes are formed *in the resin.*
The ligands taken up from the external solution or gas phase replace solvent
molecules in the solvation shell of the metal ion, or replace other ligands in
previously formed complexes. Typical "ligand-exchange" reactions are,
for example,

$$\overline{(R^-)_2[Cu(H_2O)_4^{2+}]} + 4NH_3 \rightleftharpoons \overline{(R^-)_2[Cu(NH_3)_4^{2+}]} + 4H_2O \quad (5\text{-}204)$$

$$\overline{(R^-)_2[Cu(NH_3)_4^{2+}]} + 2NH_2C_2H_4NH_2$$
$$\rightleftharpoons \overline{(R^-)_2[Cu(NH_2C_2H_4NH_2)_2^{2+}]} + 4NH_3 \quad (5\text{-}205)$$

where R^- = fixed ionic group of a cation exchanger; bars over symbols refer to the
interior of the resin.

In reaction (5-204), ammonia is sorbed by a cation exchanger in (aqueous)
Cu^{2+} form. Reaction (5-205) is a ligand exchange of ammonia for ethylene-
diamine on a similar resin. No ion exchange takes place; the ion exchanger
acts merely as a solid carrier for the complexing metal ion.

Sorption of ligands. "Ligand exchangers" (i.e., ion exchangers containing complexing metal ions) have the particular advantage of combining
high sorption capacity with high selectivity for the ligand.

The *ligand-exchange capacity* is readily estimated [136]. For example, a
styrene-type cation exchanger with an ion-exchange capacity of 5 meq/g
dry resin in H^+ form contains, when in Ni^{2+} form, about 2 mmoles Ni^{2+} per
gram dry resin. Ni^{2+} is coordinatively hexavalent. Hence ligand-exchange
capacity is about 12 mmoles/g dry Ni^{2+} resin for monodentate ligands, such
as ammonia, which occupy one coordinative valence. For bidentate
ligands, which occupy two coordinative valences, the capacity is about
6 mmoles/g. Of course, "free" ligands can be sorbed in excess over those
which are complexed by the metal ion. On the other hand, the ligand-
exchange capacity is lower if coordinative valences of the metal ion are
occupied by fixed ionic groups of the ion exchanger (see page 226).

The *selectivity* for the ligand is high when the complexes with the metal
ion are strong. There is a strong "driving force" for sorption because the
ligands are efficiently sequestered by the metal ion in the resin. The
coordinatively saturated complexes are formed in the resin even when the
ligand concentration in the external solution is very low [282]; see also Fig.
5-27. Ligand-sorption isotherms thus differ from ordinary sorption isotherms in that uptake from dilute solutions is much higher and that saturation of the sorbent is reached at much lower solution concentrations.

---

* Ligand sorption and ligand exchange are not restricted to liquid-phase operations.
For example, olefins, which form complexes with Ag^+, Cu^+, etc., can be sorbed from gas
streams [286]; see also Sec. 9-8.

The strong and selective uptake of ligands even from dilute solutions can be used for separating ligands from non-ligands (see Sec. 9-8).

Exchange of ligands. Ligand exchange between solutions and ion exchangers containing complexing metal ions is, in many respects, analogous to ion exchange. Ligand exchange, like ion exchange, is essentially a stoichiometric process. (Of course, deviations from stoichiometric behavior occur if the complexes are not coordinatively saturated or when sorption of "free" ligands is significant.) Ligand-exchange equilibria can thus be described in terms of ligand-exchange isotherms and separation factors, defined in the same way as ion-exchange isotherms and separation factors. A typical ligand-exchange isotherm is shown in Fig. 5-43.

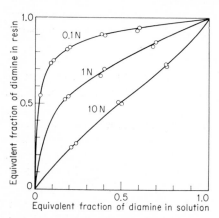

One outstanding feature of ligand exchange is that very high selectivities can be attained. The ligand exchanger prefers the ligand which has the stronger tendency to form complexes with the metal ion. Complex formation is a highly specific interaction, much more so than ordinary physical adsorption or ion exchange. Accordingly, the differences in strength of complexes of a metal ion with different ligands are, as a rule, considerable and give rise to high selectivities [135,136]. The situation resembles that in cation exchange in the presence of a complexing agent (see previous section) where high selectivities arise from differences in strength of complexes of different metal ions with an anionic ligand.

FIG. 5-43. Ligand-exchange isotherm for an ammonia/diamine exchange. The preference of the resin for the diamine (1,3-diaminopropanol-2) increases with dilution of the solution. Resin: Amberlite IRC-50 in Ni^{2+} form. *From F. Helfferich* [136].

There is a further interesting analogy between ligand-exchange and ion-exchange equilibria. The effect of the coordinative valences of the ligands is the same as that of the counter-ion valences in ion exchange [135,136]; see Sec. 5-4b, electroselectivity. This is readily shown. Consider, for example, the exchange of ammonia for a diamine in complexes with Ni^{2+} ions:

$$[Ni(NH_2RNH_2)_3^{2+}] + 6NH_3 \rightleftharpoons [Ni(NH_3)_6^{2+}] + 3NH_2RNH_2 \quad (5\text{-}206)$$

Application of the mass-action law in its simplest form gives

$$\frac{m_{Ni(NH_3)_6}m_{NH_2RNH_2}^3}{m_{Ni(NH_2RNH_2)_3}m_{NH_3}^6} = K \quad (5\text{-}207)$$

where K = molal equilibrium constant of reaction (5-206),

or, after rearrangement,

$$\frac{m_{\mathrm{Ni(NH_3)_6}}}{m_{\mathrm{Ni(NH_2RNH_2)_3}}} = K \left(\frac{m_{\mathrm{NH_3}}}{m_{\mathrm{NH_2RNH_2}}}\right)^3 m_{\mathrm{NH_3}}^3 \tag{5-208}$$

For any given constant concentration ratio $m_{\mathrm{NH_3}}/m_{\mathrm{NH_2RNH_2}}$ of the ligands, the right-hand side of Eq. (5-208) increases strongly with increasing total ligand concentration. The equation thus shows that formation of the complex with (monodentate) ammonia is favored by high solution concentration, and formation of the complex with (bidentate) diamine is favored by low solution concentration. Consequently, in ligand exchange between ion exchangers and solutions, *high solution concentration favors preference of the resin for the ligand of lower coordinative valence, and low solution concentration favors preference for the ligand of higher coordinative valence* [135,136]. A ligand-exchange isotherm which clearly shows this effect is given in Fig. 5-43. Note the similarity with the isotherm for the exchange $\mathrm{Na^+/Cu^{2+}}$ in Fig. 5-25.

The high selectivities and the ligand-valence effect make ligand exchange a very promising tool for separating ligands from one another (see also Sec. 9-8).

For a quantitative treatment of ligand-exchange equilibria, simple equations such as (5-208) are inadequate. Blocking of coordinate valences by the fixed ionic groups of the resin (see below), formation of coordinatively unsaturated and mixed complexes, and sorption of free ligands must be taken into account. Otherwise, the treatment is straightforward. By use of equations analogous to (5-161), ligand-exchange equilibria can be predicted from the respective complex-stability constants which are usually available in the literature [136].* The procedure and the simplifying assumptions involved are essentially the same as those discussed in the previous section.

Interference by ion exchange. In practical applications, displacement of the complexing metal ion from the resin by ion exchange with other cations must be avoided. Loss of metal ions from the resin results in a loss of ligand-exchange capacity. Moreover, displaced metal ions in the external solution counteract ligand sorption and ligand-exchange selectivity by forming complexes outside the resin. The metal ion can only be displaced by other cations since conservation of electroneutrality requires the presence of cations in the resin. The danger of metal-ion bleed thus is most serious when the external solution contains electrolytes in high concentrations.

Protection against metal-ion bleed can be obtained by using a resin which is highly selective for the complexing metal ion [135,136]. In particular, resins can be used which hold the metal ion by complex formation with the fixed ionic groups. In many cases, carboxylic acid groups offer sufficient protection. Chelating groups such as the iminodiacetic acid

---

* Extensive tables have been published by Bjerrum, Schwarzenbach, and Sillén [28].

groups in the resin Dowex A-1 hold the metal ion even more firmly. Of course, blocking of coordinative valences by the fixed ionic groups reduces the ligand-exchange capacity of the resin. For example, only four of the six coordinative valences of Ni^{2+} are operative in carboxylic-acid resins, and only three in iminodiacetic-acid resins:

Anion exchangers with amino groups, which complex transition-group metal ions, can also be used [286].

5-8. REACTIONS WITH MATERIALS OF LOW SOLUBILITY

Ion exchangers are able to dissolve slightly soluble solids which dissociate enough to give at least traces of ions. For example, calcium carbonate, lead sulfate, and silver chloride can be dissolved.

The mechanism of dissolution is the following. The supernatant solution in equilibrium with the solid contains a certain, though very small, amount of ions. This dissociation equilibrium between the solid and the dissolved ions is disturbed when the latter are removed from the solution by ion exchange, and is reestablished by further dissociation of the solid. In this way, the solid can be completely dissolved, provided that a sufficiently large excess of the ion exchanger is added.

This technique has been used in analytical chemistry for quantitative determinations of slightly soluble salts [44,151,227]. Examples of other potential applications are the removal of scale [24] and of superficial layers of basic lead carbonate that have formed on antique lead objects [226]. The advantage of the technique is that the removal can be achieved under mild conditions.

The success of the technique hinges mainly on the reaction rate which will be discussed in a later chapter (see Sec. 6-7). The present section deals with equilibria in three-phase systems ion exchanger/solution/solid and with the calculation of the amounts of ion exchangers required for complete dissolution of the solid.

Dissolution by a cation or anion exchanger. As a simple example, the dissolution of a 1,1-valent solid $\underline{AY}$ (for instance, AgCl) by a cation exchanger in H^+ form will be studied. With a few obvious changes, the equations also apply to dissolution by cation exchangers in other ionic forms and by anion exchangers. The extension to other than univalent ions is lengthy, but straightforward.

The solid is in equilibrium with the dissolved ions A^+ and Y^-

$$\underline{AY} \rightleftharpoons A^+ + Y^- \qquad \mathcal{K}_{sp} \equiv a_A a_Y = \text{const.} \qquad (5\text{-}209)$$

where a_i = activity of species i in solution; $\mathcal{K}_{sp}$ = solubility product of the solid; solid phases are underscored.

The cations are taken up by the cation exchanger

$$A^+ + \overline{H^+} \rightleftharpoons H^+ + \overline{A^+} \qquad \mathcal{K}_H^A \equiv \frac{\bar{a}_A a_H}{a_A \bar{a}_H} \qquad (5\text{-}210)$$

Here, $\mathcal{K}_H^A$ is the thermodynamic equilibrium constant of the ion exchange. The ion exchanger removes A^+ from the solution and thus, according to the Le Châtelier principle, promotes the dissolution of the solid. The over-all reaction is

$$\underline{AY} + \overline{H^+} \rightleftharpoons \overline{A^+} + Y^- + H^+ \qquad (5\text{-}211)$$

and the thermodynamic equilibrium constant of this process is [44]

$$\frac{\bar{a}_A a_Y a_H}{\bar{a}_H} = \mathcal{K} = \mathcal{K}_H^A \mathcal{K}_{sp} \qquad (5\text{-}212)$$

This constant $\mathcal{K}$ is the product of the ion-exchange equilibrium constant and the solubility product. The larger the constant $\mathcal{K}$, the more solid is dissolved by a given amount of the ion exchanger. Hence the dissolution is favored by a large solubility product and high selectivity of the ion exchanger for A^+ over H^+. The reason is quite obvious: large values of the two constants favor the forward reactions (left to right) in the processes (5-209) and (5-210). Furthermore, the dissolution is enhanced if the species Y is the anion of a weak acid

$$H^+ + Y^- \rightarrow HY \qquad (5\text{-}213)$$

and if the species Y forms a soluble complex with the solid, for example,

$$\underline{AY} + Y^- \rightarrow [AY_2]^- \qquad (5\text{-}214)$$

In both these cases, the forward reaction in (5-209) is promoted by partial sequestering of species Y, and in the second case the process (5-214) also contributes to the dissolution of the solid.

The amount $\bar{Q}$ of the ion exchanger (in moles) required for complete dissolution of a given amount Q_{AY}^0 of the solid (in moles) is readily estimated, as shown by the following simple calculation in which activity coefficients, electrolyte sorption by the ion exchanger, and complex formation are disregarded.

The condition for complete dissolution of the solid is that the ionic product in the solution becomes smaller than the solubility product:

$$C_A C_Y < K_{sp} \qquad (5\text{-}215)^*$$

During the dissolution by a cation exchanger, C_Y increases and C_A thus must necessarily decrease. After the solid has been dissolved, practically all ions Y^- are in the solution and practically all ions A^+ in the cation exchanger. Thus the following material balances for the final state can be written:

$$\bar{Q}_A = Q_{AY}^0 \qquad \bar{Q}_H = \bar{Q} - \bar{Q}_A = \bar{Q} - Q_{AY}^0 \qquad Q_H = Q_Y = \alpha Q_{AY}^0 \qquad (5\text{-}216)$$

where Q_i = amount of species i in the final state, i.e., after complete dissolution of solid; α = degree of dissociation of the acid HY at its concentration Q_{AY}^0/V; V = solution volume.

Introducing the selectivity coefficient K_H^A which may be written as

$$\frac{\bar{Q}_A Q_H}{Q_A \bar{Q}_H} = K_H^A \qquad (5\text{-}217)$$

one obtains from Eqs. (5-215) and (5-216)

$$\bar{Q} \geq Q_{AY}^0 \left[1 + \frac{(\alpha Q_{AY}^0)^2}{K_{sp} K_H^A V^2} \right] \qquad (5\text{-}218)^*$$

where $\bar{Q}$ is the amount of ion exchanger required for complete dissolution. This relation clearly shows the effects of the solubility product and the degree of dissociation of the acid which is formed.

The limits of applicability of the method become apparent when numerical values are inserted in the condition (5-218). For example, it is seen that the dissolution of 50 mg = 0.35 mmole AgCl ($K_{sp} = 1.6 \cdot 10^{-10}$ mole²/liter²) in 200 cm³ water, even with a rather favorable selectivity coefficient $K_H^{Ag} = 20$, requires as much as

$$\bar{Q} \geq 0.35 \cdot 10^{-3} \left[1 + \frac{(0.35 \cdot 10^{-3})^2}{1.6 \cdot 10^{-10} \cdot 20 \cdot (0.200)^2} \right] \cong 0.3 \text{ mole}$$

of cation exchanger. With a capacity of 5 meq/g, this amounts to about 60 g.[†] Hence this technique is only applicable to solids which have a relatively large solubility product, or which are salts of weak acids ($\alpha \ll 1$).

Dissolution by mixtures of cation and anion exchangers.

The dissolution of a solid takes place much more readily when a mixture of a cation and an anion exchanger, preferably in H^+ form and OH^- form, respectively,

---

* K_{sp} and K_H^A are used instead of $\mathcal{K}_{sp}$ and $\mathcal{K}_H^A$ because activity coefficients are neglected.

† This estimate is somewhat pessimistic since, actually, the Cl^- ions accumulating in the solution help to dissolve the solid by forming soluble complexes [see reaction (5-214)].

is used [151]. The anion exchanger removes the anions from the solution, replacing them by OH^-. The removal of the anions provides an additional "driving force" for the dissolution of the solid [reaction (5-209)], and, in addition, the OH^- ions released by the anion exchanger promote the cation exchange [reaction (5-210)] by combining with H^+ to form H_2O.

As before, the amount of the ion exchangers required for complete dissolution is readily estimated. This is shown by a simple example.

Suppose that a mixture of equivalent amounts, $\bar{Q}_{cat} = \bar{Q}_{an} \equiv \bar{Q}$, of the cation and the anion exchanger are used. Combining the relations

$$\frac{\bar{Q}_A C_H}{C_A \bar{Q}_H} = K_H^A \qquad \frac{\bar{Q}_Y C_{OH}}{C_Y \bar{Q}_{OH}} = K_{OH}^Y \qquad (5\text{-}219)$$

the dissociation equilibrium of water

$$C_H C_{OH} = K_w = 10^{-14} \text{ mole}^2/\text{liter}^2 \qquad (5\text{-}220)$$

and the material balances in the final state

$$\bar{Q}_H = \bar{Q}_{cat} - Q_{AY}^0 \qquad \bar{Q}_{OH} = \bar{Q}_{an} - Q_{AY}^0 \qquad (5\text{-}221)$$

with the condition (5-215), one obtains

$$\bar{Q} \geq Q_{AY}^0 \left[1 + \left(\frac{K_w}{K_{sp} K_H^A K_{OH}^Y} \right)^{1/2} \right] \qquad (5\text{-}222)$$

as the condition for complete dissolution. Inserting numerical values for the constants, one finds that 0.35 mmole AgCl can be dissolved with little more than 0.35 mmole each of the cation and the anion exchanger. This is about 0.1 to 0.2 g of high-capacity resins, as compared with 60 g if only the cation exchanger is used.

Criteria for complete dissolution of solids forming other than univalent ions can be derived in an analogous manner, but are rather lengthy. As a general rule, not much more than stoichiometric amounts of the ion exchangers are needed if

$$K_{sp}^{1/\nu} \gg K_w^{1/2} \qquad (5\text{-}223)$$

where ν = number of ions into which the solid dissociates.

For solids with lower solubility products, the amounts of ion exchangers required become prohibitive. The condition (5-223) thus shows the limitation of the technique.

5-9. EXPERIMENTAL METHODS

Equilibria with ion exchangers can usually be measured by simple means. The only points which require special attention are that the ion exchanger is properly conditioned and that certain sources of error are avoided. Several standard procedures for measuring swelling, sorption, and ion-exchange equilibria will be outlined in the following subsections. For further details, the reader is referred to the literature.

a. Conditioning and Storage

Measurements with materials as shipped by the manufacturer or freshly prepared tend to give irreproducible results. It is recommended that the material be thoroughly "conditioned" and, if possible, allowed to age for at least a few weeks. Experience has shown that the best way of conditioning an ion exchanger is to carry out a number of ion-exchange cycles. Thus, cation and anion exchangers can be conditioned by alternate treatment with NaOH and HCl (about 1 to 2 M). Between such cycles, the material should be washed thoroughly with water and occasionally with an organic solvent (methanol, ethanol). New resins may still contain soluble organic monomers or low polymers which failed to participate in forming the crosslinked network. Even more difficult to remove are traces of iron and other heavy-metal ions picked up in the course of the preparation. For the removal of ferric ions, leaching with alcoholic HCl or (for cation exchanger only) with solutions of thiocyanate, EDTA, or other complexing agents has been suggested. Conditioning is conveniently performed in a column or on a Buchner funnel.

Before an ion exchanger is used for scientific measurements, it should be ascertained that its capacity and swelling remain reproducible over several ion-exchange cycles.

Conditioned resins should be stored under dilute salt solutions (say, NaCl). When allowed to dry, the resins may require considerable time to regain their full swelling ability. On many ion-exchange resins, fungi tend to grow. This tendency, odd as it may seem, is most pronounced with phenolic resins. As a remedy it is recommended to change the supernatant solution occasionally, to add some phenol or thymol, and to wash the resin thoroughly from time to time. Strong-base anion-exchange resins should not be stored in OH$^-$ form for any length of time since the ionogenic groups decompose slowly when in OH$^-$ form. Instead, the resin should be converted to, say, the Cl$^-$ form. Cation-exchange resins are more stable, but even here storage in Na$^+$ or K$^+$ form is preferable.

b. Equilibration and Separation from the Solution

Measurements of swelling, sorption, and ion-exchange equilibria require equilibration of the ion exchanger with a solution. Usually, the ion exchanger is placed in a column and the solution is passed over it until the effluent has the same composition as the feed [112,229,236]. Alternatively, a sample of the ion exchanger (say, 1 g) is contacted successively with portions (say, 50 cm³ each) of the solution. The procedure is repeated until the composition of the solution remains unchanged while in contact with the ion exchanger. Stoppered bottles should be used in order to avoid concentration changes by evaporation of solvent.* This second procedure can also be used for ion-exchanger membranes [198,199,201] and other materials which are not in bead form.

The time of contact with the solution should be long enough for attainment of equilibrium. For strong-acid and strong-base resins of the usual bead size (20–50 mesh) and moderate crosslinking (4 to 10% DVB), about 30 min is ample. Highly crosslinked, coarse, and weak-acid or weak-base materials may require a substantially longer equilibration time.

After equilibration, the ion exchanger must be separated from the solution. The bulk solution is readily decanted or filtered off, but remaining liquid films which adhere to the beads are not as easily removed without causing the ion exchanger to lose solvent and sorbed solutes. Materials such as membranes which have large and smooth surfaces

---

* Ordinary glass is an ion exchanger, though one of very low capacity and exchange rate. Hence ordinary glass containers should not be used for storage and measurements. Pyrex glass and polyethylene are satisfactory.

may be blotted carefully with soft filter paper [63,113,155,198,201]. For ion-exchanger beads, centrifugation is preferable. The beads are transferred into a glass or plastic tube fitted at one end with a sintered glass disk or a platinum screen. The tube is then placed in a centrifuge tube [113,229]; see Fig. 5-44. To avoid solvent losses by evaporation, the centrifuge tube should be stoppered and should contain a few drops of the solution, so that the vapor phase in the tube is in equilibrium with the solution. The recommended centrifuge speed is 250 to 500 g. Spherical beads of the usual size are centrifuged for 5 to 30 min. Smaller and irregularly shaped particles should be centrifuged for a longer time. Even centrifugation still leaves traces of adherent liquid on the beads. Methods to determine the amount of retained liquid, and thus to apply corrections where necessary, have been worked out by Scatchard [259].

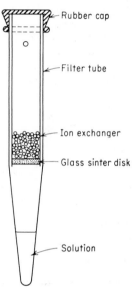

With materials of very fine particle size, the removal of adherent solution without change in composition of the ion exchanger is difficult to achieve. Here, techniques may be preferable which avoid the separation from the solution by evaluating concentration changes in the solution (see page 235) or the effluent history of a column experiment (see page 237).

c. Determination of Water or Solvent Content

Water contents of ion exchangers are determined by equilibrating a sample of the ion exchanger with the solution of interest, separating the sample from the solution, and weighing it in a stoppered weighing bottle. The sample is then dried over a desiccant (for example, P_2O_5) in vacuum at an elevated temperature, and is weighed once more in a stoppered weighing bottle. The difference between wet weight and dry weight gives the water content.

The permissible drying temperatures are rather different for the various types of ion exchangers. Strong-base anion-exchange resins are particularly sensitive and should not be exposed to temperatures above 60°C for any length of time. As a general rule, it is wise to make sure that no thermal degradation has taken place. This can be done by checking whether the ion exchanger, upon reswelling, regains its original wet weight.

Fig. 5-44. Centrifuge tube for separating ion-exchanger particles from adherent solution. *From K. W. Pepper, D. Reichenberg, and D. K. Hale* [229].

Ion exchangers hold the last traces of water very obstinately. This calls for great care in checking whether constant dry weight has been attained. A precise water-content determination requires much time (usually one week or more).

In determining the water content of a given ion exchanger in various ionic forms in equilibria with a variety of solutions, considerable time can be saved by using an indirect method, involving only one water-content measurement [134,229]. The dry weight of a known amount of the ion exchanger in an arbitrary condition can be calculated from the dry weight in the H^+ or Cl^- form, the capacity, and the counter-ion and solute contents:

$$q_{\text{dry}} = q_{\text{dry}}^0 \left[1 + 10^{-3} Q_{\text{weight}} \left(\sum_i \frac{\bar{x}_i M_i}{|z_i|} - M_A \right) \right] + \Sigma q_{\text{solutes}} \qquad (5\text{-}224)$$

where q_{dry}^0 = weight of the same amount of ion exchanger in the dry H^+ or Cl^- form containing no sorbed solutes; Q_{weight} = scientific weight capacity; $\bar{x}_i$ = equivalent ionic fraction of counter ion i; M_i = molecular weight of counter ion i; M_A = molecular weight of the reference counter ion (H^+ or Cl^-); $\Sigma q_{solutes}$ = weight of sorbed solutes.

The water contents under various conditions can thus be obtained by determining the corresponding wet weights, ionic compositions, and solute contents of one and the same sample which is then dried in the H^+ or Cl^- form or in another convenient form. To obtain best results, it is recommended to carry out the dry-weight determinations with strong-acid resins in Na^+ or K^+ form, weak-acid resins in H^+ form, strong-base resins in Cl^- form, and weak-base resins in free-base form.

The water content of strong-base resins with quaternary ammonium groups must be determined indirectly because Hofmann degradation occurs when the resin is dried in the OH^- form.

Water contents of ion-exchange resins have also been determined by Karl-Fischer titration [76a].

The techniques described above involve weighing of the swollen ion exchanger and thus require the separation of the latter from the solution. This separation is a source of errors, particularly if the ion-exchanger particles are very small and of irregular shape. Here, an alternative technique may be more practical. A weighed amount of completely dry ion-exchange material is added to a known amount of the solution. The solution contains an indicator, for example an organic dye, which cannot penetrate into the ion exchanger because of its molecular size. The solvent uptake by the ion exchanger is calculated from the increase of indicator concentration in the solution [229]. Of course, the results obtained by this method may be affected by the presence of the indicator in the equilibrating solution. Also, errors can be caused by adsorption of the indicator at the surface of the ion exchanger [259].

Solvent contents of ion exchangers in equilibrium with nonaqueous solutions or solvents can be determined in an analogous manner.

d. Water-vapor Sorption Isotherms

The most convenient method for determining water-vapor sorption isotherms is by isopiestic measurements. This technique was developed by Robinson [244] for electrolyte solutions and has been adapted to ion-exchange resins by Boyd [40].

Determination of the isotherm requires measurements of the water contents of the ion exchanger in equilibrium with water vapor of various partial pressures. The equilibration is carried out in a closed vessel (Fig. 5-45). Samples of the ion exchanger are placed in shallow silver dishes with accurately flat, polished bottoms. A similar silver dish is filled with a saturated aqueous solution of known vapor pressure. The dishes are placed inside the closed vessel where they stand on an accurately flat, gold-plated, and polished copper block. The vessel is airtight and is evacuated before the measurement. A magnetic ventilator promotes the equilibration. The vessel is immersed in a thermostat. After the ion exchanger has come to equilibrium with the water vapor, the vessel is opened and the ion exchanger is weighed in stoppered weighing bottles. The determination of the dry weight of the ion exchanger has been described previously (Sec. 5-9c).

Alternatively, a quartz-spring apparatus can be used [76a]. Here, the increase in weight of an initially dry sample upon contact with vapor of a known partial pressure is directly observed.

e. Volume and Density Determinations

The volume and density of an ion exchanger in equilibrium with a solution are readily determined with a specific-gravity bottle [113,229]. The ion exchanger is equilibrated with the solution and weighed in its swollen state (see Sec. 5-9c). The specific-gravity bottle is filled with the solution, and the ion-exchanger beads are allowed to settle into the bottle. After thermal equilibrium is attained, the bottle is weighed. The volume $\bar{V}$ of the ion exchanger is

$$\bar{V} = V_\text{b} - \frac{Q_\text{b} - \bar{Q}}{\rho} \tag{5-225}$$

where V_b = volume of the bottle; Q_b = weight of the bottle content; $\bar{Q}$ = wet weight of the ion exchanger; ρ = density of the solution.

The density $\bar{\rho}$ of the ion exchanger is

$$\bar{\rho} = \frac{\bar{Q}}{\bar{V}} \tag{5-226}$$

Determinations of the volume and density of dry or incompletely swollen ion exchangers require the use of a liquid which causes no swelling and is immiscible with the solvent

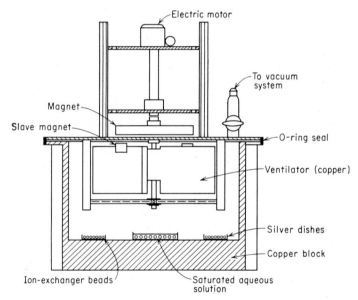

Fig. 5-45. Apparatus for isopiestic determinations of vapor-sorption isotherms. (Thermostat vessel is not shown.) *From G. E. Boyd and B. A. Soldano* [40].

in the ion exchangers [113,229]. For most determinations with dry or partially water-swollen resins, aliphatic hydrocarbons such as *n*-octane can be used. In other cases, preliminary tests should be made to find a suitable liquid. The determination itself is carried out as above.

The volume of spherical ion-exchanger particles can also be determined directly by measurement of the diameter under the microscope [49,91b] or with a microcomparator [113].

f. Sorption of Solutes

Sorption of solutes is usually determined in the following way. A known amount of the ion exchanger is equilibrated with a solution of known concentration (see Sec. 5-9b) and then separated from it and analyzed.

As a rule, sorption is reversible. In this case, the sorbed solute can be removed from the ion exchanger by washing with pure solvent and can be determined in the wash liquid by standard analytical methods [63,110,229]. The analysis gives the amount of sorbed solute. Determination of the molality of the solute in the ion exchanger requires, in addition, a knowledge of the solvent content of the latter (see Sec. 5-9c).

It is important to check whether sorption equilibrium has indeed been attained. The best test is to approach equilibrium from both sides. Two samples are used, one initially containing no solute, the other initially containing an excess of solute (sorbed from a more concentrated solution); equilibration of the two samples with a given solution should then lead to the same final solute content.

The measurement of irreversible sorption is more difficult. A possible technique is to determine the decrease in solution concentration in the course of equilibration with an ion exchanger which, initially, contains no solute [63]. Of course, swelling changes which also alter the solution concentration must be taken into account. In principle, this technique can also be used for measuring reversible sorption. However, it gives less accurate results than the method described previously.

Sorption of most inorganic solutes can also be determined by (dry or wet) combustion of the ion exchanger and analysis of the residue by standard analytical methods [146a, 179].

Serious errors may occur in determining sorption of strong electrolytes. Because of the Donnan exclusion, the electrolyte concentration in the ion exchanger is much smaller than in the solution. This is particularly true when high-capacity resins are equilibrated with dilute solutions. Small traces of solution adhering to the beads will thus cause a considerable error [91]. Especially with fine or irregularly shaped beads, a clean separation from the solution is rather difficult. The most reliable results are obtained with ion-exchanger membranes or disks with smooth surfaces from which adherent solution is readily removed [134,198,201]; see also Sec. 5-9b.

Another source of error in the determination of electrolyte sorption is hydrolysis which may take place while the solute is being removed by washing the ion exchanger with water. For example, if sorption of HCl by a strong-base anion exchanger is determined, washing with water may result in partial hydrolysis

$$H_2O + \overline{Cl^-} \rightarrow H^+ + Cl^- + \overline{OH^-} \tag{5-227}$$

especially if the ion exchanger contains a few weak-base groups [171]. The wash liquid may thus contain HCl in excess of the amount which was sorbed. This error can be eliminated by using a chloride solution, say, NaCl instead of pure water for leaching out the sorbed HCl. The chloride content of the wash liquid discourages the hydrolysis.

With weak-acid and weak-base ion exchangers, hydrolysis in the washing step can hardly be avoided. Here, it is usually preferable to determine the total counter-ion content by displacement with another counter ion. The total counter-ion content is the sum of the ion-exchange and sorption capacities of the sample (see Sec. 4-2 for difficulties in defining sorption and ion-exchange capacities).

The solute can be removed from the resin by leaching the latter in a column, or by repeated batch equilibrations with small volumes of solvent (see Sec. 5-9b). The second technique is more time-consuming, but can also be used for materials which are not in bead form.

As a rule, the amount of desorbed solute in the column effluent or in the combined wash liquids can be determined by standard analytical methods. The sensitivity of the method can be increased by using radioactive tracers. However, this technique requires more elaborate equipment and safety measures when handling higher activities and may pose waste disposal problems. Thus radioactive materials should be used only if the desired results cannot be obtained with other methods.

Sorption isotherms can also be calculated from column effluent histories. Here, no separation of the ion exchanger from the solution is necessary. This technique will be discussed in Sec. 5-9h.

g. Ion-exchange Equilibria

Ion-exchange equilibria are usually determined by equilibrating the ion exchanger with a solution containing both competing counter-ion species and analyzing the ionic composition of the ion exchanger after separation from the solution. The equilibration can be carried out in a column or by repeated batch treatment with portions of the solution (Sec. 5-9b). The separation of the ion exchanger from the solution is less critical than in electrolyte-sorption measurements; the counter-ion concentrations in the ion exchanger are usually much larger than in the solution, so that traces of adherent solution cannot cause serious errors. If electrolyte sorption is known to be small, the adherent solution may be removed by rinsing the material briefly with pure solvent. However, centrifugation, though more time-consuming, is preferable (see Sec. 5-9b). The amounts of the two competing counter ions in the ion exchanger are determined by displacing both species by treatment with a (not too dilute) solution of a third counter ion [112]. This may be done in a column or by repeated batch equilibration. The amounts of the two species are then determined in the column effluent or in the combined equilibration liquids by standard analytical methods. The third counter ion should be chosen in such a way that it does not interfere with the determinations. The displacement is facilitated by choosing a counter ion which the ion exchanger prefers to the two other species. A simpler alternative (applicable if electrolyte sorption is negligible) is to displace one of the competing species by equilibration with an excess of the other. Only the first species is then determined. The amount of the second species is calculated by difference (total ion-exchange capacity of the sample minus the amount of the first species).

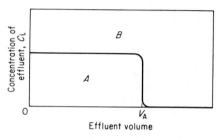

Fig. 5-46. Effluent history in displacement of a mixture of two counter ions A and B by the preferred species B (*schematic*). The mixed band ends with a sharp rear boundary. The amount of A initially in the column is the product of the (constant) effluent concentration C_A and the solution volume V_A required for displacing the mixed band.

The establishment of equilibrium may require considerable time. The best test for equilibrium is to approach it from both sides. Two samples of the ion exchanger may be used, one in A form and one in B form. After equilibration with a solution containing both species A and B, the ionic composition of both samples should be the same (for hysteresis phenomena, see page 189). In many early publications on ion-exchange equilibria, no such tests were made and equilibrium may not have been attained.

In cases in which electrolyte sorption and hydrolysis are known to be negligible, the determination of equilibrium can be carried out by an alternative and very convenient column method [57,81]. The solution containing both competing counter ions is passed through the column until the effluent has the same composition as the feed. The column is then briefly purged with pure solvent to displace the interstitial solution. After the purge, the more loosely held counter ion is displaced from the column by a solution of the preferred species. The concentrations of the two competing species in the effluent will remain constant until the mixed band ends with a sharp rear boundary (see Fig. 5-46).

The amount of the displaced species is calculated either from its steady-state concentration in the effluent and the effluent volume up to the breakthrough point (see Fig. 5-46) or from analysis of the total effluent. The amount of the other species in the column before displacement is calculated by difference as above (total ion-exchange capacity of the column minus the amount of the displaced species). The ion exchanger can remain in the column throughout the determination.

A special-purpose column for measurements at high temperatures and under pressure has been described by Kraus [178].

It is, of course, possible to equilibrate a sample of the ion exchanger in one single batch with a known volume of solution of known composition, instead of using the column or repeated-batch techniques described, previously. The advantages are that less time and solution are required for equilibration. There are, however, several disadvantages. First, the solution composition—which changes in the course of equilibration—cannot be fixed beforehand. Second, the solution *and* the ion exchanger must be analyzed unless swelling changes and electrolyte sorption are known to be negligible. In many early investigations in which equilibration was carried out in this way, the ion exchanger was not analyzed and its composition was calculated from the concentration changes in the solution by material balances, assuming the concentrations were changed by ion exchange only. Equilibrium data calculated in this way are unreliable since sorption and desorption of electrolytes and solvent, which may also change the concentrations in the solution, were not taken into account. If these effects are known to be negligible, the single-batch equilibration offers considerable advantages, especially if the concentrations in the solution can be determined without separating the latter from the ion exchanger. For example, for the ion exchange Ag$^+$/H$^+$ such a method has been developed by Högfeldt [143,145]. Here, the concentration of Ag$^+$ is determined by emf measurement (Fig. 5-47).

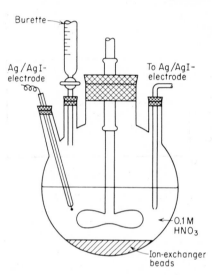

Fig. 5-47. Apparatus for determining ion-exchange isotherms involving Ag$^+$. The ion exchanger is converted stepwise to the Ag$^+$ form by successive addition of AgNO$_3$ solution from the burette. After each addition, time is allowed for establishment of equilibrium, and Ag$^+$ is then determined potentiometrically. *From E. Högfeldt* [145].

Another source of error that has been overlooked in many early publications is hydrolysis. For example, if a solution of an electrolyte BY is equilibrated with the A form of an ion exchanger which prefers H$^+$ strongly to B$^+$, the ion exchange

$$\overline{A^+} + B^+ \rightarrow \overline{B^+} + A^+ \qquad (5\text{-}228)$$

is accompanied by partial hydrolysis

$$\overline{A^+} + H_2O \rightarrow \overline{H^+} + A^+ + OH^- \qquad (5\text{-}229)$$

With zeolites, this phenomenon may be quite pronounced if the ion B$^+$ is excluded by sieve action. Furthermore, the hydrolysis (5-229) is enhanced if the ion A$^+$ is sequestered in the solution by complex formation or precipitation. A characteristic example is the reaction of a cesium chloride solution with silver analcite which excludes Cs^+ [14]:

$$\overline{Ag^+} + Cl^- + H_2O \rightleftharpoons \overline{H^+} + \underline{AgCl} + OH^- \tag{5-230}$$

The extent of hydrolysis can be determined by measuring the pH change in the solution. In earlier work, however, such tests were not made.

The quantitative determination of the competing species in the ion exchanger (after they have been displaced) and in the solution can usually be carried out by standard analytical methods. Radioactive tracers are very useful in that they permit the study of the behavior of trace components [146]. From the distribution of a radioactive trace element, valuable information can be obtained as to whether the component is present as an ion, a complex ion, or a colloid [58,196,262,265,268]. Otherwise, the use of radioactive materials should be restricted to cases in which other methods fail.

h. Ion-exchange and Sorption Isotherms

Ion-exchange and sorption isotherms can be determined point by point from a series of ion-exchange or sorption equilibrium measurements with solutions of different compositions covering the whole range of interest. This procedure, no doubt, gives the most reliable results. However, it is comparatively laborious and time-consuming.

If determination of the concentrations in the solution is sufficient to calculate the equilibrium distribution (see page 236), the "progressive-batch" method [57] is more convenient. Here, a sample of the ion exchanger in A form is converted stepwise to the B form by successive equilibrations with portions of a solution of the electrolyte BY. The concentrations of A and B in the solution are determined after each conversion step. The ionic composition of the ion exchanger is calculated by difference. Likewise, the sorption isotherm can be measured with one single sample, which is initially free of solute, by stepwise increased sorption. This technique permits the whole isotherm to be obtained from successive measurements with only one sample of the ion exchanger and without separating the latter from the solution. The results should be tested for attainment of equilibrium in the various steps by measuring the isotherm in the reverse direction also, i.e., treating the B form of the ion exchanger with solutions of AY, or measuring the desorption of the solute by stepwise treatment with pure solvent.

A very elegant and rapid alternative method has been worked out chiefly by Glueckauf [102,103], Sillén [273], and Thomas [87,88,213] (see also Sec. 9-9). Here, the whole isotherm is calculated from the effluent history of one single column experiment. In the case of sorption of a solute, the column is pretreated by feeding a concentrated solution in order to obtain a high initial sorption. The sorbed solute is then eluted with pure solvent. In the case of ion exchange, the column is pretreated by converting it to the monoionic A form, where A is preferred by the ion exchanger to B. The species A is then eluted by a solution of BY. In both cases a diffuse rear boundary (of the solute or the species A) is obtained (see Sec. 9-1). From the shape of this boundary in the effluent, the isotherm can be calculated. In ion exchange, it is essential that *the preferred species is eluted by the other one* since otherwise a self-sharpening boundary is obtained which cannot be used to calculate the isotherm. Provided that local equilibrium between the ion exchanger and the solution in the various layers of the column is attained in the elution step, there is the following functional relation between the concentration C_i of the solute or initial counter ion A in the effluent and the concentration $\bar{C}_i$ of the species in the ion exchanger in equilibrium with C_i:

$$\bar{C}_i = \frac{Q_i(V) + (V - \beta V_b)C_i}{(1 - \beta)V_b} \tag{5-231}$$

where $Q_i(V)$ = total amount of species i (solute, or counter ion A) remaining in the column after elution with solution volume V; V = elution volume at which the concentration in the effluent is C_i; V_b = total volume of the column; β = fractional void volume in the column.

[This equation is obtained from Eq. (9-3) under the conditions of local equilibrium and absence of longitudinal diffusion.] While the diffuse rear boundary migrates out of the column, the concentration C_i of the solute or the species A in the effluent decreases continuously from its maximum initial value to zero. The values of V (effluent volume) and $Q_i(V)$ (amount of species i remaining in the column) corresponding to intermediate values of C_i are obtained from the effluent history (see Fig. 5-48; $Q_i(V)$ is calculated by graphical integration). The application of Eq. (5-231) to a set of different values of C_i gives $\bar{C}_i$ as a function of C_i, i.e., the desired isotherm.

As compared with the determination of an isotherm from a large number of equilibrium measurements, this column technique has the obvious advantage of being much faster.

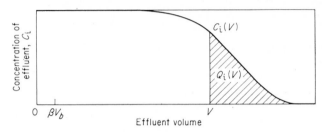

FIG. 5-48. Diffuse rear boundary in desorption or ion-exchange elution of a preferred counter ion. The diagram shows the effluent history and the quantities appearing in Eq. (5-231). *According to E. Glueckauf* [103].

Its disadvantage is that local equilibrium in the layers of the column, as assumed in the derivation of Eq. (5-231), can be attained only if the rate of ion exchange or desorption is very high, the flow rate very low, and the particle size of the ion exchanger very small. Under normal conditions, ion-exchange columns do not operate in local equilibrium. According to Glueckauf [103], a correction for deviations from local equilibrium can be applied by adding the term $(\epsilon/2N)V^2(\partial C_i/\partial V)$ to the numerator on the right-hand side of Eq. (5-231) (compare Sec. 9-9); here, ϵ ($1 \leq \epsilon \leq 2$) is a quantity which depends on the curvature of the isotherm, and N is the number of effective plates which must be determined by a separate measurement. Thomas [87] gives a similar correction. The derivation of these corrections, as outlined in Sec. 9-9, involves rather drastic simplifying assumptions about the rate laws of ion exchange or desorption. Hence, the results are reliable only as long as the correction remains small. With mineral ion exchangers, where the ion-exchange rate is rather low, the isotherms calculated by this method are often found to be badly in error [88,213], whereas satisfactory results have been obtained with ion-exchange resins of small particle size [103]. The handling of the technique requires much skill and can be recommended only to experts with experience in ion-exchange and column operation.

i. Calorimetric Measurements

Only comparatively few calorimetric measurements of the heats of swelling, sorption, and ion exchange have been reported in the past, though such measurements are not difficult to carry out. The heat evolved or absorbed can be measured directly in a common calorimeter [53,59,60,76,76a,195]. A convenient apparatus has been described by Cruickshank and Meares (see Fig. 5-49). A microcalorimeter has been developed in which the resin lies on an iron-constantan thermocouple and is wetted with the solution by a built-in micropipette [216]. In such calorimeters, the temperature change caused by the process is measured. Instead, a Bunsen-type constant-temperature calorimeter [46] can be used. Here, the heat released or absorbed causes a phase transition of an indicator substance. The extent of this phase transition is measured dilatometrically. Diphenylmethane, which undergoes a phase transition at 24.48°C, has been used as the indicator [115].

SUMMARY

Solvent uptake and swelling. Dry ion exchangers can sorb water and other solvents. The "driving forces" for solvent uptake are the solvation tendency of the counter ions and fixed ionic groups and the tendency of the highly concentrated pore liquid to dilute itself. Electrostatic repulsion between neighboring fixed charges is a possible additional factor.

Resins and other gels swell when taking up solvent. The elastic matrix is stretched to make room for solvent molecules. The expanded matrix, in turn, exerts a pressure (the so-called swelling pressure) on the pore liquid. Swelling equilibrium is attained when the swelling pressure, which tends to squeeze solvent out of the gel, balances the driving forces for solvent uptake. The swelling pressure in the common general-purpose ion-exchange resins is of the order of several hundred atmospheres. As a rule, resins swell most strongly when the degree of crosslinking, the concentration of the external solution, and the valence of the counter ion are low, when the (solvated) counter ion is large, and when no specific interactions between counter ions and fixed ionic groups occur.

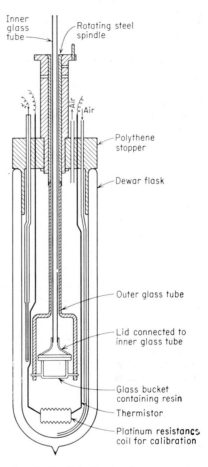

FIG. 5-49. Calorimeter for measuring heats of ion exchange, swelling, and sorption. The bucket containing the resin will tip when the lid is removed by raising the protecting inner glass tube. *From E. H. Cruickshank and P. Meares* [59].

Natural and synthetic zeolites have a rather rigid three-dimensional lattice and thus do not swell to a significant extent. However, they can accommodate solvent molecules in lattice interstices. The amount of solvent taken up is chiefly determined by the available space in the lattice.

Solvent molecules which are larger than the pore width of the zeolite are excluded by "sieve action."

Mineral ion exchangers with layer structure swell by widening their interlayer distance. In the early stages of swelling the interlayer distance increases stepwise rather than continuously ("crystalline swelling").

Sorption of solutes. Ion exchangers can sorb electrolyte and nonelectrolyte solutes from solutions. A unique feature of ion exchangers is their ability to discriminate sharply between strong electrolytes and nonelectrolytes. The latter are, as a rule, taken up much more strongly than the former.

Nonelectrolytes are sorbed in much the same way as by nonionic sorbents. The isotherms are of the same general type as the Langmuir and Freundlich isotherms, i.e., the distribution coefficient usually decreases with increasing concentration of the external solution. Sorption is favored by specific interactions between the solute and constituents of the ion exchanger, for example, by complex formation with the counter ions or London interactions with the matrix. Sorption is discouraged by the solvation tendency of the counter ions in the ion exchanger (salting out) and, particularly with zeolites, by sieve action when the solute molecules are too large to penetrate into the pores of the ion exchanger.

Sorption of *electrolytes* is affected by electrostatic forces. The tendency of the counter ions in the ion exchanger to diffuse out into the solution gives rise to an electric potential difference at the interface between the ion exchanger and the solution. This so-called Donnan potential discourages electrolyte solutes from entering the ion exchanger. Donnan exclusion of electrolytes is strongest if the ion exchanger has a high capacity and a high degree of crosslinking, if the equilibrating solution is dilute, and if the valence of the counter ion is low and that of the co-ion is high. The characteristic feature of the Donnan-type sorption isotherms of electrolytes is the *increase* of the distribution coefficient with increasing solution concentration. This is in contrast to the Langmuir- or Freundlich-type isotherms where the distribution coefficient varies in the opposite way.

Donnan exclusion of electrolytes is not universal. Strong specific interactions in the ion exchanger can result in significant electrolyte sorption. This is particularly true for cation exchangers with polyvalent cations which associate with the fixed ionic groups, and for anion exchangers with polyvalent anions such as PO_4^{3-} which trap protons and thus attract acids into the ion exchanger ("site sharing").

Ion-exchange equilibria. Ion exchangers can distinguish between different counter ions. When counter ions are exchanged, the ion exchanger usually takes up or retains certain counter ions in preference to others. This *selectivity* can arise from one or several of the following physical causes. The Donnan potential, a purely electrostatic effect, results in a preference for the counter ion of higher valence (electroselectivity), particularly when the ion-exchange capacity is high and the external solution is dilute. Specific interactions between a counter ion and the fixed ionic groups—formation of ion pairs or strong complexes—result in a preference for this ion. In resins and other gels, the tendency of the elastic matrix to contract results in a preference for the smaller ion (on a solvated equivalent-volume basis) which causes less swelling. Very large counter ions may be excluded by sieve action. The selectivity of zeolites, which have a regular and rather rigid lattice, is chiefly determined by lattice forces and by steric effects such as sieve action and space requirements of the (nonsolvated) counter ions. Ion exchange may cause a discontinuous lattice rearrangement.

The selectivity of ion exchangers is also affected by interactions in the external solution, particularly by complex formation of the counter ions with the co-ion. The counter ion which forms the weaker complex is preferred. Thus, by addition of a complexing agent to the solution, the selectivity of a given ion exchanger can be enhanced or varied. Measurements of ion-exchange equilibria with complexing agents can be used for calculating complex-stability constants.

"Ligand exchange." Ion exchangers can be used as solid carriers for metal ions which can form complexes with nonionic and anionic ligands. Such ligand exchangers can exchange ligands with solutions in essentially the same way as ordinary ion exchangers exchange counter ions. Ligand exchangers are highly selective. In particular, they can distinguish sharply between ligands which differ in their coordinative valences. A low solution concentration favors preference of the resin for the ligand with the higher coordinative valence, and vice versa.

Reactions with materials of low solubility. Ion exchangers are able to dissolve slightly soluble salts, acids, and bases. Equilibrium between the solid and the dissolved ions in the supernatant solution is disturbed when the ions are removed by ion exchange, and is re-established by further dissolution of the solid. Mixtures of cation and anion exchangers are much more efficient dissolving agents than either of the ion exchangers alone.

Quantitative theories and models. Equilibria between ion exchangers and solutions can be described in terms of abstract thermodynamics. This treatment is rigorous, universally applicable, and requires no model with particular properties, but it yields a minimum of information about the action of the various physical forces and provides no basis for predicting equilibria from fundamental data. The thermodynamic approach can be modified by introducing models with particular properties. The equations obtained in this way reflect the effects of the properties with which the model has been equipped, and thus provide a clearer insight into the action of the physical forces and a better basis for predicting equilibria. On the other hand, any commitment to a model with specific properties restricts the validity of the treatment to systems which are adequately represented by the model. Many such models have been suggested and applied. For ion-exchange resins, a very simple model which accounts for the elastic properties of the matrix has been widely and successfully used. Other, more elaborate models include further effects such as electrostatic interactions, etc., but their evaluation is much more difficult and time-consuming.

In the various thermodynamic treatments, activity coefficients are introduced to account for the effects which are not represented in the model. The definitions and numerical values of these coefficients thus depend on the properties of the model. In addition, the coefficients and equilibrium constants depend on the choice of the standard and reference states. These facts must be kept in mind when literature data are compared.

REFERENCES

1. Andelin, J., and N. Davidson, *J. Am. Chem. Soc.*, **75**, 5413 (1953).
2. Anderson, R. E., and R. D. Hansen, *Ind. Eng. Chem.*, **47**, 71 (1955).
3. Arden, T. V., and G. A. Wood, *J. Chem. Soc.*, **1956**, 1596.
3a. Arden, T. V., and M. Giddings, *J. Appl. Chem.*, **11**, 229 (1961).
4. Argersinger, W. J., Jr., and A. W. Davidson, *J. Phys. Chem.*, **56**, 92 (1952).
5. Asakura, S., N. Imai, and F. Oosawa, *J. Polymer Sci.*, **13**, 499 (1954).
6. Barrer, R. M., *Colloque international sur les réactions dans l'état solide*, Paris, 1948.
7. Barrer, R. M., *J. Chem. Soc.*, **1950**, 2342.
8. Barrer, R. M., and L. Hinds, *J. Chem. Soc.*, **1953**, 1879.
9. Barrer, R. M., and D. W. Brook, *Trans. Faraday Soc.*, **49**, 940 (1953).
10. Barrer, R. M., and J. S. Raitt, *J. Chem. Soc.*, **1954**, 4641.
11. Barrer, R. M., and D. C. Sammon, *J. Chem. Soc.*, **1955**, 2838.
12. Barrer, R. M., and D. M. MacLeod, *Trans. Faraday Soc.*, **51**, 1290 (1955).
13. Barrer, R. M., and D. C. Sammon, *J. Chem. Soc.*, **1956**, 675.
*14. Barrer, R. M., and J. D. Falconer, *Proc. Roy. Soc. (London)*, **A236**, 227 (1956).
15. Barrer, R. M., W. Buser, and W. F. Grütter, *Helv. chim. Acta*, **39**, 518 (1956).
16. Barrer, R. M., and W. M. Meier, *J. Chem. Soc.*, **1958**, 299.
*17. Barrer, R. M., *Proc. Chem. Soc. (London)*, **1958**, 99; *Brit. Chem. Eng.*, **4**, 267 (1959).
18. Barrer, R. M., and W. M. Meier, *Trans. Faraday Soc.*, **55**, 130 (1959).
19. Bauman, W. C., and J. Eichhorn, *J. Am. Chem. Soc.*, **69**, 2830 (1947).
20. Bauman, W. C., and D. F. Harrington (The Dow Chemical Company), U.S. Patent 2,738,322, 1956.
21. Bauman, W. C., and D. F. Harrington (The Dow Chemical Company), U.S. Patent 2,772,237, 1956.
*22. Bauman, W. C., R. M. Wheaton, and D. W. Simpson, in "Ion Exchange Technology," F. C. Nachod and J. Schubert (eds.), p. 182, Academic Press, Inc., New York, 1956.
23. Baumann, E. W., and W. J. Argersinger, Jr., *J. Am. Chem. Soc.*, **78**, 1130 (1956).
24. Bergman, W. E. (Phillips Petroleum Co.), U.S. Patent 2,671,035, 1954.
25. Bernhard, S. A., *J. Am. Chem. Soc.*, **74**, 4946 (1952).
26. Bishop, J. A., *J. Phys. Chem.*, **50**, 6 (1946); **54**, 697 (1950).
*27. Bjerrum, J., "Metal Ammine Formation in Aqueous Solution," P. Haase & Son, Copenhagen, 1940.
*28. Bjerrum, J., G. Schwarzenbach, and L. G. Sillén, "Stability Constants of Metal-ion Complexes," The Chemical Society, London, 1957.
29. Bloksma, A. H., *J. Colloid Sci.*, **11**, 286 (1956).

* Review articles are marked with asterisks.

30. Bonhoeffer, K. F., L. Miller, and U. Schindewolf, *Z. physik. Chem.*, **198**, 270, 281 (1951).

31. Bonner, O. D., W. J. Argersinger, Jr., and A. W. Davidson, *J. Am. Chem. Soc.*, **74**, 1044 (1952).

32. Bonner, O. D., *J. Phys. Chem.*, **58**, 318 (1954).

33. Bonner, O. D., G. D. Easterling, D. L. West, and V. F. Holland, *J. Am. Chem. Soc.*, **77**, 242 (1955).

34. Bonner, O. D., *J. Phys. Chem.*, **59**, 719 (1955).

35. Bonner, O. D., V. F. Holland, and L. L. Smith, *J. Phys. Chem.*, **60**, 1102 (1956).

36. Bonner, O. D., and L. L. Smith, *J. Phys. Chem.*, **61**, 326 (1957).

37. Bonner, O. D., and R. R. Pruett, *J. Phys. Chem.*, **63**, 1417, 1420 (1959).

38. Bonner, O. D., G. Dickel, and H. Brümmer, *Z. physik. Chem. (Frankfurt)*, **25**, 81 (1960).

39. Boyd, G. E., J. Schubert, and A. W. Adamson, *J. Am. Chem. Soc.*, **69**, 2818 (1947).

40. Boyd, G. E., and B. A. Soldano, *Z. Elektrochem.*, **57**, 162 (1953).

41. Boyd, G. E., *Z. Elektrochem.*, **57**, 170 (1953) (remark in discussion).

42. Boyd, G. E., B. A. Soldano, and O. D. Bonner, *J. Phys. Chem.*, **58**, 456 (1954).

42a. Boyd, G. E., S. Lindenbaum, and G. E. Myers, *J. Phys. Chem.*, **65**, 577 (1961).

43. Bregman, J. I., and Y. Murata, *J. Am. Chem. Soc.*, **74**, 1867 (1952).

44. Brochmann-Hanssen, E., *J. Am. Pharm. Assoc.*, **43**, 307 (1954).

45. Brønsted, J. N., *J. Am. Chem. Soc.*, **44**, 877 (1922); **45**, 2898 (1923).

46. Bunsen, R., *Ann. Physik*, **141**, 1 (1870).

*47. Buser, W., P. Graf, and W. F. Grütter, *Chimia*, **9**, 73 (1955).

48. Cady, H. H., and R. E. Connick, *J. Am. Chem. Soc.*, **80**, 2646 (1958).

49. Calmon, C., *Anal. Chem.*, **24**, 1456 (1952); **25**, 490 (1953).

50. Calmon, C. (The Permutit Co. Ltd.), U.S. Patent 2,689,829, 1954.

51. Carsten, M. E., and R. K. Cannan, *J. Am. Chem. Soc.*, **74**, 5950 (1952).

52. Chasanov, M. G., R. Kunin, and F. McGarvey, *Ind. Eng. Chem.*, **48**, 305 (1956).

53. Coleman, N. T., *Soil Sci.*, **74**, 115 (1952).

54. Cornaz, J. P., and H. Deuel, *Helv. chim. Acta*, **39**, 1220 (1956).

55. Cornaz, J. P., and H. Deuel, *Helv. chim. Acta*, **39**, 1227 (1956).

56. Coryell, C. D., 1959 (unpublished).

57. Cosgrove, J. D., and J. D. H. Strickland, *J. Chem. Soc.*, **1950**, 1845.

58. Crouthamel, C. E., and D. S. Martin, Jr., *J. Am. Chem. Soc.*, **72**, 1382 (1950).

59. Cruickshank, E. H., and P. Meares, *Trans. Faraday Soc.*, **53**, 1289 (1957).

60. Cruickshank, E. H., and P. Meares, *Trans. Faraday Soc.*, **53**, 1299 (1957); **54**, 174 (1958).

61. Curti, R., and U. Colombo, *J. Am. Chem. Soc.*, **74**, 3961 (1952).

62. Davies, C. W., and G. G. Thomas, *J. Chem. Soc.*, **1951**, 2624.

63. Davies, C. W., and G. D. Yeoman, *Trans. Faraday Soc.*, **49**, 968 (1953).

64. Davies, C. W., and G. D. Yeoman, *Trans. Faraday Soc.*, **49**, 975 (1953).

65. Davies, C. W., and B. D. R. Owen, *J. Chem. Soc.*, **1956**, 1676.

66. Davies, C. W., and B. D. R. Owen, *J. Chem. Soc.*, **1956**, 1681.

67. Davis, L. E., *J. Phys. Chem.*, **49**, 473 (1945); *J. Colloid Sci.*, **5**, 71, 107 (1950).

68. Davis, L. E., and J. M. Rible, *J. Colloid Sci.*, **5**, 81 (1950).

69. Davydov, A. T., and I. Ya. Levitskii, *Trudy Nauch.-Issledoratel Khim. Kharkov Univ.*, **10**, 221, 233 (1953); *Chem. Abstr.*, **49**, 13733, 13734 (1955). *Kolloid Zhur.*, **16**, 13 (1954); *Chem. Abstr.*, **48**, 6777 (1954).

70. Davydov, A. T., and R. Z. Davydova, *Kolloid Zhur.*, **20**, 425 (1958).

71. Dent, L. S., and J. V. Smith, *Nature*, **181**, 1794 (1958).

72. Deuel, H., J. Solms, and L. Anyas-Weisz, *Helv. chim. Acta*, **33**, 2171 (1950).

---

* Review articles are marked with asterisks.

73. Deuel, H., L. Anyas-Weisz, and J. Solms, *Experientia*, **7**, 294 (1951).
74. Deuel, H., K. Hutschneker, and J. Solms, *Z. Elektrochem.*, **57**, 172 (1953).
75. Dickel, G., and A. Meyer, *Z. Elektrochem.*, **57**, 901 (1953).
76. Dickel, G., H. Degenhart, K. Haas, and J. W. Hartmann, *Z. physik. Chem. (Frankfurt)*, **20**, 121 (1959).
76a. Dickel, G., and J. W. Hartmann, *Z. physik. Chem. (Frankfurt)*, **23**, 1 (1960).
76b. Dickel, G., *Z. physik. Chem. (Frankfurt)*, **25**, 233 (1960).
77. Dickey, F. H., *Proc. Natl. Acad. Sci.*, **35**, 227 (1948); *J. Phys. Chem.*, **59**, 695 (1955).
78. Donnan, F. G., *Z. Elektrochem.*, **17**, 572 (1911); *Z. physik. Chem.*, **A168**, 369 (1934).
79. Donnan, F. G., and E. A. Guggenheim, *Z. physik. Chem.*, **A162**, 346 (1932).
80. Dranoff, J. S., and L. Lapidus, *Ind. Eng. Chem.*, **49**, 1297 (1957); **53**, 71 (1961).
81. Duncan, J. F., and B. A. J. Lister, *J. Chem. Soc.*, **1949**, 3285; *Discussions Faraday Soc.*, **7**, 104 (1949).
82. Duncan, J. F., *Proc. Roy. Soc. (London)*, **A214**, 344 (1952).
83. Duncan, J. F., *Austral. J. Chem.*, **8**, 1 (1955).
84. Dunken, H., *Z. physik. Chem.*, **A187**, 105 (1940).
85. Ekedahl, E., E. Högfeldt, and L. G. Sillén, *Acta Chem. Scand.*, **4**, 556 (1950).
86. Faris, J. P., *Anal. Chem.*, **32**, 520 (1960).
87. Faucher, J. A., Jr., R. W. Southworth, and H. C. Thomas, *J. Chem. Phys.*, **20**, 157 (1952).
88. Faucher, J. A., and H. C. Thomas, *J. Chem. Phys.*, **22**, 258 (1954).
*89. Flory, P. J., "Principles of Polymer Chemistry," Chaps. X–XII, Cornell University Press, Ithaca, N.Y., 1953.
*90. Fowler, R. H., and E. A. Guggenheim, "Statistical Thermodynamics," Chap. X, the Macmillan Co., New York, 1939.
91. Freeman, D. H., *J. Phys. Chem.*, **64**, 1048 (1960).
91a. Freeman, D. H., *J. Chem. Phys.*, **35**, 189 (1961).
91b. Freeman, D. H., to be published.
92. Fronaeus, S., *Acta Chem. Scand.*, **5**, 859 (1951).
93. Fronaeus, S., *Acta Chem. Scand.*, **6**, 1200 (1952); **7**, 21 (1953).
94. Fronaeus, S., *Svensk Kem. Tidskr.*, **64**, 317 (1952).
95. Fronaeus, S., *Svensk Kem. Tidskr.*, **65**, 1 (1953).
96. Fronaeus, S., *Svensk Kem. Tidskr.*, **65**, 19 (1953).
97. Fronaeus, S., *Acta Chem. Scand.*, **7**, 469 (1953).
98. Fronaeus, S., *Acta Chem. Scand.*, **8**, 1174 (1954).
99. Gaines, G. L., Jr., and H. C. Thomas, *J. Chem. Phys.*, **21**, 714 (1953).
100. Gans, R., *Zentralbl. Mineral. Geol. u. Paläontol.*, **1913**; 699, 728.
100a. Gärtner, K., R. Griessbach, and E. Anton, *Kolloid Z.*, **175**, 123 (1961).
101. Giesen, J., and F. Müller (Inventa A. G.), U.S. Patent 2,916,525 (1959).
102. Glückauf, E., *Nature*, **156**, 748 (1945).
103. Glueckauf, E., *J. Chem. Soc.*, **1949**, 3280.
104. Glueckauf, E., *Proc. Roy. Soc. (London)*, **A214**, 207 (1952).
105. Glueckauf, E., and G. P. Kitt, *Proc. Roy. Soc. (London)*, **A228**, 322 (1955).
106. Gottlieb, M. H., and H. P. Gregor, *J. Am. Chem. Soc.*, **76**, 4639 (1954).
107. Greene-Kelly, R., *Trans. Faraday Soc.*, **51**, 412 (1955); **52**, 1281 (1956).
108. Greene-Kelly, R., *J. Colloid Sci.*, **11**, 77 (1956).
109. Gregor, H. P., *J. Am. Chem. Soc.*, **70**, 1293 (1948); **73**, 642 (1951).
110. Gregor, H. P., F. Gutoff, and J. I. Bregman, *J. Colloid Sci.*, **6**, 245 (1951).
111. Gregor, H. P., F. C. Collins, and M. Pope, *J. Colloid Sci.*, **6**, 304 (1951).
112. Gregor, H. P., and J. I. Bregman, *J. Colloid Sci.*, **6**, 323 (1951).
113. Gregor, H. P., K. M. Held, and J. Bellin, *Anal. Chem.*, **23**, 620 (1951).

* Review articles are marked with asterisks.

114. Gregor, H. P., *J. Am. Chem. Soc.*, **73**, 3537 (1951).
115. Gregor, H. P., B. R. Sundheim, K. M. Held, and M. H. Waxman, *J. Colloid Sci.*, **7**, 511 (1952).
116. Gregor, H. P., and M. Frederick, *Ann. N.Y. Acad. Sci.*, **57**, 87 (1953).
117. Gregor, H. P., and M. H. Gottlieb, *J. Am. Chem. Soc.*, **75**, 3539 (1953).
118. Gregor, H. P., O. R. Abolafia, and M. H. Gottlieb, *J. Phys. Chem.*, **58**, 984 (1954).
119. Gregor, H. P., J. Belle, and R. A. Marcus, *J. Am. Chem. Soc.*, **77**, 2713 (1955).
120. Gregor, H. P., M. J. Hamilton, R. J. Oza, and F. Bernstein, *J. Phys. Chem.*, **60**, 263 (1956).
*121. Griessbach, R., *Z. Elektrochem.*, **57**, 147 (1953).
*122. Griessbach, R., "Austauschadsorption in Theorie und Praxis," pp. 94, 318, Akademie-Verlag G.m.b.H., Berlin, 1957.
123. Grubhofer, N., *Naturwissenschaften.*, **42**, 557 (1955).
124. Günther-Schulze, A., *Z. Elektrochem.*, **28**, 89, 387 (1922).
125. Guggenheim, E. A., *Proc. Roy. Soc. (London)*, **A183**, 203, 213 (1944).
126. Gustavson, K. H., and P. J. Widen, *Ind. Eng. Chem.*, **17**, 577 (1925).
127. Gustavson, K. H., *J. Colloid Sci.*, **1**, 397 (1946).
128. Gustavson, K. H., and B. Holm, *Svensk Kem. Tidskr.*, **64**, 137 (1952).
129. Hale, D. K., D. I. Packham, and K. W. Pepper, *J. Chem. Soc.*, **1953**, 844.
*130. Hale, D. K., *Analyst*, **83**, 3 (1958).
*131. Harned, H. S., and B. B. Owen, "The Physical Chemistry of Electrolytic Solutions," 3d ed., p. 600 and App. A, Reinhold Publishing Corporation, New York, 1958.
132. Harris, F. E., and S. A. Rice, *J. Chem. Phys.*, **24**, 1258 (1956).
133. Hatch, M. J., J. A. Dillon, and H. B. Smith, *Ind. Eng. Chem.*, **49**, 1812 (1957).
134. Helfferich, F., and H. D. Ocker, *Z. physik. Chem. (Frankfurt)*, **10**, 213 (1957).
135. Helfferich, F., *Nature*, **189**, 1001 (1961).
136. Helfferich, F., *J. Am. Chem. Soc.*, **84**, 3237 (1962).
137. Hendricks, S. B., R. A. Nelson, and L. T. Alexander, *J. Am. Chem. Soc.*, **62**, 1457 (1940).
138. Hendricks, S. B., *J. Phys. Chem.*, **45**, 65 (1941); *J. Geol.*, **50**, 276 (1942).
*139. Hendricks, S. B., *Ind. Eng. Chem.*, **37**, 625 (1945).
140. Herber, R. H., and J. W. Irvine, Jr., *J. Am. Chem. Soc.*, **76**, 987 (1954); **78**, 905 (1956).
*141. Hirschfelder, J. O., C. F. Curtiss, and R. B. Bird, "Molecular Theory of Gases and Liquids," Chap. 4, John Wiley & Sons, Inc., New York, 1954.
142. Högfeldt, E., E. Ekedahl, and L. G. Sillén, *Acta Chem. Scand.*, **4**, 828, 829 (1950).
143. Högfeldt, E., E. Ekedahl, and L. G. Sillén, *Acta Chem. Scand.*, **4**, 1471 (1950).
144. Högfeldt, E., *Arkiv Kemi*, **5**, 147 (1952).
145. Högfeldt, E., *Acta Chem. Scand.*, **6**, 610 (1952).
146. Högfeldt, E., *Arkiv Kemi*, **7**, 561 (1954).
146a. Högfeldt, E., and P. Kierkegaard, *Acta Chem. Scand.*, **8**, 585 (1954).
147. Högfeldt, E., *Acta Chem. Scand.*, **9**, 151 (1955).
148. Hofmann, U., K. Endell, and D. Wilm, *Z. Krist., Mineral Petrog. Abt.*, **A86**, 340 (1933).
*149. Hofmann, U., *Angew. Chem.*, **68**, 53 (1956).
150. Holroyd, A., and J. E. Salmon, *J. Chem. Soc.*, **1956**, 269.
151. Honda, M., Y. Yoshino, and T. Wabiko, *J. Chem. Soc. Japan, Pure Chem. Sec.*, **73**, 348 (1952); *Chem. Abstr.*, **47**, 2568 (1953).
152. Horne, R. A., *J. Phys. Chem.*, **61**, 1651 (1957).

* Review articles are marked with asterisks.

152a. Horne, R. A., R. H. Holm, and M. D. Meyers, *J. Phys. Chem.*, **61**, 1655, 1661 (1957).

153. Horne, R. A., *J. Inorg. & Nuclear Chem.*, **6**, 338 (1958).

154. Howe, P. G., Thesis, University of London, 1953.

155. Howe, P. G., and J. A. Kitchener, *J. Chem. Soc.*, **1955**, 2143.

156. Huffman, E. H., and G. M. Iddings, *J. Am. Chem. Soc.*, **74**, 4714 (1952).

157. Hutschneker, K., and H. Deuel, *Helv. chim. Acta*, **39**, 1038 (1956).

158. Izmailov, N. A., and S. Kh. Mushinskaya, *Doklady Akad. Nauk S.S.S.R.*, **100**, 101 (1955); *Chem. Abstr.*, **49**, 14421 (1955).

159. Jenckel, E., and H. v. Lillin, *Kolloid Z.*, **146**, 159 (1956).

160. Jenny, H., *Kolloid Beih.*, **23**, 428 (1926).

161. Jenny, H., *J. Phys. Chem.*, **36**, 2217 (1932).

162. Katchalsky, A., and S. Lifson, *J. Polymer Sci.*, **11**, 409 (1953).

*163. Katchalsky, A., *Progr. Biophys.*, **4**, 1 (1954).

164. Katchalsky, A., and M. Zwick, *J. Polymer Sci.*, **16**, 221 (1955).

165. Keenan, A. G., R. W. Mooney, and L. A. Wood, *J. Phys. Chem.*, **55**, 1462 (1951).

166. Khym, J. X., and L. P. Zill, *J. Am. Chem. Soc.*, **73**, 2399 (1951); **74**, 2090 (1952).

167. Kielland, J., *J. Soc. Chem. Ind. (London)*, **54**, 232 T (1935).

168. King, E. L., and E. B. Dismukes, *J. Am. Chem. Soc.*, **74**, 1674 (1952).

169. Koschel, D., and R. Schlögl, *Z. physik. Chem. (Frankfurt)*, **11**, 137 (1957).

170. Kraus, K. A., and G. E. Moore, *J. Am. Chem. Soc.*, **73**, 13 (1951).

171. Kraus, K. A., and G. E. Moore, *J. Am. Chem. Soc.*, **75**, 1457 (1953).

172. Kraus, K. A., F. Nelson, and J. F. Baxter, *J. Am. Chem. Soc.*, **75**, 2768 (1953).

173. Kraus, K. A., F. Nelson, F. B. Clough, and R. C. Carlston, *J. Am. Chem. Soc.*, **77**, 1391 (1955).

*174. Kraus, K. A., and F. Nelson, *Proc. Intern. Conf. Peaceful Uses Atomic Energy, Geneva*, **7**, 113 (1956).

*175. Kraus, K. A., and F. Nelson, "Anion Exchange Studies of Metal Complexes," in "The Structure of Electrolytic Solutions," p. 340, W. J. Hamer (ed.), John Wiley & Sons, Inc., New York, 1959.

176. Kraus, K. A., D. C. Michelson, and F. Nelson, *J. Am. Chem. Soc.*, **81**, 3204 (1959).

177. Kraus, K. A., and R. J. Raridon, *J. Phys. Chem.*, **63**, 1901 (1959).

178. Kraus, K. A., R. J. Raridon, and D. L. Holcomb, *J. Chromatog.*, **3**, 178 (1960).

179. Kressman, T. R. E., and J. A. Kitchener, *J. Chem. Soc.*, **1949**, 1190.

180. Kressman, T. R. E., and J. A. Kitchener, *J. Chem. Soc.*, **1949**, 1201.

181. Kressman, T. R. E., and J. A. Kitchener, *J. Chem. Soc.*, **1949**, 1208.

182. Kressman, T. R. E., *J. Phys. Chem.*, **56**, 118 (1952).

183. Krishnamoorthy, C., and R. Overstreet, *Soil Sci.*, **69**, 41 (1950).

184. Kubelka, V., *Tech. Hlida Kožuiužska*, **24**, 97 (1949); *Chem. Abstr.*, **47**, 9201 (1953).

185. Kulčickyj, I., *Coll. Czech. Chem. Comm.*, **24**, 3903 (1959).

186. Kunin, R., and R. J. Myers, *Discussions Faraday Soc.*, **7**, 114 (1949).

187. Kunin, R., and F. X. McGarvey, *Ind. Eng. Chem.*, **41**, 1265 (1949).

188. Kunin, R., *Intern. Chem. Congr., New York*, 1951; ref.: *Angew. Chem.*, **64**, 340 (1952).

*189. Kunin, R., "Ion Exchange Resins," 2d ed., p. 320, John Wiley & Sons, Inc., New York, 1958.

190. Lapanje, S., and D. Dolar, *Z. physik. Chem. (Frankfurt)*, **18**, 11 (1958); **21**, 376 (1959).

191. Lazare, L., B. R. Sundheim, and H. P. Gregor, *J. Phys. Chem.*, **60**, 641 (1956).

192. Leden, I., *Svensk Kem. Tidskr.*, **64**, 145 (1952).

---

* Review articles are marked with asterisks.

193. Lindenbaum, S., C. F. Jumper, and G. E. Boyd, *J. Phys. Chem.*, **63**, 1924 (1959).

194. Lindsay, F. K., and J. S. D'Amico, *Ind. Eng. Chem.*, **43**, 1085 (1951).

195. Lisicki, Z., *Przemysl Chem.*, **6** (29), 45 (1950); *Chem. Abstr.*, **45**, 10435 (1951).

196. Lister, B. A. J., in "Ion Exchange and Its Applications," p. 112, Society Chemical Industry, London, 1954.

197. Lowen, W. K., R. W. Stoenner, W. J. Argersinger, Jr., A. W. Davidson, and D. N. Hume, *J. Am. Chem. Soc.*, **73**, 2666 (1951).

198. Mackie, J. S., and P. Meares, *Proc. Roy. Soc. (London)*, **A232**, 485 (1955).

199. Mackie, J. S., and P. Meares, *Discussions Faraday Soc.*, **21**, 111 (1956).

200. Maier, K. H., and H. Beutelspacher, *Naturwissenschaften*, **40**, 605 (1953); *Kolloid Z.*, **135**, 10; **137**, 31 (1954).

201. Manecke, G., and K. F. Bonhoeffer, *Z. Elektrochem.*, **55**, 475 (1951).

202. Manecke, G., and E. Otto-Laupemühlen, *Z. physik. Chem. (Frankfurt)*, **2**, 336 (1954).

203. Marcus, Y., *Intern. Conf. Peaceful Uses Atomic Energy, 2d Conf., Geneva*, **3**, 465 (1958).

204. Marcus, Y., and C. D. Coryell, *Bull. Research Council Israel*, **A8**, 1, (1959).

205. Matorina, N. N., and A. N. Popov, *Zhur. Fiz. Khim.*, **32**, 2557, 2772 (1958); *Chem. Abstr.*, **53**, 13727 (1959).

206. Matorina, N. N., and N. D. Safonova, *Zhur. Neorg. Khim.*, **5**, 313 (1960).

207. Matsuura, T., *Bull. Chem. Soc. Japan*, **27**, 281 (1954); *Chem. Abstr.*, **49**, 8658 (1955).

208. Mattisson, M., and O. Samuelson, *Acta Chem. Scand.*, **12**, 1386, 1395 (1958).

209. Mattson, S., *Soil Sci.*, **28**, 179 (1929).

210. Mattson, S., and L. Wiklander, *Trans. Faraday Soc.*, **36**, 306 (1940); *Soil Sci.*, **49**, 109 (1940).

211. Mayer, S. W., and S. D. Schwartz, *J. Am. Chem. Soc.*, **72**, 5106 (1950); **73**, 222 (1951).

212. Meeker, R. E., and D. B. Luten (to be published).

213. Merriam, C. N., Jr., and H. C. Thomas, *J. Chem. Phys.*, **24**, 993 (1956).

214. Michaeli, I., and A. Katchalsky, *J. Polymer Sci.*, **23**, 683 (1957).

*215. Møller, J., *Kolloid Beih.*, **46**, 1 (1937).

216. Mongar, I. L., and A. Wassermann, *J. Chem. Soc.*, **1952**, 510.

217. Mooney, R. W., A. G. Keenan, and L. A. Wood, *J. Am. Chem. Soc.*, **74**, 1371 (1952).

218. Myers, G. E., and G. E. Boyd, *J. Phys. Chem.*, **60**, 521 (1956).

219. Nelson, F., and K. A. Kraus, *J. Am. Chem. Soc.*, **77**, 329 (1955).

220. Nelson, F., and K. A. Kraus, *J. Am. Chem. Soc.*, **80**, 4154 (1958).

221. Nelson, F., R. M. Rush, and K. A. Kraus, *J. Am. Chem. Soc.*, **82**, 339 (1960).

222. Nelson, F., R. A. Day, Jr., and K. A. Kraus, *J. Inorg. & Nuclear Chem.*, **15**, 140 (1960).

223. Nikolskii, B. P., and V. I. Paramonava, *Intern. Conf. Peaceful Uses Atomic Energy, 2d Conf., Geneva*, **28**, 75 (1959).

224. Norrish, K., *Discussions Faraday Soc.*, **18**, 120 (1954).

225. Norrish, K., and J. P. Quirk, *Nature*, **173**, 255 (1954).

226. Organ, R. M., *Museums J.*, **53**, 49 (1953); *Chem. Abstr.*, **47**, 9683 (1953).

*227. Osborn, G. H., *Analyst*, **78**, 220 (1953); "Synthetic Ion Exchangers," p. 46, Chapman & Hall, Ltd., London, 1955.

228. Pauley, J. L., *J. Am. Chem. Soc.*, **76**, 1422 (1954).

229. Pepper, K. W., D. Reichenberg, and D. K. Hale, *J. Chem. Soc.*, **1952**, 3129.

230. Pepper, K. W., and D. Reichenberg, *Z. Elektrochem.*, **57**, 183 (1953).

* Review articles are marked with asterisks.

231. Peterson, S., and R. W. Jeffers, *J. Am. Chem. Soc.*, **74**, 1605 (1952); *Ann. Kentucky Acad. Sci.*, **13**, 277 (1952).

232. Peterson, S., and E. Gowen, *Ind. Eng. Chem.*, **45**, 2584 (1953).

233. Povondra, P., R. Přibil, and Z. Šulcek, *Talanta*, **5**, 86 (1960).

234. Procter, H. R., *J. Chem. Soc.*, **105**, 313 (1914).

235. Procter, H. R., and J. A. Wilson, *J. Chem. Soc.*, **109**, 307 (1916).

235a. Redfern, J. P., and J. E. Salmon, *J. Chem. Soc.*, **1961**, 291.

236. Reichenberg, D., K. W. Pepper, and D. J. McCauley, *J. Chem. Soc.*, **1951**, 493.

237. Reichenberg, D., *Research Correspondence*, **6**, 9 S (1953); *Chem. Abstr.* **47**, 2288 (1953).

238. Reichenberg, D., and D. J. McCauley, *J. Chem. Soc.*, **1955**, 2741.

239. Reichenberg, D., *Discussions Faraday Soc.*, **21**, 138 (1956).

240. Reichenberg, D., and W. F. Wall, *J. Chem. Soc.*, **1956**, 3364.

241. Rice, S. A., and F. E. Harris, *Z. physik. Chem. (Frankfurt)*, **8**, 207 (1956).

*241a. Rice, S. A., and M. Nagasawa, "Polyelectrolyte Solutions," pp. 461–495, Academic Press, Inc., New York, 1961.

242. Richardson, R. W., *Nature*, **164**, 916 (1949); *J. Chem. Soc.*, **1951**, 910; in "Ion Exchange and Its Applications," p. 167, Society Chemical Industry, London, 1954.

243. Richter, G., *Z. physik. Chem. (Frankfurt)*, **12**, 247 (1957).

*243a. Rieman III, W., *J. Chem. Education*, **38**, 338 (1961).

244. Robinson, R. A., and D. A. Sinclair, *J. Am. Chem. Soc.*, **56**, 1830 (1934).

245. Robinson, R. A., and R. H. Stokes, *Trans. Faraday Soc.*, **45**, 612 (1949).

246. Rosenberg, N. W., J. H. B. George, and W. D. Potter, *J. Electrochem. Soc.*, **104**, 111 (1957).

247. Roth, H. H., *Ind. Eng. Chem.*, **46**, 2435 (1954); U.S. Patent 2,691,644, 1954; *Ind. Eng. Chem.*, **49**, 1820 (1957).

248. Rothmund, V., and G. Kornfeld, *Z. anorg. allgem. Chem.*, **103**, 129 (1918); **108**, 215 (1919).

249. Sakai, W., and T. Seiyama, *J. Electrochem. Soc. Japan*, **19**, 343 (1951); **20**, 21 (1952); *Chem. Abstr.*, **46**, 4318 (1952). *Memoirs Fac. Eng. Kyushu Univ.*, **13**, 95 (1952), and **14**, 85 (1953); *Chem. Abstr.*, **47**, 21 (1953); **48**, 4928 (1954).

250. Saldaze, K. M., Z. G. Demonterik, and Z. V. Klimova, *Issl. Oblasti Ionoobmennoi Kromatog.*, *Akad. Nauk S.S.S.R.*, *Otdel. Khim. Nauk*, *Trudy Soveshchaniya*, **1957**, 48; *Chem. Abstr.*, **52**, 1725, 15188 (1958).

251. Salmon, J. E., and J. G. L. Wall, *J. Chem. Soc.*, **1958**, 1128.

*251a. Salmon, J. E., and D. K. Hale, "Ion Exchange. A Laboratory Manual," Academic Press, Inc., New York, 1959.

252. Samuelson, O., *Svensk Kem. Tidskr.*, **56**, 277 (1944).

253. Samuelson, O., and E. Sjöström, *Svensk Kem. Tidskr.*, **64**, 305 (1952).

254. Sansoni, B., *Angew. Chem.*, **73**, 493 (1961).

255. Sargent, R., and W. Rieman III, *J. Phys. Chem.*, **60**, 1370 (1956).

256. Saunders, L., and R. S. Srivastava, *J. Chem. Soc.*, **1952**, 2111.

257. Scatchard, G., *Chem. Revs.*, **19**, 309 (1936).

258. Scatchard, G., and R. C. Breckinridge, *J. Phys. Chem.*, **58**, 596 (1954).

259. Scatchard, G., and N. J. Anderson, *J. Phys. Chem.*, **65**, 1536 (1961).

*260. Schindewolf, U., *Z. Elektrochem.*, **62**, 335 (1958).

261. Schlögl, R., and B. Stein, *Z. physik. Chem. (Frankfurt)*, **13**, 111 (1957); *Z. Elektrochem.*, **62**, 340 (1958); **63**, 341 (1959).

262. Schubert, J., *J. Phys. Chem.*, **52**, 340 (1948).

263. Schubert, J., and J. W. Richter, *J. Phys. Chem.*, **52**, 350 (1948).

264. Schubert, J., E. R. Russell, and L. S. Myers, Jr., *J. Biol. Chem.*, **185**, 387 (1950).

265. Schubert, J., and J. W. Richter, *J. Colloid Sci.*, **5**, 376 (1950).

* Review articles are marked with asterisks.

266. Schubert, J., and A. Lindenbaum, *J. Am. Chem. Soc.*, **74**, 3529 (1952).
267. Schubert, J., *J. Phys. Chem.*, **56**, 113 (1952).
*268. Schubert, J., *Ann. Rev. Phys. Chem.*, **5**, 413 (1954).
269. Schubert, J., E. L. Lind, W. M. Westfall, R. Pfleger, and N. C. Li, *J. Am. Chem. Soc.*, **80**, 4799 (1958).
269a. Schwab, G. M., in "Ergebnisse der exakten Naturwissenschaften," vol. 7, p. 276, Julius Springer, Berlin, 1928.
270. Seim, H. J., R. J. Morris, and D. W. Frew, *Anal. Chem.*, **29**, 443 (1957).
*271. Selke, W. A., in "Ion Exchange Technology," p. 52, F. C. Nachod and J. Schubert (eds.), Academic Press, Inc., New York, 1956.
272. Sherma, J., and W. Rieman III, *Anal. Chim. Acta*, **18**, 214 (1958).
273. Sillén, L. G., *Arkiv Kemi*, **2**, 477, 499 (1950).
274. Skogseid, A., Thesis, University Oslo, 1948; U.S. Patent 2,592,350, 1950.
275. Slabaugh, W. H., *J. Am. Chem. Soc.*, **74**, 4462 (1952).
276. Soldano, B. A., and Q. V. Larson, *J. Am. Chem. Soc.*, **77**, 1331 (1955).
277. Soldano, B. A., and D. Chesnut, *J. Am. Chem. Soc.*, **77**, 1334 (1955).
278. Soldano, B. A., Q. V. Larson, and G. E. Myers, *J. Am. Chem. Soc.*, **77**, 1339 (1955).
278a. Sonesson, A., *Acta Chem. Scand.*, **15**, 1 (1961).
279. Spandau, H., and R. Kurz, *Kolloid Z.*, **150**, 109 (1957).
280. Staudinger, H., and E. Husemann, *Ber. deut. chem. Ges.*, **68**, 1618 (1935).
281. Stokes, R. H., and R. A. Robinson, *J. Am. Chem. Soc.*, **70**, 1870 (1948).
282. Stokes, R. H., and H. F. Walton, *J. Am. Chem. Soc.*, **76**, 3327 (1954).
283. Subba Rao, H. C., and M. M. David, *A. I. Ch. E. Journal*, **3**, 187 (1957).
284. Sundheim, B. R., M. H. Waxman, and H. P. Gregor, *J. Phys. Chem.*, **57**, 974 (1953).
285. Taylor, F. C., Jr., and H. L. Aamoth (The Dow Chemical Company), U.S. Patent 2,868,832, 1959.
286. Thomas, C. L. (Sun Oil Company), U.S. Patent 2,865,970, 1958.
287. Tiger, H. L., S. Sussman, M. Lane, and V. J. Calise, *Ind. Eng. Chem.*, **38**, 1130 (1946).
288. Tompkins, E. R., and S. W. Mayer, *J. Am. Chem. Soc.*, **69**, 2859 (1947).
289. Ueberreiter, K., *Z. Elektrochem.*, **57**, 188 (1953) (remark in discussion).
290. Vageler, P., and J. Woltersdorf, *Z. Pflanzenernähr. Düng. Bodenkunde*, **A15**, 329 (1930); **A16**, 184 (1930).
291. Vanselow, A. P., *J. Am. Chem. Soc.*, **54**, 1307 (1932).
292. Vermeulen, T., and N. K. Hiester, *Ind. Eng. Chem.*, **44**, 636 (1952).
*293. Verwey, E. J. W., and J. T. G. Overbeek, "Theory of the Stability of Lyophobic Colloids," chap. IV, Elsevier Press, Inc., New York, 1948.
294. Walton, H. F., *J. Phys. Chem.*, **47**, 371 (1943).
295. Weiss, D. E., *Nature*, **166**, 66 (1950).
296. Weisz, D. B., Thesis, Zurich, 1932.
*297. Wheaton, R. M., and W. C. Bauman, *Ind. Eng. Chem.*, **45**, 228 (1953); *Ann. N.Y. Acad. Sci.*, **57**, 159 (1953).
298. Whitcombe, J. A., J. T. Banchero, and R. R. White, *Chem. Eng. Progress Symp. Ser.*, **50**, No. 14, 73 (1954).
299. Wiegner, G., *J. Landwirtsch.*, **60**, 111, 197 (1912).
300. Wiegner, G., and H. Jenny, *Kolloid Z.*, **42**, 268 (1927).
301. Wiklander, L., *Svensk Kem. Tidskr.*, **57**, 54 (1945).
302. Wiklander, L., and E. Nilsson, *Acta Agr. Scand.*, **2**, 197 (1952); *Chem. Abstr.*, **47**, 6215 (1953); *J. Colloid Sci.*, **9**, 223 (1954).
303. Ziegler, M., *Angew. Chem.*, **71**, 283 (1959).
304. Zundel, G., Thesis, University of Munich, 1960.
*305. "Dowex:: ION Exchange," The Dow Chemical Company, Midland, Mich., 1959.
*306. Duolite Ion-exchange Manual, Chemical Process Co., Redwood City, Calif., 1960.

* Review articles are marked with asterisks.

6

Kinetics

The theory of ion-exchange kinetics is not nearly as far advanced as that of ion-exchange equilibria. The more recent quantitative approaches to ion-exchange equilibria include effects such as swelling pressure and specific interactions. The theory of ion-exchange kinetics, on the other hand, is still in the stage of a first approximation where such effects are not quantitatively considered. It is not unusual that time-dependent phenomena present more difficulties than equilibrium. With ion exchange, however, these difficulties are chiefly mathematical and do not obscure the fundamental features of the processes, which are well understood. Experimental and theoretical work in recent years has led to a clear-cut concept which may be considered as well established.

Any kinetic problem poses a number of questions. Usually the following four are the most interesting:

What is the mechanism of the process?

What is the rate-determining step?

What rate laws are obeyed?

How can the rate be predicted theoretically?

In ion exchange, the first two points are settled. Some work remains to be done on the third, though recent progress has been made. The fourth question is the most difficult and has not yet been satisfactorily answered. Here, the chemist must still rely on rough estimates, conclusions by analogy, or results of (independent) rate measurements.

The discussion in this chapter will be restricted to ion exchange between individual beads and a thoroughly agitated solution. Kinetics in ion-exchanger membranes and columns will be studied in later sections (Sec. 8-3 and Chap. 9, respectively).

6-1. MECHANISM OF ION EXCHANGE

The following system will be considered: spherical ion-exchanger beads of uniform size containing the counter ion A are placed in a well-stirred solution of an electrolyte BY, where B is another counter ion (Fig. 6-1). As equilibrium is approached, ions A diffuse out of the beads into the solution, and ions B diffuse from the solution into the beads (see Fig. 1-1). This interdiffusion of counter ions is what is called ion exchange. In all cases which have been studied so far, the rate-determining step of the process was established to be diffusion of the counter ions rather than an actual "chemical" exchange reaction at the fixed ionic groups, an alternative that cannot be ruled out a priori.* This shows that ion exchange, as a rule, is purely a diffusion phenomenon. Reaction rate constants may be defined formally, but in their physical interpretation they have little in common with rate constants of actual chemical reactions.†

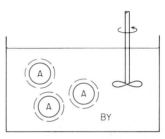

FIG. 6-1. Ion exchange between beads in A form and a well-stirred solution of BY. The liquid "films" adhering to the beads are indicated by broken lines.

Ion exchange is inherently a stoichiometric process. *Any counter ions which leave the ion exchanger are replaced by an equivalent amount of other counter ions* (for deviations, see below). This is a consequence of the electroneutrality requirement. When a counter ion moves out into the solution, the ion exchanger is left with an electric surplus charge which it must compensate by taking up another counter ion. The total counter-ion content (in equivalents) thus remains constant, irrespective of ionic composition.

Apparent deviations from stoichiometric behavior can occur because of electrolyte sorption and desorption which may accompany ion exchange and which change the co-ion content of the ion exchanger. Under normal conditions, however, Donnan exclusion keeps the co-ion content at a very low level (see Sec. 5-3c) so that deviations from stoichiometric exchange remain small. Exceptions are found when Donnan exclusion is weak. This is true in systems with concentrated solutions, low-capacity ion exchangers, strong association or ion-pair formation in the ion exchanger, and in ion exchange with weak electrolytes (organic acids, etc.). For the sake of simplicity, the discussion of these deviations will be postponed until later (see page 279).

It is true that Donnan exclusion keeps co-ions, in substantial amounts, from entering the ion exchanger during the whole process, but this does not hinder the exchange of counter ions. Electroneutrality throughout the system is preserved when the charge transfer by counter ions A is balanced by an equivalent charge transfer by counter ions B. No co-ion transfer is required. *The co-ion does not participate in ion exchange and thus has little*

---

* For one recent exception see p. 254.
† See also p. 286.

effect on the rate.*   It has been found that, indeed, the so-called "contact exchange" of (small) counter ions between ordinary ion exchangers and polyelectrolytes is not perceptibly slower than with monomeric electrolytes, though the polymeric co-ions are completely excluded from the ion exchanger by sieve action [25,65].   Counter-ion exchange can occur even between colloidal ion exchangers and ordinary ion-exchanger beads [67,76].

The stoichiometry of ion exchange requires that the fluxes (in equivalents) of the two exchanging counter ions be equal in magnitude, even though the counter-ion mobilities may be quite different.   It is important to grasp the mechanism which brings about this equivalence of fluxes.   The faster ion, of course, tends to diffuse at the higher rate.   However, any excess flux of an ion is equivalent to a net transfer of electric charge and thus produces an electric field (*diffusion potential*) which slows down the faster ion and accelerates the slower ion so that the fluxes become equal.   The fluxes of the two counter ions are electrically coupled in exactly the same way as the fluxes of the cation and anion in electrolyte diffusion in free solution.   The electric forces, though long overlooked, are one of the most important factors in ion-exchange kinetics.

6-2. THE RATE-DETERMINING STEP

It was pointed out above that the rate-determining step in ion exchange is the interdiffusion of counter ions.   This was first recognized by G. Schulze [106] as early as 1915.   Until recently, however, the importance of his work has been overlooked.   Our present knowledge is chiefly based on studies by G. E. Boyd [14], who was the first to embark on a thorough analysis of ion-exchange kinetics and to apply the Nernst concept of a liquid diffusion layer.

Let us go back to the model system shown in Fig. 6-1.   In the course of ion exchange, a counter ion A must migrate from its place within the ion exchanger into the solution.   Simultaneously, a counter ion B must go the other way and occupy the place left by ion A.   There is transfer of ions in both the ion exchanger and the solution.   In the bulk solution, any concentration differences are constantly leveled out by agitation. Here, the necessary transfer is effected by convection.   Agitation, however, affects neither the interior of the beads nor a liquid layer which adheres to the bead surfaces.   Within the beads and through this layer, the so-called "film," transport can occur by diffusion only.   Thus we are faced with two potential rate-determining steps:

1. Interdiffusion of counter ions within the ion exchanger itself (*particle diffusion*)

---

* There is, however, a more subtle co-ion effect.   The selectivity of the ion exchanger depends on the nature of the co-ion, and the rate, in turn, may be affected by the selectivity (see p. 282).

2. Interdiffusion of counter ions in the adherent films (*film diffusion*)

In practice, either step can be rate-controlling. In intermediate cases the rate may be affected by both steps.

The concept of the diffusion layer—originally developed by Nernst [81]—is an ingenious idealization. Actually, the convection of the solution by turbulent or laminar flow recedes continuously from the bulk solution to the solid surface. The film concept replaces this situation by a zone of defined thickness without any convection and with a

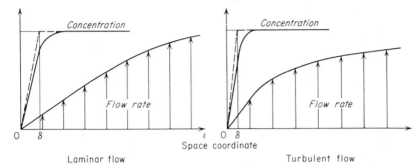

FIG. 6-2. The Nernst diffusion layer. The diagrams show the actual and the idealized concentration profiles (*solid and broken lines, respectively*) of a dissolved species which reacts instantaneously at the solid surface. The idealized profile is the tangent of the actual profile at the surface. In addition, the actual flow rates of the solutions are shown. *From W. Vielstich* [127].

sharp boundary separating it from the completely agitated solution (Fig. 6-2). Despite this drastic simplification the Nernst model, as a rule, describes diffusion phenomena at solid interfaces very accurately. This has been shown by both experimental evidence and more detailed theoretical approaches [101,127]. The "film thickness" is a fictitious quantity and cannot be measured directly. Its magnitude can be estimated from hydrodynamic or kinetic measurements and is usually of the order of 10^{-3} to 10^{-2} cm.*†

---

* The chemical engineer, as a rule, prefers to use the dimensionless Sherwood (or modified Nusselt) number (Sh) instead of the film thickness. For spherical particles, $Sh \equiv 2k_f r_0/D = 2r_0/\delta$ (k_f = mass-transfer coefficient in film; r_0 = particle radius; δ = effective film thickness; D = diffusion coefficient). The Sherwood number is a function of the Reynolds and Schmidt numbers; usually the following relations are given: $Sh \cong 0.37\ Re^{0.6}Sc^{1/3}$ for $20 < Re < 150,000$, and $Sh \cong 2 + 0.37\ Re^{0.6}Sc^{1/3}$ for $Re < 20$ (Re = Reynolds number $\equiv 2vr_0/\nu$; Sc = Schmidt number $\equiv \nu/D$; ν = kinematic viscosity; v = flow rate; see textbooks on heat transfer. Note that the heat-transfer analogues of the Sherwood and Schmidt numbers are the Nusselt and Prandtl numbers, respectively, and that many authors use the latter two names for mass-transfer phenomena also. In aqueous solutions at room temperature, $\nu \approx 10^{-2}$ cm²/sec, and $D \approx 10^{-5}$ cm²/sec, so that $Sc^{1/3} \approx 0.1$). The following other theoretical and empirical relations for the film thickness have been reported. Vielstich [127] calculated the effective film thickness on a planar surface of length l and obtained $\delta = 3l\ Re^{-1/2}Sc^{-1/3}$ for laminar flow and $\delta = l\ Re^{-0.9}Sc^{-1/3}$ for turbulent flow. For columns with spherical ion-exchanger beads, Gilliland [35] gives the empirical relation $\delta \cong 0.1r_0\ Re^{-0.84}$ and Glueckauf [37] gives the empirical approximations $\delta \approx 0.2r_0/(1 + 70r_0v)$ for low flow rates, and $\delta \approx 0.0029/v$ for high flow rates.

† For independent experimental determinations of film thicknesses at membrane surfaces, see p. 400.

Two other possible rate-determining steps have occasionally been considered. These are counter-ion exchange across the interface between ion exchanger and solution [26,27] and the actual "chemical" exchange reaction at the fixed ionic groups [10,14,78,120]. Rate control by ion exchange across the interface is very unlikely for theoretical reasons* and is not supported by experimental evidence when the latter is viewed critically (see also footnote to page 283). Rate control by the chemical exchange reaction has been ruled out for ordinary ion-exchange processes [14,44,65,94,96,119] but, according to recent findings [123a], can occur in resins with chelating groups which form sluggishly reacting complexes. Here, the rate law of a second-order reversible chemical reaction

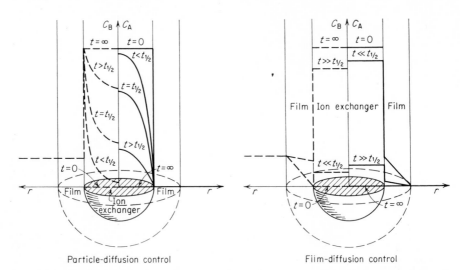

Particle-diffusion control   Film-diffusion control

FIG. 6-3. Radial concentration profiles for ideal particle diffusion control and ideal film diffusion control (schematic). The right sides of the diagrams show the profiles of species A (initially in the ion exchanger) and the left sides those of species B (initially in the solution). The various curves are for different contact times, t. *From F. Helfferich* [49].

[Eq. (6-53)] is approximately obeyed. (Occasionally, this rate law is used for ordinary ion-exchange processes also, but with little other justification than its simplicity.) The following discussion will be restricted to particle diffusion and film diffusion as potential rate-determining steps.

A simple qualitative consideration of the two limiting cases—ideal particle diffusion control and ideal film diffusion control—will help to clarify how the operating conditions determine the nature of the rate-controlling step. First, let us examine *particle diffusion control*. Here, by definition, film diffusion is so much faster than particle diffusion that concentration differences in the film are instantaneously leveled out. Concentration gradients exist only in the beads. Figure 6-3 (left) shows the radial concen-

---

* Spalding's theoretical work [112] shows that interfacial resistance to mass transfer is likely to be negligible if transition across the interface is a purely physical process such as diffusion.

tration profiles of the exchanging species. The momentary, local inter-diffusion flux is proportional to the steepness of the profile and to the interdiffusion coefficient. With an ion exchanger of, say, twice as high a concentration of fixed ionic groups, the concentration profiles would be very similar, except that all concentrations in the bead are twice as high: the whole diagram is stretched to twice its height, and the profiles thus are twice as steep. With an ion exchanger of, say, twice as large a particle diameter, the pattern of the profiles is again very similar, only the diagram is stretched horizontally, and the profiles thus are half as steep. It follows that the (momentary) exchange flux is approximately proportional to the concentration of fixed charges and to the interdiffusion coefficient in the beads and is inversely proportional to the bead radius; on the other hand, the flux is independent of the film thickness, solution concentration, and diffusion coefficients in the film.

Concentration profiles for ideal *film diffusion control* are shown in Fig. 6-3 (right). Here, by definition, particle diffusion is so much faster than film diffusion that concentration gradients exist only in the films. The same reasoning as above can be applied. It shows that, here, the flux is proportional to the solution concentration and to the interdiffusion coefficient in the film, inversely proportional to the film thickness, and independent of the fixed-charge concentration, interdiffusion coefficient in the bead, and bead radius.

The rate of ion exchange is determined by the slower of the two processes. All factors which tend to increase the rate of interdiffusion in the beads and to reduce the rate in the films favor film diffusion control. All factors with opposite tendencies favor particle diffusion control. Thus *film diffusion control may prevail in systems with ion exchangers of high concentration of fixed ionic groups, low degree of crosslinking, and small particle size, with dilute solutions, and with inefficient agitation.* (Weak crosslinking results in high interdiffusion coefficients in the beads, and inefficient agitation in large film thickness.)

The nature of the rate-determining step can be predicted by use of the simple criterion below (for derivation, see page 277):

$$\frac{X\bar{D}\delta}{CDr_0}(5 + 2\alpha_B^A) \ll 1 \qquad \text{particle diffusion control}$$

$$\frac{X\bar{D}\delta}{CDr_0}(5 + 2\alpha_B^A) \gg 1 \qquad \text{film diffusion control} \tag{6-1}$$

where X = concentration of fixed ionic groups; C = concentration of solution (in equivalents); $\bar{D}$ = interdiffusion coefficient in the ion exchanger; D = interdiffusion coefficient in the film; r_0 = bead radius; δ = film thickness; $\alpha_B^A \equiv \bar{C}_A C_B / \bar{C}_B C_A$ = separation factor [see Eq. (5-70)]; the concentrations are on the molarity scale.

In the intermediate range $[(X\bar{D}\delta/CDr_0)(5 + 2\alpha_B^A) \approx 1]$, interdiffusion is about equally fast in the bead and in the film, and both mechanisms affect the rate of ion exchange.

The criterion (6-1) is a quantitative expression of the effects of the various factors which have been discussed above. In addition, the effect of selectivity is included. This criterion is a rather rough but useful approximation. The quantities X, C, r_0, and α_B^A are usually known, for D and $\bar{D}$ the harmonic means of the individual diffusion coefficients of the counter ions A and B can be used [see Eq. (6-52)], and the film thickness δ is generally of the order of 10^{-3} to 10^{-2} cm, depending on agitation. Thus the evaluation is simple.

> *Example.* Consider the ion exchange between the Na^+ form of a sulfonated styrene-type cation exchanger of 10 per cent DVB crosslinking and 40-mesh particle size and a 1 M HCl solution. Here, $X = 2.8$ meq/cm³ (see Fig. 4-1); $C = 1$ meq/cm³; $r_0 \cong 0.02$ cm; $D/\bar{D} \approx 10$ (see Fig. 6-15 for $\bar{D}_{Na}$); $\alpha_H^{Na} \approx 1.8$ (see Fig. 5-26); $\delta \approx 10^{-3}$ cm (well-stirred solution). Introduction of these values in Eq. (6-1) gives
>
> $$\frac{2.8 \cdot 10^{-3}}{1 \cdot 10 \cdot 0.02} (5 + 2 \cdot 1.8) = 0.12$$
>
> Thus the rate is controlled by particle diffusion. On the other hand, film diffusion will become rate-controlling below a solution concentration of about 0.1 M

Note that the concentration of the solution is by no means the only factor which determines the nature of the rate-controlling step. This point has frequently been overlooked. For example, when the separation factor differs greatly from unity, it is even possible for the forward and the reverse exchange of two given ions—i.e., A for B, and B for A, respectively—under identical conditions to be controlled by different mechanisms.

Experimental methods for distinguishing between particle and film diffusion control. The best technique for distinguishing between particle and film diffusion control is the so-called "interruption test" [65]. The beads are removed from the solution for a brief period of time and are then reimmersed. The pause gives time for the concentration gradients in the beads to level out. Thus, with particle diffusion control, the rate immediately after reimmersion is greater than prior to the interruption. With film diffusion control, no concentration gradients in the beads exist, and the rate depends on the concentration difference across the film. The interruption does not affect this difference and, hence, has no effect on the rate* (Fig. 6-4).

Evidence can also be obtained by other methods which, however, are less reliable. Particle-diffusion and film-diffusion controlled ion exchange differ in their rate laws (see Fig. 6-5) and in the dependence of the rate on the particle size, solution concentration, and degree of agitation (see Table 6-1). Analysis of the experimentally observed rate laws and study of the dependence on the variables can thus help to identify the rate-controlling mechanism [20,44,65,94]. However, the conclusions are not always unambiguous. For example, the rate of particle-diffusion controlled ion exchange may,

---

* It is true that the interruption disturbs the concentration gradients in the film. However, these gradients are reestablished almost immediately (see p. 263).

under certain conditions, depend on the solution concentration (see page 279). Also, the agitation of the solution may have attained its limiting hydrodynamic efficiency, so that a change in the agitation rate can remain without effect on the ion-exchange rate even in film-diffusion controlled systems.

The theoretical aspects outlined in this section are well established. With the exception of certain exchanges in chelating resins, ion exchange was always found to be controlled by either particle diffusion or film diffusion. The experimental results are in reasonable agreement with the criterion (6-1).

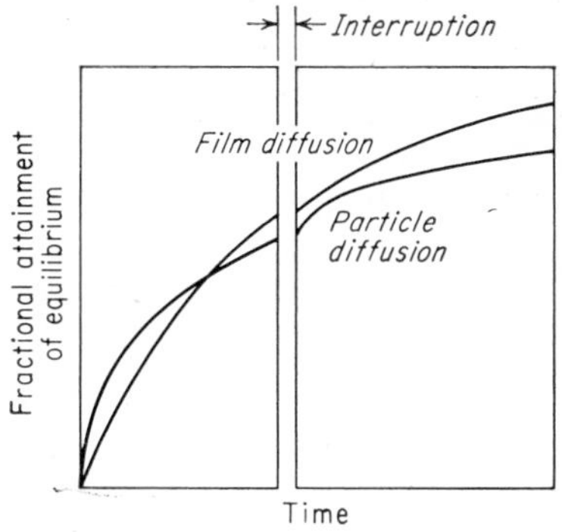

Fig. 6-4. Interruption test with film diffusion control and particle diffusion control (schematic). With particle diffusion control the interruption causes a change in the momentary exchange rate. With film diffusion control there is no such change.

6-3. RATE LAWS OF ION EXCHANGE

The rate of ion exchange is determined by diffusion processes. Rate laws can be derived by applying the well-known diffusion equations to ion-exchange systems. This task, however, is not as simple as it appears at first sight, and the problem has been solved only for certain limiting cases. The complications arise from diffusion-induced electric forces, from selectivity, specific interactions, and changes in swelling. Thus, in the general case, the differential equations and boundary conditions are nonlinear.

The simplest limiting case is isotopic exchange in a system which is in equilibrium except for isotopic distribution. Here, most of the complicating effects are absent, and a well-established theory exists. It is for this reason that isotopic exchange will be examined first. Later, the results will be generalized as far as possible for actual exchange of ions of different properties.

The study of the rate laws is preceded by a brief discussion of the fundamental equations which form the basis for the quantitative treatment of ion-exchange and sorption kinetics.

a. Fundamentals

Diffusion processes are usually described in terms of Fick's first law

$$J_i = -D \text{ grad } C_i \qquad (6-2)$$

Here, J_i is the flux (in moles per unit time and unit cross section) of the diffusing species i, C_i is its concentration (in moles per unit volume), and D is the diffusion coefficient.

The simplest case is diffusion in an ideal system, i.e., where no other simultaneous processes interfere. Here, the flux is proportional to the concentration gradient, and the diffusion coefficient thus is constant. This is readily shown by a simple statistical treatment [22]. A typical example is isotopic diffusion in a system which is in equilibrium except for isotopic distribution. The diffusion coefficient of the isotopes in such systems is called the *self-diffusion coefficient* (individual diffusion coefficient, or tracer diffusion coefficient) of the species. Its value is constant throughout any single phase of the system but, of course, depends on the nature and composition of the particular phase and on the temperature.

It is, however, dangerous to generalize on the basis of this simple situation. Whenever diffusion of a species is coupled with other processes, say, with diffusion of a different species, the diffusion coefficient is usually *not* constant. Ion exchange is a typical example. Fick's first law (6-2) can, of course, still be used, but the variation of the diffusion coefficient must be taken into account.

The theoretical prediction of individual diffusion coefficients from molecular data is a difficult problem which is still far from being satisfactorily solved. However, diffusion coefficients under various conditions for the most important ionic and molecular species have been determined by tracer measurements and other techniques. For practical applications the physical chemist, as a rule, prefers to use these tabulated values rather than concern himself with molecular mechanisms of diffusion. From this point of view, Eq. (6-2) may be considered simply as a definition of the diffusion coefficient.

In ion exchangers one is faced with a special situation. The matrix occupies a substantial fraction of the volume of the medium and obstructs diffusion. The prediction of diffusion rates in such systems is difficult, even if the diffusion coefficients of the species in ordinary aqueous systems (i.e., in the absence of the matrix) are known. The theory of ion-exchange kinetics, at least in its present form, bypasses these difficulties by considering the ion exchanger (pore liquid *and* matrix) as a single *quasi-homogeneous phase*, regardless of its inhomogeneities in molecular or colloidal dimensions and its particular geometrical structure. Thus Eq. (6-2) is applied to the ion exchanger also. The concentrations, in accordance with the concept of the quasi-homogeneous phase, are given in moles per unit volume of the swollen ion exchanger. The diffusion coefficients are defined by Eq. (6-2) and are, of course, smaller than in ordinary aqueous systems. The nature of such "effective" diffusion coefficients in macroporous or microporous media, their magnitude, and their relation to the corresponding aqueous-phase coefficients will be discussed in more detail in Sec. 6-8.

The rate of ion exchange depends on the size and shape of the beads. In the theoretical treatment it is usually assumed that all beads are spherical and uniform in size. A rigorous treatment of ion exchange with nonuniform and irregularly shaped particles is very difficult.* The most convenient approximation for such cases is to use the rate laws for uniform spherical particles, assigning an empirical "equivalent-sphere" size to the material. It has been shown that, usually, the size of the equivalent sphere is such that its surface-to-volume ratio is the same as the average surface-to-volume ratio of the actual particles [5].

The problem of deriving rate laws for ion exchange can thus be summarized as follows. Solutions of the differential equation (6-2) for spherical geometry under the appropriate initial and boundary conditions and restrictions must be found. The equation applies to both the interior of the beads and the films. However, the diffusion coefficients in these two phases are different. Furthermore, the diffusion coefficients in beads and films are not necessarily constant. Their dependence on the variables of the system must be found and taken into account.

b. Isotopic exchange

Exchange of two isotopic counter ions A and B in a system which is in equilibrium except for isotopic distribution will now be examined. It has already been pointed out that in this case the diffusion coefficient is constant. Solutions under this condition have been derived for all systems of practical interest. The most important solutions follow. First, it will be assumed that all isotope A ions are initially in the ion exchanger. Other initial conditions are discussed later. The limiting cases of ideal particle and ideal film diffusion control and the general, intermediate case are treated separately.

Particle diffusion control. The flux of the isotope A† in the ion exchanger is given by

$$J_A = -\bar{D} \text{ grad } \bar{C}_A \qquad (6-3)$$

where D = self-diffusion coefficient of the isotopes; quantities with bars refer to the interior of the ion exchanger.

The time dependence of the concentration is interrelated with the flux by the material balance (Fick's second law, often called the condition of continuity)

$$\frac{\partial \bar{C}_A}{\partial t} = - \text{ div } J_A \qquad (6-4)$$

where t = time.

---

* A mathematical treatment of diffusion phenomena (with constant diffusion coefficient) in materials with nonuniform particle size has recently been given by Pouchlý [91].

† It is sufficient to consider the flux of only one isotope. The flux of the other one is automatically equal in magnitude and opposite in sign because the system remains in equilibrium except for isotopic redistribution.

The combination of Eqs. (6-3) and (6-4) for systems with spherical geometry and with a constant diffusion coefficient gives

$$\frac{\partial \bar{C}_A}{\partial t} = \bar{D}\left(\frac{\partial^2 \bar{C}_A}{\partial r^2} + \frac{2}{r}\frac{\partial \bar{C}_A}{\partial r}\right) \tag{6-5}$$

where r = radial space coordinate = distance from bead center.

This equation must be solved under the appropriate initial and boundary conditions. In the simplest initial condition, all ions A are in the ion exchanger at a uniform concentration $\bar{C}_A^0$, and no A is in the solution:

$$\begin{aligned} r > r_0, \ t = 0 \qquad & \bar{C}_A(r) = 0 \\ 0 \le r \le r_0, \ t = 0 \qquad & \bar{C}_A(r) = \bar{C}_A^0 = \text{const.} \end{aligned} \tag{6-6}$$

where r_0 = bead radius.

Other initial distributions are discussed later (see page 265).

Two boundary conditions will be considered. The first and simpler condition applies when the concentration of A in the solution remains negligible throughout the process. This is true when a solution of constant composition is continuously passed through a thin layer of beads ("shallow bed") or, in batch experiments, if the solution volume is so large that

$$\bar{C}\bar{V} \ll CV \tag{6-7}$$

where C = total concentration of counter ions; $\bar{V}$ = total volume of ion-exchange material; V = solution volume.

This condition will be called the "infinite solution volume" condition. The second boundary condition is more general and must be used if the requirement (6-7) is not met. It will be called the "finite solution volume" condition.

Infinite solution volume. With particle diffusion rate-controlling, the concentrations at the bead surface are the same as in the bulk solution. The infinite solution volume condition thus is

$$r = r_0, \ t > 0 \qquad \bar{C}_A(t) = 0 \tag{6-8}$$

Condition (6-8) implies equilibrium at the interface, i.e., negligible resistance to diffusion across the interface.

The solution of Eq. (6-5) under the conditions (6-6) and (6-8) gives the function $\bar{C}_A(r,t)$. Integration of this function throughout the bead leads to [8,22]

$$U(t) = 1 - \frac{\bar{Q}_A(t)}{\bar{Q}_A^0} = 1 - \frac{6}{\pi^2}\sum_{n=1}^{\infty}\frac{1}{n^2}\exp\left(-\frac{\bar{D}t\pi^2 n^2}{r_0^2}\right) \tag{6-9}$$

where $\bar{Q}_A(t)$ = amount of A in the ion exchanger at time t; $\bar{Q}_A^0$ = initial amount of A in the ion exchanger; $U(t)$ is the fractional attainment of equilibrium, defined by

$U(t) \equiv (\bar{Q}_A^0 - \bar{Q}_A(t))/(\bar{Q}_A^0 - \bar{Q}_A^\infty); \ \bar{Q}_A^\infty$ = amount of A left in the ion exchanger when equilibrium is attained.

The fractional attainment of equilibrium $U(t)$ is seen to depend only on the magnitude of the dimensionless time parameter $\bar{D}t/r_0^2$. The function (6-9) is plotted in Fig. 6-5 and is tabulated in the Appendix (page 584).

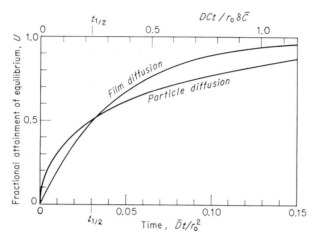

FIG. 6-5. Fractional attainment of equilibrium as a function of time for particle- and film-diffusion controlled isotopic exchange [Eqs. (6-9) and (6-22)]. Time scale at bottom is for particle diffusion control, at top for film diffusion control. The curves are normalized to give equal half times.

When $\bar{D}t/r_0^2$ is small, Eq. (6-9) does not converge rapidly. In the range $U(t) < 0.5$ the approximation

$$U(t) \cong \frac{6}{r_0} \left(\frac{\bar{D}t}{\pi} \right)^{\frac{1}{2}} - \frac{3\bar{D}t}{r_0^2} \quad (U(t) < 0.5) \qquad (6\text{-}10)$$

is more useful [22]. For $U(t) > 0.8$ the terms of higher than first order in Eq. (6-9) can be disregarded. Less accurate than Eq. (6-9), but more convenient for practical use is Vermeulen's approximation [124] which fits the whole range $0 \le U(t) \le 1$:

$$U(t) \cong \left[1 - \exp\left(-\frac{\bar{D}t\pi^2}{r_0^2} \right) \right]^{\frac{1}{2}} \qquad (6\text{-}11)^*$$

The half time $t_{\frac{1}{2}}$ of ion exchange is readily calculated from Eq. (6-9). The substitution $U(t) = 0.5$ gives

$$t_{\frac{1}{2}} = 0.030 \, \frac{r_0^2}{\bar{D}} \qquad (6\text{-}12)$$

The (relative) rate thus is *proportional to the diffusion coefficient in the ion exchanger and inversely proportional to the square of the bead radius.*

---

* See also the similar and more accurate but more complex approximation (6-41) for ion exchange. This approximation contains isotopic exchange as a limiting case ($\alpha = 1$).

The absolute amount of isotopes exchanged is, of course, also proportional to the total amount of A initially present in the beads. For the common strong-acid and strong-base ion-exchange resins and univalent counter ions ($r_0 = 0.01$ to 0.1 cm; $\bar{D} = 10^{-7}$ to 10^{-5} cm²/sec) the half time of particle-diffusion controlled ion exchange is of the order of seconds or minutes. For weak-acid, weak-base, and mineral ion exchangers and polyvalent counter ions ($\bar{D}$ much smaller) the half time may be longer by several orders of magnitude.

Finite Solution Volume. The more general finite solution volume condition is obtained from the material balance $-d\bar{Q}_A = dQ_A$. The condition is (equilibrium at the interface is assumed)

$$r = r_0,\ t > 0 \qquad \bar{C}_A(t) = \frac{3\bar{V}\bar{C}}{r_0 V C} \int_0^t J_A(t)\ dt \qquad (6\text{-}13)$$

The solution of Eq. (6-5) under the conditions (6-6) and (6-13) has been worked out by S. Paterson [87] for the corresponding heat-transfer problem. The solution is

$$U(t) = 1 - \frac{2}{3w} \sum_{n=1}^{\infty} \frac{\exp(-S_n^2 \tau)}{1 + S_n^2/9w(w+1)} \qquad (6\text{-}14)$$

where $w \equiv \bar{C}\bar{V}/CV$; $\tau \equiv \bar{D}t/r_0^2$; the quantities S_n are the roots of the equation $S_n \cot S_n = 1 + S_n^2/3w$.

Equation (6-14) converges very slowly in the range $\tau < 0.1$ (this range extends far beyond the half time of exchange). Here, Paterson gives the approximation [87]

$$U(t) = \frac{w+1}{w}\left(1 - \frac{1}{\alpha - \beta}\right.$$
$$\left. [\alpha \exp(\alpha^2 \tau)(1 + \operatorname{erf} \alpha \tau^{1/2}) - \beta \exp(\beta^2 \tau)(1 + \operatorname{erf} \beta \tau^{1/2})]\right) \qquad (6\text{-}15)$$

where α and β are the roots of the equation $x^2 + 3wx + 3w = 0$.

The function (6-15) is tabulated in the Appendix (page 585).

Film diffusion control. Rate laws for film-diffusion controlled isotopic exchange have been derived under the following simplifying assumptions:

1. Interdiffusion in the film is treated as quasi-stationary, i.e., it is assumed that diffusion across the film is fast as compared with the concentration changes at the film boundaries.

2. The film is treated as a planar layer (one-dimensional diffusion). This is admissible if the film thickness is much smaller than the bead radius.

The time lag—i.e., the time which elapses until steady-state conditions are attained—in a layer with constant boundary concentrations is about $0.5\delta^2/D$, where δ is the thickness of the layer [see Eq. (8-11)]. With $\delta \approx 10^{-3}$ cm and $D \approx 10^{-5}$ cm^2/sec, the time lag in the film is of the order of 0.1 sec. This is usually several orders of magnitude less than the half time of film-diffusion controlled ion exchange. Hence the first assumption is justified. The second assumption often holds less well.

The rate law is derived in the following way. First, the momentary quasi-stationary flux is calculated as a function of the boundary concentrations. The time dependence is introduced subsequently by calculating the changes in the boundary concentrations from the momentary flux.

Under the assumptions mentioned above, the momentary flux is constant throughout the film and, according to Eq. (6-2), is given by

$$J_A = D \frac{\Delta C_A}{\delta} \tag{6-16}$$

where $\Delta C_A \equiv C_A' - C_A$ = concentration difference between the two boundaries of the film; quantities with prime refer to the interface ion exchanger/film, without prime to the bulk solution; δ = film thickness.

The time dependence is obtained from the material balance

$$-\frac{d\bar{Q}_A}{dt} = F J_A \tag{6-17}$$

where F = total surface area of the ion exchanger,

and the equilibrium condition at the interface

$$\frac{\bar{C}_A}{C_A'} = \frac{\bar{C}}{C} \tag{6-18}$$

where $C \equiv C_A + C_B$ = total concentration of both exchanging isotopes; C is equal to C' since the system is in equilibrium except for isotopic distribution.

Combination of Eqs. (6-17) and (6-18) gives after substitution

$$-\frac{dC_A'}{dt} = \frac{3C}{r_0 \bar{C}} J_A \tag{6-19}$$

Equations (6-16) and (6-19) must be solved under the appropriate initial and boundary conditions.

The simple initial condition corresponding to uniform initial concentration $\bar{C}_A^0$ in the ion exchanger and no A in the solution is

$$r = r_0, t = 0 \qquad\qquad C_A' = \frac{\bar{C}_A^0 C}{\bar{C}} \tag{6-20}$$
$$r \geq r_0 + \delta, t = 0 \qquad C_A(r) = 0$$

Other initial distributions are discussed later (see page 265). As before, the infinite and the finite solution volume conditions will be considered.

Infinite Solution Volume. Here, the concentration of A in the bulk solution remains zero. The boundary condition at the boundary film/solution thus is

$$r \geq r_0 + \delta, \, t \geq 0 \qquad C_A(r,t) = 0 \tag{6-21}$$

The boundary condition at the interface ion exchanger/film is implicit in Eq. (6-19). The solution of Eq. (6-16) under the conditions (6-19) to (6-21) is [14]

$$U(t) = 1 - \exp\left(-\frac{3DCt}{r_0\delta\bar{C}}\right) \tag{6-22}$$

The fractional attainment of equilibrium $U(t)$ is seen to depend only on the magnitude of the dimensionless time parameter $DCt/r_0\delta\bar{C}$. The function (6-22) is plotted in Fig. 6-5. This diagram, which includes the function (6-9), illustrates the difference in kinetic behavior between particle and film diffusion control.

The half time of ion exchange is readily derived from Eq. (6-22):

$$t_{1/2} = 0.23 \, \frac{r_0\delta\bar{C}}{DC} \tag{6-23}$$

The (relative) rate thus is *proportional to the diffusion coefficient in the film and to the concentration of the solution and is inversely proportional to the bead radius, the film thickness, and the counter-ion concentration in the ion exchanger.* The half time of ion exchange depends strongly on the experimental conditions. With a typical ion-exchange resin and moderate agitation ($r_0 \approx 0.1$ cm; $\bar{C} \approx 2$ meq/cm^3; $\delta \approx 5 \cdot 10^{-3}$ cm; $D \approx 10^{-5}$ cm^2/sec) the half time of exchange with a 0.01 N solution is about 40 min, with a 0.001 N solution about $6\frac{1}{2}$ hr.

Finite Solution Volume. Here, the condition (6-21) for the boundary film/solution must be replaced by

$$r \geq r_0 + \delta, \, t > 0 \qquad C_A(r,t) = \frac{\bar{V}}{V} \, (\bar{C}_A^0 - \bar{C}_A(t)) \tag{6-24}$$

This relation is obtained from the material balance $-d\bar{Q}_A = dQ_A$. The solution of Eq. (6-16) under the conditions (6-19), (6-20), and (6-24) is

$$U(t) = 1 - \exp\left(-\frac{3D(\bar{V}\bar{C} + VC)}{r_0\delta\bar{C}V}\,t\right) \tag{6-25}$$

Intermediate range between particle and film diffusion control. A rigorous solution for the general, intermediate case in which both particle and film diffusion affect the rate has not yet been found. The mathematical difficulty is that a nonlinear boundary condition at the interface arises.

The problem becomes simpler when linear concentration profiles in the film are postulated. For isotopic exchange under the *infinite solution volume* condition, the solution for the corresponding heat-transfer problem with radiation can then be used. This solution—derived from Eqs. (6-5) and (6-16) under the conditions (6-17), (6-18), (6-20), and (6-21)—has been given by L. R. Ingersoll [59] and was first applied to ion exchange by Grossman [42]:

$$U(t) = \frac{6\Theta^2}{r_0^2} \sum_{n=1}^{\infty} \frac{A_n \sin^2(m_n r_0)}{m_n^4} \exp(-\bar{D} m_n^2 t) \qquad (6\text{-}26)$$

where
$$\Theta \equiv \frac{CD}{\bar{C}\bar{D}\delta}$$

$$A_n \equiv \frac{m_n^2 r_0^2 + (\Theta r_0 - 1)^2}{m_n^2 r_0^2 + (\Theta r_0 - 1)\Theta r_0}$$

the quantities m_n are the roots of the equation

$$m_n r_0 = (1 - \Theta r_0) \tan m_n r_0$$

Other initial conditions. In the derivations above it was assumed that the solution is initially free of species A [initial conditions (6-6) and (6-20)]. However, the treatment is readily extended to ion exchange with a solution which contains the species A at an initial concentration C_A^0. In this case, the initial conditions for particle diffusion control are

$$r = r_0, \ t = 0 \qquad \bar{C}_A(r) = \frac{C_A^0 \bar{C}}{C}$$
$$0 \leq r < r_0, \ t = 0 \qquad \bar{C}_A(r) = \bar{C}_A^0 = \text{const.} \qquad (6\text{-}27)$$

and for film-diffusion control

$$r = r_0, \ t = 0 \qquad C_A' = \frac{\bar{C}_A^0 C}{\bar{C}}$$
$$r \geq r_0 + \delta, \ t = 0 \qquad C_A(r) = C_A^0 \qquad (6\text{-}28)$$

New variables $\bar{A}$ and A can be defined: $\bar{A} \equiv \bar{C}_A - C_A^0 \bar{C}/C$ is used for particle diffusion control, and $A \equiv C_A - C_A^0$ for film diffusion control. It is readily shown that $\bar{A}$ and A obey the same differential equations and initial and boundary conditions as the variables $\bar{C}_A$ and C_A, respectively, in the previous treatment. The equations derived for the fractional attainment of equilibrium and the half times do not involve $\bar{C}_A$ or C_A explicitly and thus remain unchanged under the new initial conditions.

Initial distributions in which the ion exchanger contains the isotope B in addition to A are already covered by the previous treatment since the initial concentration of A, $\bar{C}_A^0$, was not identified with the total concentration $\bar{C}$.

Time requirement for exhaustion of the solution. The half times of exchange (6-12) and (6-23) refer to exhaustion of an ion exchanger by a solution of infinite volume. These times are characteristic of the rate of change in ionic composition within the ion exchanger and are particularly useful for designing ion-exchange columns. In batch operations, however, it is often more important to know the time which is required to remove a given ionic species from the solution. The time within which the concentration of species B is reduced to a fraction x_B of its initial value can be calculated from the relation

$$x_B(t) = 1 - \frac{\bar{C}\bar{V}}{\bar{C}\bar{V} + CV} U(t) \tag{6-29}$$

where $U(t)$ is obtained from Eq. (6-15) or (6-25). For ideal film diffusion control the time can be given explicitly:

$$t(x_B) = - \frac{r_0 \delta \bar{C} V}{3D(\bar{C}\bar{V} - CV)} \ln \left(x_B \frac{\bar{C}\bar{V} + CV}{\bar{C}\bar{V}} - \frac{CV}{\bar{C}\bar{V}} \right) \tag{6-30}$$

If a liberal excess of ion-exchange material is used ($CV \ll \bar{C}\bar{V}$), Eq. (6-30) reduces to

$$t(x_B) = - \frac{r_0 \delta V}{3\bar{V}D} \ln x_B \tag{6-31}$$

For example, 99 per cent of a counter-ion species B ($x_B = 0.01$) is removed from 100 cm³ of a very dilute solution by shaking thoroughly ($\delta \approx 5 \cdot 10^{-3}$ cm) with 5 cm³ of ion-exchanger material of fine bead size ($r_0 \approx 0.01$ cm) within about 2½ min.

Experimental evidence. The theory of isotopic exchange has been extensively confirmed by experimental studies [14–17,109–111,117,119]. It is true that these investigations do not include direct comparisons of observed rates with calculations based on independent measurements. However, the theoretical curves can be fitted to the experimental points by use of empirical (constant) diffusion coefficients. The magnitude of these diffusion coefficients is of the expected order and is in good agreement with conductivity data (see also page 332).

c. Ion Exchange

The quantitative treatment of ion exchange is, unfortunately, much more complicated than that of isotopic exchange in equilibrium systems. In actual ion exchange, the fluxes of at least two different ionic species are coupled with one another. Such processes cannot be described in terms of one constant diffusion coefficient. Further complications arise from the selectivity of the ion exchanger, specific interactions, electrolyte sorption and desorption, and changes in swelling and swelling pressure.* A rigorous treatment is quite beyond the conventional mathematical means. Solutions have been obtained only for some of the most important limiting cases, and even some of these were solved only by the use of electronic computers. However, the over-all picture is well established, and a number of general rules can be deduced.

The most important feature which distinguishes ion exchange from isotopic exchange is the *electric coupling* of the ionic fluxes. It has already been pointed out that conservation of electroneutrality requires stoichiometric exchange, i.e., the fluxes (in equivalents) of the exchanging counter ions must be equal in magnitude, since otherwise a net transfer of electric charge would result. The regulating mechanism which enforces the equality of the fluxes is the electric field (diffusion potential) set up by the diffusion process. The faster counter ion, of course, tends to diffuse at the higher rate. However, any excess charge transfer by the faster ion builds up a space charge which slows down the faster ion and accelerates the slower ion. Thus electroneutrality is preserved.† Or, in other words, one might say that the electric field generated by the diffusion process produces an electric transference of both counter ions in the direction of diffusion of the slower counter ion; this electric transference is superimposed on the diffusion. The resulting net fluxes of the counter ions are equivalent to one another, while the purely diffusional fluxes, as a rule, are not. These considerations clearly show that the action of the electric forces is an essential feature of the process and must be taken into account by any quantitative approach. Results of more recent calculations which include the electric field differ considerably from earlier theories in which this effect was omitted.

In the following, rate laws for several ideal limiting cases will be given. Deviations in actual systems will then be qualitatively discussed.

Ideal limiting laws. *The Nernst-Planck Equations.* An electric field in an electrolyte solution produces transference of the ions. In a solution of

---

* A notable exception is exchange of trace components; see Sec. 6-3d.

† Actually, generation of a space charge is a disturbance of electroneutrality. Hence, strictly speaking, it is illogical to explain conservation of electroneutrality by action of space charges. In a more rigorous treatment, the electroneutrality condition (6-36) should be replaced by the Poisson-Boltzmann equation which interrelates space charge and electric field; see, for instance, H. Oel [82]. However, even the slightest deviation from electroneutrality results in a very strong electric field which prevents further accumulation of net charge. A rigorous calculation shows that, in ion exchangers, deviations from electroneutrality remain negligible except in the electric double layer at the interface ion exchanger/solution. The composition of the double layer is irrelevant if its thickness (several angstrom units) is much smaller than the particle diameter and if the rate is controlled by diffusion in the bulk phases (equilibrium at the interface). Both conditions are met unless the ion exchanger is in colloidal form. The electroneutrality condition can thus be used even in the presence of diffusion potentials.

uniform composition, the transference $(J_i)_{el}$ of an arbitrary species i in the direction of the current is proportional to the gradient of the electric potential φ and to the concentration C_i and electrochemical valence z_i of the species:

$$(J_i)_{el} = -u_i z_i C_i \text{ grad } \varphi \tag{6-32}$$

The proportionality factor u_i is defined as the electrochemical mobility of the species.*

The electrochemical mobility is related to the individual diffusion coefficient of the species by the Nernst-Einstein equation

$$u_i = \frac{D_i \mathfrak{F}}{RT} \tag{6-33}$$

where $\mathfrak{F}$ = Faraday constant; R = gas constant; T = absolute temperature.

This relation is derived for ideal solutions.† However, experience has shown that it can be used as a good approximation even in ion exchangers. The reason may be that the smallness of the pores prevents the formation of ionic clouds. Deformation of ionic clouds by the electric field is known to contribute to the deviations from Eq. (6-33) in nonideal systems.

In solutions with concentration gradients, electric transference is superimposed on the purely statistical ("thermal") diffusion, $(J_i)_{diff}$, which is given by

$$(J_i)_{diff} = -D_i \text{ grad } C_i \tag{6-34}$$

Thus the resulting net flux of the species is [80,89]

$$J_i = (J_i)_{diff} + (J_i)_{el} = -D_i \left(\text{grad } C_i + z_i C_i \frac{\mathfrak{F}}{RT} \text{ grad } \varphi \right) \tag{6-35}$$

This relation is known as the *Nernst-Planck equation* and holds, in ideal systems, for all mobile species present. The set of Nernst-Planck equations, one for each species, must be solved under the appropriate conditions.

The Nernst-Planck equations apply whenever an electric field exists. It is completely irrelevant whether the field is generated by an external source or by diffusion within the system, since the individual ion has no means of knowing the origin of the electric field.

The Nernst-Planck equation is derived under simplifying assumptions. The effects of convection and gradients of pressure and activity coefficients are not included.

Particle Diffusion Control. The Nernst-Planck equations have been solved for particle-diffusion controlled ion exchange with the following

---

* See also footnote to p. 329.

† An excellent discussion of the Nernst-Einstein relation has recently been given by Ilschner [58]. For more complex relations between diffusion coefficients and mobilities see, for example, J. Crank [23,45a].

additional assumptions. The presence of co-ions in the ion exchanger is neglected, and the molarity of the fixed ionic groups and the individual diffusion coefficients is assumed to remain constant. The first assumption is a justified approximation if Donnan exclusion of the co-ions is strong. This is the case unless the concentration of the solution is high and the ion exchanger is weakly dissociated (see Sec. 5-3c). The other assumptions are reasonable approximations if swelling changes and specific interactions are not significant (see also page 279).

Under these assumptions, the system is subject to the restrictions

$$z_A \bar{C}_A + z_B \bar{C}_B = -\omega \bar{C} = \text{const.*} \qquad \text{electroneutrality} \qquad (6\text{-}36)$$

$$z_A J_A + z_B J_B = 0 \qquad \text{no electric current} \qquad (6\text{-}37)$$

where ω = sign of fixed ionic charges, -1 for cation exchangers, and $+1$ for anion exchangers.

The two equations (6-35) for the two counter ions A and B can be combined, eliminating the electric potential by use of Eqs. (6-36) and (6-37)† [50,51].

$$J_A = - \left[\frac{\bar{D}_A \bar{D}_B (z_A^2 \bar{C}_A + z_B^2 \bar{C}_B)}{z_A^2 \bar{C}_A \bar{D}_A + z_B^2 \bar{C}_B \bar{D}_B} \right] \text{grad } \bar{C}_A \qquad (6\text{-}38)$$

This equation may be considered as a special form of Fick's first law [Eq. (6-2)]. It describes the coupled interdiffusion in terms of one diffusion coefficient

$$\bar{D}_{AB} = \frac{\bar{D}_A \bar{D}_B (z_A^2 \bar{C}_A + z_B^2 \bar{C}_B)}{z_A^2 \bar{C}_A \bar{D}_A + z_B^2 \bar{C}_B \bar{D}_B} \qquad (6\text{-}39)$$

This interdiffusion coefficient, however, is by no means constant. Its value depends on the relative concentrations of A and B, i.e., on the ionic composition of the ion exchanger (see Fig. 6-6) which changes in the course of ion exchange. For $\bar{C}_A \ll \bar{C}_B$, the interdiffusion coefficient assumes the value $\bar{D}_A$, and for $\bar{C}_B \ll \bar{C}_A$ the value $\bar{D}_B$. *The ion present in smaller concentration has the stronger effect on the rate of interdiffusion.*‡ This general rule [48] can be deduced directly from the Nernst-Planck equation (6-35); the transference term is proportional to the concentration of the species, so that a small concentration makes this term unimportant. The physical explanation is straightforward; the electric field acts on every individual ion and

---

* See footnote to p. 267.

† A corresponding equation for univalent ions has been derived as early as 1930 by C. Wagner [128] for the migration of ions in semiconductors.

‡ This rule for coupled diffusion of two species is quite general and is not restricted to ions in ion exchangers where the coupling is enforced by the electroneutrality restriction. For example, the rule also holds for interdiffusion of the components in binary nonelectrolyte mixtures where the coupling is enforced by the constant-volume restriction (see the Hartley-Crank equation, Eq. (65) in Ref. [45a]).

thus causes large transference of the majority component while it has relatively little effect on the minority component.

Combination of Eq. (6-38) with the material balance (6-4) gives, for spherical geometry,

$$\frac{\partial \bar{C}_A}{\partial t} = \frac{1}{r^2} \frac{\partial}{\partial r} \left(r^2 \bar{D}_{AB} \frac{\partial \bar{C}_A}{\partial r} \right) \tag{6-40}$$

where $\bar{D}_{AB}$ is given by Eq. (6-39). This equation is analogous to Eq. (6-5) to which it reduces when the diffusion coefficient is constant.

Equation (6-40) is nonlinear and has not been solved analytically. However, numerical solutions have been calculated for different values

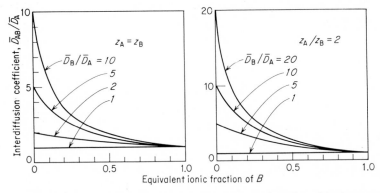

FIG. 6-6. Interdiffusion coefficient in the ion exchanger as a function of ionic composition. *Left:* exchange of ions of equal valence; *right:* univalent-bivalent exchange. The curves are calculated from Eq. (6-39) for different values of the mobility ratio $\bar{D}_B/\bar{D}_A$. *From F. Helfferich and M. S. Plesset* [51].

of the ratio $\bar{D}_A/\bar{D}_B$ and for complete conversion from A form to B form [conditions (6-8) and (6-6)] by use of an electronic computer. The results are tabulated [51,90]. An abbreviated table is given in the Appendix (see page 586). The numerical results can be expressed by the explicit approximation [51,90]

$$U(\tau) = \{1 - \exp[\pi^2(f_1(\alpha)\tau + f_2(\alpha)\tau^2 + f_3(\alpha)\tau^3)]\}^{1/2} \tag{6-41}$$

where $\tau \equiv \bar{D}_A t/r_0^2$ and $\alpha \equiv \bar{D}_A/\bar{D}_B$; for the exchange of counter ions of equal valence the coefficients are given by

$$f_1(\alpha) = -\frac{1}{0.570 + 0.430\alpha^{0.775}}$$

$$f_2(\alpha) = \frac{1}{0.260 + 0.782\alpha} \qquad \text{range of validity}$$
$$0.1 \leq \alpha \leq 10$$

$$f_3(\alpha) = -\frac{1}{0.165 + 0.177\alpha}$$

and for univalent-bivalent exchange

$\dfrac{z_A}{z_B} = \dfrac{1}{2}$ $f_1(\alpha) = -\dfrac{1}{0.64 + 0.36\alpha^{0.668}}$

$f_2(\alpha) = -\dfrac{1}{0.96 - 2.0\alpha^{0.4635}}$ $\left. \begin{array}{l} \\ \\ \end{array} \right\}$ range of validity $1 \leq \alpha \leq 20$

$f_3(\alpha) = -\dfrac{1}{0.27 + 0.09\alpha^{1.14}}$

$\dfrac{z_A}{z_B} = 2$ $f_1(\alpha) = -\dfrac{1}{0.350 + 0.650\alpha^{0.860}}$

$f_2(\alpha) = \dfrac{1}{0.030 + 1.012\alpha^{2.06}}$ $\left. \begin{array}{l} \\ \\ \\ \end{array} \right\}$ for $0 \leq \tau \leq 0.04$

$f_3(\alpha) = -\dfrac{1}{0.00265 + 0.354\alpha^{2.671}}$

range of validity
$0.05 \leq \alpha \leq 1$

$f_1(\alpha) = -\dfrac{1}{0.438 + 0.562\alpha^{0.777}}$

$f_2(\alpha) = \dfrac{1}{0.127 + 0.915\alpha^{1.057}}$ $\left. \begin{array}{l} \\ \\ \\ \end{array} \right\}$ for $\tau \geq 0.04$

$f_3(\alpha) = \dfrac{1}{0.0080 - 0.365\alpha^{0.453}}$

If $z_A = z_B$, Eq. (6-41) can also be applied to complete conversion to B form of an ion exchanger which is partially presaturated with B. In this case, the equation holds with $\alpha = \bar{x}_A^0 (\bar{D}_A/\bar{D}_B - 1) + 1$, where $\bar{x}_A^0$ is the initial equivalent ionic fraction of A in the ion exchanger [51,90]. Other cases have not been calculated. However, the computer program can be adapted without much difficulty to other conditions and parameter values.* Note that with boundary conditions other than (6-8) (no A in solution throughout the exchange) the selectivity of the ion exchanger must be taken into account. The selectivity affects the ion-exchange equilibrium at the interface ion exchanger/solution except under the condition (6-8) where B, irrespective of selectivity, is the only counter ion present at the interface (see also page 281).

It is interesting to compare the rates of forward and reverse exchange of two given counter ions, say, of H+ for Na+ and Na+ for H+. Tables of the function (6-41) are not suited for this purpose since the time parameter τ involves the diffusion coefficient of the counter ion which is initially in the ion exchanger, i.e., $\bar{D}_H$ in one case and $\bar{D}_{Na}$ in the other. When the same time scale is used for forward and reverse exchange, it becomes apparent that *the exchange is faster when the faster counter ion is initially in the ion exchanger,*

---

* In numerical integrations, Eq. (6-40) is conveniently used in its dimensionless form

$$\frac{\partial \bar{x}_A}{\partial \tau} = \frac{1}{\rho^2} \frac{\partial}{\partial \rho} \left[\rho^2 \left(\frac{1 + b\bar{x}_A}{1 + a\bar{x}_A} \right) \frac{\partial \bar{x}_A}{\partial \rho} \right]$$

where $\bar{x}_A \equiv z_A \bar{C}_A/\bar{C}$, $\rho \equiv r/r_0$, and $\tau \equiv \bar{D}_A t/r_0^2$ are the variables and $a \equiv z_A \bar{D}_A/z_B \bar{D}_B - 1$ and $b \equiv z_A/z_B - 1$ are (constant) parameters.

and that the difference in rate increases as conversion progresses. Comparisons of forward and reverse exchange rates are shown in Fig. 6-7. In the H^+/Na^+ exchanges ($\bar{D}_H/\bar{D}_{Na} \cong 7$), the half times differ by about the factor 1.6, and the times required for 90 per cent conversion by about the factor 2.5. In the Na^+/Sr^{2+} exchanges ($\bar{D}_{Na}/\bar{D}_{Sr} \cong 15$) the differences are even greater.

A rather striking feature is the behavior of the concentration profiles in the beads. These are shown in Fig. 6-8 for two extreme values of the

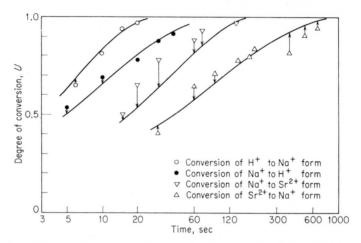

FIG. 6-7. Comparisons of forward and reverse exchange rates of two given counter ions. The exchange is faster when the faster ion (H^+ in H^+/Na^+ exchange, Na^+ in Na^+/Sr^{2+} exchange) is initially in the resin. *Circles and triangles:* experimental results by O. P. Fedoseeva [32a] with KU-2 cation exchanger (sulfonated crosslinked polystyrene); *solid lines:* theoretical curves calculated from independently determined diffusion coefficients by use of Eq. (6-41). *From F. Helfferich* [52].

mobility ratio ($\bar{D}_A/\bar{D}_B = 10$, and $\bar{D}_A/\bar{D}_B = 0.1$). If the ion initially present in the bead is much the faster one, a comparatively sharp boundary moves in toward the center of the particle. In the opposite case, the boundary becomes diffuse and the exhaustion of the bead is much more uniform. This is a consequence of the dependence of the interdiffusion coefficient on ionic composition (Fig. 6-6). In the first case, the concentration of the faster ion is low in the outer shells and high at the center of the bead. Hence, the interdiffusion coefficient decreases toward the center, and the outer shells are thus rapidly converted, whereas the exchange near the center remains slow. In the second case, the opposite holds. The interdiffusion coefficient increases toward the center; therefore the process reaches the center quickly, once the outer shells are converted.

These results show that, with counter ions of different mobilities, there is a marked difference in rate and behavior between forward and reverse exchange. However, it should be kept in mind that the comparisons were made with systems in which the ion exchanger is completely converted from A form to B form. The less complete the conversion, the less the difference between forward and reverse exchange rates. This becomes evident when the limiting case of exchange of a trace component is considered. Here the diffusion of the trace component determines the rate of both forward and reverse exchange. The interdiffusion coefficient is equal to the individual diffusion coefficient of the trace component and remains constant (see Sec. 6-3d). The only other case in which the interdiffusion coefficient is constant is exchange of counter ions of equal mobility. In these limiting cases, the equations derived for isotopic exchange can be used.

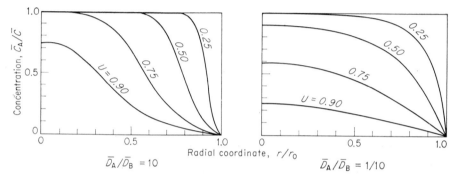

FIG. 6-8. Radial concentration profiles in particle-diffusion controlled ion exchange. The profiles are calculated from Eq. (6-40) for the mobility ratios $\bar{D}_A/\bar{D}_B = 10$ (*left*) and $\bar{D}_A/\bar{D}_B = \frac{1}{10}$ (*right*). Equal counter-ion valences and infinite solution volume are assumed. The various curves are for different degrees of conversion. *From F. Helfferich and M. S. Plesset* [51].

Film Diffusion Control. The quantitative treatment of film-diffusion controlled ion exchange is based on the same simplifying assumptions which were used for isotopic exchange; diffusion across the film is treated as a quasi-stationary and one-dimensional process (see page 262).

The treatment of particle diffusion and film diffusion differs in two aspects which should be pointed out. Within the particle, the presence of co-ions can be neglected because of the Donnan effect; within the film, however, it cannot be neglected because, here, the co-ion and counter-ion concentrations are equal. Furthermore, with film diffusion control, the selectivity of the ion exchanger must be taken into account even if the bulk solution remains free of species A throughout the exchange because, even under this condition, both counter ions are present at the interface ion exchanger/film.

As yet, only two analytical solutions for limiting cases have been found. One of them allows different mobilities of the ions, but is restricted to ions of equal valence, ion exchangers with no selectivity, and infinite solution volume. The other includes the effect of selectivity and the more general finite solution volume condition, but is applicable only to counter ions of equal mobility.

In the exchange of *ions of different mobilities*, a diffusion potential in the film arises and produces a co-ion shift. The Nernst-Planck equations (6-35) for counter ions A and B and for the co-ion Y must be solved. The restrictions in the film are (for ions of equal valence)

$$C_A + C_B = C_Y \qquad \text{electroneutrality} \qquad (6\text{-}42)$$
$$J_A + J_B = J_Y = 0 \qquad \text{no electric current} \qquad (6\text{-}43)$$

The condition $J_Y = 0$ implies the quasi-stationary state (see page 262) and the fact that the ion exchanger does not take up or release co-ions. A necessary consequence of this condition is that, in the presence of an electric field, the co-ion concentration (and thus the total concentration) in the film is *not* constant. In the quasi-stationary state, the action of the electric field on the co-ion must be balanced by a corresponding concentration gradient so that no net co-ion transfer is produced. The necessary co-ion shift occurs during the short initial time interval before the quasi-stationary state is attained.

The following initial and boundary conditions are used. The initial condition (no A in solution, no B in the ion exchanger) is

$$\begin{array}{cc} r = r_0,\ t = 0 & C'_A = C'(t = 0) \\ r \geq r_0 + \delta,\ t = 0 & C_A(r) = 0 \end{array} \qquad (6\text{-}44)$$

quantities with primes refer to the interface ion exchanger solution.

Other initial distributions are discussed later (see page 276). It is assumed that the ion exchanger has no selectivity ($\alpha_B^A = 1$). The boundary condition at the interface ion exchanger/film thus is

$$r = r_0,\ t \geq 0 \qquad C'_A(t) = \frac{\bar{C}_A(t) C'(t)}{\bar{C}} \qquad (6\text{-}45)$$

The condition at the boundary film/solution (infinite solution volume condition) is given by Eq. (6-21). The time dependence of $\bar{C}_A$ and of the flux is obtained from Eq. (6-17). Neither the initial nor the boundary condition at the interface is explicit since the quantity $C'(t)$, an eigenfunction of the set of equations, is not known beforehand.

The solution of the three equations (6-35) for the species A, B, and Y under the conditions given above is [104]

$$U(t) = \frac{D_B y^2(t) - D_A}{D_B - D_A}$$

$$\ln\left\{ \frac{y(t) - 1}{(D_A/D_B)^{1/2} - 1} \right\} + \frac{1}{2}\left(y^2(t) - \frac{D_A}{D_B} \right) + y(t) - \left(\frac{D_A}{D_B} \right)^{1/2} = -\frac{3 D_A C}{r_0 \delta \bar{C}} t \quad (6\text{-}46)$$

where $\qquad y(t) \equiv \dfrac{C'(t)}{C} = \dfrac{D_A C'_A(t) + D_B C'_B(t)}{D_B C}$

The fractional attainment of equilibrium $U(t)$ and the time t are interrelated through their mutual dependence on the mathematical parameter y. Note that arguments can be advanced against the use of the simple Nernst film model to cases as the present one where the interdiffusion coefficient in the film is variable.

In the exchange of *ions of equal mobility*, no electric field arises. There is no co-ion shift in the film and no electric transference of counter ions, and the interdiffusion coefficient is constant [see Eq. (6-39)]. The treatment differs from the calculation of isotopic exchange only in the boundary condition at the interface ion exchanger/film. Here, the selectivity affects the equilibrium:

$$\frac{\bar{C}_A C'_B}{\bar{C}_B C'_A} = \alpha^A_B \tag{5-70}$$

The separation factor α^A_B is assumed to be constant. The boundary condition thus becomes

$$r = r_0, \ t \geq 0 \qquad C'_A(t) = \frac{\bar{C}_A(t) C}{z_A \bar{C}_A(t) + \alpha^A_B (\bar{C} - z_A \bar{C}_A(t))} \tag{6-47}$$

The time dependence is obtained from the material balance (6-17). Under the finite solution volume condition (6-24) the solution is*

$$(1 - a\bar{x}^\infty_B) \ln (1 - U(t)) - (1 - a\bar{x}^\infty_B - ab) \ln \left(1 - \frac{U(t)}{1 + b/\bar{x}^\infty_B}\right) = -ct \tag{6-48}$$

where

$$a \equiv 1 - \alpha^A_B \qquad b \equiv \left[\left(\frac{1+w}{aw}\right)^2 - \frac{4}{aw}\right]^{1/2} \qquad c \equiv \frac{3ab\bar{V}D}{\delta r_0 V} \qquad w \equiv \frac{\bar{C}\bar{V}}{CV}$$

$D = D_A = D_B =$ diffusion coefficient in the film; $\bar{x}^\infty_B \equiv \frac{z_B \bar{Q}^\infty_B}{\bar{Q}} = \frac{1+w}{2aw} - \frac{b}{2}$

($\bar{x}^\infty_B$ is the relative saturation with B when equilibrium is attained).

Under the infinite solution volume condition (6-21), Eq. (6-48) reduces to*

$$\ln [1 - U(t)] + \left(1 - \frac{1}{\alpha^A_B}\right) U(t) = -\frac{3DC}{r_0 \delta \bar{C} \alpha^A_B} t \tag{6-49}$$

The half time of exchange is readily calculated from Eq. (6-49):

$$t_{1/2} = (0.167 + 0.064 \alpha^A_B) \frac{r_0 \delta \bar{C}}{DC} \tag{6-50}$$

---

* Equation (6-49) is a limiting case of a solution which was first derived by Adamson [1] and was originally supposed to cover exchange of ions of different mobilities also. Equation (6-48) is a limiting case of Dickel's extension of this solution [26]. This earlier theory, however, disregards the electric field and thus is applicable only to ions of equal mobility (see p. 278). Note that the solution given by Dickel [26] implies tacitly that $\bar{C}\bar{V} = CV$. (Dickel's experiments were designed to meet this condition.)

The relations (6-46), (6-48), and (6-49) are derived for an initial distribution where all ions A are in the ion exchanger and all ions B in the solution [conditions (6-44) and (6-20)]. If the ion exchanger is partially presaturated with species B, the fractional attainment of equilibrium can be calculated from

$$U(t) = \frac{U'(t + t_0) - \bar{x}_B^0}{1 - \bar{x}_B^0} \tag{6-51}$$

where $U'(t)$ is the right-hand side of Eq. (6-46), (6-48), or (6-49), $\bar{x}_B^0$ is the degree of presaturation, and t_0 is the time that would be required to achieve this presaturation.

It is interesting to examine the effects of selectivity and of differences in the ionic mobilities on the rate of exchange. These effects become apparent when the solutions (6-46) and (6-49) are compared with the solution (6-22) for isotopic exchange where, of course, no selectivity and no mobility difference exists. The following rules are found.

When the ion exchanger prefers the species A which it contains initially ($\alpha_B^A > 1$), the rate is lower, and when it prefers the competing species ($\alpha_B^A < 1$), the rate is higher [compare Eqs. (6-23) and (6-50)]. The ion exchanger is reluctant to release, and eager to take up, the ion it prefers. This is as one might guess intuitively. The physical cause is that preference for A leads to a comparatively small concentration of A at the solution side of the interface and thus to a small concentration difference across the film. The opposite holds if B is preferred. For $\alpha_B^A = 1$, of course, Eqs. (6-48) and (6-49) reduce to Eqs. (6-25) and (6-22), respectively, since equal mobilities and identical initial and boundary conditions have been assumed.

The effect of a difference in counter-ion mobilities is somewhat more complex. When Eq. (6-46) is applied to forward and reverse exchange of two ions with different mobilities, say H^+ and Li^+, it is seen that the rate laws differ considerably. The initial rate is lower when the ion which is originally in the ion exchanger is the faster one. This is just the opposite from particle-diffusion controlled exchange (see page 271). The explanation is straightforward. With the faster ion H^+ initially in the ion exchanger, the diffusion potential across the film is positive on the solution side and, hence, pulls anions out of the film. With the slower ion Li^+ initially in the ion exchanger, the diffusion potential has opposite sign and pushes anions into the film. The result—shown in Fig. 6-9—is electrolyte depletion at the interface and comparatively small concentration gradients in the first case, and electrolyte accumulation and comparatively large concentration gradients in the second case. The initial rates of forward and reverse exchange differ by the factor $(D_B/D_A)^{1/2}$. However, with progressing conversion to the B form, the situation is reversed since the electric potential difference and thus the co-ion accumulation or depletion decrease and the interdiffusion coefficient approaches the value D_A. The half times of forward and reverse exchange are nearly equal.

Derivation of the criterion for the rate-determining step. We are now able to derive the criterion (6-1) by which the nature of the rate-determining step can be predicted. This simple, approximate relation is obtained from Eqs. (6-12) and (6-50) which, strictly speaking, hold only for counter ions of equal mobility and infinite solution volume. By equating the right-hand sides of Eqs. (6-12) and (6-50) one finds that the (hypothetical) half times of particle- and film-diffusion controlled exchange are equal when $(\bar{C}\bar{D}\delta/CDr_0)(5 + 2\alpha_B^A) \cong 1$. This dimensionless modulus becomes smaller than unity when particle diffusion has the longer half time, and larger than unity when film diffusion has the longer half time. The slower step determines the over-all rate. Thus the value of the modulus indicates whether particle or film diffusion is rate-controlling. In Eq. (6-1), the total equivalent concentration in the ion exchanger $\bar{C}$ has been replaced for convenience by the molarity of fixed ionic groups X.

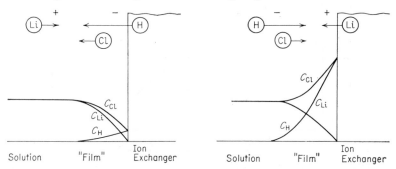

Fig. 6-9. Concentration profiles in film-diffusion controlled exchange of H+ for Li+ (*left*) and Li+ for H+ (*right*), after attainment of the quasi-stationary state (*schematic*). The electric potential difference across the film—indicated by plus and minus signs—causes co-ion accumulation at the resin surface in one case, and co-ion depletion in the other. The profiles are steeper and, hence, the (initial) rate is higher when the slower ion Li+ is initially in the ion exchanger.

There is, of course, no sharp limit between particle and film diffusion control. Both mechanisms affect the rate when their individual rates are comparable. Furthermore, Fig. 6-5 shows that (for equal half times of the two individual processes) the rate of particle diffusion is initially higher and later lower than that of film diffusion. The theoretical rate of particle diffusion at zero time is infinite, whereas the rate of film diffusion is always finite. Hence every ion exchange is film-controlled during an initial, if extremely short, period, and the tendency toward particle diffusion control increases while the exchange progresses. It should also be noted that the criterion was derived for infinite solution volume, complete conversion, and counter ions of equal mobility. For other cases, other more complex criteria may be derived from the rate laws in this section.

Earlier Theories. The rate laws given in the preceding part of this section have only recently been derived. The hitherto accepted theories of ion-exchange kinetics have adopted the conventional approach of using Fick's first law [Eq. (6-2)] with a *constant* diffusion coefficient. This is clearly tantamount to neglecting the effect of the electric field.

With *particle diffusion* rate-controlling, the treatment is the same as that for isotopic exchange, except that the self-diffusion coefficient is replaced by an empirical interdiffusion constant [37,56,65,94,98,99]. This earlier theory predicts equal rates and equal shapes of the concentration profiles for forward and reverse exchange of two counter ions. The more recent treatment, however, shows that the interdiffusion coefficient is not constant and that the rates and concentration profiles in forward and reverse exchange may differ greatly (see Figs. 6-6 to 6-8). The earlier theory has the advantage of greater simplicity and may be used as a first approximation. However, the comparison with more

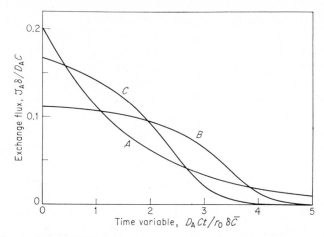

FIG. 6-10. Comparison of different theories for film-diffusion controlled ion exchange. The dimensionless diagram shows the exchange fluxes as a function of time. The curves are calculated for a mobility ratio $D_A/D_B = 9$, counter ions of equal valences, infinite solution volume, and no selectivity.

    A = rate law for isotopic exchange [Eq. (6-22)] with constant interdiffusion coefficient
        $D = 2D_A D_B/(D_A + D_B)$
    B = Adamson's theory [Eq. (6-49)]
    C = Schlögl-Helfferich theory (including the electric field [Eq. (6-46)])

rigorous solutions shows that the approximation becomes rather poor when the mobilities of the counter ions differ substantially.

A theory for *film-diffusion* controlled ion exchange has been developed by Adamson [1] and extended by Dickel [26]. These authors have used individual diffusion constants D_A and D_B, but have neglected the electric field. A comparison with the more rigorous solution (6-46) shows that this earlier theory overemphasizes the difference in rate between forward and reverse exchange [104]. (According to Adamson's equations, the initial rates differ by the factor D_A/D_B instead of $(D_A/D_B)^{1/2}$.) Adamson's more complicated equation is no better an approximation than the much simpler rate law for isotopic exchange. This is seen in Fig. 6-10 where these two rate laws are compared with the more rigorous solution (6-46) which includes the effect of the electric field. Hence the Adamson theory, though of great historical importance, should now be discarded. However, in its limiting case of equal counter-ion mobilities [Eq. (6-49)], Adamson's theory is still useful because it includes the effect of selectivity.

Deviations in actual systems. In the derivation of the ideal limiting laws in this section, the following simplifying assumptions were made. Association of fixed ionic groups with counter ions, changes in swelling and swelling pressure, gradients of activity coefficients, variation of the separation factor, and the presence of co-ions in the ion exchanger were neglected. Also, the concentration of fixed ionic groups and the individual diffusion coefficients were assumed to be constant. Furthermore, the ion exchanger was treated as a quasi-homogeneous phase. In actual systems, these simplifying assumptions are, at best, approximations. The effects mentioned immediately above have not yet been incorporated into quantitative theories. A brief qualitative discussion is given in the following.

Most of the above-mentioned effects occur within the ion exchanger and thus chiefly affect the diffusion rate in the particle. Here, *association* or *ion-pair formation* may be particularly important. It is evident that the average diffusion constant of a species is reduced when a substantial fraction of the species is immobilized by association with the fixed ionic groups. The degree of association usually varies with the ionic composition of the ion exchanger. Hence it cannot be assumed that the individual diffusion coefficient of the associating species is constant, and the quantitative treatment based on this assumption must fail. [One might argue that the assumption of a constant individual diffusion coefficient is still reasonable when applied only to the free, not to the associated, ions of the species. Now, however, the material balance (6-4) must be modified to include association and dissociation, and the total counter-ion concentration is no longer constant.] Nevertheless, some qualitative aspects of ion exchange with associating counter ions are readily deduced from the theories in this and in the preceding chapter. This will be illustrated with the exchange of H^+ for Na^+ with a weak-acid resin. When in H^+ form, the resin is very weakly dissociated and thus contains very few free ions. Hence the Donnan potential is low and the Donnan exclusion insignificant (see page 137). When placed in a solution of, say, NaCl, the resin will sorb the electrolyte almost like an ordinary, nonionic sorbent. The sorption rate depends on the concentration of the solution, even if particle diffusion is rate-controlling [95]. The ionic character of the resin shows up only in later stages of the exchange when dissociation of the weak-acid groups has made progress. The exchange rate, especially in the early stages, is low for two reasons: the concentration gradient of free H^+ ions is small because of association, and the diffusion constants are small because of the low free-water content of the resin [43]. When the resin in Na^+ form is placed n a solution of, say, HCl, the outer shells are rapidly converted to H^+ form and thus become practically nonionic. Again, Donnan exclusion becomes insignificant, electrolyte sorption occurs, and the rate of exchange thus depends on the concentration of the solution. This reverse exchange is faster than the forward exchange because the H^+ ions, upon entering the resin, are rapidly sequestered by the fixed anions. However, the rate is usually much lower than with strong-acid resins because shrinking of the beads hinders diffusion. Analogous considerations apply to exchange involving OH^- ions and weak-base resins and to other exchanges with associating counter ions.

Changes in swelling of the ion exchanger chiefly affect the individual diffusion coefficients. Diffusion is more strongly obstructed by the matrix when the solvent content of the resin is lower. Of course, a change in the resin volume also alters the bead radius and the molarity of the fixed ionic groups, but these effects are usually less important than the variation in the diffusion coefficients. Note that during the exchange of counter ions, the ion exchanger is not in swelling equilibrium with the external solution. The electric transference of counter ions by the diffusion potential in the beads causes a transfer of solvent in the same direction (see Sec. 7-3; it is irrelevant whether the counter-ion transfer is caused by an external voltage source or by a diffusion potential generated within the system in the absence of an electric current). With the faster counter ion being initially in the ion exchanger, the sign of the electric potential gradient is such that the counter ions are transferred toward the center of the bead. As a result, there is a temporary solvent accumulation in the center of the bead. Of course, as ion exchange approaches equilibrium, the electric potential gradient decays, and swelling equilibrium is reestablished. The solvent content of the beads may thus go through a maximum [52]; see Fig. 6-11. With the slower counter ion initially in the ion exchanger, the electric potential gradient has opposite sign, and the result is a temporary solvent depletion of the beads [52]; see Fig. 6-11. These transient changes in swelling tend to make the difference between forward and reverse exchange of two given counter ions even more pronounced.

The *presence of co-ions* in the ion exchanger has the following effects. Co-ions in the ion exchanger are transferred by the electric field in the direction in which the faster counter ion diffuses, i.e., opposite to the direction of solvent transference. The result thus is exactly the opposite from that in the case of the solvent, namely, a temporary co-ion depletion of the bead centers when the faster counter ion is initially in the ion exchanger, and a temporary co-ion accumulation in the bead centers when the slower counter ion is initially in the ion exchanger [52]; see Fig. 6-11. The temporary nonuniformity of the co-ion distribution in the beads reduces the electric field. Thus it reduces the force which causes the variation of the interdiffusion coefficient with ionic composition of the resin (see page 267). Hence one may expect that this variation and, consequently, the difference in rate between forward and reverse exchange of two given ions are less drastic when co-ions are present. Also, one should expect the rates of both forward and reverse exchange to be lower because a part of the electric driving force generated by diffusion of the faster ion is spent on shifting the co-ions rather than speeding up the slower counter ion.   As a rule, the effect on the ion-exchange rates is small because Donnan exclusion keeps the co-ion concentration in the ion exchanger very low.   However, the ion-exchange rates can be seriously affected in systems in which electrolyte sorption is pronounced.   This is true in systems with highly concentrated solutions or with weakly dissociated ion exchangers.

A more rigorous treatment of particle diffusion would also have to include the effect of gradients of activity coefficients [see Eq. (8-1) which

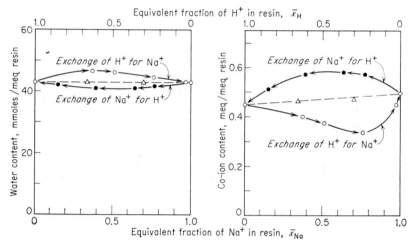

FIG. 6-11. Transient water contents (*left*) and co-ion contents (*right*) of a cation exchange resin in the course of exchange of H^+ for Na^+ (○) and Na^+ for H^+ (●), given as a function of the degree of conversion.   In the exchange of H^+ for Na^+, the water content goes through a maximum and the co-ion content through a minimum.   In the exchange of Na^+ for H^+, the opposite is true.   Resin: phenolsulfonic-acid–formaldehyde condensation polymer; solutions: 1 M HCl and NaCl.   For comparison, the equilibrium water and co-ion contents in contact with mixed HCl-NaCl solutions of 1 M total concentration are also given (Δ, *broken lines*).   *From F. Helfferich* [52].

should be used instead of Eq. (6-34)].   A physical explanation of this effect would be unduly lengthy.   Note that only the *gradients* of the activity coefficients are involved.   The absolute magnitude of the coefficients has no effect on the flux equation.   It does, however, determine the selectivity.

The *selectivity* of the ion exchanger—conveniently expressed by the separation factor—can affect the rates of both particle- and film-diffusion controlled ion exchange.   The selectivity has no influence on bulk-phase diffusion itself, but it affects the boundary condition at the surface of the particle [see Eq. (5-70)].   The preferred counter ion is taken up at a faster rate and released at a slower rate (see page 276).   There is only one limiting case in which the selectivity is irrelevant.   This is particle-diffusion controlled exchange with a solution of infinite volume and devoid of species A [boundary condition (6-8); see also page 271]. Here, the concentration of A at the interface remains effectively zero, irrespective of selectivity. The limiting law for particle diffusion control [Eq. (6-41)] was derived for this boundary condition and thus does not include the selectivity effect. The limiting laws (6-48) and (6-49) for film diffusion control were derived with the use of a constant separation factor. Thus they reflect the effect of selectivity, but not that of a variation of selectivity with ionic composition of the resin.

The separation factor depends, of course, on the nature of the ion exchanger and the counter ions. It should be noted, however, that the factor may also depend on the concentration of the solution and the nature of the co-ion. The solution concentration has a particularly strong effect when the counter ions have different valences (electroselectivity, see page 156). Here, the preference for the ion of higher valence is greater when the solution is more dilute. The co-ion can affect the selectivity by associating with one of the exchanging counter ions: the ion exchanger prefers the counter ion which does not associate with the co-ion (see page 164). Thus the exchange of, say, H^+ for Na^+ is fastest with a solution of NaOH, somewhat slower with CH_3COONa, and much slower with NaCl because the association of H^+ with the anion is strongest in the first and weakest in the last case. [Note that this effect, too, is absent when the boundary condition (6-8) is met.]

In principle, all the above-mentioned effects could be taken into account by using more refined equations for all the mobile species and integrating these under more accurate restrictions and boundary conditions. It is obvious, however, that this would be a formidable task. It is certainly impossible to obtain rigorous analytical solutions. Numerical solutions could be calculated by use of electronic computers, but numerous measurements would be necessary to establish the dependence of the various parameters and coefficients on the variables. Numerical solutions also have the disadvantage that they apply only for specific values of the parameters. The quantitative effect of a parameter can only be established and expressed by an explicit equation when a series of numerical integrations is made in which this parameter is varied and the others are kept constant. In ion-exchange kinetics, the number of parameters involved is such that a systematic investigation and tabulation of other than just the most important limiting cases hardly seems worth the effort.

Experimental evidence.   The ion-exchange rate laws given in this section are quite recent theoretical contributions and have not yet been fully confirmed by experiments.

In the case of *particle-diffusion* controlled ion exchange it had previously been claimed that the simpler rate laws for isotopic exchange apply. However, the accuracy of the measurements did not permit unambiguous conclusions.   In recent experimental tests of the newer theory, good agreement between predicted and observed rates and internal concentration profiles was obtained and, in particular, the characteristic difference in rate between forward and reverse exchange of two given counter ions was verified [52]; see also Fig. 6-7.   The temporary accumulation and depletion of co-ions and solvent—a direct consequence of the internal electric field which was disregarded in the earlier theories—is also established [52].   Additional experimental evidence in support of the more recent approach is the extensive verification of the basic equation (6-38) in steady-state measurements with ion-exchanger membranes (see Chap. 8).

Systematic experimental data on *film-diffusion* controlled ion exchange are even more scanty.   Qualitative conclusions can be derived from Dickel's work [26,27], though a quantitative evaluation is not possible.   Dickel's studies show that observed and calculated rates are in poor agreement when aqueous-phase diffusion coefficients and the earlier theories of film diffusion are used.   The deviations are greatest when the mobilities of the exchanging ions differ most, and can be qualitatively explained with the effect of the electric field.*

d. Exchange of Trace Components

A particularly simple limiting case of ion exchange is exchange of trace components.   Consider, for example, the uptake or release of traces of one counter ion in the presence of a large excess of another counter ion in both the ion exchanger and the external solution.   In such systems, the changes in composition of the ion exchanger and the solution remain on a trace level and, hence, the individual diffusion coefficients, activity coefficients, the degree of swelling, etc., remain practically constant.   Also, in interdiffusion of a trace counter ion and another counter ion which always is in large excess, diffusion of the trace ion (as the minority component) is always rate-controlling.   The simple rate laws for isotopic exchange thus apply [79], even though interdiffusion of two different counter ions occurs.   Note that the individual diffusion coefficient of the trace ion depends, of course, on the swelling condition of the ion exchanger, on specific interactions, etc.   Hence, this coefficient is not universal but depends on the nature of the system.

e. Prediction of Ion-exchange Rates

Ion-exchange rates can be predicted by the use of the rate laws given in this section when the necessary data are known.   The rate laws involve the individual diffusion coefficients of the counter ions in the ion exchanger and in the aqueous phase, the concentration of the fixed ionic groups, the solution concentration, the selectivity and the particle size of the ion

---

* Dickel interpreted his results in terms of interfacial resistance to diffusion of H^+ ions.

exchanger, and the film thickness. All except the diffusion coefficients in the ion exchanger and the film thickness are usually known or readily determined. Ways of estimating the film thickness have been mentioned in Sec. 6-2 (see footnote to page 253). As a rule, the film thickness is 10^{-3} to 10^{-2} cm. A reliable method of calculating diffusion coefficients in ion exchangers has not yet been worked out. Most investigators have approached ion-exchange kinetics from the other side, namely, they have calculated diffusion coefficients from observed rates. This line of attack is, of course, of no direct help in the prediction of rates. However, so much experimental data have been gathered in this way that at least the order of magnitude of the diffusion coefficients in a given resin can be easily estimated, unless the resin is of an unusual type. A more detailed discussion of diffusion coefficients in resins is given in Sec. 6-8.

The first step in predicting the rate of an ion-exchange process is to establish the rate-determining mechanism. For this purpose the criterion (6-1) is used. This criterion involves the interdiffusion coefficients in the ion exchanger and the film. In isotopic exchange the coefficients are, of course, equal to the self-diffusion coefficients. In ion exchange the coefficients vary with ionic composition, and suitable mean values should be used. For complete conversion of the resin from A form to B form, the average interdiffusion coefficient is

$$\bar{D}_{AB} \approx \frac{\bar{D}_A \bar{D}_B (z_A + z_B)}{z_A \bar{D}_A + z_B \bar{D}_B} \tag{6-52}$$

[Harmonic means of $\bar{D}_A$ and $\bar{D}_B$ when $z_A = z_B$; this relation follows from Eq. (6-39) with $z_A \tilde{C}_A = z_B \tilde{C}_B$.] For incomplete conversion, the average interdiffusion coefficient is more similar to the diffusion coefficient of the counter ion which is in the minority; a suitable mean value can be estimated by use of Fig. 6-6.

Once the nature of the rate-determining step is established, the rate laws for isotopic exchange can be used to calculate the order of magnitude of the rate. More accurate results are obtained with the rate laws (6-41), (6-46), (6-48), or (6-49). However, in view of the idealizations involved, the use of these more complicated equations is only worth while when the boundary conditions, restrictions, and assumptions inherent in the derivation are at least approximately met.

f. General Rules

The dependence of the ion-exchange rate on the various factors is summarized in Table 6-1. The dependences listed refer to the "relative" rather than the "absolute" rate, i.e., to approach to equilibrium rather than to the number of ions exchanged per unit time. Exceptions to these rules have been discussed in the preceding treatment.

For convenient reference, the available rate laws of isotopic exchange

Table 6-1. Dependence of the ion-exchange rate on experimental conditions

	Particle diffusion control	Film diffusion control
Counter ion mobility:		
In particle...................	$\propto \bar{D}$ *	No effect
In aqueous phase.............	No effect	$\propto D$
Co-ion mobility................	No effect	No effect
Particle size...................	$\propto 1/r_0^2$	$\propto 1/r_0$
Capacity of ion exchanger.........	No effect	$\propto 1/X$
Nature of fixed ionic groups.......	Slow when fixed ionic groups associate with counter ions†	No effect
Degree of crosslinking............	Decreases with increasing crosslinking†	No effect
Selectivity of ion exchanger.......	The preferred counter ion is taken up at higher rate and released at lower rate, except under boundary condition (6-8)	
Concentration of solution.........	No effect	$\propto C$
Solution volume.................	Decreases with increasing solution volume	
Temperature....................	Increases with temperature, ca. 4 to 8% per degree centigrade†	Increases with temperature; ca. 3 to 5% per degree centigrade†
Rate of agitation or flow..........	No effect	Increases with agitation rate‡

* Note that polyvalent cations and counter ions which associate with fixed ionic groups are particularly slow.

† This effect is reflected in the diffusion coefficients.

‡ The rate of agitation reaches a limiting hydrodynamic efficiency; beyond a critical agitation rate there is no effect on the rate of ion exchange.

Table 6-2. Rate laws of isotopic and ion exchange

	Isotopic exchange	Ion exchange
Particle diffusion control:		
Infinite solution volume..............	Eq. (6-9)*	Eq. (6-41)*†
Finite solution volume..............	Eqs. (6-14), (6-15)*	
Film diffusion control:		
Infinite solution volume..............	Eq. (6-22)	Eqs. (6-46)‡, (6-49)§
Finite solution volume..............	Eq. (6-25)	Eq. (6-48)§
General intermediate case:		
Infinite solution volume..............	Eq. (6-26)	
Finite solution volume..............		

* Tabulated in the Appendix.

† Only for counter ions of equal valence and univalent-bivalent exchange under boundary condition (6-8).

‡ Only for counter ions of equal valence and ion exchangers without selectivity.

§ Only for counter ions of equal mobility.

and ion exchange are summarized in Table 6-2. Note that the solutions for ion exchange are limiting laws derived under simplifying assumptions.

6-4. EMPIRICAL AND SIMPLIFIED RATE LAWS

The previous section has shown that the rate laws of ion exchange are rather complex, even in the comparatively simple limiting cases which have so far been solved. In a rigorous quantitative treatment of more complicated systems, for example, ion-exchange columns, tremendous mathematical difficulties are encountered. Here, simplified rate laws are widely used. In the literature on ion exchange there is no lack of such rate equations; some of them are empirical and others are based on simplified models or plausible assumptions. Most of these rate laws were found to hold quite well in the systems investigated by their originators. However, they might well fail under only slightly different conditions.* Various rate laws which have been suggested and used are listed below.

$$-\frac{1}{\bar{V}} \frac{d\bar{Q}_A}{dt} = k_1 \bar{C}_A C_B - k_2 \bar{C}_B C_A \qquad \text{(2d order/2d order)} \qquad (6\text{-}53)$$

$$[55,63,71,108,120\text{-}122,129]$$

$$= k_1 \bar{C}_A C_B - k_1 \alpha_B^A \bar{C}_B C_A \qquad \text{where } k_1 = \frac{1}{\bar{C}/a + C\alpha_B^A/b} \qquad (6\text{-}54)$$

$$[6,7,35,39,120,125]$$

$$= k_1 \bar{C}_A^{z_B} C_B^{z_A} - k_2 \bar{C}_B^{z_A} C_A^{z_B} \qquad \text{(order } z_A + z_B) \qquad (6\text{-}55) \; [31,108]$$
$$= k_1 \bar{C}_A C_B - k_2 \bar{C}_B \qquad \text{(2d order/1st order)} \qquad (6\text{-}56) \; [70,71,97,121]$$
$$= k_1 \bar{C}_A C_B \qquad \text{(2d order)} \qquad (6\text{-}57) \; [3,71,78,129]$$
$$= k_1 C_B - k_2 \bar{C}_B \qquad \text{(1st order/1st order)} \qquad (6\text{-}58) \; [4,71,97]$$
$$= k_1 C_B \qquad \text{(1st order)} \qquad (6\text{-}59) \; [108]$$

$$= k_1 \left(C_B - \frac{\bar{C}_B C}{\bar{C}} \right) \qquad (6\text{-}60) \; [108]$$

$$= k_1 \left(C_B - \frac{\bar{C}_B}{a\bar{C}_A} \right) \qquad (6\text{-}61) \; [72]$$

$$= k_1 C_B (F - a\bar{C}_B - b\bar{C}_A) \qquad (6\text{-}62) \; [34]$$

$$= \frac{15\bar{D}}{r_0^2} \left(\bar{C}_B' - \frac{\bar{Q}_B}{\bar{V}} \right) \qquad (6\text{-}63) \; [36]$$

$$= \frac{\pi^2 \bar{D}}{r_0^2} \frac{(\bar{C}_B' \bar{V})^2 - \bar{Q}_B^2}{2\bar{Q}_B \bar{V}} \qquad (6\text{-}64) \; [124]$$

$$= \frac{\pi^2 \bar{D}}{r_0^2} \frac{(\bar{C}_B' - \bar{Q}_B/\bar{V})(\tfrac{3}{4}\bar{C}_B' - \tfrac{1}{4}\bar{Q}_B/\bar{V})}{\bar{Q}_B/\bar{V}} \qquad (6\text{-}65) \; [38]$$

For the ease of comparison, the equations have been written in uniform notation. Thus some constants are named and defined in a different way from that in the original publications. In Eqs. (6-53) to (6-62) the internal concentrations are mean values ($\bar{C}_i \equiv \bar{Q}_i/\bar{V}$). Quantities with primes refer to the interface resin/solution.

In Eqs. (6-53) to (6-59), ion exchange is treated formally as a chemical reaction—reversible or irreversible—of some assumed order. The quantities k_1 and k_2 are the rate constants for the forward and reverse reactions, respectively. In principle, there is no

---

* See, for example, the test of Eq. (6-54) by Sujata [118].

objection to the formal use of such rate constants.   However, it should be kept in mind that these quantities are actually not constant and, in their physical significance, have little in common with rate constants of true chemical reactions.   Particularly the identification of the ratio k_2/k_1 with the selectivity coefficient or separation factor— as in Eq. (6-54) where $k_1\alpha_B^A$ is substituted for k_2—may well lead to serious errors.   This is borne out by the fact that the rates of forward and reverse exchange with an ion exchanger of no selectivity ($\alpha_B^A = 1$) may differ greatly [see Fig. 6-7 and Eq. (6-46)], whereas Eq. (6-54) predicts equal rates for this case.   The implied relationship holds when the system is almost in equilibrium, but does not hold when the constants are fitted to cover a range of substantial conversion.

In some of the approaches, the "mass-transfer coefficient" concept has been used for relating the rate constants (mass-transfer coefficients) to physical properties of the system.   This concept postulates that mass transfer in a phase (particle or film) is directly proportional to the existing concentration difference, irrespective of geometry. [In Eq. (6-54), the quantities a and b are the mass-transfer coefficients in the particle and the film, respectively.]   When the physical implications of this concept are studied, it is seen that particle diffusion is assumed to be controlled by the resistance of a surface shell of infinitesimal thickness and no ion-exchange capacity, while concentration differences within the particle itself are leveled out instantaneously.   The rate of particle-diffusion controlled exchange now is inversely proportional to the first power rather than to the square of the particle radius.

A slightly different approach is represented by the "linear driving force" relation (6-63).   Here it is assumed that the rate, at any time, is proportional to the distance the system is from equilibrium.   For particle diffusion control, the departure from equilibrium is given by the difference between the average internal concentration and the concentration at the surface which is in equilibrium with the solution [Eq. (6-63)]. For film diffusion control, the departure is given by the concentration difference between the bulk solution and the particle surface which is in equilibrium with the interior of the particle [see Eq. (9-13)].   The coefficients are correlated with the diffusion constants, the particle radius, etc., by fitting the curves obtained with the simplified rate functions to those calculated from more accurate rate laws.   This approach is particularly useful because of its relative simplicity.   It will be used in the quantitative treatment of ion-exchange columns (Sec. 9-9b).

The shortcomings of the simplified rate laws are obvious.   The more rigorous treatment in the previous section has shown that, as a rule, no "order" can be attributed to ion-exchange processes.   The only exception is film-diffusion controlled isotopic exchange which obeys the rate equation of a second-order–second-order reversible reaction [integration of Eq. (6-53) with $k_1 = k_2$ gives rate laws in the form of Eq. (6-22) or (6-25)]. One other point should be emphasized.   The momentary rate of particle-diffusion controlled exchange depends on the shape of the nonsteady concentration profiles within the particle and thus on the particle history.   This is clearly seen in the interruption test (Fig. 6-4).   Thus it is inherently impossible to give a universal relation between the momentary rate and the average concentrations in the particle.   No general, rigorous relation of the form $-d\bar{Q}_A/dt = f(\bar{Q}_A)$ exists.   Any such relation can be valid only for a specific set of initial and boundary conditions.

The range of validity of a simplified rate equation can only be established by a series of experiments under various conditions or by comparison with more rigorous solutions. Unfortunately, such comparisons have rarely been made.   Glueckauf [38] has compared column-effluent histories from Eqs. (6-63), (6-64), and (6-65) with the history from Eq. (6-9).   The validity range of several other approximations when used to calculate column performance has been examined by Vermeulen [126] and Opler [83].   The comparisons, however, were made only with solutions of flux equations such as (6-5) which do not include the electric field and, hence, are inadequate for counter ions of different mobilities. Thus the validity range of the various simplified rate laws is still rather uncertain.

The merits of the simplified rate laws are not that they are accurate but, rather, that they are readily integrated even under more complicated boundary conditions. In spite of their obvious shortcomings they are still indispensable for the theoretical treatment of complex phenomena such as ion exchange in columns. However, before a simplified equation is used, it should be established whether, and within which limits, it is applicable. Indiscriminate use is tantamount to looking under the street lantern for a key lost at night, for there one can see better. Often the use of even a simplified rate equation requires more mathematical effort and time than the accuracy of the result can justify.

6-5. SYSTEM WITH MORE THAN TWO COUNTER-ION SPECIES

The treatment in the previous section was restricted to exchange of two counter-ion species. Practical applications of ion exchange often involve more than two species. The following discussion outlines the theoretical treatment and some interesting qualitative aspects of such systems.

In *isotopic exchange* in systems which are in equilibrium except for isotopic distribution, it obviously makes no difference how many species are involved. The flux of any one isotope always obeys the equations which were derived in Sec. 6-3b. The same is true for exchange of trace ions.

Ion exchange in systems with more than two competing counter ions is a more complex phenomenon. Inherently, the interdependent fluxes of the species cannot be expressed in terms of only one interdiffusion coefficient. Thus the mathematical problem is one of solving three or more simultaneous differential equations, namely, the Nernst-Planck flux equations (6-35) for all counter ions. It is very unlikely that analytical solutions can be obtained. In principle, however, the equations can be integrated numerically by the use of electronic computers.*

Some interesting qualitative features of multi-counter-ion exchange can be deduced without going into mathematics. The most important factors are the relative mobilities of the counter ions and their relative affinities for the ion exchanger. The effect of the relative affinities is essentially the same as it is in systems with only two counter ions; the counter ion which is preferred by the ion exchanger is, as a rule, taken up at a higher rate and released at a lower rate than its competitors. The effect of the relative mobilities will be illustrated by two typical examples.

First, let us examine particle-diffusion controlled exchange between a resin in A form and a solution containing two electrolytes BY and CY. If the mobilities of B and C in the resin are about equal, both these species

---

* Recently, numerical solutions for three-counter-ion systems have been calculated by use of the simplified rate law (6-53) (second-order–second-order reversible reaction). The results are tabulated [30].

are taken up at approximately equal (relative) rates. The situation is different, however, if B is much more mobile than C. Now, B will rapidly replace A in the resin, and the uptake of C will lag far behind. Later, C will follow, partly replacing the B ions that were taken up in the earlier stages. Thus, the concentration of B in the resin goes through a maximum.

Another example is particle-diffusion controlled exchange between a resin which contains two counter ions A and B, and a solution of an electrolyte CY. Here, the counter ion with the higher mobility in the resin is released at the higher rate. In a solution of finite volume, the concentration of the faster ion can overshoot its equilibrium value. The reason for this overshooting is the same as in the previous case.

Similar considerations apply to other cases and to systems with more than three counter ions. The general conclusions are in good agreement with experimental observations [30,132].

6-6. KINETICS OF SORPTION AND SWELLING

Ion exchangers can take up solvent and solutes from solutions. Equilibria of solvent uptake (swelling) and solute sorption have been discussed in the previous chapter (Secs. 5-2 and 5-3). Here, the kinetics of these processes will be studied.

The mechanism by which sorption and swelling occurs is essentially a redistribution of the mobile species (solutes or solvent) by diffusion. Thus the quantitative treatment follows the same lines as the previous discussion of counter-ion exchange.

a. Sorption and Desorption of Solutes

The examination of sorption equilibria has shown that there is a fundamental difference in behavior between electrolytes and nonelectrolytes. This difference is also reflected in the kinetics of sorption. Sorption kinetics of nonelectrolytes will be discussed first.

Sorption and desorption of nonelectrolytes. It was seen in the previous sections that the flux of an ionic species, because it involves transfer of electric charge, must be electrically balanced by one or more other ionic fluxes. In contrast, the flux of a nonelectrolyte involves no charge transfer and, hence, is not electrically coupled with any other fluxes. Nonelectrolyte sorption thus is an independent process; it produces no electric field and is not directly affected by an electric field which may arise from other, simultaneous processes.

In the course of sorption, nonelectrolyte molecules must migrate across the film and through the interior of the ion-exchanger particle. Potential rate-determining steps are film diffusion and particle diffusion. In principle, the situation is the same as in ion exchange, and the same differential equations can thus be used. The diffusion coefficient of the process is the individual diffusion coefficient of the nonelectrolyte and is practically constant since no electrical coupling occurs [in the Nernst-Planck equation (6-35), the electrical transference term drops out since the electrochemical valence of the nonelectrolyte is zero]. Thus the solutions for isotopic exchange—which were derived by the use of a constant diffusion coefficient —can be applied: *nonelectrolyte sorption essentially obeys the simple rate laws of isotopic exchange*. This rule does not hold rigorously because nonelectrolyte sorption may be accompanied by changes in swelling and activity coefficients which can affect the diffusion coefficient. These effects are absent in isotopic exchange and thus are not accounted for in the rate laws. As a rule, the deviations are small unless strong specific interactions occur.

With respect to the *rate-determining step* there is a difference between exchange of counter-ion isotopes and nonelectrolyte sorption. Equations (6-12) and (6-23)—which give the half times for particle and film diffusion control, respectively—can be used for deriving a criterion similar to Eq. (6-1):*

$$\frac{\bar{C}_i \bar{D}_i \delta}{C_i D_i r_0} \ll 0.13 \qquad \text{particle diffusion control}$$

$$\frac{\bar{C}_i \bar{D}_i \delta}{C_i D_i r_0} \gg 0.13 \qquad \text{film diffusion control}$$

$$(6\text{-}66)$$

where i is the diffusing species. This criterion applies to isotopic exchange and nonelectrolyte sorption. It differs from Eq. (6-1), which was used for ion exchange, in that α_B^A is taken as unity and that the ratio $\bar{C}_i/C_i$ has not been replaced by X/C. If Eq. (6-66) is applied to a counter ion, the ratio $\bar{C}_i/C_i$ is usually much larger than unity, particularly if the ion-exchange capacity is high and the solution is dilute. A high value of this ratio favors film diffusion control. In contrast, if the criterion is applied to a nonelectrolyte, the ratio $\bar{C}_i/\bar{C}_i$ (i.e., the molar distribution coefficient) usually differs not very much from unity and depends much less on the solution concentration. Thus, here, film diffusion control is much rarer, and the solution concentration has little effect on the nature of the rate-determining step.

The *sorption rate* depends on the particle size of the ion exchanger and the diffusion coefficient of the nonelectrolyte [see Eq. (6-12)]. Diffusion coefficients in ion exchangers will be discussed in a later section (Sec. 6-8). Here it may suffice to say that the diffusion coefficient is high if the non-electrolyte molecules are small and do not interact specifically with the ion exchanger, and if the "free" solvent content (solvation shells not included) of the ion exchanger is high. Because of differences in the free-solvent

---

* A similar criterion has been given earlier by Boyd [14].

content, the rate of sorption by a given ion exchanger also depends on the ionic form of the latter. Note that the free-solvent content does not necessarily parallel the equivalent volume nor the total solvent content. For example, the usual cation-exchange resins have a higher free-water content in the K^+ form than in the Na^+ form though the equivalent volume and the total water content are higher in the Na^+ form (see Sec. 5-2b).

The same simple rate laws and rules also hold for *desorption of nonelectrolytes*.

Sorption and desorption of electrolytes.
The kinetics of sorption of an electrolyte AY by an ion exchanger in A form will now be examined.

The *mechanism* by which sorption occurs is diffusion of the mobile species. The rate-determining step can be either particle diffusion or film diffusion. More detailed considerations will show, however, that film diffusion can become rate-controlling only under exceptional conditions (see page 293). Electroneutrality requires that equivalent amounts of the counter ion A and the co-ion Y be taken up. Thus the fluxes of A and Y are electrically coupled as in electrolyte diffusion in an aqueous, homogeneous medium. However, there is one important difference between electrolyte diffusion in aqueous solutions and in ion exchangers; in a solution, the concentrations of the cation and the anion are necessarily stoichiometrically equivalent, whereas in an ion exchanger they differ by the concentration of the fixed charges. It will be seen that this difference has a characteristic effect on the kinetics.

The *rate laws* of sorption can be calculated from the Nernst-Planck equations (6-35) which hold for all mobile species. Here, the equation applies to the counter ion A and the co-ion Y. The restrictions are, as in ion exchange, the conditions of electroneutrality and absence of electric current. In *particle diffusion*, these conditions are

$$z_A \bar{C}_A + z_Y \bar{C}_Y = -\omega X = \text{const.} \qquad \text{electroneutrality} \qquad (6\text{-}67)$$

$$z_A J_A + z_Y J_Y = 0 \qquad \text{no electric current} \qquad (6\text{-}68)$$

where X = molarity of fixed ionic groups; ω = sign of fixed charges; note that the electrochemical valence z_i of the anion is negative.

The set of Eqs. (6-35), (6-67), and (6-68) is formally identical with that describing ion exchange [Eqs. (6-35) to (6-37)]; the only differences are that the index Y appears instead of B, and the constant X instead of $\bar{C}$. The combination of the equations into one differential equation describing the coupled flux thus leads to an expression which is exactly analogous to Eq. (6-38). This equation is nonlinear, and attempts to obtain general, time-dependent solutions encounter the same difficulties found in ion exchange. With electrolyte sorption, however, one is more fortunate; in the most important limiting case the equation becomes linear and is readily solved. Because of the Donnan effect (see page 135), the concentration of the co-ion in the ion exchanger is nearly always much smaller than that of the counter ion ($\bar{C}_Y \ll \bar{C}_A$). Under this condition, the equation reduces to

$$J_A = -\bar{D}_Y \operatorname{grad} \bar{C}_A \qquad (\bar{C}_Y \ll \bar{C}_A) \qquad (6\text{-}69)$$

This relation involves the diffusion coefficient of the co-ion only. *The rate of electrolyte diffusion in an ion exchanger is controlled by diffusion of the co-ion.* The physical reasons behind this rule are the same as those in interdiffusion of counter ions, namely, that the electric field has much less effect on the ion which is in the minority (see page 269). In coupled diffusion of two species it is always the minor component which determines the rate. An interesting conclusion is that various electrolytes with a common co-ion, for example, HCl, NaCl, and $CaCl_2$ in cation exchangers, are sorbed at approximately equal (relative) rates, irrespective of the differences in counter-ion mobilities. Of course, the counter ion has an indirect effect on the sorption rate in that it affects the free-solvent content of the resin and thus the mobility of the co-ion.

The diffusion coefficient in the limiting equation (6-69) is the diffusion coefficient of the co-ion and is practically constant. Hence, the solutions for particle-diffusion controlled isotopic exchange (which were derived by use of a constant diffusion coefficient) apply if the condition $\bar{C}_Y \ll \bar{C}_A$ is met, i.e., if Donnan exclusion is effective. *Electrolyte sorption essentially obeys the simple rate laws of isotopic exchange.* Of course, small deviations may occur even in the limiting case because the effects of changes in swelling and activity coefficients are not included in the simple rate laws. There can be large deviations when Donnan exclusion is not strong enough to guarantee the condition $\bar{C}_Y \ll \bar{C}_A$. Here, the mobility of the counter ion affects the rate, especially if the counter ion is the slower species.

In *film diffusion,* the electroneutrality condition is

$$z_A C_A + z_Y C_Y = 0 \qquad (6\text{-}70)$$

Combination of Eqs. (6-35) for A and Y, (6-70), and (6-68) gives

$$J_A = -D_{AY} \operatorname{grad} C_A \qquad (6\text{-}71)$$

where D_{AY} is the (constant) Nernst diffusion coefficient of the electrolyte:

$$D_{AY} = \frac{D_A D_Y (z_A - z_Y)}{z_A D_A - z_Y D_Y} \qquad (6\text{-}72)$$

Here, too, the simple rate laws of isotopic exchange are obeyed since the diffusion coefficient is constant.

Having established the rate laws for particle- and film-diffusion controlled sorption, one can return to the question of the *rate-determining step*. A criterion can be derived in exactly the same way as in the previous cases:

$$\frac{\bar{C}_Y \bar{D}_Y \delta}{C_Y D_{AY} r_0} \ll 0.13 \qquad \text{particle diffusion control}$$

$$\frac{\bar{C}_Y \bar{D}_Y \delta}{C_Y D_{AY} r_0} \gg 0.13 \qquad \text{film diffusion control}$$

(6-73)

This criterion is analogous to Eq. (6-66). Here, however, the concentration ratio involved is that of the co-ion. This ratio is usually much smaller than unity, particularly if the ion-exchange capacity is high and the solution is dilute. The low value of the ratio strongly favors particle diffusion control. Thus *film diffusion can become rate-controlling only under extreme conditions* (for example, with ion exchangers of low capacity and particle size and with highly concentrated solutions). Note that film diffusion control is favored by *high* solution concentration and *low* concentration of fixed ionic groups in the ion exchanger; this is exactly the opposite from the situation in counter-ion exchange (see page 255).

Desorption of electrolytes obeys the same simple rate laws and rules.

b. Swelling and Shrinking

The kinetics of swelling and shrinking of resins, i.e., the uptake of solvent by a dry resin and the release of solvent in the course of drying, is an interesting problem which has as yet received very little attention.

Swelling and shrinking may be described in terms of diffusion of solvent molecules. No electric coupling is involved since the solvent molecules carry no charges. In this respect, swelling resembles nonelectrolyte sorption. However, the simple rate laws which hold for nonelectrolyte sorption cannot describe swelling. Swelling and shrinking are accompanied by profound changes in the medium in which the processes take place. As swelling progresses, the matrix expands and the solvent molecules thus become more mobile. In other words, the diffusion coefficient of the diffusing species increases markedly with increasing concentration of the species. Nonelectrolyte sorption, in contrast, was described in terms of a constant diffusion coefficient.

The dependence of the diffusion coefficient of the solvent on the solvent concentration—i.e., on the extent of swelling—is so far not completely understood. Nevertheless, some qualitative conclusions can be drawn. *Swelling* progresses from the outer shells of the resin particle toward its center. Hence the mobility of the solvent is greater in the outer, already partially swollen shells. Here, swelling rapidly approaches equilibrium while the solvent has a hard time making headway into the still contracted core of the particle. The result is that the solvent advances with a comparatively sharp "front."* The movement of the front is accompanied by severe mechanical stresses which result from differences in swelling between adjacent shells of the particle. This becomes apparent when the swelling particles are observed under polarized light (Fig. 6-12).

Shrinking of a resin particle is, kinetically, not simply a reversal of swelling. Here, the outer shells are the first to lose their solvent. Thus the highest resistance to solvent diffusion is near the particle surface. Inside, the higher solvent mobility keeps the solvent concentration rather uniform. No sharp solvent "front" develops. There is little mechanical stress, and

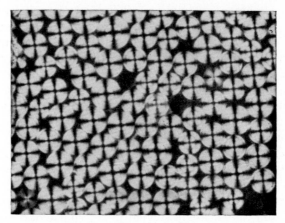

Fig. 6-12. Swelling resin beads under polarized light. Resin: crosslinked polystyrene; solvent: trichloroethane. The observation was made with cross polaroids. The characteristic transient polarization patterns indicate severe mechanical stress. *From R. M. Wheaton and D. F. Harrington* [130].

this only at the surface. Also, shrinking is much slower than swelling, particularly in the last stages where the solvent molecules which remained in the beads must travel long distances through a highly contracted resin network.

It is unlikely that swelling and shrinking can be adequately described in terms of a solvent diffusion coefficient which depends on the solvent concentration only. Rather, one must expect that this coefficient is also affected by the mechanical strain of the network [21,29] and, possibly, by time-dependent relaxation phenomena of the network [86].

It should be pointed out that these considerations apply to swelling and shrinking of resins and polymers in general. It makes little difference whether or not the resin is an ion exchanger. In fact, the theoretical and experimental studies in this field have so far almost exclusively been concerned with materials that are not ion exchangers [21,29,45,53,64,77a,86].

---

* In cellulose fibers where the situation is similar, the front can actually be seen [53].

c. Experimental Evidence

The kinetics of *nonelectrolyte sorption* has been studied repeatedly. The experimental results have confirmed the theory so well that measurements of sorption rates are used as a method for determining diffusion constants of nonelectrolytes in ion exchangers [41].

The kinetics of *electrolyte sorption* has received less attention. Accurate results are difficult to obtain. The co-ion concentration in the ion exchanger remains much smaller than in the solution. Traces of solution adhering to the beads will thus cause serious errors in the calculation of the rate from analyses of the ion exchanger (see Sec. 5-9f). In rate determinations, these errors are even more difficult to avoid than in equilibrium measurements. Calculation of the sorption rate from the concentration change in the solution is equally difficult because the relative change is very small. The experimental data on sorption by ion-exchanger beads [10] are insufficient for testing the theory. However, steady-state measurements with membranes (see Sec. 8-3b) corroborate the conclusions which were pointed out in this section.

Little has been published on the kinetics of *swelling* of ion exchangers [93,129a]. So far, no quantitative data are available. However, observations with various types of nonionic resins and polymers [22,29,45,53,64] are in good agreement with the general picture which was outlined here.

6-7. REACTIONS WITH MATERIALS OF LOW SOLUBILITY

Ion exchangers can react, to a certain extent, with solids of low solubility, for example, with calcium carbonate, lead sulfate, lead chloride, silver chloride, etc., [12,19,57,84,85]; see also Sec. 5-8. A necessary condition is that the solid dissociate at least enough to give traces of dissolved ions. Such solids can be dissolved by ion exchangers.

The mechanism of dissolution has been explained in Sec. 5-8. The ion exchanger removes one ionic species continuously from the solution. According to the solubility product, this species is continuously replaced by dissociation of the solid. This process continues until the ion exchanger is in equilibrium with the dissociation products in the solution, or, if the ion exchanger is present in sufficient excess, until the solid is completely dissolved. The amount of ion exchanger which is required for complete dissolution has been calculated in Sec. 5-8. In the following, the rate of dissolution will be studied.

Let us examine the dissolution of a finely dispersed solid AY by a granular cation exchanger in B form. The processes are

$$\underline{AY} \rightarrow A + Y \tag{6-74}$$

$$\bar{B} + A \rightarrow \bar{A} + B \tag{6-75}$$

The actual dissociation of the solid is usually a very fast process. As a rule, it is safe to assume that the solid particles are in equilibrium with the immediately adjacent layers of solution. The rate of the step (6-74) will then be limited only by diffusion across the films which surround the solid particles. In the solution, the concentration of the species A which is removed by ion exchange remains very small throughout the process. Hence the ion exchange (6-75) is also film-diffusion controlled [see Eq. (6-1)]. The rate of film diffusion processes is proportional to the surface area of the particles. Usually the surface area of the finely dispersed solid is much greater than that of the ion exchanger. Hence, as a rule, *film diffusion at the ion exchanger is the slowest step and controls the over-all rate.*

The rate of film-diffusion controlled ion exchange depends on the counter-ion mobilities, the particle size and selectivity of the ion exchanger, the temperature, and the concentration and agitation of the solution, as shown in Table 6-1. The following conclusions can be drawn. Rapid dissolution of a given solid is favored by small particle size of the resin, high mobility of the resin counter ion (preferably H^+), preference of the resin for the counter ion A which stems from the solid, high temperature, and efficient agitation.* Furthermore, dissolution is faster when the solution concentration, i.e., the solubility of the solid, is higher. Raising the temperature, as a rule, has a beneficial effect not only on the ionic mobilities but also on the solubility of the solid.

While the solid dissolves, the concentration of species Y in the solution increases. According to the solubility product this leads to a decrease in the concentration of A in the solution and thereby slows down the ion-exchange rate. This can be avoided by addition of an anion exchanger in, say, Z form which removes Y from the solution:

$$\bar{Z} + Y \rightarrow \bar{Y} + Z \tag{6-76}$$

Now, the concentrations of A and Y in the solution are kept at a steady-state level. These levels are attained when the rates of removal of A by the cation exchanger and Y by the anion exchanger become equal. The slower species, which is more slowly taken up in the earlier stages, is present in higher concentration. The concentrations of A and Y remain on the steady-state level until the degree of conversion of the ion exchangers to the A form and Y form becomes appreciable.

The accumulation of A and Y in the ion exchangers and of B and Z in the solution eventually affects the dissolution rate because it favors reversal of the ion-exchange processes (6-75) and (6-76). The reaction may even stop before the solid is completely dissolved. The smaller the amounts (in

---

* The volume capacity of the resin, though listed in Table 6-1, has no effect when a liberal excess of the resin is used. The reason is that the dissolution rate is given by the absolute rather than the relative ion-exchange rate.

equivalents) of the ion exchangers and the lower their selectivity for A and Y, the sooner this will happen. The reversal can be suppressed and the dissolution rate kept at its initial height by using a sufficient excess of the ion exchangers (so that their fractional conversion remains small), by using highly selective ion exchangers, and by avoiding the accumulation of B and Z in the solution. For example, the ion exchangers can be used in H^+ and OH^- (or CH_3COO^-) form; now, the counter ions which are released by the resins eliminate one another by combining to form water (or acetic acid). This trick, of course, is only applicable if no insoluble hydroxides or salts can precipitate.

The addition of the anion exchanger is superfluous if the solid is a salt of a weak acid. In this case the concentration of the anion in the solution automatically remains low because of association with the H^+ which is released by the cation exchanger. In some cases, the acid which is formed even enhances the dissolution of the solid by the formation of soluble complexes [19].

So far, quantitative theories for such systems with three phases have not been worked out.* Nevertheless, dissolution rates are readily estimated. This will be illustrated by a simple example.

Example. Estimate the time required for complete dissolution of finely dispersed silver chloride by a liberal excess of cation and anion exchangers in H^+ form and OH^- form, respectively. (No silver oxide will precipitate because its solubility product is much larger than that of the chloride.)

The following drastic simplifications will be used. Conservation of the steady state in the solution is assumed, the selectivities of the ion exchangers are disregarded, and film diffusion is described in terms of constant interdiffusion coefficients.

With these simplifications, the rate of silver uptake by the cation exchanger is

$$\frac{d\bar{Q}_{Ag}}{dt} = J_{Ag}F_{cat} = \frac{3\bar{V}_{cat}D_{AgH}}{r_{cat}\delta_{cat}}(C_{Ag} - C'_{Ag}) \tag{6-77}$$

where $\bar{Q}_i$ = amount of i (in moles) in ion exchanger; J_i = flux of i in film; F = total surface area, r = particle radius, and $\bar{V}$ = total volume of the ion exchanger; D_{ij} = interdiffusion coefficient of i and j in the film; δ = film thickness; subscript "cat" refers to the cation exchanger; C_{Ag} is the steady-state concentration of Ag^+ in the bulk solution, and C'_{Ag} is the concentration at the resin surface:

$$C'_{Ag} = \frac{C\bar{Q}_{Ag}}{\bar{Q}_{cat}} \tag{6-78}$$

where C = total solution concentration; $\bar{Q}_{cat}$ = amount of cation exchanger (in equivalents).

---

* Reviewers have taken to quoting Brochmann-Hanssen's thermodynamic approach [19]. It is obvious, however, that kinetic information cannot be obtained from thermodynamics.

Equations (6-77) and (6-78) give after integration

$$\bar{Q}_{\mathrm{Ag}}(t) = \frac{C_{\mathrm{Ag}}\bar{Q}_{\mathrm{cat}}}{C}\left[1 - \exp\left(-\frac{3D_{\mathrm{AgH}}C\bar{V}_{\mathrm{cat}}}{r_{\mathrm{cat}}\delta_{\mathrm{cat}}\bar{Q}_{\mathrm{cat}}}t\right)\right] \tag{6-79}$$

or

$$t(\bar{Q}_{\mathrm{Ag}}) = -\frac{r_{\mathrm{cat}}\delta_{\mathrm{cat}}\bar{Q}_{\mathrm{cat}}}{3D_{\mathrm{AgH}}C\bar{V}_{\mathrm{cat}}}\ln\left(1 - \frac{\bar{Q}_{\mathrm{Ag}}C}{\bar{Q}_{\mathrm{cat}}C_{\mathrm{Ag}}}\right) \tag{6-80}$$

which, for $\bar{Q}_{\mathrm{Ag}} \ll \bar{Q}_{\mathrm{cat}}C_{\mathrm{Ag}}/C$, reduces to

$$t(\bar{Q}_{\mathrm{Ag}}) = \frac{r_{\mathrm{cat}}\delta_{\mathrm{cat}}\bar{Q}_{\mathrm{Ag}}}{3D_{\mathrm{AgH}}C_{\mathrm{Ag}}\bar{V}_{\mathrm{cat}}} \tag{6-81}$$

Analogous relations hold for the chloride uptake by the anion exchanger. Additional conditions are

$$C = C_{\mathrm{Ag}} + C_{\mathrm{H}} = C_{\mathrm{Cl}} + C_{\mathrm{OH}} \qquad \text{electroneutrality} \tag{6-82}$$
$$d\bar{Q}_{\mathrm{Ag}} = d\bar{Q}_{\mathrm{Cl}} \qquad\qquad\qquad \text{steady state} \tag{6-83}$$
$$C_{\mathrm{Ag}}C_{\mathrm{Cl}} = K_{\mathrm{sp}} = \text{const.} \qquad \text{solubility product} \tag{6-84}$$
$$C_{\mathrm{H}}C_{\mathrm{OH}} = K_{\mathrm{w}} = \text{const.} \qquad \text{water dissociation equilibrium} \tag{6-85}$$

The steady-state concentration of silver C_{Ag} can now be calculated from Eq. (6-81), the corresponding equation for chloride uptake, and Eqs. (6-83) and (6-84) (subscript "an" refers to the anion exchanger):

$$C_{\mathrm{Ag}} = \left(K_{\mathrm{sp}}\frac{r_{\mathrm{cat}}\delta_{\mathrm{cat}}D_{\mathrm{ClOH}}\bar{V}_{\mathrm{an}}}{r_{\mathrm{an}}\delta_{\mathrm{an}}D_{\mathrm{AgH}}\bar{V}_{\mathrm{cat}}}\right)^{1/2} \tag{6-86}$$

The total steady-state solution concentration C can be calculated from Eqs. (6-86), (6-82), (6-84), and (6-85). However, if the solid is more strongly dissociated than water, it is obvious from Eq. (6-82) alone that:

If $C_{\mathrm{Cl}} \leq C_{\mathrm{Ag}}$, then $\qquad C \cong C_{\mathrm{Ag}}$

$$\qquad\qquad\qquad\qquad\qquad\qquad (K_{\mathrm{w}} \ll K_{\mathrm{sp}}) \tag{6-87}$$

If $C_{\mathrm{Ag}} \leq C_{\mathrm{Cl}}$, then $\qquad C \cong C_{\mathrm{Cl}}$

The dissolution time is calculated in the following way. First, C_{Ag} and C are calculated from the given data by use of Eqs. (6-84), (6-86), and (6-87). The values are introduced into Eq. (6-80) which gives the dissolution time when $\bar{Q}_{\mathrm{Ag}}$ is equated to the initial amount of solid.

Suppose that 0.1 g AgCl (0.7 mmole) should be dissolved by shaking with 1 g (dry weight) each of a cation and an anion exchanger of the following properties: weight capacity 4 meq/g; particle radius $r_{\mathrm{cat}} = r_{\mathrm{an}} = 0.01$ cm; wet volumes $\bar{V}_{\mathrm{cat}} = \bar{V}_{\mathrm{an}} = 1.5$ cm³. One may assume $D_{\mathrm{AgH}} \approx 2 \cdot 10^{-5}$ cm²/sec; $D_{\mathrm{ClOH}} \approx 10^{-5}$ cm²/sec; $\delta_{\mathrm{cat}} = \delta_{\mathrm{an}} \approx 10^{-3}$ cm; $K_{\mathrm{w}} = 10^{-14}$ mole²/l². The solubility product of AgCl is $K_{\mathrm{sp}} = 1.6 \cdot 10^{-10}$ mole²/l². This gives

$$C_{\mathrm{Ag}} = (K_{\mathrm{sp}}/2)^{1/2} = 0.9 \cdot 10^{-5} \text{ mole/liter}$$
$$C = C_{\mathrm{Cl}} = K_{\mathrm{sp}}/C_{\mathrm{Ag}} = 1.8 \cdot 10^{-5} \text{ mole/liter}$$
$$t = -\frac{0.01 \cdot 10^{-3} \cdot 4}{3 \cdot 2 \cdot 10^{-5} \cdot 1.8 \cdot 10^{-5} \cdot 1.5}\ln\left(1 - \frac{0.7 \cdot 1.8 \cdot 10^{-5}}{4 \cdot 0.9 \cdot 10^{-5}}\right) = 1.1 \cdot 10^{4} \text{ sec}$$

The solid is dissolved in about 3 hr. This estimate is on the conservative side since no credit has been taken for the preference of the cation exchanger for Ag^{+}.

Similar estimates can be made for other than 1,1-valent solids and for dissolution by a cation or an anion exchanger alone. One point should be emphasized: Eq. (6-80) involves the ratio C/C_{Ag} in a logarithmic function. Hence the dissolution time becomes very long if the steady-state concentrations of the ions from the solid are smaller than those of H^+ and OH^-. This shows the limitations of the technique; its use is restricted to solids with solubilities which are large enough to give ionic concentrations at least of the order of 10^{-7} mole/liter in pure water ($K_{sp}^{1/\nu} \gg 10^{-7}$ mole/liter).

Experimental data on dissolution rates are, at present, much too scanty to allow quantitative comparisons with calculations. All that can be said is that the predicted rates are of the correct order of magnitude.

6-8. DIFFUSION COEFFICIENTS IN ION EXCHANGERS

Most rate laws of ion exchange and sorption involve diffusion coefficients in ion exchangers. A reliable quantitative prediction of these coefficients is, at present, not possible for lack of an adequate theory. However, a number of qualitative rules can be deduced from simple theoretical considerations and experimental results, as discussed in the following.

a. Theoretical Considerations

Before embarking on a discussion of diffusion coefficients in ion exchangers, it is advisable to examine the general problem of diffusion in porous media more closely.

In this book, the term "porous media" is used in a very broad sense. The term is applied to all types of systems consisting of a coherent, but not necessarily rigid, structural framework with interstices ("pores") which are sufficiently wide to permit diffusion and other mass-transfer processes to take place in the medium. (A necessary condition for mass transfer is, of course, that the pore structure be "open," i.e., that the interstices be interconnected to provide uninterrupted diffusion paths across the medium.) This definition of porous media is broad enough to include, as one extreme, "macroreticular" solids with a rigid structure and macroscopic pores and, as the other extreme, "microreticular" gels such as ion-exchange resins with molecular, flexible hydrocarbon chains as the framework.

The problem of diffusion in such porous media is usually approached with the use of either of two rather different types of models. In the models of the first type, the medium is considered as consisting of *two phases*, namely, the solid framework and the intersticial pore phase. Diffusion is viewed as taking place in the pores only. In such models, diffusion is necessarily slower than in the corresponding homogeneous systems having the same composition as the pore phase. This is so for three reasons. First, only that fraction of the total cross section which is not occupied by the solid framework is available for diffusion. Second, the diffusion path is obstructed by the framework and thus is tortuous rather than straight (see Fig. 6-13). Third, the actual mobility of the diffusing species in the pores may be reduced by mechanical "friction" or other interactions with the pore walls.

In the models of the second type, the medium is considered as a single *homogeneous phase*, analogous to an ordinary solution. Self-diffusion in ion-exchange resins, for example, is assumed to be no different from that in solutions of analogous organic electrolytes. (For example, benzyltrimethylammonium chloride has been used as a model electrolyte for Dowex-1 anion exchangers in Cl^- form [79].) To be sure, in such models diffusion of the counter ion is also retarded, but this retardation, as in ordinary solutions, is essentially due to the "excluded-volume" effect (occupancy of volume and cross section by the organic ions); the tortuosity of the diffusion path and mechanical friction do not enter this molecular picture.

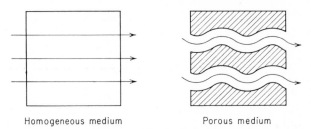

Homogeneous medium   Porous medium

FIG. 6-13. Diffusion in a porous and in a homogeneous medium (*schematic*). In the porous medium (*right*), diffusion is slower because the path is tortuous and the available cross section is smaller.

For rigid macroreticular media, models of the first type are clearly more appropriate, but for microreticular gels with molecular flexible matrices, models of the second type are more appealing though they gloss over the fact that the matrix is macromolecular and crosslinked and thus is more restricted in its mobility than truly dissolved organic ions. It appears that the behavior of the various types of ion exchangers, depending on their degree of homogeneity and the rigidity of their matrices, is intermediate between the two extreme cases represented by the models.

The rate laws in the previous sections are derived with the assumption that the ion exchanger is quasi-homogeneous, i.e., that diffusion phenomena in the ion exchanger can be described by relations which hold for homogeneous phases. This assumption does not necessarily exclude the use of a two-phase model (for limitations, see farther below). It is true that in equations such as (6-2) and (6-34), the flux and the concentration gradients are expressed in terms of total cross section and straight diffusion path, respectively. However, regardless of the particular model, the retarding effect of the matrix can be taken into account by using an "effective" intraparticle diffusion coefficient $\bar{D}_i$ which is correspondingly lower than the diffusion coefficient D_i of the species in the absence of the matrix. The essential difference between the various models is in the relations between the coefficients $\bar{D}_i$ and D_i rather than in the flux equations in which the coefficient $\bar{D}_i$ is used. Relations between $\bar{D}_i$ and D_i are of great practical interest since the latter coefficient is usually known, so that the problem of predicting ion-exchange and sorption rates can often be reduced to the simpler problem of predicting the ratio $\bar{D}_i/D_i$, i.e., the retardation by the matrix.

Adequacy of the Quasi-homogeneous Treatments. Before discussing relations between $\bar{D}_i$ and D_i, let us examine under which conditions a consistent treatment of diffusion of a species in a porous medium in terms of a unique effective diffusion coefficient is possible. The coefficient is defined in terms of the effective diffusion flux of the species [see Eq. (6-34)] which can be measured by tracer techniques in systems where no other processes interfere (equilibrium except for isotopic distribution). Actually, the effective diffusion

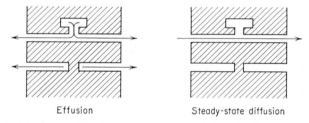

Effusion   Steady-state diffusion

Fig. 6-14. Effusion out of a slab (*left*) and steady-state diffusion across the same slab (*right*). The "blocked" and "dead-end" pores contribute to effusion, but not to steady-state diffusion.

coefficient is a macroscopic average over a large number of ions (or molecules) in pores of all different sizes, shapes, and directions and at larger and smaller distances from the pore walls, expressing the average ability of the species to make headway in any given direction. A treatment which uses such a coefficient is consistent if, and only if, all possible kinds of self-diffusion processes can indeed be described in terms of one unique coefficient. In other words, the retarding effect of a given framework on a given species must always be the same, regardless of the particular nature of the self-diffusion process. Unfortunately this is not always the case. Obvious requirements are that the porous solid be homogeneous and isotropic in dimensions which are small in comparison to the size of the sample, and that diffusion not be limited by slower processes such as slow exchange of associated and free ions or of ions in narrower pores with those in wider pores. Most ion exchangers meet these requirements. However, the obstruction by the framework may be more complex than the quasi-homogeneous treatment assumes. For example, Fig. 6-14 shows that "blocked" and "dead-end" pores participate in effusion out of a slab, but not in steady-state diffusion across the same slab. (In terms of the homogeneous-phase model, blocked and dead-end pores act as excluded volume in steady-state diffusion, but not in effusion.) The result is that effusion may occur with a higher effective diffusion coefficient than does steady-state diffusion. Such an effect has, in fact, been observed with phenolsulfonic-acid condensation polymers which are known to be inhomogeneous in colloidal dimensions [105,116]; see page 121.* Thus, at least in some cases,

---

* Concerning the interpretation of the experimental results in Refs. 105 and 116, see the Erratum in *Z. Elektrochem.*, **63**, 341 (1959).

the quasi-homogeneous treatment may fail. This is a fundamental difficulty confronting the theoretical approach to any mass-transfer phenomenon in porous media. Its resolution has so far not even been attempted.* Note, however, that such effects are consequences of particular pore geometries and are absent in homogeneous solutions; thus they are unlikely to be significant in the common ion-exchange resins (styrene- and acrylate-type addition polymers) which, because of their relatively homogeneous structure and flexibility of their matrices, behave more nearly like true solutions. Indeed, the application of the quasi-homogeneous flux equations to such resins has been highly successful [15,16,52,79,109–111]. In the following paragraphs, these equations will be assumed to hold.

Relations between intraparticle and aqueous-phase diffusion coefficients. Various models have been used for establishing relations between the effective intraparticle diffusion coefficient $\bar{D}_i$ and the diffusion coefficient D_i in the absence of the matrix. It may suffice to mention only the simplest and most widely used equations.† Wheeler [131] and Mackie [73] obtained

$$\bar{D}_i = \frac{D_i \epsilon}{2} \qquad \text{Wheeler} \tag{6-88}$$

$$\bar{D}_i = D_i \left(\frac{\epsilon}{2 - \epsilon} \right)^2 \qquad \text{Mackie} \tag{6-89}$$

where ϵ = fractional pore volume of the ion exchanger.

Mackie's relation differs from Wheeler's in that his model leads to an increase in tortuosity of the diffusion path with decreasing fractional pore volume. A much more elaborate statistical treatment has recently been given by Prager [92] who also discusses earlier approaches. His equation which applies here‡ is more complex, but deviates from Wheeler's by not more than 15 per cent. Prager's theoretical analysis shows clearly that, even with his simple two-phase model, considerable information or assumptions about the pore geometry are needed for deriving relations for the ratio $\bar{D}_i/D_i$.

Note that, in all these approaches, the ratio $\bar{D}_i/D_i$ is a function of the fractional pore volume only; hence this ratio should be the same for all mobile species in all materials of equal fractional pore volume. This conclusion (at variance with experimental results) is a consequence of the implicit assumption that the true mobility of the species in the pores is the same as in the absence of the matrix. The factors $\epsilon/2$ and $[\epsilon/(2 - \epsilon)]^2$ are merely geometrical "tortuosity factors" which account for the obstruction by the matrix, but not for retardation by interactions with the pore walls (see page 300). Such interactions may become very important in highly crosslinked resins and with polyvalent and specifically interacting counter ions. Their strength depends on the individual nature of the species and the porous medium. Hence the ratio $\bar{D}_i/D_i$ in a given material may be quite different for different species, and for a given species it may be different in different materials of equal fractional pore volume. Even the tortuosity of the material can affect different species in a different way if the pores of various sizes are not equally accessible to all species [72c,105].

Recently, corrections for such effects have been attempted by the use of the so-called Faxén equation [69,77,88]. Faxén [32] has calculated the reduction in mobility of a

---

* Interesting theoretical and experimental studies with a simple model with dead-end sources or sinks have recently been reported by Goodknight [40]. See also Rose's studies with electrical analogues [96a].

† See also Refs. [11], [72a], and [72b].

‡ Equation (63) in Prager's paper. Note that the derivation is restricted to steady-state diffusion.

spherical particle in a cylindrical pore by friction with the pore walls. This mobility reduction, expressed in terms of a "drag factor" F, is

$$F = 1 - 2.104 \frac{d_i}{d_p} + 2.09 \left(\frac{d_i}{d_p}\right)^3 - 0.95 \left(\frac{d_i}{d_p}\right)^5 \tag{6-90}$$

where d_i = diameter of the diffusing species; d_p = pore diameter.

The stronger retardation of larger species is in qualitative agreement with experimental results. However, one cannot expect Faxén's purely mechanical model with its drastic idealizations to be quantitatively adequate for microreticular ion-exchange resins. Aside from the fact that application of the concept of mechanical friction on a molecular scale is questionable, Faxén's model does not include molecular interactions due, for example, to electrostatic or London forces between the species and the fixed ionic groups or the matrix.

A quite different model in which such interactions play the major part has been suggested much earlier by Boyd [14]. This author assumes, in essence, that most of the counter ions are localized while only a few diffuse in "macropores" containing solution of about the same composition as the external solution. Boyd's relation, which does not include the tortuosity of the macropores, is

$$\bar{D}_i = \frac{D_i \epsilon}{\lambda_i'} \tag{6-91}$$

where λ_i' = molar distribution coefficient of species i, defined by Eq. (5-29). Boyd's model drastically overemphasizes one single effect, but it reflects in a qualitatively correct way the experimentally observed increase in counter-ion mobility and decrease in co-ion mobility with increasing concentration of the external solution (see page 307). Note that Eq. (6-91), because it involves λ_i', leads to an effective individual diffusion coefficient which depends on the ionic composition of the resin even if the fractional pore volume remains constant.

Boyd [14] and other authors [61,62] have also suggested that, particularly in weakly crosslinked resins, the mechanism of counter-ion diffusion may be one of "surface migration" along the chains of the matrix. Relations derived from such models are difficult to test since they involve unknown surface migration coefficients.

None of the theoretical relations which have so far been developed is entirely satisfactory. Reliable predictions of diffusion coefficients in ion exchanger would require more information and much more elaborate models.

b. Experimental Evidence

The experimental evidence on "effective" diffusion coefficients in ion exchangers is summarized in the following. The data on which the discussion is based were obtained from self-diffusion measurements with radioactive tracers in membranes, rods, and spherical beads (see Sec. 6-9c) and from electric conductivity studies (see Sec. 7-5).

The diffusion coefficient of a species in an ion exchanger depends on the size, valence, and chemical nature of the species; on the degree of swelling, mesh width, charge density, and chemical nature of the matrix; on the composition of the pore liquid; and on the temperature. These various factors will now be discussed in a qualitative way.

Size of the Species. As in ordinary solutions, the smaller species are the faster ones (provided that no other effects interfere). In most of the common ion exchangers, the species retain their solvation shells at least partially. Here, the size of the solvated species determines the mobility. For example, the mobilities of the alkali-metal ions in weakly and moderately crosslinked aqueous ion-exchange resins increase in the sequence

$$Li^+ < Na^+ < K^+ < Rb^+ \leq Cs^+ \tag{6-92}$$

In very highly crosslinked resins and in zeolites there is little room for solvation. Here, the size of the nonsolvated species determines the mobility and, accordingly, the sequence (6-92) is reversed. Because of interaction with the pore walls, the mobilities in ion exchangers usually decrease more strongly with increasing size of the species than in ordinary solutions [68]; the mobility becomes very small when the size of the species approaches the mesh width of the matrix [66].

Valence and Chemical Nature of the Species. The mobility of a species in the pores may be reduced by other than the geometric effects discussed above. It has been found that, as a rule, the retardation is stronger for counter ions than for co-ions, and stronger for polyvalent than for monovalent counter ions [15,16,54,56,68,74,100,109–111]. This effect is particularly noticeable in high-capacity resins and is more pronounced in cation exchangers than in anion exchangers. The difference in retardation between polyvalent and monovalent counter ions is observed even when the environment is identical [111], for example, in simultaneous self-diffusion in heteroionic resins (see Fig. 6-17), and can thus not be explained by differences in swelling alone. The most likely explanation is *electrostatic attraction* of the counter ions by the fixed ionic groups; this attraction is, of course, stronger for polyvalent counter ions and does not affect co-ions.

The retarding interaction with the framework may be other than electrostatic. *Specific chemical interaction* also results in a lower mobility of the species involved. An example is the Skogseid resin which is specific for K^+ (see pages 43 and 162) and in which the diffusion coefficient of K^+ is abnormally low [133]. London forces acting between the species and the matrix are likely to have a similar retarding effect.

A nice parable illustrating this situation has been given by Wyllie [115]. He compares the ion exchanger to an assembly hall in which two politicians are on their way down the aisle to the speaker's platform. If one of the politicians is more popular than the other, he will be hindered more than his opponent by the necessity of shaking hands frequently with enthusiastic supporters. Although their speed of walking between handshakes may be identical, the politician who is subjected more frequently to handshaking will have a lower average speed of progression. By analogy, the species with the higher affinity for the fixed ionic groups or for the matrix must be expected to have a lower effective diffusion coefficient in the ion exchanger. However, there is no simple quantitative relation between the relative strength of interaction (a thermodynamic quantity that can be expressed by the activity coefficient) and the relative mobility of the species (a kinetic quantity expressed by the diffusion coefficient). Experience has shown that, as a rule, the relative retardations $D_i/\bar{D}_i$ of various species in a given ion exchanger differ less than the relative affinities $\bar{\gamma}_i/\gamma_i$. Thus the effect is smaller than might have been expected.

Swelling and Mesh Width of the Ion Exchanger.   The effects of swelling and mesh width on diffusion are obvious.   The retardation by the framework increases with decreasing fractional pore volume (i.e., with shrinking of the resin) and decreasing mesh width of the matrix [15,43,68,87a,109–111]. The latter effect becomes particularly important when the mesh width and the diameter of the diffusing species are comparable.

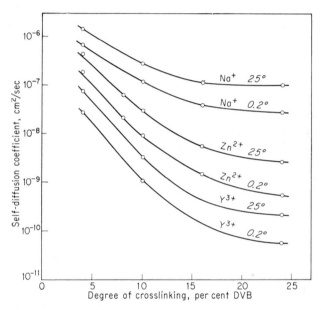

Fig. 6-15. Dependence of the self-diffusion coefficient on the degree of crosslinking. Self-diffusion coefficients of Na^+, Zn^{2+}, and Y^{3+} at 0.2° and 25°C in sulfonated styrene-type cation exchangers.   The crosslinking is given in terms of the nominal DVB content. *From B. A. Soldano* [109].

It appears that resins with very high solvent contents (80 per cent or more) may behave differently.   It has been found that, here, the self-diffusion coefficients can *decrease* with increasing fractional pore volume [62].   This surprising effect has been tentatively explained with a model according to which the main resistance to counter-ion diffusion is across the gaps between adjacent matrix chains, while diffusion along the chains is relatively unhindered.   With increasing fractional pore volume the gaps widen and the resistance to diffusion thus increases.

The dependence of swelling on the structure and composition of the ion exchanger and on external conditions has been discussed in detail in Sec. 5-2.   One of the most important factors is the *degree of crosslinking*. Its effect is shown in Fig. 6-15.

The mobilities usually parallel the free-water content of the resin rather than the total water content. For example, the diffusion coefficients of sorbed nonelectrolytes are usually larger in the K^+ form of a resin than in the Na^+ form [41]. In the K^+ form, the free-water content is higher though the total water content is lower (see Sec. 5-2b). It appears that hydration shells obstruct diffusion about as much as the matrix does.

Concentration of Fixed Ionic Groups and Chemical Nature of the Matrix. The dependence of the diffusion coefficients on the concentration of the

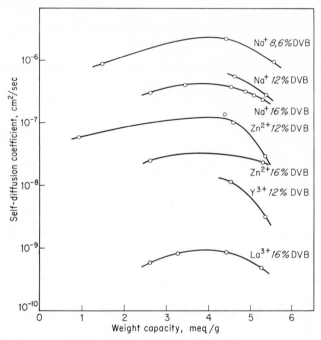

FIG. 6-16. Dependence of the self-diffusion coefficient on the weight capacity of the ion exchanger. Self-diffusion coefficients of Na^+, Zn^{2+}, and Y^{3+} at 25°C in sulfonated styrene-type cation exchangers. The capacity was varied by partial thermal desulfonation. *From data by G. E. Boyd, B. A. Soldano, and O. D. Bonner* [17].

fixed ionic groups has not yet been sufficiently elucidated. Results obtained by Boyd [17] are shown in Fig. 6-16. The diffusion coefficients of the counter ions have maxima in resins of intermediate capacities. However, as the authors point out, their procedure of varying the capacity also affects the degree of crosslinking and swelling. From a purely theoretical point of view one should expect that the counter-ion mobilities increase with decreasing capacity (and thus decreasing electrostatic retardation), provided, of course, that swelling remains the same.

The chemical nature of the matrix can affect the diffusion coefficients by specific interactions such as London forces. This effect has already been discussed.

Composition of the Pore Liquid. The pore liquid can be considered as the medium in which the actual diffusion takes place. Hence its composition must affect the mobilities of the species. The nature of the *solvent* chiefly determines the viscosity and the extent of ionic solvation. These effects are obvious. Also, there may be mutual interactions between various counter ions. Experiments by Soldano and Boyd [109,111] could be interpreted to indicate the existence of such an effect (see Fig. 6-17). As a rule, the self-diffusion coefficient of a species is increased by the presence of a faster one and is decreased by the presence of a slower one. However, it may well be that this is largely or entirely due to the change in free-water content accompanying the introduction of the other species. This effect has already been discussed.

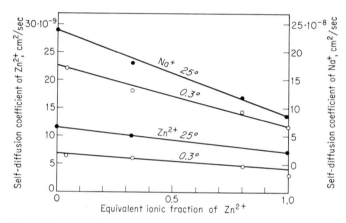

Fig. 6-17. Dependence of self-diffusion coefficients on ionic composition of the ion exchanger. Self-diffusion coefficients of Na^+ and Zn^{2+} at 0.3°C (○) and 25°C (●) in a (heteroionic) sulfonated styrene-type cation exchanger of 16 per cent DVB. *From B. A. Soldano and G. E. Boyd* [111].

A rather interesting phenomenon is the dependence of the diffusion coefficients in ion-exchange resins on the *concentration of the external solution* with which the resin is in equilibrium. When the solution concentration is increased, the free-water content of the resin decreases. A corresponding decrease in the diffusion coefficients might be expected. This is indeed so for the co-ion [103,119], but the diffusion coefficient of the counter ion usually increases [60,96,103,119]; see Fig. 6-18. This increase apparently occurs because of the increased co-ion concentration in the pores.

Two possible explanations for the unexpected behavior of the counter-ion mobility have been offered. Schlögl [103] pictures the interior of the resin as a field of potential-energy troughs representing the fixed charges. In order to move from one trough to another, the counter ion has to pass the potential-energy barrier in between. The co-ions provide additional troughs of high mobility and thus facilitate the migration of the counter ions. In this way, the (average) mobility of the counter ions is increased when the co-ion concentration is increased.   In Wyllie's picture (see page 304) the co-ions would represent admirers who, while shaking hands, accompany the politician rather than remain at their place.   Spiegler [114] has pointed out that the effect may also be due to nonuniformity of the resin.   In resins with "island" structure (see page 121) most of the original counter ions are in the tightly crosslinked islands, whereas most of the sorbed electrolyte is in between in the weakly crosslinked regions where diffusion is less obstructed.   Sorbed counter ions thus are more mobile than the original ones.   As a result, the average counter-ion mobility increases with increasing electrolyte sorption, i.e., with increasing concentration of the external solution.

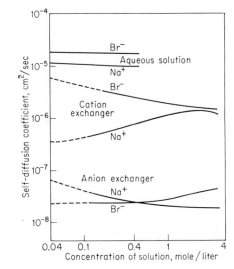

Fig. 6-18. Dependence of the self-diffusion coefficients of the counter ion and the co-ion on the concentration of the external solution.   Cation exchanger: phenolsulfonic-acid–formaldehyde condensation polymer; anion exchanger: polyethyleneimine–epichlorohydrin condensation polymer.   *From R. Schlögl* [103].

Temperature.   As in ordinary solutions, diffusion coefficients in ion exchangers increase with increasing temperature.   As a rule, the increase in mobility with temperature is somewhat greater in ion exchangers than in ordinary aqueous solutions (activation energy of diffusion in standard ion-exchange resins is about 6 to 10 kcal/mole, as compared to about 3 to 6 kcal/mole in solutions) [15,109,110].   Likely explanations are that, with increasing temperature, retarding specific or electrostatic interactions become weaker, the matrix becomes more flexible, and the ions become smaller because solvation is reduced.

For zeolites, Barrer has recently discovered interesting correlations between the activation energy of counter-ion diffusion, the polarizability of the counter ion, and the distance between adjacent fixed charges [9].   For alkali ions in analcite, Barrer finds that the activation energy consists of two contributions, namely, a polarization-independent contribution of about 10 kcal/mole which he correlates with the periodic change in field strength along the diffusion path, and another contribution which is proportional to the polarizability.

Absolute values of diffusion coefficients of univalent cations in strong-acid, moderately crosslinked resins are about $\frac{1}{5}$ to $\frac{1}{20}$ of the corresponding coefficients in water. For bivalent and trivalent cations, the ratios are about $\frac{1}{10}$ to $\frac{1}{100}$ and $\frac{1}{100}$ to $\frac{1}{1000}$, respectively. In the standard anion exchangers, the ratio is about $\frac{1}{2}$ to $\frac{1}{10}$ and depends much less on the counter-ion valence. In weak-acid and weak-base resins and in zeolites the diffusion coefficients are usually smaller by several orders of magnitude [9,20,43].

6-9. EXPERIMENTAL METHODS

a. Ion-exchange Materials

The rates of ion exchange and sorption depend on the size and shape of the ion-exchanger particles. Reproducible results can only be obtained if particle size and shape are well defined. The particles should be carefully selected. The use of strictly spherical beads of uniform size is recommended for rate measurements and is indispensable for determinations of diffusion coefficients. Broken or cracked beads should be discarded. A bead fraction of uniform size can be obtained by repeated sieving. Beads of irregular shape can be sorted out by placing the material on a slightly sloping planar surface, on which spherical beads roll down fastest.

b. Rate of Ion Exchange

Ion-exchange rates can be measured in batch and "shallow-bed" experiments. In the latter, a rapid stream of solution is passed through a thin layer of ion-exchanger beads. Both these techniques are described in this section. Note that the boundary conditions in the two techniques are different: batch experiments are made with solutions of finite volume, whereas in shallow-bed runs the infinite solution volume condition is closely approached. Both methods can be applied to ion exchange as well as to isotopic exchange.

Batch Technique. A known amount of an ion exchanger in A form is contacted with a solution of BY of known concentration and volume. Exchange of A for B takes place in a closed vessel. Agitation is provided by stirring or shaking. The rate of exchange can be determined by measuring either the uptake of B by the ion exchanger or the increase in concentration of A in the solution. The ion exchanger can only be analyzed after separation from the solution. Thus a number of experiments are required for determining the uptake as a function of contact time. The concentration change in the solution can be determined by analysis of aliquots withdrawn at various times without interrupting the process. This procedure is usually more convenient.

A simple and convenient technique has been worked out by Boyd and Soldano [15]. The ion exchanger (about 1 to 4 g) is equilibrated with a solution which is spiked with a radioactive isotope of the counter ion. The material is then leached with water until the effluent is free of radioactivity. A known amount of pure water (150 cm³) is used to wash the radioactive ion exchanger into the reaction vessel. The stirrer in the vessel is started. After thermal equilibrium is attained, electrolyte solution (50 cm³) is added. This initiates the counter-ion exchange. The increase in radioactivity in the solution with time is determined by withdrawing aliquots (1 microliter) and counting in a suitable counter. The radioactivity in the solution is proportional to the fractional attainment of equilibrium. The authors have used the technique for isotopic exchange, but it can be applied equally well to ion exchange. Note that the ion exchanger is in contact with pure water when the exchange is initiated by adding the electrolyte; isotopic exchange thus takes place in a system which is not strictly in equilibrium except for isotopic distribution.

A slightly different technique has been developed by Kressman [65]. The ion exchanger is placed in a platinum-wire cage which constitutes the center part of a centrifugal stirrer (Fig. 6-19). The stirrer is started and immersed in the electrolyte solution. The centrifugal force presses the beads against the walls of the cage. Solution is forced out radially through the layer of beads and the openings provided in the casing. Fresh solution is sucked in at the center through the bottom of the cage. Thus the beads

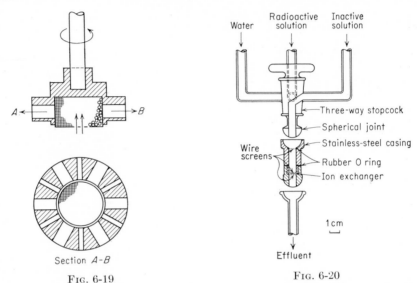

Section A-B

Fig. 6-19   Fig. 6-20

Fig. 6-19. Centrifugal stirrer for ion-exchange rate measurements. The central part of the stirrer is a platinum wire cage which holds the ion-exchanger beads. Centrifugal action produces a rapid circulating flow of solution entering the cage at the bottom and leaving it through the wall and the radial holes in the casing. *From T. R. E. Kressman and J. A. Kitchener* [65].

Fig. 6-20. Apparatus for measuring ion-exchange rates by the shallow-bed technique. *From G. E. Boyd, A. W. Adamson, and L. S. Myers, Jr.* [14].

are subjected to a rapid, circulating flow of solution. The rate of exchange can be determined as before by withdrawing aliquots from the solution at different times. The use of the centrifugal stirrer has the advantage that ion exchanger and solution can be separated almost instantaneously by raising the (still rotating) stirrer out of the solution. This is especially useful for interruption tests.

In the techniques described above, aliquots must be withdrawn for analysis. This is avoided in a technique developed by Dickel [26]. Here, ion exchange is carried out in a conductivity cell. The changing conductivity of the solution is continuously recorded and is used to calculate the composition of the solution. This technique is very convenient. However, it is restricted to exchange of ions of sufficiently different mobilities in the aqueous phase.*

---

* In the apparatus described by Dickel, ion-exchanger beads can come in between the electrodes and affect the conductivity measurement, particularly if the conductivity

Shallow-bed Technique. A thin layer of ion-exchanger particles in A form is placed on a fine platinum screen or a glass sinter disk. A solution of BY is forced through the layer at a high flow rate [13,14,31,119]; see Fig. 6-20. The flow rate must be kept strictly constant. The change in effluent composition with time is measured. This can be done by collecting and analyzing samples or, more conveniently, by continuous recording of the radioactivity of an isotope of species A in the effluent which is passed through a counter. The measurement gives the exchange flux as a function of time. The fractional attainment of equilibrium as a function of time can be obtained from the flux by graphical integration. The technique is applicable to ion exchange and isotopic exchange.

As compared with the batch technique, the shallow bed has the following advantages and disadvantages. The exchange takes place under the simpler infinite solution volume condition, a fact which facilitates the calculation of diffusion coefficients from the measured rate. No samples are withdrawn. However, in order to meet the infinite solution volume condition which is implied in the evaluation, only a very small concentration of species A in the effluent can be tolerated. This requires a very high flow rate and a large solution throughput. The determination of the small amounts of A in the presence of a large excess of B calls for special analytical methods. Radioactivity measurements are most suitable. Continuous recording is very convenient, but is less accurate than counting of samples where the statistical error can be reduced by prolonging the counting time. A further disadvantage of the shallow-bed technique is its sensitivity to fluctuations in flow rate.

c. Determination of Diffusion Coefficients in Ion Exchangers

The most accurate and convenient techniques for determining effective individual diffusion coefficients in ion exchangers are based on isotopic redistribution measurements. The coefficients can be calculated from the rates of isotopic interdiffusion under various conditions. Three different types of techniques have been developed. These involve rate measurements of, first, isotopic exchange between ion exchangers and solutions, second, isotopic exchange within ion exchangers which are not in contact with solutions, and, third, steady-state isotopic diffusion across ion-exchanger membranes. All these techniques are generally applicable to counter ions, co-ions, sorbed species, and the solvent in monoionic as well as in heteroionic ion exchangers, provided, of course, that a suitable isotope exists.* Either radioactive or stable tracers can be used. Radioactive tracers are more convenient because their determination is much simpler.

Alternatively, diffusion coefficients can be calculated from various other ion-exchange, diffusion, and conductivity measurements. However, these techniques are less generally applicable and less accurate.

Isotopic exchange between ion exchangers and solutions. Rate measurements of isotopic exchange with ion-exchange beads, as described in Sec. 6-9b, can be used for calculating the self-diffusion coefficient of the tagged counter ion [14,15,109–111,119]. Equation (6-9) or (6-14) is used for the evaluation, depending on whether the infinite or the

---

of the beads is much larger than that of the solution. This can be avoided by a slightly different construction of the cell.

* A necessary condition is that isotopic redistribution occur exclusively by diffusion of the species under investigation. This may not always be the case. For example, results obtained by Adamson and Irani [2] in experiments with tagged water molecules seem to indicate that mechanisms other than diffusion of H_2O may contribute to the redistribution of H and O tracers. Later investigators [28], however, have failed to reproduce this effect and have questioned its existence.

finite solution volume condition applies. The beads must be spherical and uniform in size. The experimental conditions should be chosen in such a way that particle diffusion is the rate-controlling step. In the intermediate range between particle and film diffusion control, less accurate but essentially correct results can be obtained by use of the approximation (6-26) [119].

This technique, as well as those described farther below, is not restricted to counter ions. The experimental procedures and mathematical evaluation methods are essentially the same when the tagged species is a co-ion or a sorbed solute or solvent molecule [16,119]. Also, it makes no difference whether the ion exchanger is monoionic or heteroionic [111].

Alternatively, the measurements can be made with rods or strips of uniform cross section [96,123] or disks of uniform thickness [103]. Large particles such as rods and disks have several advantages over small beads. First, the geometrical parameters (cross section and length, or surface and thickness) needed for the mathematical evaluation can be measured more conveniently and more accurately. Second, the exchange is slower and thus its rate is easier to determine. Third, there is less tendency toward film diffusion control. Unfortunately, only relatively few ion exchangers can be prepared in the form of flawless coherent rods or disks.

The mathematical evaluation of such rate measurements with rods, strips, and disks depends on the experimental conditions. The respective solutions of the diffusion equation and convenient evaluation methods are given in standard textbooks on diffusion. Two techniques will be given here as characteristic examples.

Effusion out of a Rod [123]. The rod is equilibrated with a solution containing a radioactive tracer of the species under investigation. The rod is then removed from the solution, is insulated except for one end, and is placed into a counter. In the actual measurement the free end of the rod is exposed to an inactive solution flowing past at a high rate, and the radioactivity of the rod is continuously recorded. The mathematical treatment is that of one-dimensional diffusion out of a finite body into a semi-infinite, well-mixed medium. The solution of this diffusion problem is

$$\frac{\bar{Q}(t)}{\bar{Q}^0} = 1 - \frac{2}{a}\left(\frac{\bar{D}t}{\pi}\right)^{1/2} \left\{1 - 2\sum_{n=1}^{\infty} (-n)^{n+1} Hh_1\left[na\left(\frac{2}{\bar{D}t}\right)^{1/2}\right]\right\} \qquad (6\text{-}93)$$

where $\bar{Q}(t)$ = amount of tracer in the rod at time t; $\bar{Q}^0$ = amount at time $t = 0$; a = length of the rod.

The function Hh_1 is tabulated [18]. In the early stages ($\bar{D}t/a^2 < 3 \cdot 10^{-3}$) the expression in braces can be neglected. Equation (6-93) is used for calculating the diffusion coefficient $\bar{D}$ from the decrease in radioactivity in the rod with time. In addition, Thomas [123] gives the solution for the case in which a thin membrane separates the rod from the solution. The evaluation does not require a knowledge of the membrane properties. Thomas used such membranes for confining clay pastes.* The solution for the rod with membrane can also be used for eliminating errors caused by partial film diffusion control since a liquid film affects the rate in the same way as a superficial membrane.

---

* Such measurements with pastes yield the "effective diffusion coefficient" in the paste rather than the diffusion coefficient in the colloid particles which constitute the paste; isotopic redistribution within the paste is likely to be extraparticle- rather than intraparticle-diffusion controlled.

Diffusion into a Rod from a Solution of Finite Volume [96]. In this technique, the rod is initially free of radioactivity and is insulated except for one end which is exposed to a radioactive solution. The solution is rapidly circulated past the rod and through a counter. The radioactivity of the solution decreases with time and is continuously recorded. The experimental conditions are chosen in such a way that practically no radioactivity reaches the far end of the rod. Thus the mathematical treatment is that of one-dimensional diffusion from a finite, well-mixed medium into a semi-infinite body. The solution of this diffusion problem is

$$\frac{Q}{Q^0} = \exp\left[\left(\frac{\bar{C}}{C}\right)^2 \cdot \frac{q^2\bar{D}t}{V^2}\right] \text{erfc}\left[\left(\frac{\bar{C}}{C}\right)\frac{q(\bar{D}t)^{1/2}}{V}\right] \tag{6-94}*$$

where q = cross section of the rod; C = concentration of the tagged species; V = solution volume.

A more convenient approximation has been given by Thomas [96].

Isotopic redistribution within insulated ion exchangers. Isotopic redistribution measurements can also be made with ion exchangers which are not in contact with solutions [61,62,68,113]. These techniques are usually somewhat less accurate than those described above, but they have the great advantage that the solvent content of the ion exchanger can be varied systematically and independently.

The measurements are usually made with rods or strips. The water content can be adjusted by partial dehydration. The rod is then insulated except for one end which, before insulation, is briefly exposed to a highly radioactive solution (as a rule, a few microliters of solution are ample). The spread of the radioactive tracer in the rod can be observed by taking autoradiographs of the rod at different times [113]. Alternatively, one can allow sufficient time for substantial spread and then cut the rod into segments and determine their tracer contents [61,62,68]. The mathematical treatment is that of one-dimensional diffusion from an (instantaneous) planar source into a semi-infinite body. The solution is

$$\bar{C}(x,t) = \frac{\bar{Q}^0}{q(\pi\bar{D}t)^{1/2}} \exp\left(-\frac{x^2}{4\bar{D}t}\right) \tag{6-95}$$

where $\bar{Q}^0$ = total amount of tracer; x = distance from the end of the rod where the tracer was initially deposited.

Exact determinations of $\bar{C}(x,t)$ are impossible when the rod is cut into only a few thick segments, since the analysis gives only the average concentration in the segment. In this case, the evaluation should be made with the integrated form of Eq. (6-95) [22],

$$\bar{Q}(x_1,x_2,t) = q \int_{x_1}^{x_2} \bar{C}(x,t)\,dx = \frac{\bar{Q}^0}{\pi^{1/2}}\left[\text{erf}\left(\frac{x_2}{2(\bar{D}t)^{1/2}}\right) - \text{erf}\left(\frac{x_1}{2(\bar{D}t)^{1/2}}\right)\right] \tag{6-96}*$$

where $\bar{Q}(x_1,x_2,t)$ is the amount of tracer in the segment between the planes at the distances x_1 and x_2 from the end of the rod.

Alternatively, the measurements can be made with stacks of disks or membranes [24]. One set of disks is tagged with a radioactive tracer, another set is left inactive. The stack is then assembled in such a way that the radioactive disks are on one side and the inactive ones on the other side. Sufficient time for substantial isotopic exchange between the disks is allowed. Then the stack is disassembled, and the tracer contents of the individual disks are determined. The mathematical solution of this diffusion problem

---

* The functions erf (x) and erfc (x) are tabulated in the Appendix (page 590).

is (provided that the exchange has not reached the far ends of the stack) [22]

$$\bar{C}(x,t) = \frac{\bar{C}_0}{2} \operatorname{erfc}\left(\frac{x}{2(\bar{D}t)^{1/2}}\right) \tag{6-97}*$$

where $\bar{C}_0$ = initial tracer concentration in the radioactive disks; x = distance from the boundary between the initially active and inactive disks.

The function (6-97) is shown in Fig. 6-21. The diffusion coefficient can also be calculated from the amount $\bar{Q}(t)$ of tracer that has diffused into the initially inactive part of the stack [22]:

$$\bar{D} = \frac{\pi}{t}\left[\frac{\bar{Q}(t)}{q\bar{C}_0}\right]^2 \tag{6-98}$$

Alternatively, Matano's "slope method" can be used [22,75]. It can be shown that

$$\bar{D} = -\frac{1}{2t(\partial\bar{C}/\partial x)}\int_0^{\bar{C}(x_1)} x \, d\bar{C} \tag{6-99}$$

The diffusion coefficient can thus be calculated from the concentration gradient (slope

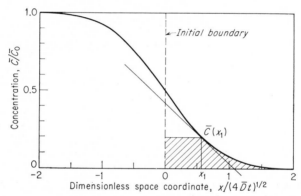

FIG. 6-21. Concentration profile of a tracer which was initially at uniform concentration in the left half of the medium (i.e., at $x \leq 0$). The profile is time-independent when plotted versus the dimensionless space coordinate $x/(4\bar{D}t)^{1/2}$. The tangent and the integral required for evaluation by the slope method Eq. (6-99) are shown. *From J. Crank* [22].

of the tangent in Fig. 6-21) and the integral $\int_0^{\bar{C}(x_1)} x \, d\bar{C}$ (shaded area in Fig. 6-21), both at an arbitrary point x_1. The advantage of using disk stacks is that cutting of the usually rather brittle ion exchanger is avoided. The disadvantage is that films or voids between the disks may give rise to errors.

Various modifications of these techniques have been reported [22,107,113].

Steady-state isotopic diffusion across membranes. Diffusion coefficients can be calculated from steady-state isotopic diffusion across ion-exchanger membranes [46,103,105, 116,133–135]. The phenomenon as such will be discussed in more detail in Sec. 8-3a.

---

* See footnote to previous page.

The membrane is inserted between two solutions which are identical in composition, except that one of them is tagged with a tracer. After an initial time lag (see page 351), a steady state in the membrane is attained, and the tracer flux across the membrane thus becomes time-independent. The steady state is preserved as long as the difference in the tracer concentrations between the two solutions has not significantly diminished. In the steady state, the tracer concentration in the initially inactive solution increases linearly with time. The diffusion coefficient of the tagged species in the membrane is calculated from this increase [102]:

$$\bar{D} = \frac{d(C''/C')}{dt} \frac{V''Cd}{\bar{C}q} \tag{6-100}$$

where d = membrane thickness; q = membrane cross section; C' and C'' are the tracer concentrations in the initially active and inactive solutions, respectively; C and $\bar{C}$ are the (total) concentrations in the solutions and the membrane, respectively, of the species of which the tracer is an isotope; V'' = volume of the initially inactive solution.

This relation is obtained from the steady-state isotopic flux $J = \bar{D}\bar{C}'/d$, the material balance $V''dC''/dt = qJ$, and the equilibrium condition at the membrane surface $\bar{C}'/\bar{C} = C'/C$.

The radioactivity in the initially inactive solution can be determined either by counting aliquots withdrawn at different times or by continuous recording in a counter through which the solution is circulated (see Fig. 6-22). The advantages and disadvantages of continuous recording are the same as in the nonstationary techniques (see page 311).

Equation (6-100) implies steady-state conditions and ideal particle diffusion control. In order to obtain a sufficiently long period of steady-state diffusion, the time lag should be short and the change in tracer concentrations in the solutions should be slow. The time lag is proportional to the square of the membrane thickness (see page 351), and the tracer transfer across the membrane is proportional to the membrane cross section and inversely proportional to the membrane thickness. Hence, the membrane should have a small cross section and be as thin as is compatible with preservation of particle diffusion control, and the solution volumes should be as large as is practical in view of the amount of radioactive material needed. Small deviations from the steady state in later stages can be accounted for by a simple correction. Small deviations from ideal particle diffusion control can be taken into account by using the quantity $d + 2\delta\bar{D}\bar{C}/DC$ instead of the membrane thickness d (see Eq. (8-7) [47]).

A nonstationary method of calculating the diffusion coefficient can be combined with the steady-state measurement [46,134,135]. From the steady-state increase in radioactivity in the initially inactive solution, the hold-up time t_e can be obtained (see Fig. 8-5). This quantity is related to the diffusion coefficient by [8,22,33]*

$$\bar{D} = \frac{d^2}{6t_e} \tag{6-101}$$

[see Eq. (8-12)]. This method, however, is not very accurate.

Steady-state measurements have one important advantage over the nonstationary techniques. Under suitable experimental conditions, the steady state is preserved for a considerable length of time. Thus the (linear) increase in radioactivity with time—from which the diffusion coefficient is calculated—can be determined rather accurately

---

* Frisch's mathematical treatment [33] gives correlations for nonconstant diffusion coefficients.

from a large number of measurements. The chief disadvantage of the technique is that the evaluation involves the concentration of the tagged species in the membrane. This quantity must be determined by an additional measurement.

Other methods. Various other methods not involving tracers can be used for calculating or estimating diffusion coefficients in ion exchangers. All of them, however, have limitations and shortcomings.

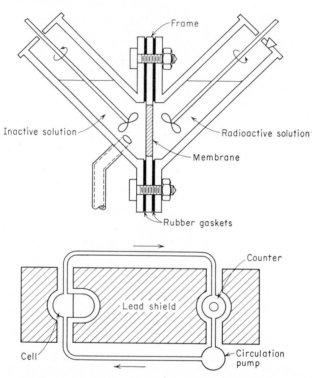

Fig. 6-22. Apparatus for measuring steady-state isotopic diffusion across ion-exchanger membranes. The initially inactive solution is circulated at high flow rate through a counter. Both solutions are agitated by high-speed stirrers [116].

The diffusion coefficient of the counter ion in monoionic resins can be calculated from electric conductivity measurements [52,74,113]. The measurements and their evaluation are discussed in the next chapter (see Sec. 7-5 and page 332). The external solution must be dilute so that Donnan exclusion of the co-ion is effective. The main disadvantage of this method is that a correction for convection conductivity must be made. The determination of the correction term requires additional measurements and is difficult.

Average interdiffusion coefficients of exchanging counter ions can be estimated from measurements of ion-exchange rates rather than of isotopic exchange rates [20,65,94]. However, such coefficients are not well defined. For example, different coefficients are obtained for forward and reverse exchange of two given counter ions in the same resin. Thus the method only gives an order-of-magnitude orientation.

The diffusion coefficient of the co-ion can be obtained from rate measurements of electrolyte sorption (see Sec. 6-6a) [10] or, preferably, of steady-state electrolyte diffusion across an ion-exchanger membrane [103] (see Secs. 8-3b and 8-10a). The external solution must be dilute so that Donnan exclusion is efficient and, hence, diffusion of the co-ion is rate-controlling.

Diffusion coefficients of sorbed nonelectrolytes can also be determined by such sorption or diffusion-rate measurements [41]. Here, solutions of higher concentrations can be used.

In view of the advantages of the tracer techniques, recourse to other methods should only be taken for valid reasons, for example, if isotopes are not available or are too expensive.

SUMMARY

Ion exchange is a diffusion process. Its mechanism is a redistribution of the counter ions by diffusion. The co-ion has relatively little effect on the kinetics and the rate of ion exchange.

The rate-determining step in ion exchange is interdiffusion of the exchanging counter ions either within the ion exchanger itself (particle diffusion) or in an adherent liquid "film" which is not affected by agitation of the solution (film diffusion). Film diffusion control is favored by high capacity, low degree of crosslinking, and small particle size of the ion exchanger; by low concentration and weak agitation of the solution; and by preference of the ion exchanger for the counter ion which is taken up from the solution. A simple criterion can be used for predicting whether particle or film diffusion will be rate-controlling under a given set of conditions.

In the theoretical treatment of ion-exchange kinetics, the ion exchanger is considered as a quasi-homogeneous phase. The mathematical problem is to solve the differential equations for homogeneous-phase diffusion in the (spherical) bead and in the film under the appropriate boundary conditions. The simplest case is isotopic exchange in systems which are in equilibrium except for isotopic distributions. Here, the diffusion coefficient (the self-diffusion coefficient of the isotopes) is constant. Rigorous solutions are available for all conditions of practical interest. Exchange of counter ions of different properties, however, is a more complex phenomenon. Electroneutrality requires that the fluxes of the exchanging counter ions be equivalent so that no net transfer of charge occurs. This equivalence of the fluxes is brought about by an electric field which arises automatically and enforces the required balance by slowing down the faster counter ion and accelerating the slower one. The coupled interdiffusion can still be described in terms of one interdiffusion coefficient, but this coefficient depends on the ionic composition of the ion exchanger and thus is variable. Its local value is chiefly determined by the counter ion which is in the minority. Further complications arise from the selectivity of the ion exchanger and from changes in swelling, activity coefficients, and association or ion-pair formation. Solutions have been obtained for a few ideal limiting cases only. The following general rules can be deduced. Forward and reverse exchanges of two given counter ions occur at different rates.

Particle-diffusion controlled exchange is more rapid when the counter ion which is initially in the ion exchanger is the faster one. For film-diffusion controlled exchange, the opposite holds. The counter ion which is preferred by the ion exchanger is taken up at the higher rate and released at the lower rate. The current theories are inadequate for counter ions which associate with the fixed ionic groups (H^+ in weak-acid and OH^- in weak-base resins, etc.). The dependence of the ion- (or isotopic-) exchange rate on experimental conditions is well understood. Factors which favor high rates are high counter-ion mobilities, small particle size and low degree of crosslinking of the ion exchanger, preference of the ion exchanger for the counter ion which is taken up, high concentration and efficient agitation of the solution, and elevated temperatures.

Although a comprehensive quantitative treatment of exchange processes with three or more counter-ion species has so far not been attempted, the following qualitative rules are readily deduced. The relative exchange rates of the various species depend chiefly on their relative affinities for the ion exchanger and on their relative mobilities. The counter ion which is preferred by the ion exchanger or which is more mobile is taken up at the higher rate. The counter ion which is preferred or is less mobile is released at the lower rate. The concentration of the faster species may overshoot its equilibrium concentration in the ion exchanger or in the solution.

Nonelectrolyte sorption can be rather accurately described in terms of a constant diffusion coefficient. The kinetics thus essentially obeys the same simple rate laws as isotopic exchange. Electrolyte sorption involves coupled diffusion of the counter ion and the co-ion; electroneutrality requires that the fluxes of these species be equal. The co-ion, because of the Donnan effect, is in the minority and hence determines the rate. The same simple rate laws as in isotopic exchange (constant diffusion coefficient) apply, provided that Donnan exclusion is strong.

Swelling and shrinking of ion-exchange resins are complex phenomena which have so far received little attention. Swelling proceeds with a sharp solvent "front" which advances toward the center of the resin particle. Shrinking occurs without such a front and is much slower than swelling.

Ion exchangers can dissolve solids of low solubility, provided that the latter dissociate enough to form at least traces of dissolved ions. Dissolution is fastest when a cation exchanger and an anion exchanger are used simultaneously. As a rule, the rate-determining step is film diffusion at the ion exchangers. No rigorous quantitative theories have so far been developed, but the order of magnitude of the dissolution rate is readily predicted.

The rate laws of ion exchange and sorption involve the "effective" diffusion coefficients of the mobile species in the ion exchanger. The present state of the theory does not permit these coefficients to be calculated from more fundamental data. However, the dependence of the coefficients on the experimental conditions is qualitatively well understood, and published experimental data on various types of ion exchangers provide a reliable basis for predicting at least the order of magnitude of the coefficients in a given system.

REFERENCES

1. Adamson, A. W., and J. J. Grossman, *J. Chem. Phys.*, **17**, 1002 (1949).
2. Adamson, A. W., and R. R. Irani, *J. Am. Chem. Soc.*, **79**, 2967 (1957); *J. chim. phys.*, **55**, 102 (1958).
3. Amundson, N. R., *J. Phys. Chem.*, **52**, 1153 (1948).
4. Amundson, N. R., *J. Phys. Chem.*, **54**, 812 (1950).
5. Aris, R., *Chem. Eng. Sci.*, **6**, 262 (1957).
6. Baddour, R. F., D. J. Goldstein, and P. Epstein, *Ind. Eng. Chem.*, **46**, 2192 (1954).
7. Baddour, R. F., and R. D. Hawthorn, *Ind. Eng. Chem.*, **47**, 2517 (1955).
*8. Barrer, R. M., "Diffusion in and through Solids," pp. 29, 50, Cambridge University Press, New York, 1941.
9. Barrer, R. M., and L. V. C. Rees, *Nature*, **187**, 768 (1960).
10. Bauman, W. C., and J. Eichhorn, *J. Am. Chem. Soc.*, **69**, 2830 (1947).
11. Bell, J. R., and P. Grosberg, *Nature*, **189**, 980 (1961).
12. Bergman, W. E. (Phillips Petroleum Co.), U.S. Patent 2,671,035, 1954.
13. Bieber, H., F. E. Steidler, and W. A. Selke, *Chem. Eng. Progr. Symp. Ser.*, **50**, No. 14, 17 (1954).
14. Boyd, G. E., A. W. Adamson, and L. S. Myers, Jr., *J. Am. Chem. Soc.*, **69**, 2836 (1947).
15. Boyd, G. E., and B. A. Soldano, *J. Am. Chem. Soc.*, **75**, 6091 (1953).
16. Boyd, G. E., and B. A. Soldano, *J. Am. Chem. Soc.*, **75**, 6105 (1953).
17. Boyd, G. E., B. A. Soldano, and O. D. Bonner, *J. Phys. Chem.*, **58**, 456 (1954).
18. British Association for the Advancement of Science, "Mathematical Tables," 1931.
19. Brochmann-Hanssen, E., *J. Am. Pharm. Assoc.*, **43**, 307 (1954).
20. Conway, D. E., J. H. S. Green, and D. Reichenberg, *Trans. Faraday Soc.*, **50**, 511 (1954).
21. Crank, J., *J. Polymer Sci.*, **11**, 151 (1953).
*22. Crank, J., "The Mathematics of Diffusion," Oxford University Press, New York, 1956.
*23. Crank, J., *Discussions Faraday Soc.*, **23**, 99 (1957).
24. DeLopez-Gonzales, J., and H. Jenny, *J. Colloid Sci.*, **14**, 533 (1959).
25. Deuel, H., L. Anyas-Weisz, and J. Solms, *Experientia*, **7**, 294 (1951).
26. Dickel, G., and A. Meyer, *Z. Elektrochem.*, **57**, 901 (1953).
27. Dickel, G., and L. v. Nieciecki, *Z. Electrochem.*, **59**, 913 (1955).
28. Douglass, D. C., and D. W. McCall, *J. Chem. Phys.*, **31**, 569 (1959).
29. Downes, J. G., *J. Polymer Sci.*, **36**, 519 (1959).
30. Dranoff, J. S., and L. Lapidus, *Ind. Eng. Chem.*, **50**, 1648 (1958); **53**, 71 (1961).
31. DuDomaine, J., R. L. Swain, and O. A. Hougen, *Ind. Eng. Chem.*, **35**, 546 (1943).
32. Faxén, H., *Ann. Physik*, **68**, 89 (1922); *Ark. Mat. Astron. Fys.*, **17**, No. 27 (1922).
32a. Fedoseeva, O. P., E. P. Cherneva, and N. N. Tunitskii, *Zhur. Fiz. Khim.*, **33**, 936, 1140 (1959).
33. Frisch, H. L., *J. Phys. Chem.*, **61**, 93 (1957).
34. Fujita, H., *J. Phys. Chem.*, **56**, 949 (1952).

---

* Review articles are marked with asterisks.

35. Gilliland, E. R., and R. F. Baddour, *Ind. Eng. Chem.*, **45**, 330 (1953).
36. Glueckauf, E., and J. I. Coates, *J. Chem. Soc.*, **1947**, 1315.
*37. Glueckauf, E., in "Ion Exchange and Its Applications," edited by the Society of Chemical Industry, London, 1955, p. 34.
38. Glueckauf, E., *Trans. Faraday Soc.*, **51**, 1540 (1955).
39. Goldstein, S., *Proc. Roy. Soc. (London)*, **A219**, 151 (1953).
40. Goodknight, R. C., W. A. Klikoff, Jr., and I. Fatt, *J. Phys. Chem.*, **64**, 1162 (1960).
41. Gregor, H. P., F. C. Collins, and M. Pope, *J. Colloid Sci.*, **6**, 304 (1951).
42. Grossman, J. J., and A. W. Adamson, *J. Phys. Chem.*, **56**, 97 (1952).
43. Haagen, K., *Z. Elektrochem.*, **57**, 178 (1953).
44. Hale, D. K., and D. Reichenberg, *Discussions Faraday Soc.*, **7**, 79 (1949).
45. Hartley, G. S., Faraday Soc. Discussion on Swelling and Shrinking, **1946**, p. 6.
45a. Hartley, G. S., and J. Crank, *Trans. Faraday Soc.*, **45**, 801 (1949).
46. Helfferich, F., *Z. Elektrochem.*, **56**, 947 (1952).
47. Helfferich, F., *Z. physik. Chem. (Frankfurt)*, **4**, 386 (1955).
48. Helfferich, F., *Discussions Faraday Soc.*, **21**, 83 (1956).
*49. Helfferich, F., in *Ullmann's Encyklopädie der technischen Chemie*, 3d ed., Urban & Schwarzenberg, vol. 8, p. 787, Munich, 1957.
50. Helfferich, F., *J. chim. phys.*, **55**, 157 (1958).
51. Helfferich, F., and M. S. Plesset, *J. Chem. Phys.*, **28**, 418 (1958).
52. Helfferich, F., *J. Phys. Chem.*, **66**, 39 (1962).
53. Hermans, P. H., and D. Vermaas, *J. Polymer Sci.*, **1**, 149 (1946).
54. Heymann, E., and I. J. O'Donnell, *J. Colloid Sci.*, **4**, 405 (1949).
55. Hiester, N. K., and T. Vermeulen, *J. Chem. Phys.*, **16**, 1087 (1948).
56. Holm, L. W., *J. Chem. Phys.*, **22**, 1132 (1954).
57. Honda, M., Y. Yoshino, and T. Wabiko, *J. Chem. Soc. Japan, Pure Chem. Sect.*, **73**, 348 (1952); *Chem. Abstr.*, **47**, 2568 (1953).
58. Ilschner, B., *Z. Elektrochem.*, **62**, 989 (1958).
*59. Ingersoll, L. R., O. J. Zobel, and A. C. Ingersoll, "Heat Conduction," pp. 169–174, McGraw-Hill Book Company, Inc., New York, 1948.
60. Ishibashi, N., T. Seiyama, and W. Sakai, *J. Electrochem. Soc. Japan*, **23**, 182 (1955); *Chem. Abstr.*, **49**, 14524 (1955).
61. Jakubovic, A. O., G. J. Hills, and J. A. Kitchener, *J. chim. phys.*, **55**, 263 (1958).
62. Jakubovic, A. O., G. J. Hills, and J. A. Kitchener, *Trans. Faraday Soc.*, **55**, 1570 (1959).
63. Juda, W., and M. Carron, *J. Am. Chem. Soc.*, **70**, 3295 (1948).
64. King, G., *Trans. Faraday Soc.*, **41**, 325 (1945).
65. Kressman, T. R. E., and J. A. Kitchener, *Discussions Faraday Soc.*, **7**, 90 (1949).
66. Kressman, T. R. E., *J. Phys. Chem.*, **56**, 118 (1952).
67. Krishnamoorthy, C., and A. D. Desai, *Soil Sci.*, **76**, 307 (1953); **79**, 159 and 215 (1955).
68. Lagos, A. E., and J. A. Kitchener, *Trans. Faraday Soc.*, **56**, 1245 (1960).
69. Lane, J. A., and J. W. Riggle, *Chem. Engr. Progr. Symp. Ser.*, **55**, (24), 127 (1959).
70. Lapidus, L., and N. R. Amundson, *J. Phys. Chem.*, **54**, 821 (1950).
71. Lapidus, L., and N. R. Amundson, *J. Phys. Chem.*, **56**, 373 (1952).
72. Lapidus, L., and J. B. Rosen, *Chem. Eng. Progr. Symp. Ser.*, **50**, No. 14, 97 (1954).
72a. Laufer, M. A., *Biophys. J.*, **1**, 205 (1961).
72b. Lorenz, P. B., *Nature*, **189**, 386 (1961).
72c. Mackay, D., *J. Phys. Chem.*, **64**, 1718 (1960).
73. Mackie, J. S., and P. Meares, *Proc. Roy. Soc. (London)*, **A232**, 498 (1955).

---

* Review articles are marked with asterisks.

74. Manecke, G., and E. Otto-Laupemühlen, *Z. physik. Chem. (Frankfurt)*, **2**, 336 (1954).

75. Matano, C., *Japan. J. Phys.*, **8**, 109 (1933).

76. Møller, J. *Kolloid Beih.*, **46**, 1 (1937).

*77. Monet, G. P., *Chem. Eng. Progr. Symp. Ser.*, **55**, No. 24, 1 (1959).

77a. Müller, F. H., and E. Helmuth, *Kolloid Z.*, **177**, 1 (1961).

78. Nachod, F. C., and W. Wood, *J. Am. Chem. Soc.*, **66**, 1380 (1944); **67**, 629 (1945).

79. Nelson, F., *J. Polymer Sci.*, **40**, 563 (1959).

80. Nernst, W., *Z. physik. Chem.*, **2**, 613 (1888) and **4**, 129 (1889).

81. Nernst, W., *Z. physik. Chem.*, **47**, 52 (1904).

82. Oel, H. J., *Z. physik. Chem. (Frankfurt)*, **10**, 165 (1957).

83. Opler, A., and N. K. Hiester, Tables for Predicting the Performance of Fixed Bed Ion Exchange and Similar Mass Transfer Processes, *Stanford Research Inst. Rept.*, 1954.

84. Organ, R. M., *Museums J.*, **53**, 49 (1953); *Chem. Abstr.*, **47**, 9683 (1953).

85. Osborn, G. H., *Analyst*, **78**, 220 (1953).

86. Parks, G. S., *J. Polymer Sci.*, **11**, 97 (1953).

87. Paterson, S., *Proc. Phys. Soc. (London)*, **59**, 50 (1947).

87a. Pepper, K. W., and D. Reichenberg, *Z. Elektrochem.*, **57**, 183 (1953).

88. Peterson, M. A., and H. P. Gregor, *J. Electrochem. Soc.*, **106**, 1051 (1959).

89. Planck, M., *Ann. Phys. and Chem.*, **39**, 161 (1890).

90. Plesset, M. S., F. Helfferich, and J. N. Franklin, *J. Chem. Phys.*, **29**, 1064 (1958).

91. Pouchlý, J., *Chem. Listy*, **52**, 996 (1958); *Coll. Czech. Chem. Com.*, **24**, 3007 (1959).

92. Prager, S., *J. Chem. Phys.*, **33**, 122 (1960).

93. Pulido, C., *Acta Chem. Scand.*, **10**, 49 (1956).

94. Reichenberg, D., *J. Am. Chem. Soc.*, **75**, 589 (1953).

95. Reichenberg, D., 1957 (unpublished).

96. Richman, D., and H. C. Thomas, *J. Phys. Chem.*, **60**, 237 (1956).

96a. Rose, W., H. C. Tung, and C. Newman, *J. Phys. Chem.*, **65**, 1440 (1961).

97. Rosen, J. B., and W. E. Winsche, *J. Chem. Phys.*, **18**, 1587 (1950).

98. Rosen, J. B., *J. Chem. Phys.*, **20**, 387 (1952).

99. Rosen, J. B., *Ind. Eng. Chem.*, **46**, 1590 (1954).

100. Rosenberg, N. W., J. H. B. George, and W. D. Potter, *J. Electrochem. Soc.*, **104**, 111 (1957).

101. Schlegelmilch, W., *Z. physik. Chem.*, **214**, 165 (1960).

102. Schlögl, R., and F. Helfferich, *Z. Elektrochem.*, **56**, 644 (1952).

103. Schlögl, R., *Z. Elektrochem.*, **57**, 195 (1953).

104. Schlögl, R., and F. Helfferich, *J. Chem. Phys.*, **26**, 5 (1957).

105. Schlögl, R., and B. Stein, *Z. physik. Chem. (Frankfurt)*, **13**, 111 (1957); *Z. Elektrochem.*, **62**, 340 (1958).

106. Schulze, G., *Z. physik. Chem.*, **89**, 168 (1915).

107. Schurig, H., Thesis, Göttingen, 1959.

108. Selke, W. A., and H. Bliss, *Chem. Eng. Progr.*, **46**, 509 (1951).

109. Soldano, B. A., *Ann. N.Y. Acad. Sci.*, **57**, 116 (1953).

110. Soldano, B. A., and G. E. Boyd, *J. Am. Chem. Soc.*, **75**, 6099 (1953).

111. Soldano, B. A., and G. E. Boyd, *J. Am. Chem. Soc.*, **75**, 6107 (1953).

112. Spalding, D. B., *Internat. J. Heat & Mass Transfer*, **2**, 283 (1961).

113. Spiegler, K. S., and C. D. Coryell, *J. Phys. Chem.*, **57**, 687 (1953).

114. Spiegler, K. S., unpublished, 1954.

*115. Spiegler, K. S., and M. R. J. Wyllie, in "Physical Techniques in Biological Research," G. Oster and A. Pollister (eds.), vol. 2, p. 301, Academic Press, Inc., New York, 1956.

* Review articles are marked with asterisks.

116. Stein, B., Thesis, Göttingen, 1956.

117. Sugai, S., and J. Furuichi, *J. Chem. Phys.*, **23**, 1181 (1955); *J. Phys. Soc. Japan*, **10**, 1032 (1955); *Chem. Abstr.*, **50**, 6136 (1956).

118. Sujata, A. D., J. T. Banchero, and R. R. White, *Ind. Eng. Chem.*, **47**, 2193 (1955).

119. Tetenbaum, M., and H. P. Gregor, *J. Phys. Chem.*, **58**, 1156 (1954).

120. Thomas, H. C., *J. Am. Chem. Soc.*, **66**, 1664 (1944).

121. Thomas, H. C., *Ann. N.Y. Acad. Sci.*, **49**, 161 (1948).

122. Thomas, H. C., in "Ion Exchange," F. C. Nachod (ed.), p. 29, Academic Press, Inc., New York, 1949.

123. Thomas, H. C., *Proc. Natl. Acad. Sci.*, **42**, 909 (1956).

123a. Turse, R., and W. Rieman III, *J. Phys. Chem.*, **65**, (1961).

124. Vermeulen, T., *Ind. Eng. Chem.*, **45**, 1664 (1953).

125. Vermeulen, T., and N. K. Hiester, *J. Chem. Phys.*, **22**, 96 (1954).

*126. Vermeulen, T., *Advances in Chem. Eng.*, **2**, 147 (1958).

127. Vielstich, W., *Z. Elektrochem.*, **57**, 646 (1953).

128. Wagner, C., *Z. physik. Chem.*, **B11**, 139 (1930).

129. Walter, J. E., *J. Chem. Phys.*, **13**, 332 (1945).

129a. Westermark, T., *Acta Chem. Scand.*, **14**, 1858 (1960).

130. Wheaton, R. M., and D. F. Harrington, *Ind. Eng. Chem.*, **44**, 1796 (1952).

131. Wheeler, A., *Advances in Catalysis*, **3**, 249 (1951).

132. Wiesner, W., Thesis, Köthen, 1953.

133. Woermann, D., K. F. Bonhoeffer, and F. Helfferich, *Z. physik. Chem. (Frankfurt)*, **8**, 265 (1956).

134. Wright, M. L., *Trans. Faraday Soc.*, **49**, 95 (1953); **50**, 89 (1954).

135. Wright, M. L., *Discussions Faraday Soc.*, **16**, 58 (1954).

* Review articles are marked with asterisks.

7

Electrochemical Properties

Swollen ion exchangers may be considered as concentrated electrolytes in which one ionic species, the fixed ionic groups, is immobile. The electrochemical properties of such materials are unusual and have received considerable attention. In recent times, they have found more and more practical applications. Most of these applications involve ion-exchanger membranes which will be discussed in a separate chapter (Chap. 8). Before studying specific systems in detail, we shall examine the fundamental electrochemical properties of ion exchangers as such. In this chapter, a general qualitative survey of the phenomena and a brief quantitative treatment will be given.

7-1. ELECTRIC CONDUCTIVITY

The specific electric conductivity of a material is essentially given by the concentrations and mobilities of the charge carriers (electrons or ions) which the material contains. Ion exchangers, like electrolyte solutions, contain mobile ions and are ionic conductors. Ionic concentrations in the usual ion-exchange resins are quite high (generally above 1 molar). Thus the electric conductivity is considerable, though the ionic mobilities in the resins are lower than in aqueous solutions of comparable concentrations. Mineral ion exchangers, on the other hand, are rather poor conductors because, here, the ionic mobilities are smaller by several orders of magnitude.

The mobility of an ion can be expressed in terms of its diffusion coefficient [see Eq. (6-33) and Sec. 7-4]. Diffusion coefficients in ion exchangers and their dependence on the various physical factors have been discussed at length in Sec. 6-8. Thus the factors which determine the electric conductivity of ion exchangers are readily understood. High specific conductivity is favored by:

High concentration of the fixed ionic groups
Low degree of crosslinking of the ion exchanger

Small size and low valence of the counter ions

High concentration of the solution which is in equilibrium with the ion exchanger

Elevated temperature

The concentrations of the fixed ionic groups and of the solution determine the concentrations of the charge carriers in the ion exchanger; the degree of

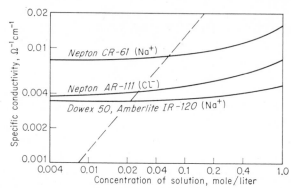

F<small>IG</small>. 7-1. Specific conductivities of various ion exchangers in Na$^+$ form or Cl$^-$ form in equilibrium with NaCl solutions. The specific conductivity of the solution is given as a broken line.

crosslinking, the nature of the counter ions, and the temperature determine their mobilities.

Absolute values of the specific conductivity of common ion-exchange resins in alkali-metal-ion or halide-ion form are of the order of 10^{-3} to 10^{-1} ohm^{-1} cm^{-1}.

The conductivity of an ion exchanger is not constant but depends on the nature of the counter ion and, to a lesser degree, on the concentration of the solution with which the ion exchanger is in equilibrium. As long as the solution is rather dilute ($C \ll X$), the conductivity of the ion exchanger, which has the higher ionic concentration, is greater than that of the solution. When the solution concentration is increased, the concentration in the ion exchanger also increases, but to a lesser degree. Hence the conductivity of the solution increases faster than that of the ion exchanger and eventually becomes the larger one. The effect of higher ionic concentration in the ion exchanger is now offset by that of the higher ionic mobilities in the solution (see Fig. 7-1). The point at which the conductivities of ion exchanger and solution are equal is called the *equiconductance point*.

The fact that the conductivity of the ion exchanger is much larger than that of a dilute solution can be used for regeneration of ion-exchange beds and for ionic separations. If a direct current is passed through an ion-exchange column, the charge transfer is accomplished chiefly by the counter ions in the ion-exchanger beads. Thus a counter-ion species introduced at the "upstream" electrode (cations at the anode, anions at the cathode) will efficiently displace the counter ions which were initially present in the beads

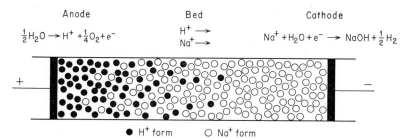

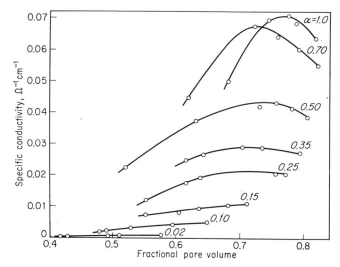

Fig. 7-2. Electrolytic regeneration of a cation exchanger (*schematic*). The ion-exchange bed is placed between two perforated platinum electrodes. H^+ ions entering at the anode displace Na^+ ions from the bed. *From K. S. Spiegler [50].*

[19,29,31,34,49,50]; see Fig. 7-2. If a mixture of several species is introduced and subsequently displaced by a "chaser," the species of the mixture will separate into individual bands following one another in the sequence of decreasing mobility [28,47,49,50].

Interesting results have been obtained with partially dehydrated ion exchangers [8,15,18a]. As a rule, the self-diffusion coefficient of the counter ion decreases with progressing dehydration, and so does the specific conductivity of the ion exchanger. However, exceptions may occur. The specific conductivity may go through a maximum at a certain swelling state (see Fig. 7-3). Two causes can bring about such an effect. First, in weakly

Fig. 7-3. Specific conductivity of a weak-acid cation exchanger (crosslinked polymethacrylic acid), shown as a function of the degree of swelling. The various curves correspond to different degrees of neutralization with KOH. *From experimental results by A. Despić and G. T. Hills [8].*

crosslinked resins, the effective self-diffusion coefficient of the counter ion may be increased by partial dehydration because shrinking of the resin reduces the "jumping" distance from chain to chain (see also page 305) [15]. Second, shrinking of the resin increases the number of counter ions per unit volume. This increase in the number of charge carriers may outweigh the decrease in their mobility. Mineral ion exchangers do not shrink when being dehydrated. Hence, both potential causes are absent and, indeed, a steady decrease in specific conductivity with progressing dehydration is observed [2]. Completely dehydrated ion exchangers are rather poor conductors [7].

7-2. TRANSFERENCE NUMBERS AND TRANSPORT NUMBERS

The *transference number** t_i of a species i is defined as the number of moles of the species transferred by 1 faraday of electricity through a stationary cross section in the direction of positive current—a complete definition only when the frame of reference is specified. The electric current induces convection in the pores. Thus it makes a difference whether the matrix, the solvent, or the pore liquid is considered as stationary [36,37]. A spectator riding on a solvent molecule or floating in the pore liquid will see the matrix being "transferred." In the following, the matrix is chosen as the frame of reference. Transference of the solvent must thus be considered. According to the definition given above, the transference numbers of anions are negative since anions are transferred in the direction opposite to that of positive electric current.

The *transport number** of a species is defined as the fraction of the electric current which is carried by the species. According to this definition, the transport number is the product of the transference number and the electrochemical valence of the species. The transport numbers are positive for all ions and zero for the (electrically neutral) solvent. By definition, the sum over all transport numbers is equal to unity:

$$\sum_i z_i t_i = 1 \tag{7-1}$$

---

* In the literature, the term transference number is often used interchangeably with transport number. Further misunderstandings can arise from the fact that several frames of reference can be chosen to define both these quantities. Possible frames of reference are the matrix, the center of gravity of the pore liquid, and the solvent in the pores. In the last case, either the total or only the "free" solvent (solvation shells not included) can be chosen ("Hittorf" and "true" transference numbers). Another point which is likely to cause confusion is that the terms transference number and transport number are often used tacitly for the *integral* transference and transport numbers in membrane systems where the actual (differential) numbers are functions of the space coordinate. The integral transference number will be discussed in Sec. 8-8c.

In homogeneous electrolyte solutions the concentrations of the cation and the anion are necessarily stoichiometrically equivalent. Hence the ratio of the transference numbers is determined solely by the ratio of the ionic mobilities. In ion exchangers the situation is different. Here, the concentration of the counter ion exceeds that of the co-ion by far, particularly if the solution which is in equilibrium with the ion exchanger is dilute (Donnan exclusion, see Sec. 5-3c). If an electric field is applied to the ion exchanger, the transport of the electric current thus is accomplished nearly exclusively by the counter ions. The transport number of the counter ion (or the sum over the transport numbers of all counter-ion species) is nearly unity. *Electric current in an ion exchanger transfers predominantly counter ions.* However, when the concentration of the solution is increased, the Donnan exclusion of the co-ion becomes less efficient. The increasing concentration of the co-ion in the ion exchanger causes a decrease in the transport number of the counter ion.

7-3. TRANSFERENCE OF SOLVENT; CONVECTION CONDUCTIVITY

A constant electric field applied to an electrolyte solution causes the cations to migrate to the cathode and the anions to the anode. The electric field, like any other force, accelerates the particle on which it acts. As the ions gather speed, however, their "friction" with the surrounding medium increases in proportion to their velocity. Thus the ions attain a constant final velocity in which the acceleration by the field and the deceleration by friction balance one another. This steady-state condition is reached in a very short time after the electric field has been imposed.

An electrolyte solution contains cations and anions in stoichiometrically equivalent concentrations. Here, the electric field imparts equal over-all momentum to the cations and anions; since friction equals the electric driving force, both species convey equal over-all momentum to the solvent: the forces exerted on the solvent by the cations and anions balance one another exactly, irrespective of differences in rate of migration and ionic valence. (It is true that, for instance, a 2,1-valent electrolyte contains twice as many anions as cations, but the electric force acting on the bivalent cation is twice as large as that acting on the monovalent anion; thus every cation imparts twice as much momentum to the solvent as an anion.) Except for solvation shells *no* solvent is transferred.

In ion exchangers the situation is different. Here, the counter ions are in the majority and, hence, impart more momentum to the solvent than do the co-ions (see Fig. 7-4). Solvent is carried along by the counter ions, or, in other words, there is convection in the direction of counter-ion transfer [42]. The rate of this convection depends chiefly on the counter-ion concentration, the electric field, and the flow resistance of the ion-exchange material. The convection of the pore liquid is superimposed on the migration of the ions relative to the pore liquid. The counter ions "swim with a fair tide," the co-ions against the tide. Relative to the matrix, the counter ions move faster than they would in a stationary liquid. By adding to the rate of counter-ion transfer, the convection of the pore liquid increases the electric conductivity of the material [22,32,42,48,52]. This surplus conductivity due to convection is called *convection conductivity*.*

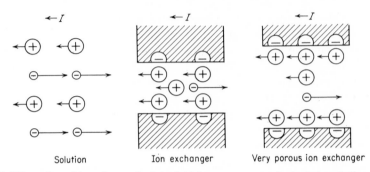

Fig. 7-4. Migration of ions in an electric field in an aqueous electrolyte solution (*left*), in an ordinary cation exchanger (*middle*), and in a highly porous cation exchanger (*right*). Where the cations outnumber the anions, convection of solvent in the direction of cation transference is induced. This is the case in the pore of the ordinary cation exchanger and at the pore walls of the highly porous cation exchanger.

The factors on which the convection conductivity depends are readily deduced from the considerations above. Convection conductivity is high in ion exchangers with a high concentration of fixed charges (high counter-ion concentration) and a low flow resistance, and when the exchanger is in equilibrium with dilute solution (low co-ion concentration).

7-4. QUANTITATIVE RELATIONS

The phenomena which are produced by an electric field acting on an ion exchanger depend chiefly on the concentrations and mobilities of the mobile ions and on the properties of the ion-exchange material. An adequate description can be given in terms of the thermodynamics of irreversible processes [11]. This description, however, is somewhat abstract. For the physical interpretation of the important factors and for predicting the behavior of given systems a model must be used. The treatment given in the following paragraphs is based on a simple model.

---

* Convection conductivity is closely related to the "surface conductivity" in Smoluchowski's theory of capillary systems [3,44]. If the pore width is much larger than the Debye-Hückel ionic cloud, the counter-ion concentration is in excess near the pore walls only. In such systems the electric field produces a convection near the pore walls, and Smoluchowski's model applies. In the usual ion exchangers, however, the pore width is much smaller, and thus convection occurs in the whole pore cross section.

The ion exchanger is considered as a porous system which is homogeneous in macroscopic dimensions. No detailed information or assumptions about the structure of the pores (shape, width, degree of branching) are required. All quantities used (concentrations, fluxes, current density, gradients, etc.) refer to unit volume, cross section, and length of the total ion-exchange material rather than to the pores. Thus they are accessible by macroscopic measurement. Only two quantities are used to characterize the pore geometry: the (macroscopic) flow resistance and the fractional pore volume. It is assumed that the distribution of mobile species within the pores is uniform. This assumption is a good approximation in the usual ion exchangers in which the pore width is too small to permit the formation of diffuse double layers at the pore walls (pore width much smaller than Debye-Hückel cloud of fixed ionic groups). This model was first formulated clearly by G. Schmid [40]. For ion exchangers it has proved to be very useful.

In this chapter, the discussion is restricted to the interior of an ion exchanger. The discussion deals with processes occurring in a volume element of the material which is in equilibrium before the electric field is applied, and in which the electric current produces no concentration changes. Thus there are no gradients of concentrations, activity coefficients, and pressure, and the transport of mobile species is due solely to electric transference and convection.

The rate of motion of an ion i relative to the surrounding liquid in an electric field is proportional to the force with which the field acts on the ion. This force is the product of the electrical potential gradient grad φ and the ionic valence z_i. The proportionality factor is, by definition, the electrochemical mobility u_i of the ion.* The electric transference $(J_i)_{el}$ of the species i *relative to the surrounding pore liquid* is the product of the rate of motion and the concentration $\bar{C}_i$ of the species

$$(J_i)_{el} = -z_i \bar{C}_i \bar{u}_i \, \text{grad} \, \varphi \qquad (6\text{-}32)$$

In the ion exchanger, the transference *relative to the matrix* results from superposition of the transference relative to the pore liquid and transport by convection of the pore liquid. According to the thermodynamics of irreversible processes [11] the latter is the product of the concentration $\bar{C}_i$ and the rate $\mathfrak{v}$ at which the center of gravity of the pore liquid moves

$$(J_i)_{con} = \bar{C}_i \mathfrak{v} \qquad (7\text{-}2)$$

---

* According to this definition, the electrochemical mobility u_i is the rate of motion of an ion propelled by unit force. The mobility is positive for cations and anions. The force can be expressed in electric or cgs units (Planck, in his definition, used the force 1 dyne). Often a different definition is used according to which the electrochemical mobility is the rate of motion in the direction of positive current at the field strength of 1 volt/cm. The mobility so defined is negative for anions. The conversion factor interrelating electric and cgs units is 1 volt · coulomb · cm^{-1} = 10^7 dyne.

Thus the transference relative to the matrix is

$$J_i = (J_i)_{el} + (J_i)_{con} = -z_i \bar{C}_i \bar{u}_i \, \mathrm{grad} \, \varphi + \bar{C}_i \mathfrak{v} \qquad (7\text{-}3)$$

Note that all quantities in Eq. (7-3) refer to unit dimensions of the ion-exchange material, not of the pores. The vector $\mathfrak{v}$ is the "linear" convection rate in the direction of the current rather than the actual rate of motion in the tortuous pores. In the same way, grad φ refers to unit length of the material, not of the tortuous pore path. The concentration $\bar{C}_i$ is per unit volume of the over-all material rather than of the pore liquid.

Every mole of species i carries the electric charge z_i faraday. Thus the electric current density I (net charge transfer per unit time and unit cross section of the material) is

$$I = \mathfrak{F} \sum_i z_i J_i \qquad (7\text{-}4)$$

Conservation of electroneutrality requires that the electric charges of all species balance one another everywhere in the system

$$\sum_i z_i \bar{C}_i + \omega X = 0 \qquad (7\text{-}5)$$

> where X = concentration of fixed charges; ω = sign of fixed charges (-1 for cation exchangers, $+1$ for anion exchangers).

The rate of motion $\mathfrak{v}$ of the center of gravity of the pore liquid (convection rate) is proportional to the force with which the electric field acts on a volume element of the pore liquid. The proportionality factor is, by definition, the reciprocal of the specific flow resistance of the material.* The electric surplus charge per unit volume of pore liquid (not including the matrix volume) is $-\omega \mathfrak{F} X/\epsilon$ (ϵ = fractional pore volume). Thus the convection rate is [38,39]

$$\mathfrak{v} = \frac{\omega \mathfrak{F} X}{\rho_0 \epsilon} \, \mathrm{grad} \, \varphi = \omega \bar{u}_0 \, \mathrm{grad} \, \varphi \qquad \left(\bar{u}_0 \equiv \frac{\mathfrak{F} X}{\rho_0 \epsilon} \right) \qquad (7\text{-}6)$$

> where ρ_0 = specific flow resistance of the ion exchanger.

The introduction of the quantity $\bar{u}_0$ as defined above (it has the dimension of an electrochemical mobility and may be called the "mobility" of the pore liquid) will prove to be useful in later calculations.

Combining Eqs. (7-3) to (7-6) one obtains the following relations for the

---

* "Specific" is meant to indicate that ρ_0 is the flow resistance of the unit cube of the material. The specific flow resistance of a given ion exchanger is *not* a characteristic constant since its magnitude depends on the pore width and the viscosity of the pore liquid and thus on the ionic form of the ion exchanger, the nature of the solvent, etc.

current density I in a cross section normal to the direction of the current*

$$I = -\mathfrak{F} \left(\sum_i z_i^2 \bar{u}_i \bar{C}_i + \bar{u}_0 X \right) \text{grad } \varphi \qquad (7\text{-}7)\dagger$$

and for the specific conductivity $\bar{\kappa}$ (i.e., the conductivity of the unit cube of the material)

$$\bar{\kappa} = -\frac{I}{\text{grad } \varphi} = \mathfrak{F} \left(\sum_i z_i^2 \bar{u}_i \bar{C}_i + \bar{u}_0 X \right) \qquad (7\text{-}8)\dagger$$

The second term in Eq. (7-8) is due to convection conductivity. Hence the convection conductivity $\bar{\kappa}_0$ and its fractional contribution to the total conductivity are

$$\bar{\kappa}_0 = \bar{u}_0 \mathfrak{F} X \qquad (7\text{-}9)\dagger$$

$$\frac{\bar{\kappa}_0}{\bar{\kappa}} = \frac{\bar{u}_0 X}{\sum_i z_i^2 \bar{u}_i \bar{C}_i + \bar{u}_0 X} \qquad (7\text{-}10)\dagger$$

Equation (7-9) shows that the convection conductivity can be considered formally as the contribution of the fixed ionic groups to the total conductivity [42]. The relative importance of convection conductivity increases with the ratio $\bar{u}_0/\bar{u}_i$. The quantity $\bar{u}_0$ is proportional to the concentration of fixed ionic groups and inversely proportional to the flow resistance [see Eq. (7-6)]. Hence convection conductivity is most important in high-capacity ion exchangers with low flow resistance. According to Eq. (7-10), high ionic valences and electrolyte sorption (resulting in higher ionic concentrations $\bar{C}_i$) reduce the relative contribution of convection conductivity. However, all these factors are more or less interrelated. For instance, low flow resistance is likely to be accompanied by high ionic mobilities, high ionic valence by low ionic mobility, and a high concentration of fixed ionic groups by high flow resistance.

The transference numbers $\bar{t}_i$ can be obtained by use of Eqs. (7-3) and (7-6) which give

$$J_i = -\bar{C}_i(z_i\bar{u}_i - \omega\bar{u}_0) \text{grad } \varphi \qquad (7\text{-}11)$$

Thus the transference number is

$$\bar{t}_i = \frac{\mathfrak{F} J_i}{I} = \frac{\bar{C}_i(z_i\bar{u}_i - \omega\bar{u}_0)}{\sum_i z_i^2 \bar{u}_i \bar{C}_i + \bar{u}_0 X} \qquad (7\text{-}12)$$

---

* Note that the units must be used consistently. If current density and field strength are expressed in electric units, the definition of mobility to be used is the rate of motion at unit electric force.

† Corresponding equations for the case of a 1,1-valent electrolyte have been derived previously by G. Schmid [42].

Equations (7-8), (7-9), and (7-12) involve the ionic mobilities $\bar{u}_i$ and the quantity $\bar{u}_0$ (or ρ_0). These quantities are still unknown and must be calculated from independent measurements if the conductivity, convection conductivity, and transference numbers are to be predicted. In ideal systems the electrochemical mobility u_i (as defined by Planck, i.e., on the cgs scale) is related to the self-diffusion coefficient D_i by

$$u_i = \frac{\mathfrak{F}}{RT} D_i \tag{6-33}$$

In ion exchangers, this so-called Nernst-Einstein relation is found to hold rather well (see page 268). By use of Eq. (6-33) the mobilities $\bar{u}_i$ can be calculated from self-diffusion measurements. The independent determination of the specific flow resistance ρ_0 is more cumbersome. For ion exchangers in bead form no methods have so far been worked out. However, the quantities $\bar{u}_0$ or ρ_0 can be calculated from measurements of the hydrodynamic and electroosmotic permeabilities of membranes [see Eq. (8-129)]. For practical purposes, a rough estimate by analogy is often sufficient. The specific flow resistance of common ion-exchange resins is usually of the order of 10^{12} to 10^{14} g cm^{-3} sec^{-1}.

The specific conductivity of ion exchangers can be measured with rather simple means. (With beads, however, the results are not very accurate.) For this reason, most investigators have approached the problem from the other side, calculating diffusion coefficients from conductivity data. An ion exchanger in pure A form and devoid of sorbed electrolyte contains the counter ion A as the only mobile ionic species. If the concentration of fixed ionic groups and the flow resistance are known, the diffusion coefficient of A can be calculated from the specific conductivity of the material by use of Eqs. (7-8) and (6-33). The correction for convection conductivity is often neglected because the necessary data are lacking [25–27]. On the other hand, the comparison of self-diffusion and conductivity data can be used to calculate the convection conductivity and thus the flow resistance [8,13,48,49].

The simple treatment given here involves several idealizations. The objections that may be raised against expressing transport phenomena in porous media in terms of effective mobilities or diffusion coefficients have been discussed in Sec. 6-8a. The uniformity of distribution of the species in the pore liquid is another simplifying assumption. The use of the Nernst-Einstein relation (6-33) amounts to disregarding any "coupling" of fluxes other than by induced convection. Probably more serious than all these idealizations is an implicit assumption in the application of Eq. (7-2) to porous media. This equation implies that convection—in the absence of any other force—carries all particles in the pore liquid at the same rate. It disregards the fact that exchange of momentum with the pore walls by mechanical or molecular interactions may retard the various species to different degrees. Let us resort to a crude analogy, a rubber tube through which a constant flow of water carries sand and pebbles. Because of differences in friction the pebbles will move at a slower pace than the smaller sand particles, and these will move slower than the extremely small water molecules. The consistent application of Eq. (7-2), however, would lead to equal rates of motion for pebbles, sand, and water. Similarly, one must expect that, in ion exchangers, the rate of transport by convection is different for different ions. For example, very large or specifically interacting ions may be more strongly retarded than others. A more refined theory will have to include this effect.* Of course, the relations become more complex since individual interaction parameters for all mobile species must be introduced, whereas the simple approach given above involves only one quantity (the specific flow resistance) characteristic of the "friction" with the matrix.

Experimental results are, in most cases, in reasonable qualitative agreement with the theory. For quantitative comparisons the experimental data are still insufficient. In particular, independent measurements of diffusion coefficients have rarely been made and flow-resistance data are lacking. Conspicuous deviations are found with polyvalent, strongly bound counter ions such as TiO^{2+}. Here, convection in the direction of co-ion transfer has been observed (negative electroosmosis; see Sec. 8-8b) [33]. Most likely this anomalous behavior is due to the differences in interaction which were discussed above.

7-5. EXPERIMENTAL METHODS

The specific conductivity of ion-exchange materials is readily determined. Various methods are discussed in the following paragraphs. The convection conductivity, however, cannot be measured directly. It can be calculated either from conductivity and self-diffusion data (see Sec. 7-4) or from determinations of the flow resistance. Measurements of the flow resistance and of transport and transference numbers will be described in the next chapter (Sec. 8-9c).

The most accurate conductivity data are obtained when the ion exchanger is used in the form of rods, ribbons, or disks (membranes). The resistance of such materials can be measured in a cell with platinum or copper-bronze electrodes which are in direct contact with the ion exchanger [1,6,17,18,20,21,30,33,48,50,53,54]; see Fig. 7-5. An alternative technique is to clamp the membrane between two solutions of identical composition and measure the resistance between two electrodes dipping into the solutions [4,5,10,23,25–27,41,45,46]; see Fig. 7-6. The resistance is usually measured by an ordinary bridge circuit (Fig. 7-7). A more elaborate precision circuit has been described by Shedlowsky [14,43]. As a rule, the measurement is carried out with alternating current (1,000 cycles). In measurements with electrodes in direct contact with the ion exchanger, the specific

---

* An excellent approach along these lines has recently been given by K. S. Spiegler [51].

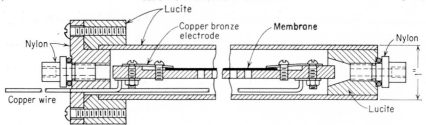

FIG. 7-5. Cell for measuring electric conductivities of ion exchangers. An ion-exchanger rod or ribbon is clamped between copper-bronze electrodes. The cell may be flushed continuously with water or dilute solutions. The electrode distance is about 5 in. *From K. S. Spiegler* [50].

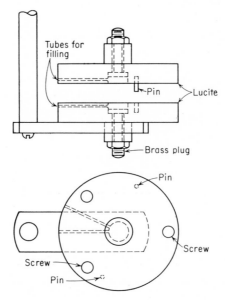

FIG. 7-6. Cell for measuring electric conductivities of ion-exchanger membranes with electrodes that are not in contact with the membrane. The cell is attached to a stirring rod and rotates in the equilibrating solution. *From J. W. Lorimer, E. I. Boterenbrood, and J. J. Hermans* [23].

conductivity $\bar{\kappa}$ is calculated from the resistance $\mathfrak{R}$, the cross section q of the rod or ribbon, and the distance l between the electrodes

$$\bar{\kappa} = \frac{l}{\mathfrak{R}q} \tag{7-13}$$

More accurate results are obtained by difference measurements with varying electrode distances [8,13,14]. Here, errors due to surface contact resistances largely cancel.

$$\bar{\kappa} = \frac{\Delta l}{\Delta \mathfrak{R}\, q} \tag{7-14}$$

where Δl = difference of electrode distances; $\Delta \mathfrak{R}$ = difference of measured resistances.

Measurements with electrodes which are in direct contact with the material can also be made with partially desolvated ion exchangers [8,13,14].

Measurements with electrodes dipping into solutions on both sides of an ion-exchanger membrane yield the total resistance $\mathfrak{R}_c$ of the cell. This resistance is the sum of the solution resistance $\mathfrak{R}_0$ and the membrane resistance. The solution resistance is conveniently

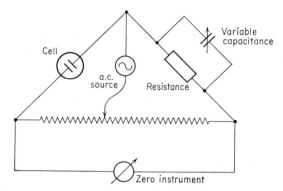

FIG. 7-7. Bridge circuit for conductivity measurements.

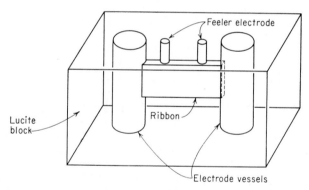

FIG. 7-8. Cell for measuring electric conductivities of ion exchangers. A rod or ribbon is mounted in a Lucite block. Direct current is passed through the rod. The conductivity is calculated from the electric potential difference between the two feeler electrodes. *From J. W. Lorimer* [24].

determined by a blank measurement without membrane. The specific conductivity of the membrane material is

$$\bar{\kappa} = \frac{d}{q}(\mathfrak{R}_c - \mathfrak{R}_0) \tag{7-15}$$

where d = membrane thickness; q = membrane cross section.

Any errors due to surface contact resistances are eliminated in this technique. The accuracy hinges, however, on the exact determination of a difference between two resistivities ($\mathfrak{R}_0$ and $\mathfrak{R}_c$). This difference may be comparatively small, particularly if the ion exchanger is a good conductor and the solution is dilute.

This disadvantage is avoided in a third technique. Here, a constant direct current of strength i is passed through a rod or ribbon of ion-exchange material which is clamped lengthwise between two identical solutions. The specific conductivity is calculated from the electric potential difference $\Delta\varphi$ (in volts) between two feeler electrodes [24]; see Fig. 7-8.

$$\bar{\kappa} = \frac{i\,l}{\Delta\varphi\,q} \qquad (7\text{-}16)$$

where l = distance between the feeler electrodes.

In many cases the ion exchanger cannot be prepared in the form of rods, ribbons, or membranes. Here, the resistance of an ion-exchange bed must be measured. The measurement itself presents no serious difficulties [12,16,35,50]; see Sec. 9-12, Fig. 9-33. However, the calculation of the specific conductivity of the ion-exchange material from the conductivity of the bed is a problem which has not yet been satisfactorily solved.* An accurate value of the specific conductivity is obtained only at the equiconductance point where the specific conductivities of the ion exchanger and the interstitial solution are equal. Nevertheless, the method yields valuable qualitative information and can be used to obtain relative values. The conductivity of ion-exchange beds will be discussed in greater detail in Sec. 9-11.

SUMMARY

Ion exchangers contain mobile ions in high concentrations. Hence they are good ionic conductors. The electric current is carried predominantly by the counter ions, which are in great excess over the co-ions. Counter-ion transference thus exceeds co-ion transference by far, particularly when Donnan exclusion of the co-ion is strong. The specific electric conductivity is chiefly determined by the concentration and the mobility of the counter ions.

The ions, when migrating under the influence of an electric field, impart momentum to the solvent. In the pores of an ion exchanger, the counter ions outnumber the co-ions. Hence, momentum transfer by the counter ions predominates, and the solvent is carried along in the direction of counter-ion transfer. This electroosmotic convection, in turn, contributes to the conductivity of the ion exchanger. The conductivity contribution from convection is called convection conductivity.

Electrochemical mobilities and diffusion coefficients are interrelated. Conductivities can be calculated from counter-ion diffusion coefficients, and vice versa. A correction for convection conductivity should be made.

REFERENCES

1. Beattie, I. R., *Trans. Faraday Soc.*, **51,** 712 (1955).
2. Beattie, I. R., and A. Dyer, *Trans. Faraday Soc.*, **53,** 61 (1957).

---

* A formula derived by son Frey [9] has been used for this purpose [16]. However, son Frey's derivation is based on a specific model of the two-phase system (regular interpenetrating network of uniform rods of the components). In ion-exchange beds this model is very unrealistic.

*3. Bjerrum, N., and E. Manegold, *Kolloid Z.*, **43**, 5 (1928).

4. Carr, C. W., and K. Sollner, *J. Gen. Physiol.*, **28**, 119 (1944).

5. Carr, C. W., H. P. Gregor, and K. Sollner, *J. Gen. Physiol.*, **28**, 179 (1945).

6. Clarke, J. T., J. A. Marinsky, W. Juda, N. W. Rosenberg, and S. Alexander, *J. Phys. Chem.*, **56**, 100 (1952).

7. Dedek, J., J. Henry, S. Lange, and G. Rens, *Sucre Belge*, **70**, 145 (1950); *Chem. Abstr.*, **45**, 3177 (1951).

8. Despić, A., and G. J. Hills, *Trans. Faraday Soc.*, **51**, 1260 (1955).

9. Frey, G. S. son, *Z. Elektrochem.*, **38**, 260 (1932).

10. Gregor, H. P., and K. Sollner, *J. Phys. Chem.*, **50**, 53 (1946).

11. Groot, S. R. de, "Thermodynamics of Irreversible Processes," p. 94, North Holland Publ. Co., Amsterdam, 1951.

12. Heymann, E., and I. J. O'Donnell, *J. Colloid Sci.*, **4**, 405 (1949).

13. Hills, G. J., J. A. Kitchener, and P. J. Ovenden, *Trans. Faraday Soc.*, **51**, 719 (1955).

14. Hills, G. J., A. O. Jakubovic, and J. A. Kitchener, *J. Polymer Sci.*, **19**, 382 (1956).

15. Jakubovic, A. O., G. J. Hills, and J. A. Kitchener, *Trans. Faraday Soc.*, **55**, 1570 (1959).

16. Jenckel, E., and H. v. Lillin, *Kolloid Z.*, **146**, 159 (1956).

17. Juda, W., and W. A. McRae, *J. Am. Chem. Soc.*, **72**, 1044 (1950).

18. Juda, W., N. W. Rosenberg, J. A. Marinsky, and A. A. Kasper, *J. Am. Chem. Soc.*, **74**, 3736 (1952).

18a. Kawasaki, K., *J. Colloid Sci.*, **16**, 405 (1961).

19. Kosaka, Y., and A. Sato, *J. Chem. Soc. Japan, Ind. Chem. Sect.*, **55**, 628 (1952); *Chem. Abstr.*, **48**, 6623 (1954).

20. Kosaka, Y., A. Sato, and S. Tajima, *J. Chem. Soc. Japan, Ind. Chem. Sect.*, **56**, 279 (1953); *Chem. Abstr.*, **48**, 9759 (1954).

21. Kressman, T. R. E., *Nature*, **165**, 568 (1950).

22. Lorenz, P. B., *J. Phys. Chem.*, **56**, 775 (1952).

23. Lorimer, J. W., E. I. Boterenbrood, and J. J. Hermans, *Discussions Faraday Soc.*, **21**, 141 (1956).

24. Lorimer, J. W., *Discussions Faraday Soc.*, **21**, 198 (1956).

25. Manecke, G., and K. F. Bonhoeffer, *Z. Elektrochem.*, **55**, 475 (1951).

26. Manecke, G., *Z. Elektrochem.*, **55**, 672 (1951); *Z. physik. Chem.*, **201**, 193 (1952).

27. Manecke, G., and E. Otto-Laupemühlen, *Z. physik. Chem. (Frankfurt)*, **2**, 336 (1954).

28. Manecke, G., *Naturwissenschaften*, **39**, 62 (1952).

29. Miyamoto, S., and T. Sasaki, *J. Chem. Soc. Japan, Pure Chem. Sect.*, **73**, 926 (1952); *Chem. Abstr.*, **47**, 6277 (1953).

30. Nagamatsu, M., T. Seiyama, and W. Sakai, *J. Electrochem. Soc. Japan*, **22**, 362 (1954); *Chem. Abstr.*, **49**, 9415 (1955).

31. Nagasawa, M., S. Ozawa, and I. Kagawa, *J. Chem. Soc. Japan, Ind. Chem. Sect.*, **57**, 372 (1954); *Chem. Abstr.*, **49**, 4205 (1955).

32. Overbeek, J. T. G., *J. Colloid Sci.*, **8**, 420 (1953).

33. Rosenberg, N. W., J. H. B. George, and W. D. Potter, *J. Electrochem. Soc.*, **104**, 111 (1957).

34. Sasaki, T., and S. Miyamoto, Japanese Patent 1575, 1954.

35. Sauer, M. C., Jr., P. F. Southwick, K. S. Spiegler, and M. R. J. Wyllie, *Ind. Eng. Chem.*, **47**, 2187 (1955).

36. Scatchard, G., *J. Am. Chem. Soc.*, **75**, 2883 (1953).

*37. Scatchard, G., *Discussions Faraday Soc.*, **21**, 27 (1956).

---

* Review articles are marked with asterisks.

38. Schlögl, R., Z. physik. Chem. (Frankfurt), **3**, 73 (1955).
39. Schlögl, R., and U. Schödel, Z. physik. Chem. (Frankfurt), **5**, 372 (1955).
40. Schmid, G., Z. Elektrochem., **54**, 424 (1950).
41. Schmid, G., and H. Schwarz, Z. Elektrochem., **55**, 295 (1951).
42. Schmid, G., Z. Elektrochem., **56**, 181 (1952).
43. Shedlovsky, T., J. Am. Chem. Soc., **52**, 1806 (1930).
*44. Smoluchowski, M. v., in "Handbuch der Elektrizität und des Magnetismus," L. Graetz (ed.), vol. 2, 1921.
45. Sollner, K., and H. P. Gregor, J. Colloid Sci., **6**, 557 (1951); **7**, 37 (1952).
*46. Sollner, K., J. Electrochem. Soc., **97**, 139C (1950); Ann. N.Y. Acad. Sci., **57**, 177 (1953).
47. Spiegler, K. S., and C. D. Coryell, J. Phys. Chem., **56**, 106 (1952).
48. Spiegler, K. S., and C. D. Coryell, J. Phys. Chem., **57**, 687 (1953).
*49. Spiegler, K. S., J. Electrochem. Soc., **100**, 303C (1953).
*50. Spiegler, K. S., in "Ion Exchange Technology," F. C. Nachod and J. Schubert (eds.), p. 118, Academic Press, Inc., New York, 1956.
51. Spiegler, K. S., Trans. Faraday Soc., **54**, 1409 (1958).
52. Staverman, A. J., Trans. Faraday Soc., **48**, 176 (1952).
53. Tajima, S., Y. Kosaka, K. Kosaka, and A. Sato, J. Electrochem. Soc. Japan, **22**, 67 (1954); Chem. Abstr., **48**, 13344 (1954).
54. Winger, A. G., G. W. Bodamer, and R. Kunin, J. Electrochem. Soc., **100**, 178 (1953).

* Review articles are marked with asterisks.

8

Ion-exchanger Membranes

Ion-exchanger membranes are of recent origin. The preparation of such products was first announced about ten years ago. Nevertheless, the theories of membranes are further advanced than those of many other ion-exchange systems and can account reasonably well for even the most complex phenomena. This fact and the unusually large number of experimental and theoretical publications on membranes reflect the exceptional attention which this field has received by physical, physiological, and industrial chemists. It is true, however, that the origins of the theories are older than the ion-exchanger membranes themselves. As early as 1935—in the same year in which ion-exchange resins were first prepared—membrane potentials observed with physiological and collodion membranes were explained in terms of a theory in which the ion-exchange properties of these materials are an essential factor. Later, the fundamentals of this theory were extensively confirmed by measurements with resinous ion-exchanger membranes. The quantitative treatment given in this chapter is based largely on this early pioneer work.

The great interest in ion-exchanger membranes is chiefly due to their exceptional electrochemical properties. Many attempts have been made to use ion-exchanger membranes as simple models for physiological membranes. The results have thus far not been too encouraging, but there is no doubt that the elucidation of the behavior of ion-exchanger membranes with a known and relatively simple structure will contribute greatly to the understanding of the processes occurring in the much more complex nerve and cell membranes. In chemical technology, the preparation of chemically and mechanically resistant ion-exchanger membranes has opened the way to new processes which may have a great future. Here, however, in contrast to most other uses of ion exchangers, the theory is still well ahead of practical application.

It is beyond the scope of this book to give a detailed account of all the various theories that have been developed to describe the behavior of membrane systems. The treatment here is restricted essentially to one rather simple approach, with the chief objective of providing a sound understanding of the various physical factors involved.

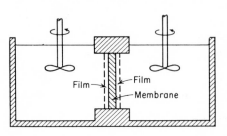

FIG. 8-1. Membrane cell with a membrane between two well-stirred solutions. The stirring does not affect adherent Nernst "films" at the membrane surfaces.

All phenomena described in this chapter occur in systems in which a membrane separates two solutions (Fig. 8-1). If the solution volumes are sufficiently large, the system attains a quasi-stationary state, i.e., the processes in the membrane become time-independent. Most of the discussion will be restricted to this state. Time-dependent phenomena—such as the behavior of membrane systems exposed to alternating current and other periodic membrane processes*—require a more sophisticated approach and are not included in the presentation.

8-1. CHARACTERISTIC PROPERTIES OF ION-EXCHANGER MEMBRANES

A "membrane," according to the usual definition, is a solid or liquid film or layer with a thickness which is small compared to its surface. In the case of ion-exchanger membranes, a broader definition has come into use. It includes any ion-exchange material, irrespective of its geometrical form, which can be used as a separation wall between two solutions. Many common ion-exchanger membranes are planar disks about 1 mm in thickness. However, cylindrical plugs [46,79] or single beads glazed into frames [6] are also called membranes. In some experiments, ribbons of ion-exchange material in contact with the solutions only at their ends have been used [91,94]. Even these are called membranes though, here, the "thickness" of the separation wall (length of the ribbon) is large compared to its "surface" (cross section of the ribbon). The broader definition is justified by its usefulness. The membrane potentials—and these belong to the most important membrane phenomena—are little affected by the geometrical shape of the membrane. Within wide limits they are the same for disks, plugs, and ribbons if these are prepared from identical ion-exchange material.

Ion-exchanger membranes combine the ability to act as a separation wall between two solutions with the chemical and electrochemical properties

---

* See T. Teorell [129].

of ion exchangers.   The most important of these are the pronounced differences in permeability for counter ions, co-ions, and neutral molecules, and their high electric conductivity.

When in contact with electrolyte solutions of low or moderate concentrations, the membrane contains a large number of counter ions but relatively few co-ions (Donnan exclusion; see Sec. 5-3c).   Counter ions are admitted to the membrane and thus have little difficulty in passing through from one solution to the other.   Co-ions, on the other hand, are rather efficiently excluded from the membrane and thus find it difficult to pass through.   *The membrane is permselective for counter ions.*   Ion-exchanger membranes closely approach the behavior of the hypothetical, ideally semipermeable membrane (permeable for one species, but not for the other) which has been used since Nernst for many theoretical derivations and fictitious thermodynamic cycles.   The permselectivity is reflected not only in differences in permeability, but also in the electric potential difference which arises between the two solutions (membrane potential).   However, when the concentrations of the solutions are increased, the Donnan exclusion becomes less effective and thus the permselectivity is reduced.

Two different types of ion-exchanger membranes are in use.   They are often called "homogeneous" and "heterogeneous" membranes (see also Sec. 3-6).   "Homogeneous" membranes are coherent ion-exchanger gels in the shape of disks, ribbons, etc.   Their structure is that of the usual ion-exchange resins.   Of course, they are homogeneous only in dimensions which are large as compared to the mesh width of the matrix.   "Heterogeneous" membranes consist of colloidal ion-exchanger particles embedded in an inert binder (polystyrene, polyethylene, wax, etc.; see Fig. 8-2).   Their mechanical stability is superior, but their electrochemical properties such as conductivity and barrier action are not as good as those of the homogeneous membranes [24].   With the recent syntheses of homogeneous or almost homogeneous membranes with greatly improved mechanical characteristics, however, the heterogeneous membranes have lost much of their appeal.   For scientific investigations, homogeneous membranes have been preferred even in the past because of their more uniform structure.

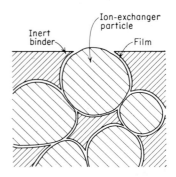

Fig. 8-2. Structure of a "heterogeneous" membrane (*schematic*).   Colloidal ion-exchanger particles (1 to 10 μ in diameter) are embedded in an inert binder.   Liquid films may form between the particles and the binder.

8-2. MODELS AND THEORETICAL APPROACHES

The current theories of membrane systems can be classified into three more or less distinct groups [102]. The groups differ from one another in the models on which they are based.

The theories of the first group consider the membrane as a surface of discontinuity separating the two adjacent phases and setting up different resistances to the passage of the various molecular and ionic species. The driving forces for particle transfer across the membrane are the *differences* in the general chemical potentials between the two adjacent phases [66,80, 122,131].

The theories of the second group consider the membrane as a quasi-homogeneous intermediate phase of finite thickness. Here, the driving forces are the local *gradients* of the general chemical potentials in the layer. Convection may also contribute to particle transfer within the membrane [16,18,34,41,42,44,51–57,69,70,90,99–101,104,121,125].

The theories of the third group consider the membrane as a series of potential-energy barriers. Thus the membrane is an inhomogeneous intermediate layer. An (irregular) spatial lattice is formed because the probability of finding a particle is higher in the positions between the activation thresholds. The driving forces arise from the differences between the transition probabilities in opposite directions normal to the membrane [11,49,140]. When the number of activation thresholds becomes very large and the distance between the lattice points sufficiently small—a situation usually found in ion exchangers—these theories give the same result as those of the second group.

The theories of the first group have the advantage of being relatively simple. For ion-exchanger membranes, however, they are often inadequate. The treatment given in this chapter deals chiefly with processes occurring *within* the membrane. For such a purpose the theories of the second group are the proper choice.

The most important theories of the second group are based either on quasi-thermodynamics or on thermodynamics of irreversible processes. The fundamental difference between these two approaches will be discussed later (Sec. 8-4). Here, it may suffice to say that quasi-thermodynamics can be used only to calculate membrane potentials and electric transference, whereas the thermodynamics of irreversible processes also gives the fluxes of the various species. Moreover, quasi-thermodynamics is restricted to isothermal systems, whereas thermodynamics of irreversible processes is not.

The thermodynamics of irreversible processes [22] has often been used to describe membrane phenomena, along the lines of either first- or second-group theories [42,44,51,52,54,66,80,121,122,131]. A system of equations for the fluxes of the various species, of the electric current, and of heat can be set up. Some of the coefficients in this set of equations can be eliminated by use of the Onsager correlations. Thus it should be possible to predict all membrane phenomena from only a limited number of measurements. Such a treatment is still quite general, and only the physical interpretation of the coefficients requires the use of a model. Some of the most interesting current work on membrane systems follows these lines [52,54,121]. These theories, however, are still in an early stage of their development. A general, unified treatment including systems with concentration gradients in the membrane (allowing for the concentration dependence of the various coefficients) has not yet been achieved.*

In this chapter, a similar but less elaborate approach is chosen. The use of simpler flux equations permits a broader range of membrane phenomena to be covered and serves better to establish the relations with other phenomena discussed in other chapters. From the more rigorous thermodynamics of irreversible processes this treatment differs in that cross coefficients (which describe mutual "coupling" of individual fluxes other than by electric forces and convection) are omitted, that only isothermic systems are considered, and that a specific model is used. From the still simpler Nernst-Planck flux equations the treatment differs in that activity coefficients and convection are included. The model used is the same as in the two previous chapters: the ion exchanger is considered as a quasi-homogeneous phase in which one ionic species (the fixed ionic groups) is immobile. This model was first successfully applied to membranes by Teorell [125] and K. H. Meyer [70]. Its implications have been critically discussed in previous chapters (see pages 301 and 332). In "homogeneous" resinous membranes the basic assumptions can be considered as rather good approximations. For "heterogeneous" membranes this theory holds only as far as the equations for the behavior of porous plugs (see Sec. 9-11) approach those of homogeneous membranes.

The use even of the simpler Nernst-Planck flux equations (6-35) in ion-exchange kinetics was seen to encounter mathematical difficulties (see Sec. 6-3c). Fortunately, the treatment of steady-state membrane phenomena is easier since only time-independent solutions are required. Therefore it is often possible to use the more refined flux equations and thus to account for the most serious deviations from ideal behavior.

The flux equations on which the treatment in this chapter is based contain as "driving forces" the gradient of the chemical potential of the species, the gradient of the electric potential,† and the convection of the pore liquid. Limiting cases of these equations have been derived and used in the

---

* See also the recent review by Bergsma [4].

† As a rule, an electric potential gradient exists even if no external field is applied; see p. 267.

two previous chapters.   The equations and restrictions can be summarized as follows:

The over-all flux J_i of an arbitrary species i is composed of three additive terms: the diffusion flux $(J_i)_{\text{diff}}$ caused by the chemical potential gradient of the species, the electric transference $(J_i)_{\text{el}}$ caused by the electric potential gradient, and the transfer $(J_i)_{\text{con}}$ caused by convection.   The diffusion flux is

$$(J_i)_{\text{diff}} = -D_i C_i \text{ grad } \mu_i = -D_i(\text{grad } C_i + C_i \text{ grad ln } f_i) \qquad (8\text{-}1)$$

where μ_i = chemical potential of species i; f_i = molar activity coefficient of species i.

This relation differs from the simpler Eq. (6-34) in that the effect of the activity coefficient is explicitly taken into account.   For convenience, the activity is defined according to Eq. (5-54), thus including the effect of pressure.   The electric transference is

$$(J_i)_{\text{el}} = -u_i z_i C_i \text{ grad } \varphi = -D_i z_i C_i \frac{\mathfrak{F}}{RT} \text{ grad } \varphi \qquad (6\text{-}32)$$

and the transfer by convection is

$$(J_i)_{\text{con}} = C_i \mathfrak{v} \qquad (7\text{-}2)$$

where $\mathfrak{v}$ = rate of motion of the center of gravity.

Thus the over-all flux is given by

$$J_i = (J_i)_{\text{diff}} + (J_i)_{\text{el}} + (J_i)_{\text{con}}$$
$$= -D_i \left(\text{grad } C_i + z_i C_i \frac{\mathfrak{F}}{RT} \text{ grad } \varphi + C_i \text{ grad ln } f_i \right) + C_i \mathfrak{v} \qquad (8\text{-}2)$$

Equation (8-2) is more rigorous than the Nernst-Planck equation (6-35) which was used for ion-exchange kinetics, since it includes activity coefficients and convection.   A limiting case of this equation is Eq. (7-3) which was used for systems without concentration gradients where, of course, the first and third term disappear.

The physical interpretation and the idealizations involved have been discussed in the derivation of the simpler equations (6-35) and (7-3) (see pages 268 and 332).   Briefly, the most serious simplifications are these. Equation (6-32) in the form given here implies the validity of the Nernst-Einstein relation (6-33) between the individual diffusion coefficient and the electrochemical mobility.   This is equivalent to neglecting "coupling" of individual fluxes other than by electric forces and convection. In Eq. (7-2) any differences in interaction of the various species with structural parts of the ion exchanger have been disregarded.

The flux equation (8-2) applies to all mobile species in the system.   The set of flux equations—one equation for every species—is subject to the restriction of electroneutrality[*]

$$\sum_i z_i \bar{C}_i + \omega X = 0 \tag{7-5}$$

Furthermore, the fluxes are related to the current density by

$$I = \mathfrak{F} \sum_i z_i J_i \tag{7-4}$$

Both these equations have been derived and used in the previous chapters.

The discussion in this chapter is restricted to the most important (and most simple) limiting case: the steady or quasi-stationary state. This state is attained after a certain time lag (see page 351), provided that the boundary conditions remain constant. In practice, the system attains the quasi-stationary state if the volumes of the solutions are so large that their concentrations do not appreciably change in the time it takes for an ion to cross the membrane. In the steady or quasi-stationary state, the concentrations are time-independent. Hence, according to Eq. (6-4),

$$\operatorname{div} J_i = 0 \tag{8-3}$$

It is also assumed that, at the interfaces, the adjacent layers of membrane and solution are in equilibrium (no interfacial resistance to diffusion), that the species cross the membrane as such (no complexing with other mobile species in the membrane), and that their motion is not geometrically coupled (as in "one-way" flow in unbranched pores which are too narrow for ions to pass one another). Thus the treatment does not cover the hypothetical biological "carrier" mechanisms in which a mobile complexing agent in the membrane acts as sort of a "streetcar," nor does it cover "single-file" diffusion and other geometrical anomalies.

The set of equations (8-2), (7-5), (7-4), and (8-3) constitutes the mathematical basis for the quantitative treatment. In the following sections it will be applied to various membrane systems. General solutions can be obtained if a few further simplifications are made, but they are complex and difficult to interpret and to evaluate (see Secs. 8-5 and 8-8c). However, simpler and more rigorous solutions can be given for the most important particular systems. These will be discussed in more detail.

8-3. DIFFUSION ACROSS MEMBRANES

A characteristic feature of ion-exchanger membranes is the large difference in permeability for counter ions and co-ions (*permselectivity*). Furthermore, there is a large difference in the resistance of the membrane to diffusion of electrolytes and nonelectrolytes.

---

[*] See footnote to p. 267.

The diffusion of an ionic species across the membrane is not an independent phenomenon. Any ionic flux involves a transfer of electric charge. In the absence of an electric current this charge transfer must be balanced by one or more other ionic fluxes. The compensation of the fluxes is brought about by the electric potential gradient (diffusion potential) built up by the diffusion process. In contrast, diffusion of a nonelectrolyte involves no charge transfer and thus is not coupled with other fluxes. These characteristics of the fluxes, the action of the diffusion potential in the membrane, and the permselectivity for counter ions are the key to the understanding of diffusion phenomena in membrane systems.

In certain cases, the behavior of the system is not exclusively determined by the processes occurring within the membrane. In the bulk solutions, the concentration levels are kept uniform by stirring. The agitation of the solutions, however, does not affect the liquid Nernst diffusion layers, the "films," which adhere to the membrane surfaces (see Sec. 6-2). The overall diffusion rate from bulk solution on one side to bulk solution on the other side may be controlled by diffusion in either the membrane (*membrane diffusion control*) or the films (*film diffusion control*). Affected are not only the diffusion rate, but also the electric potential difference between the solutions. Even extremely violent agitation may be insufficient to overcome film diffusion control. The theoretical treatment of such cases must include the effect of the films.

The migration of solvent across the membrane (*osmosis*) is a very interesting phenomenon. Its anomalous behavior and its effect on ionic diffusion will be discussed separately (Sec. 8-6). The effect on diffusion in ordinary ion-exchanger membranes is usually rather small and will be disregarded in the present section.

In the following, it will be assumed that the membrane surfaces are planar and parallel to one another and that the membrane cross section is uniform. This is true for the usual disks, ribbons, and cylindrical (homogeneous) plugs, but not for conical plugs and materials of irregular shape. All fluxes then are normal to the membrane surfaces (one-dimensional diffusion) and constant in the steady state. Thus absolute values can be used instead of vectors, and differential quotients d/dx (x = space variable normal to the membrane surfaces) instead of gradients

a. Self-diffusion and Isotopic Diffusion

First, let us examine self-diffusion of an arbitrary species (counter ion, co-ion, or nonelectrolyte) across the membrane in a system which is in equilibrium. Self-diffusion in such a system is defined as the diffusion of the molecules of the species from the bulk solution on one membrane side into the bulk solution on the other side. (Of course, self-diffusion always occurs simultaneously in both directions.)

Consider the flux of the molecules (designated by A) from the left to the right membrane side. Since the system is in equilibrium, there are no gradients of activity coefficients, of the electric potential, and of pressure, and no convection occurs. Therefore the flux equation (8-2) for the molecules A reduces to

$$J_A = -D \frac{dC_A}{dx} \tag{8-4}$$

where D is the self-diffusion coefficient of the species in question. This relation holds in both the membrane and the films. Also, in the steady

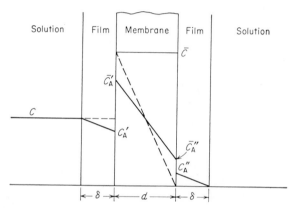

FIG. 8-3. Counter-ion concentration profile in steady-state isotopic diffusion across an ion-exchanger membrane (*schematic*). *Solid line:* partial film diffusion control. *Broken line:* ideal membrane diffusion control.

state [Eq. (8-3)], the fluxes in the membrane and in the films are equal. Integration of Eq. (8-4) and equating the fluxes in membrane and films gives (see also Fig. 8-3).

$$J_A = D \frac{C - C_A'}{\delta} = \bar{D} \frac{\bar{C}_A' - \bar{C}_A''}{d} = D \frac{C_A''}{\delta} \tag{8-5}$$

where indices ' and " refer to the left and right interface membrane/film, respectively; quantities with bars refer to the membrane phase; δ = film thickness;* d = membrane thickness; C = concentration of species in question.

The equilibrium conditions at the phase boundaries (no interfacial resistance to diffusion, see Sec. 6-2) is

$$\frac{C_A'}{C} = \frac{\bar{C}_A'}{\bar{C}} \qquad\qquad \frac{C_A''}{C} = \frac{\bar{C}_A''}{\bar{C}} \tag{8-6}$$

---

* For calculation of the film thickness, see p. 400 and footnote to p. 253. A more elaborate procedure has been described by Mackay [53].

From Eqs. (8-5) and (8-6) one obtains the self-diffusion flux [25]

$$J_A = -\frac{\bar{D}\bar{C}}{d(1 + 2\bar{D}\bar{C}\delta/DCd)} \tag{8-7}$$

The relation (8-7) applies to all mobile species, no matter whether they are counter ions, co-ions, or nonelectrolytes, and is rigorous as far as the film concept holds.

In practice, self-diffusion is measured by tagging the species in question with an isotopic tracer which is added to the solution on one membrane side. It is readily seen that Eq. (8-7) also holds for tracer diffusion in equilibrium systems when $\bar{C}$ in the numerator is taken as the tracer concentration which the membrane would have if it were in equilibrium with the tagged solution.

The rate-determining step. The rate of self-diffusion can be controlled by diffusion either across the membrane or across the films. A criterion indicating the nature of the rate-determining step is readily derived [25]. It follows from Eq. (8-7) that

$$\begin{aligned}
\frac{DCd}{\bar{D}\bar{C}\delta} \gg 2 \qquad & J_A = \frac{\bar{D}\bar{C}}{d} \\
\frac{DCd}{\bar{D}\bar{C}\delta} \ll 2 \qquad & J_A = \frac{DC}{2\delta}
\end{aligned} \tag{8-8}$$

In the first case, the rate is seen to be completely membrane-diffusion controlled, and in the second case completely film-diffusion controlled. The nature of the rate-determining step thus depends on the magnitude of the dimensionless modulus $DCd/\bar{D}\bar{C}\delta$. Film diffusion control is favored by a high diffusion coefficient in the membrane, small membrane thickness, inefficient agitation (resulting in thick films), and a low value of the ratio $C/\bar{C}$ of the concentrations of the species in solution and membrane. The situation is quite similar to that in kinetics of ion exchange and sorption with beads [see Eqs. (6-1), (6-66), and (6-73)].

In a typical ion-exchanger membrane system ($D/\bar{D} \approx 5$; $d \approx 0.1$ cm; $\delta \approx 0.003$ cm) the quotient $Dd/\bar{D}\delta$ is of the order of 100 to 200. This quotient is approximately the same for all species. The magnitude of the ratio $C/\bar{C}$, however, depends greatly on the nature of the diffusing species. For *co-ions*, the concentration in the ion exchanger is smaller than in the solutions. The ratio $C/\bar{C}$ is always larger than unity and becomes very large with dilution of the solutions (Donnan equilibrium; see Sec. 5-3c). Hence, if the solutions are stirred at all, film diffusion can become rate-controlling only under extreme conditions. For *nonelectrolytes*, the ratio $C/\bar{C}$ is usually not too far from unity and depends little on concentration (see Sec. 5-3b). Here, too, membrane diffusion control prevails under the usual conditions. For *counter ions*, however, the ratio $C/\bar{C}$ is smaller than unity and becomes extremely small when the solutions are strongly diluted (see Sec. 5-3c). Here, film diffusion control is quite common. As in counter-ion exchange with granules or beads (Sec. 6-2) and for the same physical reasons, film diffusion control is favored by high concentration of the fixed ionic groups and low concentration of the solutions (see also Fig. 8-4). If the concentration X of the fixed ionic groups in the membrane system mentioned above is 5 N, the limit between film and membrane diffusion control is at solution concentrations of the order of 10^{-2} N (in this range, $\bar{C} \approx X$).

The criterion (8-8) shows that self-diffusion of counter ions is most likely to be film-diffusion controlled. The physical explanation is straightforward. By definition, film diffusion control implies that the resistance to permeation is much larger in the films than in the membrane. This situation is most likely to occur in the case of species for which the membrane is highly permeable.

Self-diffusion flux, permeability, and permselectivity.

The permeabilities of an ion-exchanger membrane for counter ions, co-ions, and nonelectrolytes are quite different. The differences are most strongly pronounced when the concentration of fixed ionic groups is high and the solutions are dilute.

According to Eq. (8-8), the self-diffusion flux across the membrane—membrane diffusion being rate-controlling—is proportional to the self-diffusion coefficient and the concentration of the species in the membrane and inversely proportional to the membrane thickness. In a given membrane, the self-diffusion coefficients of different species are usually of the same order of magnitude (except in cases of strong interactions or steric hindrance); however, the concentrations of counter ions, co-ions, and nonelectrolytes in the membrane may differ by several orders of magnitude.

The concentration of the *counter ion* in the membrane is larger than in the solutions. Because of the electroneutrality requirement it can never become smaller than that of the fixed ionic groups. Hence the self-diffusion flux of the counter ion is large and becomes practically independent of the concentration of the solutions when these are sufficiently dilute.* In this concentration range the flux across a typical ion-exchanger membrane ($d \approx 0.1$ cm; $X \approx 5$ N $= 5 \cdot 10^{-3}$ eq/cm^3; $\bar{D} \approx 2 \cdot 10^{-6}$ cm^2/sec) is of the order of 10^{-7} equivalents per second and square-centimeter membrane cross section.

The concentration of the *co-ion* in the membrane is smaller than in the

---

* Note that film diffusion becomes rate-controlling at very low concentrations of the solutions. In the range of film diffusion control the flux is proportional to the concentration of the solutions (see Fig. 8-4).

solutions. Because of the Donnan exclusion it becomes very small when the solutions are dilute. Hence the self-diffusion flux of the co-ion is small and decreases strongly with dilution of the solutions (Fig. 8-4). In the typical membrane with the properties given above, the co-ion concentration in the membrane in equilibrium with 0.1 N solutions is of the order of 10^{-3} to 10^{-2} N. Here, the co-ion flux thus is roughly three orders of magnitude

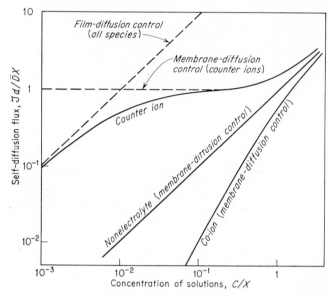

FIG. 8-4. Self-diffusion of counter ions, co-ions, and nonelectrolytes across a membrane. The curves are calculated for $Dd/\bar{D}\delta = 200$, univalent ions, equal mobilities of all species, and activity coefficients equal to unity. The co-ion and nonelectrolyte fluxes are completely membrane-diffusion controlled whereas the counter-ion flux changes from film diffusion to membrane diffusion control.

smaller than that of the counter ion. The limiting laws for very dilute solutions will be given later [Sec. 8-3b, Eq. (8-30)].

The concentration of a *nonelectrolyte* is generally of the same order of magnitude in the ion exchanger and in the solutions, except if specific interactions cause strong sorption or if sieve action prevents sorption. Hence the self-diffusion flux of the nonelectrolyte is usually approximately proportional to the concentration of the solutions (Fig. 8-4). In the membrane with the properties given above, and for 0.1 M nonelectrolyte concentration in the solutions, the self-diffusion flux of the nonelectrolyte is of the order of 10^{-9} to 10^{-8} moles per second and square-centimeter membrane cross section.

The situation is somewhat more complex in weak-acid and weak-base ion-exchanger membranes [30,33,87]. Here, the ionic concentrations as well as swelling and thus the diffusion coefficients depend strongly on the pH within the ion exchanger. The pH inside is a function of the equivalent ionic fraction $x_H \equiv C_H/C$ of the H^+ ion in solution. In weak-acid ion exchangers there is association of H^+ with fixed ionic groups if x_H in solution is high. This reduces the counter-ion concentration in the membrane, the efficiency of Donnan exclusion of the co-ion, and swelling and diffusion coefficients. Hence the self-diffusion fluxes of counter ions and nonelectrolytes decrease with increasing x_H, whereas in the case of the co-ion the effects of lower mobility and higher concentration in the membrane counteract one another. In weak-base membranes there is an analogous dependence on x_{OH} in the solutions.

The self-diffusion flux of a species across a layer can be used as a quantitative measure of the *permeability** for this species. The large differences in the so defined permeabilities for counter ions, co-ions, and nonelectrolytes are seen in Fig. 8-4 where the self-diffusion fluxes are shown as a function of the solution concentration.

Frequently, diffusion across a membrane is described in terms of *permeability coefficients*. The permeability coefficient P_i of a species i is a phenomenological quantity defined by the relation

$$J_i = P_i \frac{\Delta C_i}{d} \tag{8-9}$$

where ΔC_i is the concentration difference between the solutions on either membrane side. A comparison with Eqs. (8-5) to (8-8) shows that the permeability coefficient depends on the concentrations and the distribution ratio $\bar{C}_i/C_i$. Therefore its usefulness is limited.

The characteristic difference in membrane permeability for counter ions and co-ions is called *permselectivity*. Occasionally, the permselectivity of a membrane has been quantitatively defined as [132]

$$\Pi_A \equiv \frac{z_A(\bar{t}_A - t_A)}{1 - z_A t_A} \tag{8-10}$$

where Π_A = permselectivity, z_A = valence, and t_A = transference number of the counter ion.

The permselectivity is not a membrane constant, but depends on the nature of counter ion and co-ion and on the concentration of the solutions. Ideal permselectivity means that the permeability for the co-ion is negligible as compared to that for the counter ion. In this case, Π_A is unity.

Time lag. The "time lag" is the time which elapses until the diffusion of a species across a layer has attained the steady (or quasi-stationary) state. The flux has approached its eventual steady-state value to within 3 per cent in the time

$$t_a = 0.42 \frac{d^2}{\bar{D}} \tag{8-11}$$

[The numerical factor in Eq. (8-11) depends on the specified closeness of approach to the steady state.] A more unambiguously defined quantity is

---

* Note that the permeability for the solvent is usually defined in a different way (for hydrodynamic and electroosmotic permeability, see Sec. 8-8b).

the "hold-up" time; in a diagram where the (cumulative) amount diffused is plotted versus time, as in Fig. 8-5, the hold-up time is the intersect

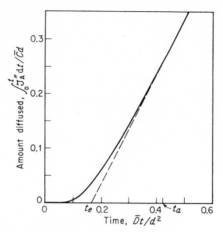

FIG. 8-5. Time lag in isotopic diffusion. The dimensionless diagram shows the amount diffused as a function of time [Eq. (8-17)]. The time lag t_a and the hold-up time t_e are indicated. *From J. Crank* [10].

of the prolongation of the steady-state straight line with the time axis. The hold-up time is [1]

$$t_e = \frac{d^2}{6\bar{D}} \tag{8-12}$$

Derivation. Time lag and hold-up time are calculated from the time-dependent solution of the flux equation with constant boundary conditions. Equation (6-2) in combination with the continuity condition (6-4) gives, for one-dimensional diffusion

$$\frac{\partial \bar{C}_A}{\partial t} = - \operatorname{div} J_A = \bar{D}_A \frac{\partial^2 \bar{C}_A}{\partial x^2} \tag{8-13}$$

With the initial condition

$$t = 0, \, 0 < x \leq d \qquad \bar{C}_A(x) = 0 \tag{8-14}$$

(membrane initially devoid of A) and the boundary conditions

$$\begin{array}{ll} x = 0 & \bar{C}_A(x,t) = \bar{C} \\ x = d & \bar{C}_A(x,t) = 0 \end{array} \tag{8-15}$$

the solution is

$$\bar{C}_A(x,t) = \bar{C}\left(1 - \frac{x}{d}\right) - \sum_{n=1}^{\infty} \frac{2\bar{C}}{n\pi} \exp\left\{-\bar{D}t\left(\frac{n\pi}{d}\right)^2\right\} \sin \frac{n\pi x}{d} \tag{8-16}$$

The flux J_A'' across the boundary at $x = d$ (i.e., at the far side of the membrane) is accordingly

$$J_A''(t) = -\bar{D}\left(\frac{\partial \bar{C}_A}{\partial x}\right)_{x=d} = \bar{D}\frac{\bar{C}}{d} - \bar{D}\frac{2\bar{C}}{d}\sum_{n=1}^{\infty} \exp\left\{-\bar{D}t\left(\frac{n\pi}{d}\right)^2\right\} \cos(n\pi) \tag{8-17}$$

The first term gives the flux in the steady state, and the second gives the deviation. Allowing a 3 per cent deviation and solving for t, one obtains Eq. (8-11). Integrating the second term within the limits $t = 0$ and $t = \infty$ and dividing by the first term, one obtains Eq. (8-12).

The time lag and the hold-up time are proportional to the square of the membrane thickness, inversely proportional to the self-diffusion coefficient in the membrane, and independent of cross section and concentrations. Hence the time lag is, as a rule, of the same order of magnitude for counter ions, co-ions, and nonelectrolytes. In a typical ion-exchanger membrane ($\bar{D} \approx 2 \cdot 10^{-6}$ cm^2/sec, $d \approx 0.1$ cm), the time lag is of the order of $\frac{1}{2}$ hr.

Equations (8-11) and (8-12) are derived with a constant diffusion coefficient and thus are rigorous only for self-diffusion and tracer diffusion. The relations, however, are very useful approximations for other cases, particularly since they can be applied to films as well as to membranes.* Before applying a theory which assumes a steady or quasi-stationary state, one should ascertain with Eq. (8-11) whether this assumption holds for the system under consideration.

b. Diffusion of an Electrolyte

Let us consider a system in which a membrane is between two solutions of the same electrolyte. The electrolyte diffuses from the more concentrated solution across the membrane into the more dilute solution. The steady-state flux of the electrolyte and the concentration profiles of the ions will be calculated. Complete membrane diffusion control is assumed since film diffusion can be rate-controlling only under extreme conditions.

There are only two mobile ionic species present, the cation and the anion. In such systems, the effect of gradients of activity coefficients can be taken into account and no assumptions regarding the constancy of diffusion coefficients and of the fixed-charge concentration are required. In this section, it is assumed that convection is insignificant (the effect of convection on electrolyte diffusion will be discussed in Sec. 8-6). Under these conditions, the system of equations given in Sec. 8-2 is

$$J_+ = -\bar{D}_+\left(\frac{d\bar{C}_+}{dx} + z_+\bar{C}_+\frac{\mathcal{F}}{RT}\frac{d\varphi}{dx} + \bar{C}_+\frac{d\ln\bar{f}_+}{dx}\right)$$

$$J_- = -\bar{D}_-\left(\frac{d\bar{C}_-}{dx} + z_-\bar{C}_-\frac{\mathcal{F}}{RT}\frac{d\varphi}{dx} + \bar{C}_-\frac{d\ln\bar{f}_-}{dx}\right)$$

(8-18)

$$z_+\bar{C}_+ + z_-\bar{C}_- + \omega X = 0 \qquad \text{electroneutrality} \qquad (8\text{-}19)$$

$$z_+J_+ + z_-J_- = 0 \qquad \text{no electric current} \qquad (8\text{-}20)$$

$$J_+, J_- = \text{const.} \qquad \text{quasi-stationary state} \qquad (8\text{-}21)$$

Subscripts $+$ and $-$ refer to cation and anion, respectively.

---

* For calculations with nonconstant diffusion coefficients, see Frisch [17].

Equation (8-20) is particularly important for understanding the behavior of the system. This relation states that the fluxes of the cation and the anion are necessarily stoichiometrically equivalent. Inequality of the fluxes would amount to a net transfer of electric charge and thus, in the absence of an electric current, disturb electroneutrality. Actually, the ion of higher mobility tends to move faster, but this produces an electric field (diffusion potential) which slows down the faster ion and speeds up the slower one, thus enforcing the equivalence of the fluxes (see also Sec. 6-3c).

Using the relation

$$\bar{f}_+^{z_+} \bar{f}_-^{-z_-} = \bar{f}_\pm^{z_+ - z_-} \tag{8-22}$$

between the single activity coefficients $\bar{f}_+$ and $\bar{f}_-$ and the mean activity coefficient $\bar{f}_\pm$ of the electrolyte and introducing relative concentrations $\bar{\chi}_+$ and $\bar{\chi}_-$ defined by

$$\bar{\chi}_+ \equiv \frac{z_+ \bar{C}_+}{X} \qquad \bar{\chi}_- \equiv -\frac{z_- \bar{C}_-}{X} \tag{8-23}$$

one obtains from Eqs. (8-18) to (8-21)

$$
\begin{aligned}
z_+ J_+ &= -\bar{D}_+ X \frac{a\bar{\chi}_+ - 1 + a\bar{\chi}_+(\bar{\chi}_+ + \omega)\mathrm{d}\ln \bar{f}_\pm/\mathrm{d}\bar{\chi}_+}{b\bar{\chi}_+ - 1} \frac{\mathrm{d}\bar{\chi}_+}{\mathrm{d}x} \\
&= F(\bar{\chi}_+) \frac{\mathrm{d}\bar{\chi}_+}{\mathrm{d}x}
\end{aligned}
\tag{8-24}
$$

where $a \equiv (z_+ - z_-)/\omega z_-$; $b \equiv (z_+ \bar{D}_+ - z_- \bar{D}_-)/\omega z_- \bar{D}_-$; the function $F(\bar{\chi}_+)$ is defined by Eq. (8-24).

By integration of Eq. (8-24) across the membrane the *electrolyte flux* is obtained

$$z_+ J_+ = -\frac{1}{d} \int_{'}^{''} F(\bar{\chi}_+) \, \mathrm{d}\bar{\chi}_+ \tag{8-25}*$$

The *concentration profile* $\bar{\chi}_+(x)$* cannot be expressed explicitly. It can be calculated, however, from

$$x(\bar{\chi}_+) = \frac{d \displaystyle\int_{\bar{\chi}_+(x=0)}^{\bar{\chi}_+(x)} F(\bar{\chi}_+) \, \mathrm{d}\bar{\chi}_+}{\displaystyle\int_{\bar{\chi}_+(x=0)}^{\bar{\chi}_+(x=d)} F(\bar{\chi}_+) \, \mathrm{d}\bar{\chi}_+} \tag{8-26}$$

By Eqs. (8-25) and (8-26), the flux and the concentration profile are given as functions of the boundary concentrations $\bar{\chi}_{+(x=c)}$ and $\bar{\chi}_{+(x=d)}$ in the

---

* It is sufficient to calculate the cation flux and concentration profile. The cation and anion fluxes are stoichiometrically equivalent [Eq. (8-20)]; the anion concentration profile readily obtained from that of the action by Eq. (8-19).

membrane. These, in turn, can be calculated from the concentrations of the solutions by use of the Donnan equilibrium (5-57). Here, the Donnan equilibrium can be written*

$$\bar{\chi}_+^{-z_-}(\bar{\chi}_+ + \omega)^{z_+} = \left(\frac{Cf_\pm}{X\bar{f}_\pm}\right)^{z_+ - z_-} \tag{8-27}$$

where $C = z_+C_+ = -z_-C_- =$ equivalent concentration of the solution.

The integrals in Eqs. (8-25) and (8-26) must be evaluated graphically, unless the dependence of the quantities X, $\bar{f}_\pm$, $\bar{D}_+$, and $\bar{D}_-$ on the concentration variable $\bar{\chi}_+$ can be expressed by simple analytical relations.† If these quantities are constant, Eq. (8-24) can be integrated explicitly. The integrated form, however, is of little practical use since the conditions are usually not met unless the concentrations of the solutions are much smaller than that of the fixed ionic groups, and in this case the treatment can be greatly simplified.

If the concentrations of the solutions are much smaller than that of the fixed ionic groups, the Donnan exclusion of the co-ion becomes very strong. In cation exchangers, $\bar{\chi}_+$ approaches unity, and in anion exchangers it approaches zero. Thus Eq. (8-24) reduces to

$$z_+J_{+(\lim\bar{\chi}_+\to1)} = -\bar{D}_- \frac{X\,d\bar{\chi}_+}{dx} \quad \text{for cation-exchanger membranes}$$

$$z_+J_{+(\lim\bar{\chi}_+\to0)} = -\bar{D}_+ \frac{X\,d\bar{\chi}_+}{dx} \quad \text{for anion-exchanger membranes}$$

$$\tag{8-28}$$

These relations involve the diffusion coefficient of the co-ion only, not that of the counter ion. *The rate of electrolyte diffusion is controlled by diffusion of the co-ion* [26,98]. This is another example of the general rule that the diffusion rate is controlled by the species which is in the *minority* (see interdiffusion of counter ions, Sec. 6-3c, and electrolyte sorption, Sec. 6-6a). An interesting consequence is that, say, HCl and NaCl diffuse across a cation-exchanger membrane at about equal rates, provided that the solutions are dilute and that the activity coefficients (and thus the boundary values of $\bar{\chi}_+$) and the swelling condition

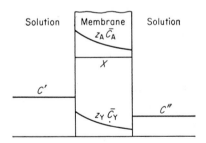

FIG. 8-6. Concentration profiles in steady-state electrolyte diffusion across a membrane (*schematic*).

(and thus $\bar{D}_{\text{Cl}}$) are not strongly affected by the counter ion.

---

* The activities and activity coefficients are defined according to Eq. (5-54), including the effect of pressure (see p. 344).

† J. S. Mackie [56] gives an explicit integration in which X, $\bar{D}_+$, and $\bar{D}_-$ are assumed to be constant and $\bar{f}_\pm$ is approximated by an empirical function.

The limiting laws (8-28) in combination with the Donnan equilibrium (8-27) express—within the limits of their applicability—the dependence of the electrolyte flux on the concentrations of the solutions, on the concentration of fixed ionic groups, and on the ionic valences. For the sake of simplicity this dependence will be discussed in a system in which the concentration X of fixed ionic groups is constant and the liquid phase on one membrane side is pure solvent ($C'' = 0$). In the limiting case $C' \ll X$, Eq. (8-27) reduces to

$$\chi_- = \left(\frac{Cf_\pm}{X\bar{f}_\pm}\right)^{(z_+-z_-)/z_+} \qquad \text{for cation exchangers}$$

$$\chi_+ = \left(\frac{Cf_\pm}{X\bar{f}_\pm}\right)^{(z_--z_+)/z_-} \qquad \text{for anion exchangers} \tag{8-29}$$

Introducing these relations into Eq. (8-28), one obtains after integration

$$z_+J_+ = \frac{\bar{D}_-}{d}\frac{C'f_\pm}{\bar{f}_\pm}\left(\frac{C'f_\pm'}{X\bar{f}_\pm}\right)^{-z_-/z_+} \qquad \text{for cation-exchanger membranes}$$

$$z_+J_+ = \frac{\bar{D}_+}{d}\frac{C'f_\pm}{\bar{f}_\pm}\left(\frac{C'f_\pm'}{X\bar{f}_\pm}\right)^{-z_+/z_-} \qquad \text{for anion-exchanger membranes} \tag{8-30}$$

These relations show that the electrolyte flux becomes extremely small when the ratio C'/X is small. *A high capacity ion-exchanger membrane between dilute solutions acts as a barrier which prevents electrolyte diffusion almost completely.* Furthermore, Eqs. (8-30) reflect the effect of the ionic valences. The dependence of the flux on the ratio C'/X—and thus the barrier action between dilute solutions—is stronger when the counter-ion valence is low and the co-ion valence is high. The reason is that Donnan exclusion of the co-ion, the cause of the barrier action, is stronger when the valences are such (see Sec. 5-3c). In actual systems, the dependence on the concentrations and valences is usually less pronounced than Eqs. (8-30) seem to indicate because, as a rule, the effect of the activity coefficients is in the opposite direction.

The Eqs. (8-30) also describe self-diffusion of co-ions across the membrane, provided the solutions are sufficiently dilute ($C \ll X$).

The most serious simplification in the derivations above is that *convection* has been disregarded in the flux equations (8-18). Simplified solutions which include convection have been obtained by Schlögl [100] and Meares [69]. The effect of convection will be discussed in Sec. 8-6.

Furthermore, it should be emphasized that the equations were derived for homogeneous membranes. In heterogeneous membranes the situation may be very different. Here, diffusion along thin liquid films between the colloidal ion-exchanger particles and the inert binder may still occur when the particles themselves become impermeable for the electrolyte [24], see Fig. 8-2. Hence the limiting laws (8-30) cannot be expected to hold for such "leaky" membranes. The porous plug model (Sec. 9-11) is likely to give better answers.

The general conclusions in this section have been qualitatively confirmed by experiments with homogeneous membranes [56,62,69]. In particular, it has recently been verified that different electrolytes with a common co-ion diffuse at approximately equal rates, i.e., that co-ion diffusion is rate-controlling [75]. No investigations, however, have so far been reported in which the diffusion coefficients were determined by independent methods.

c. Interdiffusion of Counter Ions

Ion-exchanger membranes, while acting as a barrier for co-ion and electrolyte diffusion, are readily permeable for counter ions. Thus an exchange of counter ions between the solutions on either membrane side can take place at a considerable rate. The mechanism of such processes is interdiffusion of counter ions which can occur even if the membrane is impermeable for co-ions.

Interdiffusion of isotopes in systems which are in equilibrium except for isotopic distribution obeys the laws of self-diffusion. These laws have already been discussed (Sec. 8-3a). Now, interdiffusion of different counter-ion species will be studied.

Bi-ionic systems. In the so-called bi-ionic systems, the membrane is between two solutions with different counter ions A and B but with a common co-ion Y:

$$AY \quad | \quad \text{membrane} \quad | \quad BY \qquad (8\text{-}31)$$

In systems with concentrated solutions, the flux of co-ions across the membrane cannot be neglected (even if the co-ion concentrations in both solutions are equal, there is usually a transfer of co-ions caused by the electric potential gradient in the membrane). In such cases, no simple solution of the flux equations can be obtained, and the fluxes and concentration profiles must be calculated from the general integration of the flux equations which will be discussed in Sec. 8-5.* On the other hand, if the concentrations of the solutions are much smaller than that of the fixed ionic groups, the membrane is permselective for counter ions, i.e., the co-ion flux is insignificant. In this case, simple and more rigorous solutions of the flux equations can be given.

---

* A simpler treatment for concentrated solutions has recently been given by Mackay [55a]. Convection is included, but the treatment is restricted to counter ions of equal valence, constant co-ion activity throughout the membrane is postulated, and a number of additional simplifications are made.

The permeability of the membrane for counter ions is large. It may be substantially larger than that of the films, particularly if the solutions are dilute. Hence the process is often film-diffusion controlled. The nature of the rate-determining step can be predicted by use of the criterion (8-8). The two limiting cases of ideal membrane and ideal film diffusion control will be studied, and an approximation for the intermediate region in which the effects of the two mechanisms overlap will be outlined.

The treatment in the following does not include convection. This simplification is much less serious here than in electrolyte diffusion because the leading terms in the flux equations are nearly always much larger than the convection term.

Complete Membrane Diffusion Control. For the specific case of inter-diffusion of two counter ions A and B, and when convection and presence of co-ions are disregarded, the set of equations given in Sec. 8-2 becomes

$$J_A = -\bar{D}_A \left(\frac{d\bar{C}_A}{dx} + z_A \bar{C}_A \frac{\mathcal{F}}{RT} \frac{d\varphi}{dx} + \bar{C}_A \frac{d \ln \bar{f}_A}{dx} \right)$$

$$J_B = -\bar{D}_B \left(\frac{d\bar{C}_B}{dx} + z_B \bar{C}_B \frac{\mathcal{F}}{RT} \frac{d\varphi}{dx} + \bar{C}_B \frac{d \ln \bar{f}_B}{dx} \right)$$

(8-32)

$$z_A \bar{C}_A + z_B \bar{C}_B = -\omega \bar{C} \qquad \text{electroneutrality} \qquad (8\text{-}33)$$

$$z_A J_A + z_B J_B = 0 \qquad \text{no electric current} \qquad (8\text{-}34)$$

$$J_A, J_B = \text{const.} \qquad \text{quasi-stationary state} \qquad (8\text{-}35)$$

where $\bar{C}$ = total counter-ion concentration (in equivalents); ω = sign of fixed membrane charges.

From these equations, the interdiffusion flux and the concentration profiles can be obtained. Important for understanding the behavior of the system is, again, the condition (8-34); the fluxes of the two counter ions must balance one another exactly since there is no net transfer of electric charge. As in other systems, the compensation of the fluxes is enforced by the electric field (diffusion potential).

Introducing equivalent ionic fractions $\bar{x}_A$ and $\bar{x}_B$, defined by

$$\bar{x}_A \equiv \frac{z_A \bar{C}_A}{-\omega \bar{C}} \qquad\qquad \bar{x}_B \equiv \frac{z_B \bar{C}_B}{-\omega \bar{C}} \qquad (8\text{-}36)$$

one obtains by combination of Eqs. (8-32) to (8-35) [28]

$$z_A J_A = -\bar{D}_A \bar{D}_B (-\omega \bar{C}) \left[\frac{\bar{x}_A(z_A - z_B) + z_B - \bar{x}_A(1 - \bar{x}_A) d \ln K_{aB}^{\prime A} / d\bar{x}_A}{\bar{x}_A(\bar{D}_A z_A - \bar{D}_B z_B) + \bar{D}_B z_B} \right] \frac{d\bar{x}_A}{dx}$$

$$= G(\bar{x}_A) \frac{d\bar{x}_A}{dx} \qquad (8\text{-}37)$$

where the function $G(\bar{x}_A)$ is defined by this equation; $K_{aB}^{\prime A} \equiv (\bar{C}_A/a_A)^{z_B} (a_B/\bar{C}_B)^{z_A}$ $= \bar{f}_A^{z_A}/\bar{f}_B^{z_B}$ is the corrected molar selectivity coefficient of the ion exchange A + $\bar{B} \rightleftharpoons B + \bar{A}$ [see Eq. (5-77)].

Integration of Eq. (8-37) across the membrane with the boundary conditions $x = 0$, $\bar{x}_A = 1$; and $x = d$, $\bar{x}_A = 0$ gives the interdiffusion flux

$$z_A J_A = -\frac{1}{d} \int_0^1 G(\bar{x}_A) \, d\bar{x}_A \tag{8-38}*$$

The concentration profile $\bar{x}_A(x)$ cannot be written explicitly. It can be calculated from

$$x(\bar{x}_A) = \frac{d \int_{\bar{x}_A(x)}^1 G(\bar{x}_A) \, d\bar{x}_A}{\int_0^1 G(\bar{x}_A) \, d\bar{x}_A} \tag{8-39}$$

The integrals in Eqs. (8-38) and (8-39) must be evaluated graphically unless the dependence of the quantities $\bar{C}$, K'^A_{aB}, $\bar{D}_A$, and $\bar{D}_B$ on $\bar{x}_A$ can be expressed by simple analytical functions. If these quantities are constant, Eq. (8-37) can be integrated explicitly to give [26,28]

$$z_A J_A = \frac{\bar{D}_A \bar{D}_B (-\omega \bar{C})}{(\bar{D}_A z_A - \bar{D}_B z_B)d} \left[z_A - z_B + \frac{z_A z_B (\bar{D}_A - \bar{D}_B)}{\bar{D}_A z_A - \bar{D}_B z_B} \ln \frac{\bar{D}_A z_A}{\bar{D}_B z_B} \right] \tag{8-40}$$

$$x(\bar{x}_A) = d \left\{ \frac{\bar{x}_A - 1 + \dfrac{z_A z_B(\bar{D}_A - \bar{D}_B)}{(z_A - z_B)(\bar{D}_A z_A - \bar{D}_B z_B)} \ln \left[\dfrac{\bar{D}_B z_B}{\bar{D}_A z_A} + \bar{x}_A \left(1 - \dfrac{\bar{D}_B z_B}{\bar{D}_A z_A} \right) \right]}{\dfrac{z_A z_B(\bar{D}_A - \bar{D}_B)}{(z_A - z_B)(\bar{D}_A z_A - \bar{D}_B z_B)} \ln \dfrac{\bar{D}_B z_B}{\bar{D}_A z_A} - 1} \right\}$$

$$\tag{8-41}$$

In the case of equal counter-ion valences ($z_A = z_B$), Eqs. (8-40) and (8-41) reduce to [26]

$$z_A J_A = \frac{\bar{D}_A \bar{D}_B (-\omega \bar{C})}{(\bar{D}_A - \bar{D}_B)d} \ln \frac{\bar{D}_A}{\bar{D}_B} \qquad \text{for } \bar{D}_A \neq \bar{D}_B$$

$$= \frac{\bar{D}_A(-\omega \bar{C})}{d} \qquad \text{for } \bar{D}_A = \bar{D}_B \tag{8-42}$$

and

$$\bar{x}_A(x) = \frac{\bar{D}_A}{\bar{D}_A - \bar{D}_B} \left[\left(\frac{\bar{D}_B}{\bar{D}_A} \right)^{x/d} - \frac{\bar{D}_B}{\bar{D}_A} \right] \qquad \text{for } \bar{D}_A \neq \bar{D}_B$$

$$= 1 - \frac{x}{d} \qquad \text{for } \bar{D}_A = \bar{D}_B \tag{8-43}$$

The function $G(\bar{x}_A)$ and thus Eqs. (8-38) and (8-39) do *not* involve the concentrations of the solutions. Hence the flux and the concentration profiles are independent of the concentrations of the solutions, provided that membrane diffusion is rate-controlling.

The *interdiffusion flux*, according to Eq. (8-40), is proportional to the

---

* It is sufficient to calculate the flux and concentration profile of species A only. The fluxes of A and B are stoichiometrically equivalent [Eq. (8-34)]; the concentration profile of B is readily obtained from that of A by Eq. (8-33).

total equivalent concentration of counter ions and thus (since $\bar{C} \approx X$) approximately proportional to the concentration of fixed ionic groups. Furthermore, the flux is inversely proportional to the membrane thickness. The absolute magnitude of the flux is of the same order as in self-diffusion of counter ions (see Sec. 8-3a).

The shape of the *concentration profiles* depends chiefly on the mobility ratio $\bar{D}_A/\bar{D}_B$ of the two counter ions in the membrane. The membrane accumulates the slower ion (see Fig. 8-7) [26,28]. This effect is a consequence of the general rule which says that the (local) interdiffusion coefficient is chiefly determined by the species which is in the minority (see Sec. 6-3c). In the membrane layers near the solution of AY the concentration of B is small and the interdiffusion coefficient approaches the value of $\bar{D}_B$. On the other side the concentration of A is small and the interdiffusion coefficient approaches $\bar{D}_A$. The interdiffusion flux is the product of interdiffusion coefficient and concentration gradient and is constant throughout the membrane. Thus, where the interdiffusion coefficient is large, the concentration gradient must be small, and vice versa. Therefore the profiles are steeper on the side facing the solution of the faster ion (compare the profiles for NaCl/HCl and NaCl/SrCl₂ in Fig. 8-7).

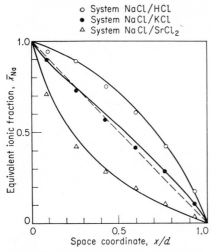

○ System NaCl/HCl
● System NaCl/KCl
△ System NaCl/SrCl₂

FIG. 8-7. Theoretical and experimental concentration profiles in bi-ionic membrane systems with complete membrane diffusion control. *Solid lines:* calculated from selectivity and self-diffusion data; *circles and triangles:* experimental points. *Systems:* phenolsulfonic-acid membrane between 0.1 N solutions. *From data by F. Helfferich and H. D. Ocker* [28].

The (corrected) selectivity coefficient appears only in the form of the differential quotient $d \ln K_{aB}^{\prime A}/d\bar{x}_A$. The absolute value of the coefficient is irrelevant. Thus the shape of the profiles does *not* depend on whether A or B is preferred by the ion exchanger in equilibrium with a solution containing both these species. Such a dependence was erroneously assumed in earlier theories. The dependence of the selectivity coefficient on ionic composition may result in S-shaped profiles (see the profile for NaCl/KCl in Fig. 8-7).

The theoretical treatment is in quantitative agreement with experimental results [28,55,84]. This is particularly true for the concentration profiles (see Fig. 8-7).

Complete Film Diffusion Control. In this limiting case, the membrane offers very much less resistance to counter-ion diffusion than the films.

The membrane, however, prevents co-ion transfer from one solution to the other. In the films, the situation is similar to that in film-diffusion controlled exchange of counter ions (Sec. 6-3c, Fig. 6-9). The diffusion potentials in the films cause an initial co-ion shift. There is an accumulation of co-ions at the interface membrane/film facing the solution of the faster

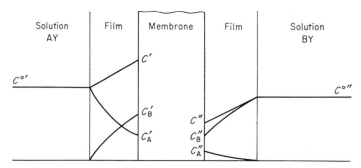

Fig. 8-8. Concentration profiles in a film-diffusion controlled bi-ionic system (*schematic*). There is co-ion accumulation in the film on the side of the faster counter ion (A) and co-ion depletion in the other film.

ion, and a depletion on the other side (Fig. 8-8). The steady (or quasi-stationary) state is attained when the concentration gradient of the co-ion and the electric potential gradient balance one another so as to produce no further co-ion flux.

This system is more complex than the previous one because the films contain three mobile ionic species. An analytical solution can be given if the counter ions have equal valences ($z_A = z_B$) and if the concentration dependence of the activity coefficients (in both membrane and films) is disregarded. The set of equations to be solved then is*

$$J_A = -D_A \left(\frac{dC_A}{dx} + z_A C_A \frac{\mathfrak{F}}{RT} \frac{d\varphi}{dx} \right)$$

$$J_B = -D_B \left(\frac{dC_B}{dx} + z_B C_B \frac{\mathfrak{F}}{RT} \frac{d\varphi}{dx} \right)$$

$$J_Y = -D_Y \left(\frac{dC_Y}{dx} + z_Y C_Y \frac{\mathfrak{F}}{RT} \frac{d\varphi}{dx} \right) \tag{8-44}$$

$$
\begin{array}{ll}
z_A C_A + z_B C_B + z_Y C_Y = 0 & \text{electroneutrality} \\
z_A J_A + z_B J_B = 0 & \text{no electric current} \\
J_Y = 0 & \text{permselectivity} \\
J_A, J_B = \text{const.} & \text{quasi-stationary state}
\end{array}
$$

The equations must be solved separately for both films. The boundary conditions at the interfaces membrane/film are eigenvalues of the system; however, they are interrelated by $x_A' = x_A''$ (this follows from the assumed independence of activity coefficients on con-

---

* Note that objections can be raised against the application of the Nernst film concept to cases which involve a variable diffusion coefficient.

centration).   Under the boundary conditions at the boundaries solution/film

$$
\begin{aligned}
x &= -\delta & z_A C_A &= (C^0)' & z_B C_B &= 0 \\
x &= d + \delta & z_A C_A &= 0 & z_B C_B &= (C^0)''
\end{aligned}
\tag{8-45}
$$

the solution is

$$
z_A J_A = \frac{D_A D_B [-\omega (C^0)']}{(D_A - D_B)\delta\alpha} \frac{[(D_A/D_B)^\alpha - 1]}{[(C^0)'/(C^0)''(D_A/D_B)^\alpha + 1]}
\tag{8-46}
$$

where $\alpha \equiv z_Y/(z_Y - z_A)$

The total equivalent concentrations at the interfaces membrane/film are

$$
\begin{aligned}
C' &= \frac{[(C^0)' + (C^0)''][(C^0)'/(C^0)''](D_A/D_B)^\alpha}{1 + [(C^0)'/(C^0)''](D_A/D_B)^\alpha} \\
C'' &= \frac{(C^0)' + (C^0)''}{1 + [(C^0)'/(C^0)''](D_A/D_B)^\alpha}
\end{aligned}
\tag{8-47}
$$

The flux is proportional to the concentration of the solutions (if the ratio $(C^0)'/(C^0)''$ is kept constant) and inversely proportional to the film thickness. Its absolute value is of the same order of magnitude as in film-controlled self-diffusion of counter ions (see Sec. 8-3a).

So far, no experimental data on completely film-controlled interdiffusion of counter ions are available.

Partial Film Diffusion Control. Both membrane and film diffusion affect the over-all rate if the resistances of membrane and films to diffusion become comparable. In principle, it is possible to calculate the interdiffusion rate by solving the flux equations in membrane and films simultaneously. Even in the simplest cases, however, transcendental equations are obtained which are difficult to evaluate. Calculation by successive approximations [26] is more convenient. This procedure is outlined in the following.

Integral interdiffusion coefficients $\tilde{D}_{AB}$ for membrane and films are defined by

$$
\tilde{D}_{AB} \equiv J_A \frac{l}{C_A' - C_A''} = J_B \frac{l}{C_B'' - C_B'}
\tag{8-48}
$$

where C_i' and C_i'' = concentrations of species i at the left and right boundary, respectively, of the layer under consideration (membrane or film) of thickness l.

The values of these coefficients can be roughly estimated. They are used to obtain a first approximation for the concentrations at the interfaces by use of the steady-state condition and the interface equilibria. There is another functional relation between the coefficients and the concentrations at the interfaces, namely, the integrated forms of Eqs. (8-37) and (8-44). Introducing the first approximation for the interface concentrations as boundary conditions into these equations gives a second approximation for the interdiffusion coefficients. This procedure can be repeated until the required accuracy is obtained. The interdiffusion flux can now be calculated directly from Eq. (8-48).

A characteristic feature of systems with counter ions of different valences is that the tendency toward film diffusion control is much more pronounced on the membrane side facing the solution of the counter ion of lower valence. The ion exchanger prefers the counter ion of higher valence (electroselectivity, see page 156). Thus the presence of a small number of counter ions of the higher valence in the film on the side of the counter ion of lower valence is sufficient to produce a drastic change in the intramembrane concentrations at the interface. This reduces the concentration gradients in the membrane, thus causing a deviation from complete membrane diffusion control. In contrast, the presence of a small amount of counter ions of the lower valence in the other film has little effect. Suppressing film diffusion control by strong agitation is therefore much more difficult in the solution of the counter ion of lower valence.

A similar procedure of correcting for partial film diffusion control as well as convection has been described in more detail by Mackay [53] who also obtained reasonable agreement with experimental results [55].

Extension to Other Systems. The treatment given here is readily extended to membrane systems such as

$$\text{AY, BY} \quad | \quad \text{membrane} \quad | \quad \text{AY, BY} \qquad (8\text{-}49)$$

in which both solutions contain both counter ions in arbitrary concentrations. In such systems the calculation even for complete membrane diffusion control involves the ion-exchange equilibria at the interfaces and thus the selectivity coefficient. The relations obtained are somewhat more complex, but the same principal rules are obeyed. Of course, systems of the type (8-49) are limiting cases of the multi-ionic systems (8-50) for which simplified solutions are given below.

Multi-ionic systems. In the so-called multi-ionic systems, the membrane is between two solutions containing the electrolytes AY, BY, CY, . . . and LY, MY, . . . , respectively,

$$\text{AY, BY, CY, . . .} \quad | \quad \text{membrane} \quad | \quad \text{LY, MY, NY, . . .} \qquad (8\text{-}50)$$

This is a situation often encountered in physiological membrane systems. Therefore multi-ionic systems are particularly interesting.

One of the most outstanding features of physiological membranes is their high permselectivity. The permeability of a membrane may be quite different for different ions even of equal valence. Therefore the flux ratios J_A/J_B, J_A/J_C, . . . , J_L/J_M, . . . in multi-ionic systems are even more interesting than the absolute values of the various fluxes. Indeed, it is found that ion-exchanger membranes also display striking permeability differences which cannot be explained by differences in the individual diffusion coefficients alone [76,117].

As in bi-ionic systems, the calculation of fluxes and concentration profiles in systems with concentrated solutions requires evaluation by use of the general integration of the flux equations (see Sec. 8-5). A simple solution of the flux equations is only possible if the co-ion flux can be neglected and if all counter ions have the same valence. Furthermore, convection and gradients of activity coefficients must be disregarded. In the following, it will be assumed that the individual diffusion coefficients and the concentration of the fixed ionic groups are constant and that the system is membrane-diffusion controlled. Under these conditions and assumptions, the system of equations given in Sec. 8-2 has the form

$$J_i = -\bar{D}_i \left[\frac{d\bar{C}_i}{dx} + z_i \bar{C}_i \frac{\mathscr{F}}{RT} \frac{d\varphi}{dx} \right] \tag{8-51}$$

$$z_i \sum_i \bar{C}_i = -\omega \bar{C} \qquad \text{electroneutrality} \tag{8-52}$$

$$\sum_i J_i = 0 \qquad \text{no electric current} \tag{8-53}$$

$$J_i = \text{const.} \qquad \text{quasi-stationary state} \tag{8-54}$$

where subscript i refers to all counter ions; $J_Y = 0$.

As a rule, it is desired to express the fluxes and profiles as functions of the concentrations (or activities) in the solutions. In this case, a relation between the intramembrane boundary concentrations and the activities in the solution is required. For counter ions of equal valence z_i, the equilibrium at the interface [obtained from Eqs. (8-73) and (8-52)] is*

$$\bar{C}_A = \frac{-\omega \bar{C} a_A}{z_i \bar{f}_A \sum_i (a_i / \bar{f}_i)} \tag{8-55}$$

The fluxes and concentration profiles as calculated from Eqs. (8-51) to (8-55) are [27]

$$J_A = \frac{\bar{D}_A \bar{C}'_A}{d} \frac{\sum_k \bar{D}_k \bar{C}''_k}{\sum_j \bar{D} \bar{C}'_j - \sum_k \bar{D}_k \bar{C}''_k} \ln \frac{\sum_j \bar{D} \bar{C}'_j}{\sum_k \bar{D}_k \bar{C}''_k}$$

$$= \frac{\bar{D}_A(-\omega \bar{C}) a_A}{z_i \bar{f}_A d} \frac{B_k}{(A_k B_j - A_j B_k)} \ln \frac{A_k B_j}{A_j B_k} \tag{8-56}$$

$$\bar{C}_A(x) = \bar{C}'_A \frac{\sum_j \bar{D}_j \bar{C}'_j}{\sum_j \bar{D}_j \bar{C}'_j - \sum_k \bar{D}_k \bar{C}''_k} \left[\left(\frac{\sum_k \bar{D}_k \bar{C}''_k}{\sum_j \bar{D}_j \bar{C}'_j} \right)^{x/d} - \frac{\sum_k \bar{D}_k \bar{C}''_k}{\sum_j \bar{D}_j \bar{C}'_j} \right]$$

$$= \frac{(-\omega \bar{C}) a_A}{z_i \bar{f}_A} \frac{A_k B_j}{A_j (A_k B_j - A_j B_k)} \left[\left(\frac{A_j B_k}{A_k B_j} \right)^{x/d} - \frac{A_j B_k}{A_k B_j} \right] \tag{8-57}$$

where subscript j refers to counter ions A, B, C, . . . (originally on the left membrane side), and subscript k to counter ions L, M, . . . (originally on right membrane side); the quantities A and B are defined by

$$A_i \equiv \sum_i \frac{a_i}{\bar{f}_i} \qquad B_i \equiv \sum_i \frac{\bar{D}_i a_i}{\bar{f}_i}$$

---

* Note that the effect of swelling pressure is included in the activities; see p. 344.

The flux ratio of two counter ions A and B present on the same membrane side is readily derived from Eq. (8-56)

$$\frac{J_A}{J_B} = \frac{\bar{D}_A a_A \bar{f}_B}{\bar{D}_B a_B \bar{f}_A} \tag{8-58}$$

Several interesting conclusions can be deduced from Eqs. (8-56) and (8-58). First, the flux of species A depends on the intramembrane activity coefficients and thus on the relative affinity of the membrane for the ion A. The equations show that *the membrane is more permeable for the species it prefers* (provided that this effect is not offset by a lower mobility of this species). The physical explanation is simple. High affinity for A results in a high boundary concentration $\bar{C}'_A$ and thus in a steep concentration profile (see Fig. 8-9). It is often true, however, that an ion which is preferred has a somewhat lower mobility in the membrane (see page 304). Thus the effect stressed here is usually not as strong as one might expect at first sight.

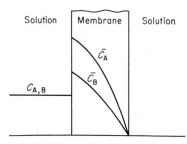

FIG. 8-9. Concentration profiles of two competing counter ions A and B in a multi-ionic system (*schematic*). The concentrations of A and B in the solution are equal. Species A is preferred by the membrane material and thus has the steeper profile and the larger flux.

The second conclusion is that, according to Eqs. (8-56) and (8-58), the flux ratio of two counter ions present on the same side of the membrane is *independent* of the properties and concentrations of the counter ions on the other membrane side. Furthermore, the flux ratio J_A/J_B is related to the bi-ionic potential in the cell

$$\text{AY} \quad | \quad \text{membrane} \quad | \quad \text{BY}$$

and can be predicted from this potential [27,76]; compare Sec. 8-4d, Eq. (8-86).

The equations are readily applied to systems in which one or several counter ions are present on both sides of the membrane. The flux of such a counter ion, say, species A, is obtained in the following way. The ions A on the left and right membrane side are arbitrarily designated A′ and A″, respectively. The fluxes of A′ and A″ are given by Eq. (8-56). The net flux of A from left to right then is

$$J_A = J'_A - J''_A = \frac{\bar{D}_A(-\omega\bar{C})(a'_A B_k - a''_A B_j)}{z_i \bar{f}_A d(A_k B_j - A_j B_k)} \ln \frac{A_k B_j}{A_j B_k} \tag{8-59}$$

The net flux is positive (i.e., is from left to right) if $a'_A B_k > a''_A B_j$. This can be the case even if $a'_A < a''_A$: *a counter ion can diffuse from the solution where its activity is lower into the solution where its activity is higher.* This diffusion to a higher activity level can occur when the competing counter ions j on the low-activity side are either much slower or have lower activities or less affinity for the membrane than the counter ions k on the other side ($B_j < B_k$), i.e., if A' has less efficient competition than A''. The required energy for this anomalous diffusion is provided by normal diffusion of other counter ions in opposite direction.

Probably the most serious simplification in the derivations above is the assumption that the activity coefficients are constant throughout the membrane. In systems with highly selective membranes—and these are naturally the most interesting—this assumption is usually incorrect. Nevertheless, it can be expected that, even in such cases, the equations describe the behavior of the system at least qualitatively.

The theory has been reasonably well confirmed by measurements of diffusion fluxes. This is particularly true for Eq. (8-58) and the relation between the flux ratio of two counter ions and their bi-ionic potential [76]. These measurements, however, did not include independent determinations of the diffusion coefficients.

d. Diffusion of a Nonelectrolyte

The flux of a nonelectrolyte from a more concentrated into a more dilute solution across a membrane will now be examined. A nonelectrolyte flux does not involve electric-charge transfer and, hence, is not electrically coupled with other fluxes. The simple laws which were derived for self-diffusion (constant diffusion coefficient) are obeyed with only minor deviations which are due to the concentration dependence of the activity coefficient and diffusion coefficient and to convection (osmosis).

The electrochemical valence of the nonelectrolyte is zero. The flux equation (8-2) thus reduces to

$$J_N = -D_N \left(\frac{dC_N}{dx} + C_N \frac{d \ln f_N}{dx} \right) + C_N \mathfrak{v} \qquad (8\text{-}60)$$

where subscript N refers to the nonelectrolyte.

The convection velocity $\mathfrak{v}$ is proportional to the osmotic pressure difference between the solutions (provided that all solutes are nonelectrolytes) and can thus be determined by an independent measurement. The general equation (8-60) can be integrated, but cannot be written explicitly in the form $J_N = \int_{'}^{''} f(\bar{C}_N) \, d\bar{C}_N$. The integral, however, can be evaluated numerically or graphically by successive approximations. If $\bar{D}_N$ and $\bar{f}_N$ are constant and $\mathfrak{v}$ is negligible, the integrated form reduces to

$$J_N \cong \frac{\bar{D}_N}{d}(\bar{C}_N' - \bar{C}_N'') = \frac{\bar{D}_N \lambda_N'}{d}(C_N' - C_N'') \qquad (8\text{-}61)$$

where $\lambda_N' \equiv \bar{C}_N/C_N = f_N/\bar{f}_N$ = molar distribution coefficient of the nonelectrolyte.

Equation (8-61) gives the flux as a function of the solution concentrations C_N' and C_N'' at the interfaces. With complete membrane diffusion control these are equal to the concentrations in the bulk solutions. With partial film diffusion control one obtains

$$J_N = \frac{\bar{D}_N}{d}\frac{\lambda_N'(C_N^{0\prime} - C_N^{0\prime\prime})}{1 + 2\lambda_N'\bar{D}_N\delta/D_N d} \qquad (8\text{-}62)$$

where superscript 0 refers to the bulk solutions.

[Compare the analogous relation (8-7).] Film diffusion control is rare because the modulus $D_N d/\lambda_N'\bar{D}_N\delta$ [see Eq. (8-8)] is usually much smaller than unity.

J. S. Mackie [57] has given an analytical integration which, within certain limits, includes the concentration dependence of the activity coefficient and the diffusion coefficient as well as convection. In the calculation of the correction term for convection, $\bar{D}_N$ and $\bar{f}_N$ are assumed to be constant. In the integration of the main term the coefficients are approximated by the empirical expressions $\bar{D}_N = \bar{D}_0 + k\bar{C}$ and $\ln \bar{f}_N = a\bar{C}_N + b$ ($\bar{D}_0$, a, b, and k are constants). The result is

$$J_N = \frac{a\bar{D}_0 + k}{2d}(\bar{C}_N'^2 - \bar{C}_N''^2) + \frac{ka(\bar{C}_N'^3 - \bar{C}_N''^3)}{3d} + \frac{\bar{C}_N'' - \bar{C}_N'\exp(\mathfrak{v}d/\bar{D}_0)}{1 - \exp(\mathfrak{v}d/\bar{D}_0)}\mathfrak{v} \qquad (8\text{-}63)$$

This relation is valid only for systems with dilute solutions.

According to the approximation (8-61), the flux of the nonelectrolyte is proportional to the diffusion coefficient in the membrane, the distribution coefficient, and the concentration difference between the solutions, and inversely proportional to the membrane thickness. The absolute magnitude of the flux is of the same order as in self-diffusion of nonelectrolytes (see Sec. 8-3a).

Within the limits determined by the simplifying assumptions involved, the equations are in good agreement with experimental results [57,62,84].

e. Simultaneous Diffusion of Electrolytes and Nonelectrolytes

Nonelectrolyte diffusion across a membrane is little affected by simultaneous diffusion of an electrolyte, and vice versa. The electric potential gradient built up by electrolyte diffusion does not act on the nonelectrolyte molecules. It may only affect the convection. On the other hand, nonelectrolyte diffusion does not alter the electric potential gradient. Of course, the presence of one solute causes changes in the activity coefficient of the other and in swelling, but all these effects are usually minor. Thus the relations derived for electrolyte and nonelectrolyte diffusion are rather good approximations even in systems which contain both these species. The large permeability differences in such systems can be used for separations [62].

This last point may be illustrated by the permeability difference in a very simple system in which an electrolyte and a nonelectrolyte diffuse from a solution containing both species in equal concentration C' into pure solvent on the other membrane side. Neglecting activity coefficients and equating $\lambda'_N = 1$ one obtains the following limiting law for dilute solutions ($C' \ll X$) by use of Eqs. (8-30) and (8-61)

$$\frac{J_N}{z_+ J_+} = \frac{\bar{D}_N}{\bar{D}_-} \left(\frac{X}{C'} \right)^{-z_-/z_+} \quad \text{for cation-exchanger membranes}$$

$$= \frac{\bar{D}_N}{\bar{D}_+} \left(\frac{X}{C'} \right)^{-z_+/z_-} \quad \text{for anion-exchanger membranes} \tag{8-64}$$

The flux ratio can become very large. It increases with increasing concentration of fixed ionic groups and with dilution of the solution. Furthermore, the flux ratio depends on the ionic valences. The ratio is larger when the valence of the counter ion is smaller than that of the co-ion [62]. This is readily explained by the dependence of electrolyte sorption on the ionic valences (Sec. 5-3d). Thus, for separating a nonelectrolyte from a 2,1-valent electrolyte an anion-exchanger membrane is more efficient than a cation-exchanger membrane of equal capacity, and with a 1,2-valent electrolyte the use of the cation-exchanger membrane is more advantageous.

The conclusions deduced from Eq. (8-64) are qualitatively confirmed by experiments [62].

8-4. MEMBRANE POTENTIALS

Two electrolyte solutions which are separated by a permeable or semi-permeable membrane differ in their electric potential. The electric potential difference is called *membrane potential* and can be measured by inserting suitable electrodes into the solutions.

The existence of an electric potential difference between two electrolyte solutions in systems with or without a membrane is a consequence of the electroneutrality requirement. Conservation of electroneutrality prohibits the accumulation of net charge anywhere in the system. Thus, in the absence of electric current, all ionic fluxes must balance one another exactly so that no net electric charge is transferred. Initially, an extremely small net charge transfer may occur, but just this charge shift causes an electric potential difference which affects the ionic fluxes and enforces their compensation. This point will be further illustrated by specific examples in later parts of this section.

The relative permeabilities—i.e., the relative ease with which various ionic species can migrate across the membrane—depend on the properties of the ions and the membrane. The membrane potential, which must bring about the balance of the ionic fluxes, thus also depends on the properties of the membrane. This is true for its magnitude as well as for its sign.

The membrane potential is usually independent of the thickness, cross section, and shape of the membrane. The equations in the following are valid for any geometrical shape, regular or irregular, of the separation wall between the two solutions, provided that the wall is not "leaky." Two reservations must be made, however. First, a change in the membrane shape does affect the potential if it changes the nature of the rate-determining step (membrane or film diffusion); second, the transient potentials before attainment of the steady state and the time required for attaining the steady state depend on the shape and thickness of the membrane.

The existence of an electric potential difference is proof that the system can do work. The energy source is the free energy of mixing of the two solutions. A fraction of this free energy is obtained as electric energy when the diffusion potential or membrane potential is used as a voltage source. The lower the free energy losses due to irreversible phenomena— in this case to diffusion—the higher is the degree of free-energy utilization. In systems without a separating membrane which obstructs diffusion, the degree of utilization is very small. In contrast, in systems with ideally permselective membranes which prevent electrolyte diffusion completely, the utilization is 100 per cent if the current is withdrawn reversibly. This latter situation is approached in concentration cells with dilute solutions and high-capacity ion-exchanger membranes. The electric current which a membrane cell can supply is discussed in Sec. 8-8a. The present section deals with membrane potentials in the absence of an electric current.

The membrane potential itself cannot be measured directly. By necessity, any measurement can only give the electromotive force (emf) of the whole cell

$$\text{electrode} \mid \text{solution 1} \mid \text{membrane} \mid \text{solution 2} \mid \text{electrode} \qquad (8\text{-}65)$$

$$\underbrace{\text{electrode potential}} \qquad \underbrace{\text{membrane potential}} \qquad \underbrace{\substack{\text{electrode} \\ \text{potential}}}$$

which, in addition to the membrane potential, involves the two electrode potentials. The emf can be calculated theoretically by the use of quasi-thermodynamics or thermodynamics of irreversible processes.

Quasi-thermodynamics and Thermodynamics of Irreversible Processes. There is a fundamental difference between these two lines of approach.[*] A brief discussion may serve to point out the limitations of the earlier quasi-thermodynamic theories and to clarify the inherent assumptions in the treatment in this section.

Quasi-thermodynamics is not interested in the particle fluxes. One might say that the quasi-thermodynamic approach consists in taking a snapshot of the system and calculating the emf from the changes which a reversible electric current would produce in the

---

[*] See also G. Scatchard [92].

system if it were "frozen" in the state in which the photographic picture was taken. This procedure gives directly the emf of the cell. No model is needed. Taking the snapshot, however, is often not as simple as it may seem. A rigorous treatment would require the knowledge of the composition of every differential layer of the diffusion zone (i.e., the concentration profiles of all species). Since obtaining this information experimentally is usually too lengthy a task or even quite impossible, the quasi-thermodynamic treatment is forced to make assumptions about the condition of the system. A characteristic example is the well-known assumption first made by Henderson [29], according to which every differential layer of the diffusion zone has a composition which can be obtained by mixing appropriate amounts of the solutions on either side of the zone. The only systems in which no such assumptions are necessary are those with only two mobile ionic species. Here, the membrane potential is completely determined by the boundary conditions, i.e., the compositions of the solutions (and, of course, the membrane properties). If there are several diffusion layers, however, the boundary conditions must be known for each of them. This is true, for example, in systems with partial film diffusion control.

The *thermodynamics of irreversible processes* [22], in contrast to quasi-thermodynamics, does not require prior knowledge of the concentration profiles. The set of equations of thermodynamics of irreversible processes interrelates all occurring "fluxes" (of species, electric current, heat, etc.) and "driving forces" (gradients of chemical potentials, electric potential, temperature, etc.). From measurements of a sufficient number of "phenomenological coefficients," all fluxes and forces—and hence also the emf—can be calculated, without knowledge of the profiles and without using the concept of "reversible energy production" on which quasi-thermodynamics is based. Furthermore, thermodynamics of irreversible processes is applicable also to nonisothermal systems and includes coupling of fluxes which is not covered by quasi-thermodynamics.

The treatment given in this chapter is based on the equations derived and discussed in Sec. 8-2 and can be classified as a simplification of thermodynamics of irreversible processes (see also page 343). The previous section has shown that fluxes, concentration profiles, and (in systems with partial or complete film diffusion control) phase boundary concentrations can be calculated by integrating the flux equations under the appropriate restrictions and boundary conditions. The flux equations also involve the gradient of the electric potential. Hence they can be integrated to give the membrane potential. The calculation of the emf of the cell by this method requires separate computation of all additive potential differences involved. These "single" potential differences are the electrode potentials, the phase boundary potentials, and the diffusion potential within the membrane. In the case of film diffusion control, the diffusion potentials in the films must be added. Such a "splitting" of the emf into single potential differences is considered as unrealistic by representatives of rigorous thermodynamics [23,81] because their existence can principally not be proven by direct measurement. Despite such objections on purely theoretical grounds, the separate computation of the single potential differences serves best to elucidate the phenomena which occur in the various parts of the system.

All these methods—quasi-thermodynamics, thermodynamics of irreversible processes, and the flux equations used here—lead to identical results if the quasi-thermodynamic treatment is based on the concentration profiles calculated from the flux equations, and if coupling is disregarded in the thermodynamics of irreversible processes.

In this chapter, the flux equations will be used to calculate membrane potentials in concentration cells, bi-ionic cells, and multi-ionic cells. This study of particular systems is preceded by a general discussion of the various potential differences which contribute to the emf of a membrane cell.

a. Membrane Potential, Electrode Potentials, and EMF

The electromotive force (emf) of a cell such as (8-65) consists of the membrane potential and the electrode potentials. The *membrane potential* is defined as the electric potential difference between the two bulk solutions. It consists of the diffusion potential within the membrane, the phase-boundary potentials (Donnan potentials, see next section), and, in systems with partial or complete film diffusion control, the diffusion potentials in the films.

The membrane potential is a "single" potential difference between two phases and, as such, is thermodynamically undefined and cannot be measured directly. Any electric potential measurement always gives the emf of a complete cell. In order to obtain the membrane potential from the emf, assumptions about the *electrode potentials*—which also are single potential differences—must be made.

A standard procedure in electrochemistry is the use of *calomel electrodes* in potential measurements:

$$\text{Hg}|\text{Hg}_2\text{Cl}_2\Big|{\text{KCl} \atop \text{saturated}}\Big|\text{solution 1}\Big|\text{membrane}\Big|\text{solution 2}\Big|{\text{KCl} \atop \text{saturated}}\Big|\text{Hg}_2\text{Cl}_2|\text{Hg}$$

$$(8\text{-}66)$$

Usually it is assumed that the electrode potentials of the calomel electrodes balance one another exactly, so that the membrane potential and the emf of the cell are equal. It can be shown that this assumption is equivalent to a definition of single-ion activity coefficients. If the solutions contain polyvalent ions or polyelectrolytes, the physical significance of the single-ion activity coefficients defined in this way becomes questionable.* Because of the KCl "bridges" in the cell (8-66), the rigorous theoretical expression for the emf involves mixed-electrolyte activity coefficients which are difficult to evaluate [23].

The diffusion potentials at the KCl bridges—problem children of electrochemistry—can be avoided by the use of "direct" *reversible electrodes* which are inserted directly into the solutions. An example is

$$\text{Ag}|\text{AgCl} \quad | \quad \text{NaCl} \quad | \quad \text{membrane} \quad | \quad \text{KCl} \quad | \quad \text{AgCl}|\text{Ag} \quad (8\text{-}67)$$

The electrodes are reversible with respect to the Cl^- ion present in both solutions. The potential of a reversible electrode is a function of the activity of the ion involved (Cl^- in the case of Ag/AgCl electrodes). Thus the two electrode potentials are usually not equal, and the membrane potential differs from the emf. The calculation of the membrane potential from the emf requires, as in cells with calomel electrodes, an assumption about single-ion activity coefficients. But here, one is free to choose any desired definition.* The theoretical expression for the emf of the cell involves only

---

* This point has been discussed in detail by K. S. Spiegler and M. R. J. Wyllie [120].

mean electrolyte activities. Reversible electrodes thus have great advantages [39]. The number of ions for which reversible electrodes exist is limited, however.

The potential, E_{el}, of an electrode (i.e., the electric potential difference between electrode and solution) which is reversible with respect to the ion j is given by

$$E_{el} = E_0 + \frac{RT}{z_j \mathfrak{F}} \ln a_j \tag{8-68}$$

where $\mathfrak{F}$ = Faraday constant; a_j = activity of ion j; E_0 = standard electrode potential.

The equation for the emf of the cell involves the difference of the two electrode potentials. This difference is

$$\Delta E_{el} = \frac{RT}{z_j \mathfrak{F}} \ln \frac{a_j''}{a_j'} \tag{8-69}$$

Equation (8-69), as does the expression for the membrane potential, contains single-ion activities which are principally inaccessible to thermodynamic measurement. If the emf, however, is formed by adding the membrane potential and the difference of the electrode potentials, the single activities cancel or combine by necessity to form mean activities (see also pages 140 and 412).

In the following, expressions for the membrane potential rather than for the emf will be given because the latter depends on the properties of the electrodes with which it is measured.

b. Phase-boundary Potentials (Donnan Potentials)

As a rule, two phases in contact with one another differ in their electric potential, irrespective of whether or not they are in equilibrium. The electric potential difference is called the *phase-boundary potential.** The phase-boundary potential between an ion exchanger and a solution is usually called the *Donnan potential.*†

The Donnan potential arises from the unequal equilibrium distribution of the mobile ions. Electroneutrality requires that, in the ion exchanger, the fixed charges are electrically balanced by counter ions which are in

---

* A more detailed examination shows that, even in the hypothetical case of a mathematically sharp phase boundary, the electric potential and the concentrations of the mobile ions change gradually rather than stepwise from one bulk phase to the other [78,96]. The changes occur within a narrow region on either side of the interface. This region is the electric double layer. Its thickness, however, is only of the order of a few hundred angstrom units or less. In the usual ion-exchanger membrane systems, both the membrane and the films are much thicker than the electric double layers. Hence it is safe to ignore this detail and to base the derivations on discontinuous changes in the concentrations and the electric potential at the interfaces.

† In honor of F. G. Donnan and his work in this field [13]; see page 135.

excess of the co-ions. These counter ions cannot diffuse out (unless when being replaced by others) since the resulting charge transfer creates an electric potential difference, the Donnan potential, which pulls them back. This has been discussed in detail in Sec. 5-3c.

The Donnan potential is an equilibrium phenomenon. Equations (5-39) and (5-55), which give the Donnan potential, were derived for equilibrium systems. They can also be used, however, in nonequilibrium systems in which fluxes across the interfaces occur, provided that there is equilibrium at the interfaces, i.e., that the interfaces offer no resistance to diffusion. This assumption is taken for granted (see pages 254 and 345). Note that the Donnan potential, under this condition, is an equilibrium potential, i.e., its effect on the ionic fluxes is exactly balanced by other forces; there is no net driving force at the interfaces [127].

The mechanism of the Donnan potential may be illustrated by a derivation which is based on the flux equations [97], i.e., by a kinetic rather than by a thermodynamic approach as in Chap. 5. For this purpose, one rewrites the flux equation (8-2) in the following form

$$J_i = -D_i C_i \left(\text{grad} \ln a_i + \frac{z_i \mathfrak{F}}{RT} \text{grad} \ \varphi \right) + C_i \mathfrak{v} \tag{8-70}$$

At the interface ion exchanger/solution, the gradients of the activity and the electric potential become very much larger than the flux and the convection term (this is equivalent to assuming equilibrium at the interface). Thus, at the interface, Eq. (8-70) reduces to

$$\frac{z_i \mathfrak{F}}{RT} \text{grad} \ \varphi = - \text{grad} \ln a_i \tag{8-71}$$

This relation shows clearly the balance of forces at the interface. Integration of Eq. (8-71) across the interface gives

$$E_{\text{Don}} \equiv \bar{\varphi} - \varphi = - \frac{RT}{z_i \mathfrak{F}} \ln \frac{\bar{a}_i}{a_i} = - \frac{RT}{z_i \mathfrak{F}} \ln \frac{\bar{C}_i \bar{f}_i}{C_i f_i} \tag{8-72}$$

where E_{Don} = Donnan potential.

This result is identical to Eq. (5-55), which was derived thermodynamically. Note that in both the flux equation (8-70) and the derivation of Eq. (5-55) the activity a_i was defined according to Eq. (5-54), i.e., including the effect of pressure. Instead, the activity can be defined according to Eq. (5-8). In this case the flux equation will contain a pressure term, and the expression for the Donnan potential becomes identical to Eq. (5-39) which was used in Chap. 5. In the following sections, the simpler relation (8-72) will be used. In membrane systems there is little need to state the effect of swelling pressure explicitly since the pressure difference at the interface is an equilibrium phenomenon, i.e., its effect on the fluxes is balanced by other forces.

Equation (8-72) can be used to derive, for later use, the important relations for sorption equilibrium of an electrolyte AY (page 354) and for ion-exchange equilibrium of two counter ions A and B (page 364). According to Eq. (8-72), the quantity $(\bar{a}_i/a_i)^{1/z_i}$ is equal for all ionic species A, B, . . . , Y, . . . present in the system, regardless of whether they are counter ions or co-ions:

$$\left(\frac{\bar{a}_A}{a_A}\right)^{1/z_A} = \left(\frac{\bar{a}_B}{a_B}\right)^{1/z_B} = \cdots = \left(\frac{\bar{a}_Y}{a_Y}\right)^{1/z_Y} = \cdots \tag{8-73}$$

Thus one obtains

$$\bar{a}_A^{-z_Y}\bar{a}_Y^{z_A} = a_A^{-z_Y}a_Y^{z_A} \tag{8-74}$$

and

$$\frac{\bar{a}_A^{z_B}}{\bar{a}_B^{z_A}} = \frac{a_A^{z_B}}{a_B^{z_A}} \tag{8-75}$$

These relations hold irrespective of whether or not other species are present. Except for the inclusion of the swelling-pressure effect into the activites, Eqs. (8-73) to (8-75) are identical to the relations (5-158), (5-44), and (5-90) which have previously been used.

c. Concentration Potentials

In concentration cells, the membrane is between two solutions containing the same electrolyte in different concentrations (see Sec. 8-3b). The membrane potential in such a system is called *concentration potential*.

The physical interpretation of the concentration potential is straightforward. As a rule, the membrane is more permeable for the counter ion. Thus the counter ion tends to diffuse more rapidly across the membrane than the co-ion. Any excess counter-ion diffusion, however, results in a net transfer of electric charge. The electric field built up in this way enforces equivalence of the counter-ion and co-ion fluxes. With cation-exchanger membranes, the electric potential in the dilute solution thus is more positive than in the concentrated solution. With anion-exchanger membranes the opposite holds. The electric potential difference is the concentration potential.

An ion-exchanger membrane between dilute solutions acts as a barrier across which almost no electrolyte can diffuse. Thus practically no irreversible processes occur and, theoretically, the free energy of the system can be completely converted into electric energy. The membrane potential reaches the thermodynamic limiting value. This limiting case is particularly important.

The concentration potential can be calculated from Eqs. (8-18) to (8-21) which have been used in Sec. 8-3b for calculating the electrolyte flux. Solving these equations for the electric potential gradient and integrating across the membrane, one obtains

$$\bar{E}_{\text{diff}} \equiv \bar{\varphi}'' - \bar{\varphi}' = -\frac{RT}{z_A\mathfrak{F}}\left[\ln\frac{\bar{a}_A''}{\bar{a}_A'} - (z_Y - z_A)\int_{'}^{''}\bar{t}_Y \, d\ln\bar{a}_{\pm}\right] \tag{8-76}$$

where A = counter ion; Y = co-ion; $\bar{t}_i$ = transference number of species i in the membrane; note that, in the absence of convection, $\bar{t}_i = z_i\bar{C}_i\bar{D}_i/(z_A^2\bar{C}_A\bar{D}_A + z_Y^2\bar{C}_Y\bar{D}_Y)$ [compare Eq. (7-12)].

Equation (8-76) gives the diffusion potential *within* the membrane. The membrane potential is the sum of this diffusion potential and the Donnan potentials [Eq. (8-72)]:*

$$E_\mathrm{m} \equiv \varphi'' - \varphi' = \bar{E}_\mathrm{diff} + E'_\mathrm{Don} - E''_\mathrm{Don}$$

$$= -\frac{RT}{z_\mathrm{A}\mathfrak{F}}\left[\ln\frac{a''_\mathrm{A}}{a'_\mathrm{A}} - (z_\mathrm{Y} - z_\mathrm{A})\int_{'}^{''}\bar{t}_\mathrm{Y}\mathrm{d}\ln a_\pm\right] \quad (8\text{-}77)$$

The integral can be evaluated graphically.

The right-hand side of Eq. (8-77) can be split into two terms. The first term gives the thermodynamic limiting value of the concentration

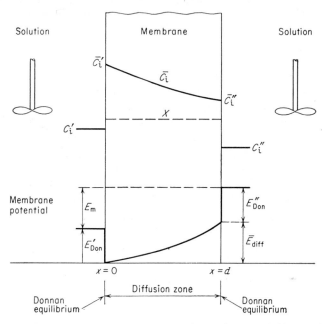

FIG. 8-10. Profiles of counter-ion concentration and electric potential in a cation-exchanger membrane (*schematic*). The system is a concentration cell. *From R. Schlögl* [99].

potential, and the second the deviation due to the co-ion flux. With an ideally permselective membrane ($\bar{t}_\mathrm{Y} = 0$) the second term vanishes and Eq. (8-77) reduces to the so-called *Nernst equation*

$$E_\mathrm{m} = -\frac{RT}{z_+\mathfrak{F}}\ln\frac{a''_+}{a'_+} \quad \text{for ideal cation permselectivity}$$

$$= \frac{RT}{-z_-\mathfrak{F}}\ln\frac{a''_-}{a'_-} \quad \text{for ideal anion permselectivity} \quad (8\text{-}78)$$

---

* Note that the Donnan potential E''_Don enters with opposite sign (see Fig. 8-10). Equation (8-77) also involves the substitution $\bar{a}_\pm = a_\pm$ according to Eq. (8-74); this substitution implies that the membrane is uniform, i.e., that all differential membrane layers behave alike (cf. Ref. 97).

This limiting law can also be derived thermodynamically. With the usual ion-exchanger membranes, Eq. (8-78) holds reasonably well within the concentration range of about 10^{-4} to 10^{-1} N. Deviations at higher solution concentrations are caused by co-ion transference, and at lower concentrations by H^+ or OH^- ions (stemming from dissociation of H_2O) which compete with the electrolyte counter ion [95]. With univalent counter ions, the limiting value of the membrane potential (at room temperature) is 59 mv per power of 10 of the activity ratio of the solutions.

The two terms in Eq. (8-77) are always opposite in sign. The deviation term is proportional to the average transference number of the co-ion in the membrane. This number may become large if the co-ion is more mobile than the counter ion and if there is little Donnan exclusion of the co-ion. Thus the relative importance of the deviation term increases with increasing mobility ratio $\bar{D}_Y/\bar{D}_A$, solution concentration, counter-ion valence, and affinity of the membrane for the electrolyte, and with decreasing fixed-charge concentration and co-ion valence (see Sec. 5-3c). The deviation term in Eq. (8-77) may even outweigh the leading term. The membrane potential, however, can vary only between the two limiting values for ideal cation permselectivity and ideal anion permselectivity.

In systems with weak-acid or weak-base membranes and acids and bases, respectively, as electrolytes, the lack of Donnan exclusion is particularly conspicuous. Here, the limiting value of the membrane potential is reached only with very dilute solutions [30,33,87]. More striking still is the behavior of systems with cation-exchanger membranes and strongly preferred polyvalent counter ions such as ThO^{2+}. Here, the transport number of the co-ion is the larger one even when the solutions are very dilute. With respect to its potential and its permeability the membrane acts like an anion-exchanger membrane [38,89]; see also page 138.

"*Membrane Electrodes.*" Within the range of validity of the limiting law (8-78), an ion-exchanger membrane can be used for determining ionic activities. The measurement is made in a cell with a membrane which is ideally permselective for the ion A. One compartment of the cell is filled with a standard solution of known activity a'_A. The unknown activity a''_A in the solution on the other membrane side can be calculated from the membrane potential by use of Eq. (8-78). The half-cell

$$Hg|Hg_2Cl_2 \quad | \quad KCl \text{ saturated} \quad | \quad \text{solution } AY \quad | \quad \text{membrane} \quad (8\text{-}79)$$

acts as an electrode which is reversible with respect to the ion A ("membrane electrode") [7,8,20,46,63,64,94,95,109,112,115,118]. Membrane electrodes have the great advantage that they can be built for almost any ion. A serious limitation, however, is their inability to distinguish adequately between different ions of equal sign (see also page 385).

Effect of Convection. In the derivation of Eqs. (8-77) and (8-78), the effect of convection has been disregarded. Therefore these equations only hold for membranes of high flow resistance. Integration of the flux equations with convection terms is possible, but rather cumbersome. The integral obtained is complex and difficult to evaluate (see Secs. 8-6 and 8-8c). It may suffice to say that, at low solution concentrations, convection as an irreversible process always lowers the absolute value of the concentration potential.

The effect of convection becomes apparent in Scatchard's [90] quasi-thermodynamical relation for the concentration potential of a 1,1-valent electrolyte

$$E_m = -\frac{RT}{\mathfrak{F}}\left\{\ln\frac{a_+''}{a_+'} - \int_{'}^{''} \frac{\dfrac{\bar{u}_-}{\bar{u}_+}[(1+B^2)^{1/2}-1] - \dfrac{\bar{u}_w\bar{\gamma}_\pm}{\bar{u}_+\gamma_\pm}B}{2+\left(1-\dfrac{\bar{u}_-}{\bar{u}_+}\right)[(1+B^2)^{1/2}-1]}\, d\ln a_\pm^2\right\} \quad (8\text{-}80)$$

where u_i = mobility of species i; m_i = molality of species i; $\bar{\gamma}_\pm$ = mean molal activity coefficient; $B \equiv 2a_\pm/\bar{\gamma}_\pm\bar{m}_R$; $\bar{m}_R$ = molality of fixed ionic groups; $\bar{u}_w$ is the "mobility" of the solvent (to be determined from electroosmotic transference).

At low solution concentrations ($B \ll 1$), Eq. (8-80) reduces to

$$E_m = -\frac{RT}{\mathfrak{F}}\left\{\ln\frac{a_+''}{a_+'} - \int_{'}^{''}\left[\frac{\bar{u}_-}{\bar{u}_+}\left(\frac{a_\pm}{\bar{\gamma}_\pm\bar{m}_R}\right)^2 - \frac{\bar{u}_w\bar{\gamma}_\pm}{\bar{u}_+\gamma_\pm}\left(\frac{a_\pm}{\bar{\gamma}_\pm\bar{m}_R}\right)\right]d\ln a_\pm^2\right\} \quad (8\text{-}81)$$

The first term is the thermodynamic limiting value of the concentration potential, the second is the correction for co-ion transference, and the third is the correction for convection. With dilution of the solutions, the second term decreases in proportion to the second power of the solution activity, and the third term in proportion to only the first power. If the flow resistance of the membrane is small (high value of $\bar{u}_w$), there may well be a concentration range in which the convection term is still noticeable, whereas the co-ion transference term has become insignificant.

The Historical Teorell-Meyer Equation. For a 1,1-valent electrolyte and constant values of $\bar{D}_+/\bar{D}_-$, $\bar{f}_\pm$, $f_\pm$, and X (concentration of fixed ionic groups), Eq. (8-77) can be integrated explicitly

$$E_m = \frac{RT}{\mathfrak{F}}\left[\omega\ln\frac{C''(\sqrt{4C'^2+A^2}+A)}{C'(\sqrt{4C''^2+A^2}+A)} + U\ln\frac{\sqrt{4C'^2+A^2}-\omega XU}{\sqrt{4C''^2+A^2}-\omega XU}\right] \quad (8\text{-}82)$$

where
$$A \equiv \frac{X\bar{f}_\pm}{f_\pm} \qquad U \equiv \frac{\bar{D}_+-\bar{D}_-}{\bar{D}_++\bar{D}_-}$$

This equation was derived as early as 1935 by Teorell [125] and K. H. Meyer [70]. The latter author also described a graphic method by which the parameters U [or $\bar{D}_+/\bar{D}_- = (U+1)/(U-1)$] and A can be determined from a series of potential measurements with various concentrations C' and a constant concentration ratio C'/C'' (Fig. 8-11) [70,73]. This convenient method has often been used. For resinous ion-exchanger membranes, however, it gives only approximate results because both parameters usually depend on concentration.

Experimental Evidence. No other membrane phenomena have been studied as frequently and thoroughly as concentration potentials. The basic conception of the early Teorell-Meyer theory—initially developed for physiological membranes—has been extensively confirmed. The more elaborate forms of this theory which have been given here are in satisfactory agreement with experimental results [6,9,19,20,30,37,58,61,63,70,91,98,106, 113,115,132,136,137].

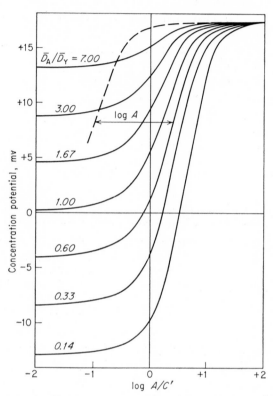

FIG. 8-11. Evaluation of concentration potentials by the Meyer-Sievers method. The *solid lines* are theoretical concentration potentials [from Eq. (8-82)] for a cation-exchanger membrane, a 1,1-valent electrolyte, and a constant solution-concentration ratio C'/C'' = 2 as a function of $\log A/C'$. The various curves are for different mobility ratios $\bar{D}_A/\bar{D}_Y$. Experimental values are plotted in the same graph versus $-\log C'$ (*broken line*). The experimental curve is shifted horizontally until it coincides with one of the theoretical curves. The shift gives $\log A$, and the coinciding theoretical curve gives $\bar{D}_A/\bar{D}_Y$. *From K. H. Meyer* [73].

d. Bi-ionic Potentials

A bi-ionic cell contains two electrolyte solutions AY and BY:

$$AY \quad | \quad \text{membrane} \quad | \quad BY \qquad (8\text{-}31)$$

The membrane potential in such a cell is called *bi-ionic potential.*

Bi-ionic potentials are complex phenomena. Even a qualitative interpretation requires a detailed examination of the system. The process occurring in a bi-ionic cell is interdiffusion of the two counter ions A and B within the membrane and the films (see Sec. 8-3c). The faster counter ion tends to diffuse at a higher rate. The resulting electric field enforces the equivalence of the counter-ion fluxes. The electric potential difference (interdiffusion potential) between the boundaries of the diffusion layer depends primarily on the charge sign and the mobility ratio of the counter ions. With a cation-exchanger membrane, the electric potential is more positive on the side facing the solution of the slower cation, and with an anion-exchanger membrane it is more negative on the side of the slower anion. The membrane potential, however, is not equal to the interdiffusion potential and may even have opposite sign. The membrane potential—defined as the potential difference between the bulk solutions—also includes the Donnan potentials at the membrane interfaces (Fig. 8-12). Each Donnan potential depends on the nature of the counter ion present and on the solution concentration. This dependence has been explained in Sec. 5-3c. Taking all effects together: with cation-exchanger membranes, the electric potential tends to be more positive in the solution which is more dilute or contains the counter ion of lower mobility, lower valence, or lower affinity for the ion exchanger. With anion-exchanger membranes the opposite holds. The

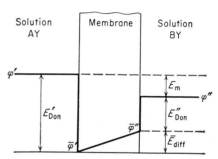

FIG. 8-12. Electric-potential profile in a membrane-diffusion controlled bi-ionic system (schematic). The membrane potential E_m consists of the interdiffusion potential $\bar{E}_{diff}$ in the membrane and the Donnan potentials E_{Don}. In the particular case shown, the interdiffusion potential and the membrane potential have opposite signs.

situation is further complicated by the fact that a change from membrane- to film-diffusion control may deeply affect the Donnan and diffusion potentials, particularly if the counter ions have different valences. Without a detailed analysis of all these factors, not even the sign of the bi-ionic potential can be predicted.

The counter-ion fluxes in bi-ionic cells are considerable and may change the composition of the solutions unless precautions are taken. The following quantitative treatment is restricted to constant solution compositions (quasi-stationary state).

The counter-ion fluxes and concentration profiles in bi-ionic systems have been calculated in Sec. 8-3c. The same equations can be used to calculate the membrane potential. Note that the presence of co-ions in the membrane and convection is neglected.* The limiting cases of

---

* Inclusion of co-ion transfer requires evaluation of the general integral given in Sec. 8-5. Solutions which, with certain simplifying assumptions, account for convection have been given by Mackay [53,55a].

complete membrane diffusion and film diffusion control and the intermediate case of partial film diffusion control will be discussed.

Complete Membrane Diffusion Control. The interdiffusion potential in the membrane is calculated from Eqs. (8-32) to (8-35):

$$
\bar{E}_{\text{diff}} = \frac{RT}{\mathfrak{F}} \left[\int_{'}^{''} \frac{\bar{D}_{\text{B}} - \bar{D}_{\text{A}} + (\bar{D}_{\text{A}}\bar{x}_{\text{A}}/z_{\text{B}})(\text{d} \ln K_{a\text{B}}'^{\text{A}}/\text{d}\bar{x}_{\text{A}})}{\bar{x}_{\text{A}}(\bar{D}_{\text{A}}z_{\text{A}} - \bar{D}_{\text{B}}z_{\text{B}}) + \bar{D}_{\text{B}}z_{\text{B}}} \, \text{d}\bar{x}_{\text{A}} - \frac{1}{z_{\text{B}}} \ln \frac{\bar{f}_{\text{B}}''}{\bar{f}_{\text{B}}'} \right]
$$

$$
= \frac{RT}{\mathfrak{F}} \left[\int_{'}^{''} H(\bar{x}_{\text{A}}) \, \text{d}\bar{x}_{\text{A}} - \frac{1}{z_{\text{B}}} \ln \frac{\bar{f}_{\text{B}}''}{\bar{f}_{\text{B}}'} \right] \quad (8\text{-}83)
$$

where the function $H(\bar{x}_{\text{A}})$ is defined by Eq. (8-83).

The membrane potential is obtained by adding the difference of the two Donnan potentials (see Fig. 8-12):

$$
E_{\text{m}} = \bar{E}_{\text{diff}} + E_{\text{Don}}' - E_{\text{Don}}''
$$

$$
= \frac{RT}{\mathfrak{F}} \left[\int_{'}^{''} H(\bar{x}_{\text{A}}) \, \text{d}\bar{x}_{\text{A}} + \frac{1}{z_{\text{A}}z_{\text{B}}} \left(\ln K_{a\text{B}}'^{\text{A}'} - z_{\text{B}} \ln \frac{\bar{C}'}{C'} - z_{\text{A}} \ln \frac{C''}{\bar{C}''} \right) \right.
$$

$$
\left. + \ln \frac{f_{\text{A}}'^{1/z_{\text{A}}}}{f_{\text{B}}''^{1/z_{\text{B}}}} \right] \quad (8\text{-}84)
$$

where $K_{a\text{B}}'^{\text{A}'}$ is the corrected molar selectivity coefficient at the left membrane interface, where $\bar{x}_{\text{A}} = 1$.

Explicit integration is possible if $\bar{D}_{\text{A}}/\bar{D}_{\text{B}}$, $\ln K_{a\text{B}}'^{\text{A}}$, and $\bar{C}$ are constant. After rearrangement, Eq. (8-84) then becomes

$$
E_{\text{m}} = \frac{RT}{\mathfrak{F}} \left[\frac{\bar{D}_{\text{B}} - \bar{D}_{\text{A}}}{\bar{D}_{\text{A}}z_{\text{A}} - \bar{D}_{\text{B}}z_{\text{B}}} \ln \frac{\bar{D}_{\text{B}}z_{\text{B}}}{\bar{D}_{\text{A}}z_{\text{A}}} + \frac{1}{z_{\text{A}}z_{\text{B}}} \ln K_{a\text{B}}'^{\text{A}} + \frac{z_{\text{A}} - z_{\text{B}}}{z_{\text{A}}z_{\text{B}}} \ln \frac{\bar{C}}{C'} + \frac{1}{z_{\text{B}}} \ln \frac{C'}{C''} \right.
$$

$$
\left. + \ln \frac{f_{\text{A}}'^{1/z_{\text{A}}}}{f_{\text{B}}''^{1/z_{\text{B}}}} \right] \quad (8\text{-}85)
$$

For counter ions of equal valences ($z_{\text{A}} = z_{\text{B}}$), Eq. (8-85) further reduces to

$$
E_{\text{m}} = \frac{RT}{z_{\text{A}}\mathfrak{F}} \ln \frac{\bar{D}_{\text{A}}a_{\text{A}}'\bar{f}_{\text{B}}}{\bar{D}_{\text{B}}a_{\text{B}}''\bar{f}_{\text{A}}} \quad (8\text{-}86)
$$

This relation was given as early as 1942 by Marshall [65].

In bi-ionic cells with counter ions of *equal* valence, the membrane potential [Eq. (8-86)] is practically independent of concentration, provided that the activity ratio $a_{\text{A}}'/a_{\text{B}}''$ of the solutions is kept constant. In cells with counter ions of *different* valences, however, the membrane potential [Eq. (8-85)] varies approximately linearly with the logarithm of the solution concentration (see Fig. 8-14). This variation is reflected in the third term of Eq. (8-85) and stems from the difference of the two Donnan potentials.

Bi-ionic potential measurements with counter ions of equal valence can be used for determining the *mobility ratio* $\bar{D}_A/\bar{D}_B$ in the membrane.   This ratio can be calculated by use of Eq. (8-86) from one potential measurement with solutions of known activities and a membrane of known (corrected) selectivity coefficient $K_{aB}'^A = \bar{f}_B/\bar{f}_A$.   A more reliable procedure has been described by Wyllie [139].   In one series of measurements, the activity of the solution AY is kept constant and the activity of the solution BY is varied. In a second series of measurements a_{BY} is kept constant and a_{AY} is varied.   When plotted versus the logarithm of solution activity, the potentials fall on two straight lines which intersect at $a_{AY} = a_{BY}$ (Fig. 8-13).   The mobility ratio is calculated from the membrane

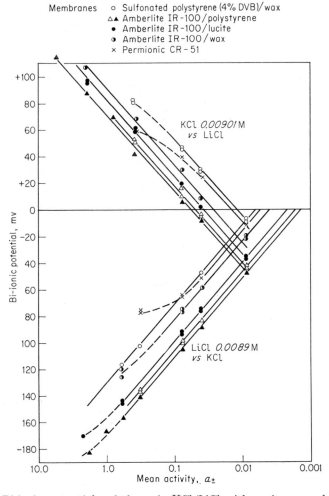

Membranes   o Sulfonated polystyrene (4% DVB)/wax
△▲ Amberlite IR-100/polystyrene
• Amberlite IR-100/lucite
◐ Amberlite IR-100/wax
× Permionic CR-51

Fig. 8-13. Bi-ionic potentials of the pair KCl/LiCl with various membranes.   The curves with negative slope are the potentials with $a_{KCl} = 0.01$ as a function of log a_{LiCl}. The curves with positive slope are the potentials with $a_{LiCl} = 0.01$ as a function of log a_{KCl}.   The mobility ratio $\bar{D}_K/\bar{D}_{Li}$ can be calculated from the curves if the selectivity is known.   *From M. R. J. Wyllie and S. L. Kanaan* [139].

potential at this intersection point.   Note that the equation used implies complete membrane diffusion control and constancy of the mobility ratio and the selectivity coefficient.

Complete Film Diffusion Control.   The behavior of film-diffusion controlled bi-ionic systems has been discussed in Sec. 8-3c.   Within the membrane there are no concentration gradients and, hence, no interdiffusion potential.   The membrane potential thus consists of the two interdiffusion potentials in the films and the two Donnan potentials.   For cells with counter ions of equal valence the membrane potential can be calculated from Eqs. (8-44) and (8-47):

$$E_m = E'_{\text{diff}} + E'_{\text{Don}} - E''_{\text{Don}} + E''_{\text{diff}}$$
$$= \frac{RT}{z_A \mathfrak{F}} \ln \frac{(C^0)' D_A}{(C^0)'' D_B} \tag{8-87}$$

where $(C^0)'$ and $(C^0)''$ are the concentrations in the two bulk solutions.

Note that activity coefficients and diffusion constants were assumed to be independent of concentration.

For counter ions of different valences, no simple solution is obtained.   An approximation, however, can be given.   Consider a fictitious system in which the solutions are separated by an intermediate aqueous layer impermeable for co-ions.   No membrane is present.   The potential difference across such a layer is readily calculated.   For counter ions of equal valences, the result is identical to Eq. (8-87).   For counter ions of different valences the potential difference is

$$E_m = \frac{RT}{\mathfrak{F}} \frac{D_A(C^0)' - D_B(C^0)''}{z_A D_A(C^0)' - z_B D_B(C^0)''} \ln \frac{z_A D_A(C^0)'}{z_B D_B(C^0)''} \tag{8-88}$$

Replacing membrane and films by the fictitious aqueous layer is equivalent to neglecting the effect of electrolyte accumulation and depletion (see Fig. 8-8) on the membrane potential.

The bi-ionic potential in film-diffusion controlled systems is larger in absolute value than the liquid-junction potential between the solutions.   Across the membrane, no co-ion transference can occur.   Thus the membrane potential must be strong enough to enforce complete equivalence of the counter-ion fluxes.   On the other hand, across a liquid junction, co-ions are transferred by the junction potential and assist in balancing the charge transfer by counter ions.

It is interesting to compare the bi-ionic potentials in membrane-diffusion and film-diffusion controlled systems with counter ions of different valences [Eqs. (8-85) and (8-88)].   With equal solution concentrations on either side of the membrane, the potential is concentration-dependent in the case of membrane diffusion control, and concentration-independent in the case of film diffusion control.   The membrane potentials in the two limiting cases may differ greatly and may even have opposite signs (Fig. 8-14). Thus the membrane potential is very strongly affected by the mechanism which determines the diffusion rate [26,93].

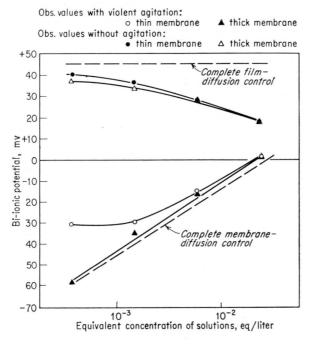

Fig. 8-14. Bi-ionic potentials between HCl and $CaCl_2$ solutions of equal normality. The theoretical potentials for ideal membrane diffusion and ideal film diffusion control (*broken lines*) have opposite sign and may differ by more than 100 mv. Experimental values obtained with agitation deviate from ideal membrane diffusion control only at very low concentrations and with thin membranes. When agitation is stopped, the system switches to partial or complete film diffusion control. Membranes: Amberplex C-1, thickness 0.08 and 0.30 cm, respectively. *From G. Scatchard and F. Helfferich* [93].

Partial Film Diffusion Control. The membrane potential can be calculated by the approximation method which has been used for calculating the counter-ion fluxes (Sec. 8-3c). First, the concentrations at the interfaces membrane/film are determined by successive approximations. These concentrations constitute the limits of integration in the calculation of the interdiffusion potentials in membrane and films. The Donnan potentials are obtained from Eq. (8-72). The membrane potential is the sum of all five single potential differences [26].

Extension to Other Boundary Conditions. The treatment is readily extended to cells of the type (8-49) in which both counter-ion species are present in both solutions (see page 363).

Experimental Evidence. A wealth of experimental results have been collected since Michaelis [74], in 1933, published the first measurements of bi-ionic potentials [3,14,21,28,55,55a,59,65,72,76,79,84,93,114–116,139]. Most of this work, however, was restricted to univalent ions and did not include independent determinations of diffusion coefficients and selectivity coefficients. The theory outlined here is of recent origin and has been tested only in a few systems where it gave very satisfactory results [26,28, 55,84].

e. Multi-ionic Potentials

In multi-ionic cells, both solutions contain various counter ions A, B, C, . . . , and L, M, . . . , respectively:

$$\text{AY, BY, } \ldots \quad | \quad \text{membrane} \quad | \quad \text{LY, MY, } \ldots \quad (8\text{-}50)$$

The membrane potential in such a cell is called *multi-ionic potential*.

In this section, a simple expression for the multi-ionic potential is given. It is derived from Eqs. (8-51) to (8-54) which have been used in Sec. 8-3c. Note that equal counter-ion valences,* ideal permselectivity, complete membrane diffusion control, constant activity coefficients, and absence of convection have been assumed. The interdiffusion potential in the membrane is obtained from the equations by solving for the electric potential gradient and integrating across the membrane:

$$\bar{E}_{\text{diff}} = \frac{RT}{z_i \mathfrak{F}} \ln \frac{\sum_j \bar{D}_j \bar{C}'_j}{\sum_k \bar{D}_k \bar{C}''_k} \qquad (8\text{-}89)$$

The membrane potential is [27,138]

$$E_m = \bar{E}_{\text{diff}} + E'_{\text{Don}} - E''_{\text{Don}} = \frac{RT}{z_i \mathfrak{F}} \ln \frac{\sum_j (\bar{D}_j a'_j / \bar{f}_j)}{\sum_k (\bar{D}_k a''_k / \bar{f}_k)} \qquad (8\text{-}90)$$

where subscripts j refer to counter ions A, B, . . . , and subscripts k to counter ions L, M, . . .

Membrane Electrodes in Mixed Electrolytes. The determination of the activity of an ion A in a solution of AY, BY, CY, . . . by means of a membrane electrode (see page 376) is a special multi-ionic problem. The system is

$$\begin{array}{c}\text{AY} \\ \text{(reference solution)}\end{array} \quad \bigg| \quad \text{membrane} \quad \bigg| \quad \text{AY, BY, CY, } \ldots \qquad (8\text{-}91)$$

---

* Occasionally the Henderson equation for the liquid-junction potential [29] has been used in deriving a simple relation for the multi-ionic potential with counter ions of different valences. In such systems, however, Henderson's assumption about the composition of the diffusion zone (see p. 370) does not hold.

An ideally specific membrane (i.e., permeable for A only) would give the concentration potential

$$E_{\mathrm{m}} = \frac{RT}{z_A \mathfrak{F}} \ln \frac{a'_A}{a''_A} \qquad (8\text{-}78)$$

Here, the unknown activity a''_A in the mixture can be calculated from the observed membrane potential and the reference activity a'_A. On the other hand, a nonideal membrane which is permeable also for B, C, etc. (but not for Y) gives the multi-ionic potential (equal counter-ion valences are assumed)

$$E_{\mathrm{m}} = \frac{RT}{z_i \mathfrak{F}} \ln \frac{\bar{D}_A a'_A / \bar{f}_A}{\displaystyle\sum_i (\bar{D}_i a''_i / \bar{f}_i)} = \frac{RT}{z_i \mathfrak{F}} \ln \frac{a'_A}{a''_A + \dfrac{\bar{D}_B \bar{f}_A}{\bar{D}_A \bar{f}_B} a''_B + \dfrac{\bar{D}_C \bar{f}_A}{\bar{D}_A \bar{f}_C} a''_C + \cdots} \qquad (8\text{-}92)$$

Equation (8-92) reduces to Eq. (8-78) if, and only if, all quotients $\bar{D}_i \bar{f}_A / \bar{D}_A \bar{f}_i$ ($i \neq A$) disappear. The logarithms of these quotients are proportional to the bi-ionic potentials in the systems BY/AY, CY/AY, etc., with equal activities in both solutions [see Eq. (8-86)]. Hence the bi-ionic potentials with solutions of the interfering ions quantitatively characterize the specificity of the membrane electrode [135].

Experimental Evidence. Multi-ionic potentials have so far been measured only with counter ions of equal valences. In this work, the diffusion coefficients have not been determined by independent methods. Nevertheless, the theory can be considered as qualitatively confirmed [15].

f. Nonisothermal Membrane Potentials

As a rule, there is an electric potential difference between electrolyte solutions of different temperatures, even if the solutions are of identical composition. In all other sections it has been assumed that the systems are isothermal. Nonisothermal membrane potentials can be calculated by the use of thermodynamics of irreversible processes. For solutions of identical composition and under equal hydrostatic pressure, the relation [31]

$$d\varphi = -\frac{1}{\mathfrak{F}} \sum_i \bar{t}_i Q_i^* \, d \ln T \qquad (8\text{-}93)$$

where Q_i^* = heat of transference of species i,

is obtained. Integration of this relation gives the membrane potential. However, the relation for the emf of the cell also involves the temperature coefficients of the electrode potentials and is difficult to evaluate.

In the past, little attention has been devoted to nonisothermal membrane systems. The only measurements so far reported are by Ikeda [35] who found a temperature coefficient of the potential of 0.05 mv/deg (the warmer solution having the more positive potential) with dilute KCl solutions and a cation-permselective collodion membrane.

8-5. GENERAL INTEGRATION OF THE NERNST-PLANCK EQUATIONS*

In the preceding sections, the set of equations given in Sec. 8-2 has been used to calculate ionic fluxes, concentration profiles, and membrane potentials in specific systems.

---

* The general integration is not required in other parts of the book. This section may be skipped without loss in continuity.

The solutions derived are limiting cases of the general solution which will be shown in this section.

A general integration of the flux equations is possible if absence of convection, complete membrane-diffusion control, and constancy of activity coefficients, diffusion coefficients, and fixed-charge concentration is assumed. With these idealizations, the flux equations (8-2) reduce to the Nernst-Planck equations [77,85]

$$J_i = -D_i \left(\text{grad } C_i + z_i C_i \frac{\mathfrak{F}}{RT} \text{grad } \varphi \right) \tag{6-35}$$

These equations are interconnected by the electroneutrality restriction (7-5) and the charge-conservation relation (7-4). This set of equations has been solved for steady state [condition (8-3)] and one-dimensional geometry. Earlier solutions for special cases have been given by Planck [85], Behn [2], Pleijel [86], Goldman [18], and Teorell [127]. A quite general solution for arbitrary electrolyte mixtures, charged and uncharged membranes, and with and without external electric field has been derived by Schlögl [99].

The boundary conditions for the integration are the concentrations of all ionic species at the membrane/solution interfaces (i.e., at $x = 0$ and $x = d$). These intramembrane boundary concentrations are calculated from the solution concentrations by use of the Donnan relation (8-73).

For the integration, the ionic species are classified in "valence groups" z_k. For example, with the three electrolytes CaCl$_2$, NaCl, and KBr, the groups are

$$z_1 = +2 \text{ (for Ca}^{2+}) \qquad z_2 = +1 \text{ (for Na}^+ \text{ and K}^+) \qquad z_3 = -1 \text{ (for Cl}^- \text{ and Br}^-)$$

The subscript k is the group index (here, k = 1,2,3). Another subscript j is used to denote the individual species within a group. Thus, $\bar{C}_{jk}$ is the concentration of the jth ion in the group k. The integration makes use of the "group concentrations" $\bar{C}_k$ and the "anion-plus-cation concentration" $\bar{c}$ ("Totalkonzentration" in Schlögl's paper). They are defined by

$$\bar{C}_k \equiv \sum_j \bar{C}_{jk} \qquad \bar{c} \equiv \sum_k \bar{C}_k$$

Integration across the membrane gives the *flux* of the ion jk:

$$J_{jk} = -\frac{\bar{D}_{jk}}{d} \frac{\bar{C}_{jk}'' \xi^{z_k} - \bar{C}_{jk}'}{\bar{C}_k'' \xi^{z_k} - \bar{C}_k'} \cdot \zeta_k \left(\frac{1}{z_k} - q_1 \right) \cdots \left(\frac{1}{z_k} - q_{n-1} \right) (\bar{c}'' - \bar{c}' - \omega X \ln \xi) \tag{8-94}$$

Here, $\xi \equiv \exp(\mathfrak{F}\varphi/RT)$; the normalization of the electric potential, φ, is such that $\bar{\varphi} = 0$ at $x = 0$; superscripts $'$ and $''$ refer to the left and right membrane interface, respectively; ζ_k is defined by

$$\frac{1}{\zeta_k} \equiv \prod_{\substack{i \neq k}}^{i=1,\ldots n} \left(\frac{1}{z_k} - \frac{1}{z_i} \right)$$

The parameters $q_1, q_2, \ldots, q_{n-1}$ are obtained from the relation

$$\ln \xi = q \ln \frac{\sum_k \dfrac{z_k \bar{C}_k'}{q - 1/z_k}}{\sum_k \dfrac{z_k \bar{C}_k''}{q - 1/z_k}}$$

Note that Eq. (8-94) is not restricted to zero electric current.

Combination of Eqs. (8-94) and (7-4) gives the *electric current density*

$$I = \mathfrak{F} \sum_{k} \sum_{j} z_k J_{jk} \tag{8-95}$$

The fluxes and the current density depend, of course, on the electric potential difference between the solutions. The *current-voltage characteristic* of the system is obtained in the following way. First, the current density is calculated and plotted as a function of $\ln \xi$. Then the difference between the two Donnan potentials [obtained from Eq. (8-72)] is added to the intramembrane potential corresponding to $\ln \xi$. The *membrane potential* in the limiting case of zero electric current corresponds to the point on the current-voltage characteristic where $I = 0$.

The *concentration profiles* are calculated by the following method. First, the "characteristic roots" $Q_1, Q_2, \ldots, Q_{n-1}$ must be determined. These roots are functions of the concentrations at the location x and satisfy the relation

$$\ln \xi(x) = q \ln \frac{(q - Q_1') \cdots (q - Q_{n-1}')}{(q - Q_1(x)) \cdots (q - Q_{n-1}(x))} \tag{8-96}$$

for every value of $q = q_1, q_2, \ldots, q_{n-1}$. Here, Q_i' is the value of Q_i at $x = 0$. Substituting q in Eq. (8-96) successively by $q_1, q_2, \ldots, q_{n-1}$ one obtains $(n - 2)$ relations between $Q_1, Q_2, \ldots, Q_{n-1}$ at the location x:

$$A_1 \cdot |(q_1 - Q_1) \cdots (q_1 - Q_{n-1})|^{q_1} = A_2 \cdot |(q_2 - Q_1) \cdots (q_2 - Q_{n-1})|^{q_2}$$
$$= \cdots = A_{n-1} \cdot |(q_{n-1} - Q_1) \cdots (q_{n-1} - Q_{n-1})|^{q_{n-1}} \tag{8-97}$$

where $\qquad\qquad 1/A_1 \equiv |(q_1 - Q_1') \cdots (q_1 - Q_{n-1}')|^{q_1}$, etc.

A specific value of Q_1 is arbitrarily chosen and introduced into Eq. (8-97) to give the corresponding values of $Q_2, \ldots, Q_{n-1}$. These values are used for calculating the group concentrations at the (still unknown) location x:

$$z_k \bar{C}_k(x) = -\omega X \zeta_k \left(\frac{1}{z_k} - Q_1 \right) \cdots \left(\frac{1}{z_k} - Q_{n-1} \right) \tag{8-98}$$

Now, $\ln \xi(x)$ is calculated by introducing the numerical values of the roots into Eq. (8-96) and using, say, $q = q_1$. Finally, the value of x is obtained from

$$\frac{x}{d} = \frac{\bar{c}(x) - \bar{c}' - \omega X \ln \xi(x)}{\bar{c}'' - \bar{c}' - \omega X \ln \xi(d)} \tag{8-99}$$

The individual ionic concentrations $\bar{C}_{jk}(x)$ are given by

$$\frac{\bar{C}_{jk}(x)\xi(x)^{z_k} - \bar{C}_{jk}'}{\bar{C}_k(x)\xi(x)^{z_k} - \bar{C}_k'} = \frac{\bar{C}_{jk}''\xi(d)^{z_k} - \bar{C}_{jk}'}{\bar{C}_k''\xi(d)^{z_k} - \bar{C}_k'} \tag{8-100}$$

Repetition of this procedure with different values of Q_1—and thus of x—yields the various $\bar{C}_{jk}$ as functions of x, i.e., the concentration profiles.

The calculation of fluxes and current densities and particularly of membrane potentials and concentration profiles by this method is not quite simple and is rather time-consuming. The interested reader is referred to Schlögl's paper [99] in which details of the derivation and calculation, practical examples, and possible short cuts are discussed.

The integration is quite general and holds—under the assumptions mentioned at the outset—for systems of arbitrary complexity. Simpler solutions are found if, and only if, the electric potential is a linear function of x. It can be shown that this condition is met in the "monogroup" case, i.e., if all mobile species in the membrane belong to the

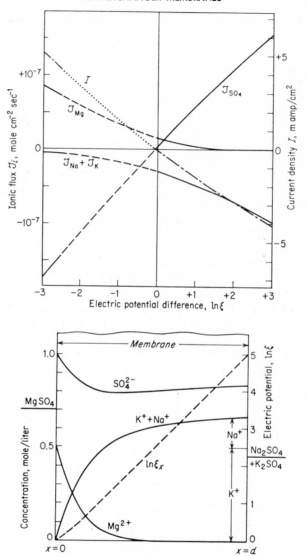

FIG. 8-15. Theoretical fluxes, current density, and concentration profiles in an anion-exchanger membrane under the following conditions:

Concentration of fixed ionic groups 1.0 meq/cm³
Left solution MgSO₄ 0.707 N
Right solution K₂SO₄ 0.677 N + Na₂SO₄ 0.229 N
Diffusion coefficients $\bar{D}_{Mg} = 3 \cdot 10^{-6}$ cm²/sec $\bar{D}_{K} = 5 \cdot 10^{-6}$ cm²/sec
                       $\bar{D}_{SO_4} = 3 \cdot 10^{-6}$ $\bar{D}_{Na} = 3 \cdot 10^{-6}$

Upper diagram: fluxes and current density as a function of the electric potential difference ln ξ. *Broken and dotted lines:* interpolation in the irregularity range of the parameter function ln ξ (q). *Lower diagram:* concentration profiles for ln $\xi = 5$. Note the minimum in the profile of SO_4^{2-}. *From R. Schlögl* [99].

same valence group (see Secs. 8-3c and 8-4e). The integration becomes simpler still if only two mobile ionic species are present. Here, more elaborate solutions can be given which include the effects of activity coefficients, of variable diffusion coefficients, etc. (see Secs. 8-3b,c and 8-4c,d). The most important simpler cases have been discussed in the previous sections.

8-6. ANOMALOUS OSMOSIS

In previous sections, diffusion of solutes across membranes has been examined. Diffusion of solvent, however, has been disregarded. Solvent diffusion (*osmosis*) across ion-exchanger membranes is a very interesting phenomenon. Effects are observed which are not found with nonionic membranes.

Let us consider a simple concentration cell. The solutions on either membrane side differ in concentration but contain the same solute throughout. No external electric field is applied.

With membranes which are nonionic or completely impermeable for the solute, the solvent flux is from the dilute to the concentrated solution and is proportional to the osmotic pressure difference between the two solutions. This pressure difference is readily determined in a cell in which the solutions are in closed compartments carrying capillaries (see Fig. 8-29). Osmosis makes the level in the capillary with the concentrated solution rise until the hydrostatic counter pressure balances the osmotic pressure difference. The osmotic pressure difference is given almost entirely by the total concentrations of the dissolved species (ions or molecules) and depends very little on the individual nature of the latter. Osmosis is said to be "normal" if this simple law is obeyed, i.e., if the levels in the capillaries attain the theoretical height.

With ion-exchanger membranes and electrolytes as solutes, the osmotic behavior is "anomalous." In the capillary with the concentrated solution there may be a transient rise of the level to many times the theoretical height (*anomalous positive osmosis*) or even a depression (*negative osmosis*).* Here, obviously, the osmotic pressure difference is not the only driving force for solvent transfer. Both anomalous positive and negative osmosis involve transfer of solvent against the gradient of its general chemical potential. This requires energy which must be supplied by another process, namely, by diffusion of the solute. Anomalous osmosis cannot occur with membranes which are completely impermeable for the solute.

A quantitative theory of anomalous osmosis has been developed by Schlögl [100] who integrated the flux equations including the convection terms.† The essential features of this theory are as follows.

---

* See Söllner [110,111] who also summarized previous experimental results, and Refs. 32, 45, 130.

† Schlögl's integration is restricted to one 1,1-valent electrolyte; activity coefficients, diffusion coefficients, specific flow resistance, fixed-charge concentration, and fractional pore volume are assumed to be constant.

There are two driving forces which act on the pore liquid in the membrane and produce convection. The first force is the pressure gradient, the second the electric potential gradient. The effect of pressure is obvious. The electric field produces convection because the pore liquid carries a net electric charge which balances the fixed membrane charges (see Sec. 7-3).

It is readily shown that the effect of pressure alone always results in *positive osmosis*. The swelling pressure, i.e., the pressure difference between ion exchanger and solution, is higher on the side of the dilute solution. Thus, with solutions under equal hydrostatic pressure, the pressure *in* the membrane is higher on the side of the dilute solution and drives the solvent toward the concentrated solution. (Note that at the interfaces themselves there is equilibrium, i.e., interfacial differences in pressure, electric potential, and concentrations exactly balance one another.)

The effect of pressure may be enhanced, partly balanced, or even outweighed by the electric field. Strong diffusion potentials arise when the mobilities of the counter ion and the co-ion differ greatly. The faster ion tends to diffuse at the higher rate and thus to build up a space charge of its sign on the side facing the dilute solution. If the counter ion is the faster one, the resulting electric field—in addition to enforcing equivalence of the ionic fluxes—drives the electrically charged pore liquid as a whole toward the concentrated solution. The effect of the electric field thus adds to that of pressure and produces *anomalous positive osmosis*. On the other hand, if the co-ion is the faster one, the electric field has opposite sign and drives the pore liquid toward the dilute solution. The electric field may be stronger than the pressure. In this case there is *negative osmosis*.

The interaction of pressure and electric field and their relative importance depends on the flow resistance of the membrane material and on the ionic mobilities. Pressure alone produces a shift of the electrically charged pore liquid and thus a counteracting electric potential difference. This counteracting force is proportional to the charge shift produced, i.e., it is large in membranes with low flow resistance, with high concentration of fixed charges (high net charge of the pore liquid), and with ions of low mobility (the faster the ions, the more readily is the electric potential gradient leveled out by transference).

In membranes with little resistance to solvent flow and with ions of low mobility, osmosis may deeply affect the electrolyte flux. Very strong positive osmosis may carry the electrolyte from the dilute to the concentrated solution ("incongruent salt flux"). Here, solvent diffusion provides the energy required for transferring the electrolyte against its chemical potential gradient.

Earlier investigators have contended that anomalous osmosis arises from heteroporosity of the membrane. Schlögl's theory, in contrast to these earlier approaches, requires no assumptions about the pore geometry and thus shows that anomalous osmosis is the rule with ionic solutes and charged membranes of any structure. This theory explains qualitatively the experimental data which have been accumulated. These data, however, are

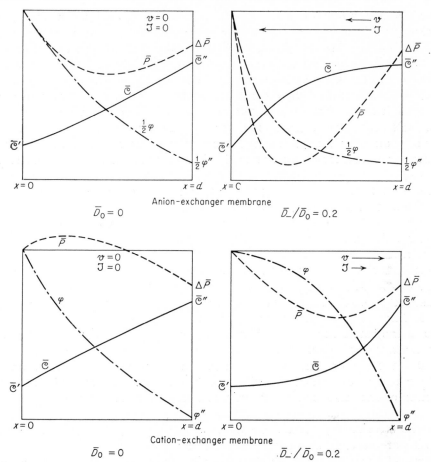

FIG. 8-16. Theoretical concentration, potential, and pressure profiles in various membranes in concentration cells. The electric potential $\bar{\varphi}$ and the pressure $\bar{P}$ are plotted from the upper limit of the diagram; $\bar{c} = \bar{C}_+ + \bar{C}_-$ is the "anion-plus-cation concentration." The profiles are calculated for systems with one 1,1-valent electrolyte with a very mobile cation ($\bar{D}_+ \gg \bar{D}_-$). *Left:* diagrams for membranes with high flow resistance. *Right:* diagrams for low flow resistance [the quantity $\bar{D}_0$ is defined in Eq. (8-134)]. The anion-exchanger membrane with low flow resistance shows negative osmosis; the cation-exchanger membrane with low flow resistance shows anomalous positive osmosis and incongruent salt flux. *From R. Schlögl* [100].

insufficient for quantitative tests because other properties of the systems (flow resistance, diffusion coefficients, etc.) have not been measured.

8-7. STREAMING POTENTIAL, STREAMING CURRENT, AND ELECTROLYTE FILTRATION

In the preceding sections, systems have been examined in which the solutions are under equal hydrostatic pressure. The following discussion deals with the effect of excess hydrostatic pressure exerted on one of the solutions.   The pressure difference gives rise to three important phenomena: streaming potential, streaming current, and electrolyte filtration.

Excess pressure applied to the solution on one membrane side forces pore liquid through the membrane.   The pore liquid carries a net electric charge.   Hence, its displacement builds up an electric potential difference, the so-called *streaming potential* (Fig. 8-17).   The streaming potential produces two effects.   First, it acts on the electrically charged pore liquid as a whole, partly balancing the effect of pressure and thus reducing the flow across the membrane.   Second, it accelerates the co-ions and slows

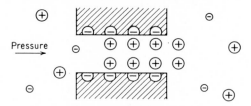

FIG. 8-17. Origin of the streaming potential (*schematic*).   Excess hydrostatic pressure on one solution causes displacement of the pore liquid and thus a shift of net electric charge.

down the counter ions so that both species, despite their different concentrations, transfer equivalent amounts of electric charge.   The electric field makes the counter ions swim against the tide and the co-ions with the tide. The effect of pressure, however, is necessarily stronger than the counteracting electric field which it has generated.   Thus, relative to the matrix, both species are carried along with the solvent flow.

The streaming potential can be short-circuited by reversible electrodes which are attached to the membrane surfaces and are connected with one another.   Now, there is no electric field across the membrane.   The net charge transfer resulting from excess counter-ion flux produces an electric current in the electrode circuit.   This current is called *streaming current.*

With ion-exchanger membranes of high permselectivity, there is strong Donnan exclusion of the co-ion.   Electrolyte transfer across the membrane remains small because of the lack of co-ions, in spite of the streaming potential which enhances the co-ion flux.   Solvent transfer is obstructed not nearly as much.   Thus, the electrolyte is partially held back by the membrane (*electrolyte filtration*) [67,107].   This filter action is electrostatic and not due to a mechanical sieve effect.   Thus it is the rule even if the pore width of the membrane is considerably larger than the ionic diameters [67,107].

Streaming potential.   The calculation of the streaming potential in systems with solutions of different concentrations is rather complex.   The derivation in the following is restricted to systems where the solutions are of identical composition and where electrolyte accumulation and depletion at the membrane surfaces (resulting from filter action) is suppressed by strong agitation. The effect of electrolyte accumulation and depletion will be discussed farther below (see page 395).

Under the assumptions mentioned immediately above there are no concentration gradients within the membrane. Thus the ionic fluxes are given by

$$J_i = -z_i \bar{C}_i \bar{u}_i \frac{\Delta \bar{\varphi}}{d} + \bar{C}_i \mathfrak{v} \tag{7-3}$$

where $\Delta \bar{\varphi} \equiv \bar{\varphi}'' - \bar{\varphi}'$.

Two driving forces act on the electrically charged pore liquid, namely, the pressure gradient and the electric potential gradient (see Sec. 8-6). A short calculation gives the rate of motion $\mathfrak{v}$ of the center of gravity of the pore liquid

$$\mathfrak{v} = -\frac{\Delta \bar{P}}{\rho_0 d} + \omega \bar{u}_0 \frac{\Delta \bar{\varphi}}{d} \qquad \left(\bar{u}_0 \equiv \frac{\mathfrak{F} X}{\rho_0 \epsilon} \right) \tag{8-101}$$

where $\Delta \bar{P} \equiv \bar{P}'' - \bar{P}'$; P = pressure; ρ_0 = specific flow resistance; ω = sign of fixed charges; ϵ = fractional pore volume.

Equations (7-3) and (8-101) are subject to the restrictions

$$\sum_i z_i \bar{C}_i + \omega X = 0 \qquad \text{electroneutrality} \tag{7-5}$$

$$\sum_i z_i J_i = 0 \qquad \text{no electric current} \tag{8-102}$$

With solutions of identical composition, there is no difference in the Donnan potentials and swelling pressures between the two membrane interfaces. Thus $\Delta \bar{P}$ and $\Delta \bar{\varphi}$ equal the hydrostatic pressure difference ΔP and the electric potential difference $\Delta \varphi$ (streaming potential), respectively, between the two solutions. Solving Eqs. (7-3), (8-101), (7-5), and (8-102) for $\Delta \varphi$ and using Eq. (7-8) one obtains the streaming potential

$$\Delta \varphi = \frac{\omega X}{\rho_0 \left(\sum_i z_i^2 \bar{C}_i \bar{u}_i + X \bar{u}_0 \right)} \Delta P = \frac{\omega X \mathfrak{F}}{\rho_0 \bar{\kappa}} \Delta P \tag{8-103}*$$

where $\bar{\kappa}$ = specific electric conductivity of the membrane.

According to Eq. (8-103), the streaming potential is proportional to the hydrostatic pressure difference and inversely proportional to the specific flow resistance of the membrane. There is little dependence on fixed-charge concentration and specific conductivity since their effects largely

---

* A corresponding equation for one 1,1-valent electrolyte has been given by G. Schmid [107,108]. See also Eqs. (8-104) and (8-105).

cancel. The concentration of the solutions affects the streaming potential only in so far as both the conductivity and the flow resistance of the membrane increase with the solution concentration when the latter becomes comparable to the fixed-charge concentration. The streaming potential does not depend on the membrane thickness. The streaming potential across a typical ion-exchanger membrane ($X \approx 2$ N $= 2 \cdot 10^{-3}$ mole/cm^3; $\bar{\kappa} \approx 10^{-2}\Omega^{-1}$ cm^{-1}; $\rho_0 \approx 10^{13}$ g cm^{-3} sec^{-1}) is of the order of a few millivolts per atmosphere pressure difference between the solutions.

Streaming current. The streaming current is calculated in a similar way. Here, $\Delta\bar{\varphi} = 0$, since the streaming potential is short-circuited. Instead of Eq. (8-102) the relation

$$I = \mathfrak{F} \sum_i z_i J_i \qquad (7\text{-}4)$$

for the electric current density I is used. Solving Eqs. (7-3), (8-101), (7-5), and (7-4) for I, one obtains the streaming current

$$I_{\Delta\varphi=0} = \frac{\omega X \mathfrak{F}}{\rho_0 d} \Delta P \qquad (8\text{-}104)*$$

The streaming current is proportional to the hydrostatic pressure difference and the fixed-charge concentration and inversely proportional to the specific flow resistance and the membrane thickness. The concentration of the solutions has an effect only in so far as it may influence the flow resistance. With a typical ion-exchanger membrane ($X \approx 2$ N $= 2 \cdot 10^{-3}$ mole/cm^3; $\rho_0 = 10^{13}$ g cm^{-3} sec^{-1}; $d \approx 0.1$ cm) the streaming current is of the order of 0.1 to 1 ma/cm^2 per atmosphere pressure difference between the solutions.

Ionic fluxes. The flux of an arbitrary ion j across the membrane (in the absence of electric current) can be calculated from Eqs. (7-3), (8-101), and (8-103)

$$J_j = - \frac{\Delta P}{\rho_0 d} (\bar{C}_j + \omega X \bar{t}_j) \qquad (8\text{-}105)*$$

where t_j = transference number of species j; see Eq. (7-12).

This relation holds for counter ions and co-ions. In highly permselective membranes the co-ion fluxes become very small. If only one counter-ion species is present, its flux is also very small (in this case, $z_A \bar{C}_A \rightarrow -\omega X$, and $z_A \bar{t}_A \rightarrow 1$). If several counter ion species are present, however, the faster species migrates toward the solution of higher pressure and the slower species toward the solution of lower pressure. With the faster species, the

---

* See footnote to p. 393.

transference caused by the streaming potential outweighs the transport by convection; with the slower species it does not. Such "sorting effects" will be discussed in a later section (see Sec. 8-9).

Electrolyte filtration. The quantitative treatment of electrolyte filtration is rather complex. The principal factors involved, however, are readily shown by simple equations which hold for systems with only one electrolyte and with equal solution concentrations on both membrane sides. According to Eq. (8-105) the electrolyte flux (in equivalents per unit time and unit membrane cross section) across the membrane is

$$z_A J_A = - \frac{\Delta P}{\rho_0 d} (z_A \bar{C}_A + \omega X z_A \bar{t}_A) \tag{8-106}$$

The volume transfer (volume per unit time and unit membrane cross section) across the membrane is obtained from Eqs. (8-101) and (8-103):

$$\dot{V} = \epsilon \mathfrak{v} = - \frac{\Delta P}{\rho_0 d} \epsilon \left(1 - \frac{\bar{u}_0 \mathfrak{F} X}{\bar{\kappa}} \right) \tag{8-107}$$

Dividing Eq. (8-106) by Eq. (8-107) and using Eqs. (7-8), (7-12), and (7-5), one obtains the concentration C_s of the solution which leaves the membrane on the side of lower pressure ("streaming concentration")

$$C_s = \frac{z_A J_A}{\epsilon \mathfrak{v}} = \frac{-z_A \bar{C}_A z_Y \bar{C}_Y (z_A \bar{u}_A - z_Y \bar{u}_Y)}{\epsilon (z_A^2 \bar{C}_A \bar{u}_A + z_Y^2 \bar{C}_Y \bar{u}_Y)} \tag{8-108}$$

In the limiting case of almost ideal permselectivity ($\bar{C}_Y \ll \bar{C}_A$), Eq. (8-108) reduces to

$$C_{s(\lim \bar{c}_Y \to 0)} = -z_Y \bar{C}_Y \frac{z_A \bar{u}_A - z_Y \bar{u}_Y}{\epsilon z_A \bar{u}_A} \tag{8-109}$$

The filter action can be quantitatively characterized by the ratio C/C_s, where C is the solution concentration (in equivalents per unit volume). When $\bar{C}_Y$ is substituted by use of the limiting law (8-29), the ratio becomes

$$\left(\frac{C}{C_s} \right)_{(\lim C_Y \to 0)} = \left(\frac{X}{C} \right)^{-z_Y/z_A} \left(\frac{\bar{f}_\pm}{f_\pm} \right)^{(z_A - z_Y)/z_A} \frac{\epsilon z_A \bar{u}_A}{z_A \bar{u}_A - z_Y \bar{u}_Y} \tag{8-110}$$

This relation shows that filter action increases with increasing ratio X/C and is stronger with counter ions of lower valence and co-ions of high valence.

Effect of Electrolyte Accumulation and Depletion at the Membrane Surfaces. As a result of filter action, the electrolyte is held back at the membrane surface on the side of higher pressure, and a dilute solution leaves the membrane on the other side. With highly permselective membranes, this effect may be so strong that even violent agitation of the solution is insufficient to keep the electrolyte concentrations constant up to the membrane surfaces. The consequence is electrolyte accumulation in the Nernst film on the side of higher pressure, and electrolyte depletion in the film on the other side. Concentration gradients in the membrane and the films are built up, filter action declines, and the streaming potential is changed.

These effects show up most clearly in the behavior of the streaming poten-

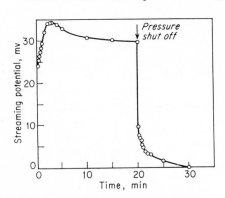

FIG. 8-18. Streaming potential as a function of time. *System:* collodion membrane between $2 \cdot 10^{-4}$ M KCl solutions; excess pressure on one solution 63.5 mm Hg. *From G. Schmid and H. Schwartz* [107].

tial [107]. When pressure is first applied, the streaming potential assumes the value given by Eq. (8-103). Subsequently, electrolyte accumulation and depletion cause an additional concentration potential across the membrane. The (over-all) streaming potential shows a transient rise. After a certain time, the streaming concentration on the low-pressure side rises because of the higher concentration at the membrane surface on the other side. This causes the streaming potential to drop until a steady state is attained. When the pressure is shut off, the potential difference does not break down immediately. It takes some time until the concentration gradient and the concentration potential have disappeared. A characteristic experimental curve is shown in Fig. 8-18.

The initial and steady-state streaming potentials are usually similar. The filter action, however, decreases sharply from its initial value and can be held on a significant level only by violent agitation.

The quantitative treatment of the steady state is complex, even with solutions of equal composition. It requires the simultaneous solution of the flux equations (8-2), the convection equation (8-101), and the Donnan equilibria (8-72) under the conditions of electroneutrality, absence of electric current, and the continuity condition in the films

$$\frac{\partial}{\partial x} \left(\frac{2 D_+ D_-}{D_+ + D_-} \frac{\partial C}{\partial x} \right) - \mathfrak{v} \frac{\partial C}{\partial x} = \frac{\partial C}{\partial t} = 0 \qquad (8\text{-}111)$$

Within the membrane the mathematical problem is the same as in anomalous osmosis. The only difference is that, here, the boundary concentrations are eigenvalues rather than being directly obtained from the solution concentrations.

Probably the most serious idealization in the derivation of the equations in this chapter is the assumption that there are no specific interactions between the various mobile species and the matrix or fixed ionic groups. This idealization and its consequences have been discussed in Sec. 7-4. Nevertheless, the equations are at least qualitatively successful in explaining experimental results [67,107].   For quantitative comparisons the available data are insufficient.

8-8. TRANSPORT OF ELECTRIC CURRENT ACROSS MEMBRANES

The preceding sections were devoted to systems in which no external electric field was applied.   The following discussion deals with the effect of an electric current which is passed through a membrane cell:

$$\text{cathode} \quad | \quad \text{solution 1} \quad | \quad \text{membrane} \quad | \quad \text{solution 2} \quad | \quad \text{anode} \quad (8\text{-}112)$$

Membranes with high concentration of fixed ionic groups have good electric conductivity.   The electric current is carried by ions.   In cells of the type (8-112) there is ionic transference superimposed on ionic diffusion.   Ionic transference also causes convection of the pore liquid (electroosmosis; Sec. 8-8b).

The electric current transfers many more counter ions than co-ions. This effect can be utilized for removing electrolytes from solutions by electrodialysis (Sec. 8-8a).

The validity of the flux equations is not restricted to systems without electric current.   The individual ion has no means of knowing whether the electric field in the membrane has been generated by a diffusion process within the system or by a voltage source outside.   The general integration (Sec. 8-5), which includes the condition of zero electric current only as a limiting case, can thus be applied to cells of the type (8-112) also.   In this integration, however, it was assumed that no convection occurs.   With high current densities and membranes of low flow resistance, the effect of convection cannot be neglected.   The treatment in this section includes convection.

a. Ionic Transference and Electrodialysis

Cells with "direct" reversible electrodes.   The effect of electric current is best shown by a practical example.   Consider the cell

$$- \quad \text{Ag|AgCl} \quad | \quad \text{NaCl} \quad | \quad \begin{array}{c} \text{cation-exchanger} \\ \text{membrane} \end{array} \quad | \quad \text{NaCl} \quad | \quad \text{AgCl|Ag} \quad +$$

$$(8\text{-}113)$$

The electrodes are reversible with respect to the co-ion (Cl^-).   The electric current transfers ions across the membrane.   This process is called *electrodialysis*.

With an ideally permselective membrane there is transference only of the counter ion (Na^+).   The reactions produced by the electric current are

Cathode	Membrane	Anode
$AgCl + e^- \rightarrow \underline{Ag} + Cl^-$	$\leftarrow\mid\!- Na^+$	$Cl^- + \underline{Ag} \rightarrow \underline{AgCl} + e^- \quad (8\text{-}114)$

One faraday of electricity passed through the cell produces one equivalent of Cl⁻ at the cathode, transfers one equivalent of Na⁺ across the membrane, and consumes one equivalent of Cl⁻ at the anode. Thus the NaCl content of the cathode compartment is increased by one equivalent, and that of the anode compartment is decreased by one equivalent. The *current efficiency*—defined as the change in equivalent content per faraday—is unity. The electric energy is stored by the system as free energy and can be recovered completely by using the resulting concentration potential as a voltage source.

Actual membranes are not ideally permselective. In a cell with a non-ideal membrane the electrode reactions are the same, but the electric current also transfers Cl⁻ ions from the cathode to the anode compartment. With solutions of equal concentration on both membrane sides the number of equivalents of Na⁺ transferred by one faraday is, by definition, $\bar{t}_{Na}$. Thus the current efficiency is equal to $\bar{t}_{Na}$ and is less than unity. With arbitrary electrolytes, the current efficiency is quite generally

$$q_I = \sum_j z_j \bar{t}_j \qquad (8\text{-}115)$$

Summation is carried out over all counter-ion species.

The counter-ion transference numbers decrease with increasing solution concentration (see Sec. 7-2), and so does the current efficiency.

Equation (8-115) only holds as long as the solution concentrations have not been changed significantly by the electrodialysis process. The progressing electrolyte accumulation in one compartment and depletion in the other cause electrolyte diffusion which counteracts transference and thus reduces the current efficiency.

The effects of transference and diffusion are not additive. Their complex interaction can only be resolved by integrating the flux equations. This integration (including convection) will be given in Sec. 8-8c. At the moment, it may suffice to point out qualitatively how the current efficiency is affected by the operating conditions. Electric transference, in the absence of diffusion, is proportional to the current density and (at constant current density) independent of the membrane thickness. The rate of diffusion, in the absence of electric transference, is inversely proportional to the membrane thickness. Within certain limits the adverse effect of diffusion on current efficiency can thus be minimized by choosing thick membranes and operating with a high current density. Several other points must be considered, however. First, the energy requirement is higher with thick membranes and high current densities because the required operating voltage and the resistive losses (heat evolution) are higher. Second, beyond a certain critical current density the current efficiency drops sharply (see farther below). Increase in fixed-charge concentration and decrease in solution concentration have a beneficial effect on the current efficiency since both reduce the rate of diffusion and increase the transference numbers of the counter ions. With dilute solutions, however, the critical current density is lower and the electric resistance of the cell is higher. Finally, the diffusion rate depends on the concentration difference between the solutions. The adverse effect of diffusion thus becomes stronger as electrodialysis progresses.

Critical Current Density. The current density cannot be increased beyond a certain critical value without causing a sharp drop in the current efficiency and an equally sharp rise in the energy requirement. In the membrane, the current is carried almost exclusively by the counter ion, whereas in the solution it is carried by both the counter ion and the co-ion. Thus the transference of the counter ion away through the membrane is higher than the transference in the solution up to the membrane surface. The difference must be made up by convection (agitation) and diffusion. Convection does not affect the Nernst film at the membrane surface. Across this film, the missing counter ions can be supplied by diffusion only. The maximum possible diffusion flux across the film is proportional to the solution concentration. With dilute solutions and high current densities there is electrolyte depletion at the membrane surface. The ohmic resistance and thus the voltage drop increase until water is dissociated. The H^+ ions (OH^- ions in the case of an anion-exchanger membrane) now compete with the electrolyte counter ion for being transferred across the membrane, and the OH^- ions (H^+ ions with anion-exchanger membranes) are transferred back into the solution. The current efficiency drops because of H^+ (or OH^-) transfer, and the energy requirement rises because, in addition to the energy of transference, the dissociation energy of water is consumed [48,88].

The critical current density is readily calculated. For the sake of simplicity it will be assumed that only one electrolyte AY is present and that the membrane is ideally permselective. In this case, there is no net co-ion flux and the electric current density is

$$I = \mathfrak{F} z_A J_A \tag{8-116}$$

Integration of the Nernst-Planck equations (6-35) in the film under the restrictions of electroneutrality ($z_A C_A + z_Y C_Y = 0$) and zero co-ion flux ($J_Y = 0$) gives

$$z_A J_A = -D_A \frac{C^0 - C''}{\delta} \left(1 - \frac{z_A}{z_Y}\right) \tag{8-117}$$

where C^0 = equivalent concentration in bulk solution; C'' = equivalent concentration at membrane surface.

The critical current density I_{cr} is reached when C'' becomes zero [81a, 83,88]; see Fig. 8-19

$$I_{cr} = \frac{\mathfrak{F} D_A C^0}{\delta} \left(1 - \frac{z_A}{z_Y}\right) \tag{8-118}$$

With a 0.01 M solution of a 1,1-valent electrolyte ($C^0 = 10^{-5}$ mole/cm^3; $z_A = -z_Y = 1$; $D_A \approx 10^{-5}$ cm^2/sec) and reasonable agitation ($\delta \approx 10^{-3}$ cm) the critical current density is as low as 20 ma/cm^2. This stresses the need for efficient agitation in electrodialytic demineralization.

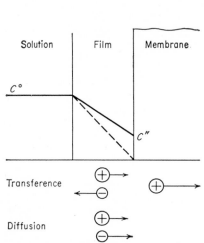

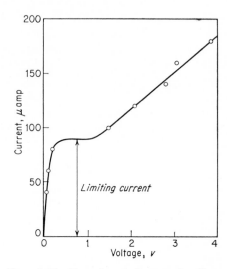

FIG. 8-19. Concentration profile of an electrolyte in the film during electrodialysis. The critical current density is reached when the profile has the steepest possible slope (*broken line*).

FIG. 8-20. Experimental current-voltage characteristic of an ion-exchanger membrane. The curve has a pronounced plateau at the critical current density. *System:* cation-exchanger membrane Amberplex C-10 of 0.126 cm^2 cross section between 0.01 M NaCl solutions. *From A. M. Peers* [83].

Equation (8-118) can also be used for calculating the film thickness from experimental measurements of the critical current density [83]; see Fig. 8-20.

Cells with inert electrodes. Quite similar considerations apply to cells with inert instead of reversible electrodes. The electrode reactions, of course, are different. In a cell with NaCl solutions, the processes are

$$\begin{array}{ccc} \text{Cathode} & \text{Membrane} & \text{Anode} \\ H_2O + e^- \rightarrow \tfrac{1}{2}H_2 + OH^- & \leftarrow\!\!\!\mid Na^+ & \tfrac{1}{2}H_2O \rightarrow H^+ + \tfrac{1}{4}O_2 + e^- \end{array} \quad (8\text{-}119)$$

In the anode compartment NaCl is converted to HCl, and in the cathode compartment NaOH is formed. This procedure can be used for preparing an acid from its salt [50, 119,132]. As electrodialysis progresses, the current efficiency drops more rapidly than in cells with reversible electrodes because H$^+$ ions also are transferred across the membrane. This is not the case, however, when the acid formed is undissociated or is insoluble and precipitates.

Multicompartment cells. Electrodialysis can also be carried out in cells with more than two compartments and more than one membrane. Consider a three-compartment cell

$$
\begin{array}{ccc}
 & \text{cation-exchanger} & \text{anion-exchanger} \\
 & \text{membrane} & \text{membrane}
\end{array}
$$

$$
\text{cathode} \mid \text{solution 1} \qquad \| \qquad \text{solution 2} \qquad \| \qquad \text{solution 3} \mid \text{anode}
$$

$$\tag{8-120}$$

The electric current transfers cations and anions out of solution 2 into solutions 1 and 3, respectively. With permselective membranes there is little back-transfer of anions from solution 1 and of cations from solution 3 into solution 2. The net effect is deionization of the solution in the center compartment [71]. The nature of the electrodes is of minor importance since the electrode reactions have little effect on the deionization in the center compartment.

In a cell of the type (8-120) and filled with NaCl solutions of equal concentrations, 1 faraday of electricity transfers $(\bar{t}_{Na})_{cat}$ equivalents of Na^+ across the cation-exchanger membrane out of the center compartment and $(\bar{t}_{Na})_{an}$ equivalents across the anion-exchanger membrane into the center compartment (subscripts "cat" and "an" refer to the respective membranes). The net NaCl removal from the center compartment thus is $(\bar{t}_{Na})_{cat} - (\bar{t}_{Na})_{an}$. The current efficiency—i.e., the number of equivalents removed per faraday—is quite generally

$$q_I = |(\Sigma z_+\bar{t}_+)_{cat} - (\Sigma z_+\bar{t}_+)_{an}| \tag{8-121}$$

The concentrations in the compartments change as electrodialysis progresses. The effects of counteracting diffusion and of electrolyte depletion at the membrane surfaces are the same as in two-compartment cells.

For plant-scale demineralization, the use of multicompartment cells with large numbers of alternating cation- and anion-exchanger membranes in series is advantageous [5,40, 47,71,119,131a,133]. The electric current causes electrolyte depletion in every other cell, namely, in the cells with cation-exchanger membranes on the cathode side, and electrolyte accumulation in the cells in between (Fig. 8-21). In such operations the energy

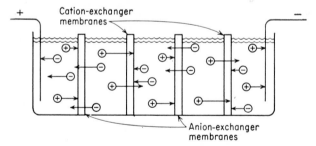

FIG. 8-21. Multicompartment cell for electrodialytic demineralization (*schematic*). Plant-scale installations have a much larger number of compartments. *From Angew. Chemie,* **67,** 15 (1955).

requirement is the most important factor. The energy required for the removal of a given amount of electrolyte depends not only on the current efficiency but also on the operating voltage. A current in the desired direction, i.e., causing further depletion of the more dilute solutions, can be forced through the cell only if the voltage applied is higher than the sum of the membrane potentials. The excess voltage required to attain the desired current density depends on the ohmic resistance of the cell. Hence the inter-membrane distances should be as small as possible to keep the resistance low. The cell resistance increases with progressing depletion of the dilute solutions. Furthermore, it increases with current density because of electrolyte depletion at the membrane surfaces (see page 399). The theoretical minimum energy requirement for the removal of a given amount of electrolyte can be calculated thermodynamically. It corresponds to reversible transference of the electrolyte across ideally permselective membranes at minimum operating voltage and infinitesimal current density. The actual process operates with higher voltage and lower efficiency and thus requires more energy. The excess energy is irreversibly spent for co-ion transference, production of joule heat, and compensation of diffusion [119,131a].

Membrane Accumulators. The electrodialysis in a two-compartment or multicompartment cell can be reversed. A cell in which the alternating compartments are filled with concentrated and dilute solutions (or solvent) acts as a voltage source ("membrane accumulator") [60,71,82]. All membrane potentials have equal sign. Their sum is the cell voltage.

b. Electroosmosis

In cells of the type (8-112) or (8-120), the electric current causes not only transference of ions but also convection of the pore liquid and thus transference of solvent. This phenomenon is called *electroosmosis*. The pore liquid carries a net electric charge of the same sign as the counter ions. Therefore it is transferred in the same direction as the counter ions (see Sec. 7-3). This convection is superimposed on the ionic transferences. Hence the counter-ion flux is larger and the co-ion flux smaller than in systems without convection. The effect of convection on ionic transference is accounted for in the transference numbers [see Eq. (7-12)]. The transference of solvent will now be examined.

Simple relations for electroosmosis can only be given for cells with solutions of equal concentration and with no film effects. Here, no concentration gradients exist. Integration of Eqs. (7-6) and (7-7) across the membrane gives the convection rate $\mathfrak{v}$ and the current density I:

$$\mathfrak{v} = \frac{\omega \bar{u}_0 \, \Delta \bar{\varphi}}{d} \tag{8-122}$$

$$I = -\frac{\mathfrak{F} \left(\sum_i z_i^2 \bar{u}_i \bar{C}_i + \bar{u}_0 X \right) \Delta \bar{\varphi}}{d} = -\frac{\bar{\kappa} \, \Delta \bar{\varphi}}{d} \tag{8-123}$$

The volume transfer per unit time and unit membrane cross section (not pore cross section!) is

$$\dot{V} = \epsilon \mathfrak{v} \tag{8-124}$$

The volume transfer at unit current density is, by definition, the "electroosmotic permeability" D_e [105,108]. One obtains from Eqs. (8-122) to (8-124)

$$D_e \equiv \left(\frac{|\dot{V}|}{I} \right)_{\Delta P = 0} = \frac{\epsilon \bar{u}_0}{\mathfrak{F} \left(\sum_i z_i^2 \bar{C}_i \bar{u}_i + X \bar{u}_0 \right)} = \frac{\mathfrak{F} X}{\rho_0 \bar{\kappa}} \tag{8-125}$$

The electroosmotic permeability is inversely proportional to the specific flow resistance ρ_0 and independent of the membrane thickness. There is little dependence on fixed-charge concentration and specific conductivity since their effects largely cancel. With increasing solution concentration the flow resistance and the specific conductivity increase and the electroosmotic permeability drops.

The *transference number of the solvent* $\bar{t}_0$ is defined as the number of solvent moles transferred by 1 faraday of electricity in the direction of the current. This quantity is calculated in the following way. The over-all volume transferred by 1 faraday is $-\omega D_e \mathfrak{F}$. The contribution from ionic transference must be subtracted:

$$\bar{t}_0 = - \frac{\omega D_e \mathfrak{F} + \sum_i v_i \bar{t}_i}{v_0} \tag{8-126}$$

where v_i = partial molar volume of ion i; subscript 0 refers to solvent.

The solvent transference number is positive for cation exchangers ($\omega = -1$) and negative for anion exchangers ($\omega = 1$).

Equation (8-126) gives the transference number of total solvent including solvation shells. Instead, the transference number of the "free" solvent can be calculated by using the solvated ionic volumes instead of the partial volumes. The difference between total solvent and free solvent transference is $\sum_i Z_i \bar{t}_i$, where Z_i is the solvation number of species i. This approach in combination with self-diffusion and conductivity measurements has been used for determining ionic solvation numbers [12,134]. The underlying assumptions are essentially the same as in the determination of solvation numbers in homogeneous solutions from the difference between "Hittorf" and "true" transference numbers.

The calculation of electroosmotic transference requires a knowledge of the quantity $\bar{u}_0 \equiv \mathfrak{F}X/\rho_0\epsilon$ and hence of the specific flow resistance ρ_0. The latter can be directly determined by measuring the "permeability" D_h of the membrane with short-circuited streaming potential ($\Delta\bar{\varphi} = 0$) [108]. The permeability is defined as the volume transfer per unit time and unit membrane cross section at unit pressure difference. According to Eqs. (8-101) and (8-124) the permeability is

$$D_h \equiv - \left(\frac{\dot{V}}{\Delta P} \right)_{\Delta\varphi=0} = \frac{\epsilon}{\rho_0 d} \tag{8-127}$$

Alternatively, the specific flow resistance can be determined by measuring the "hydrodynamic permeability" D_h'' of the membrane at zero electric current ($I = 0$), i.e., without short-circuiting the streaming potential. This measurement is simpler. According to Eqs. (8-101), (8-103), and

(8-124) the hydrodynamic permeability is

$$D_h'' \equiv -\left(\frac{\dot{V}}{\Delta P}\right)_{I=0} = \frac{\epsilon}{\rho_0 d}\left(1 - \frac{(\mathfrak{F}X)^2}{\rho_0 \bar{\kappa}\epsilon}\right) \tag{8-128}$$

Measurements of the two permeabilities, D_h and D_h'', can be used for determining the convection conductivity $\bar{\kappa}_0$. Equations (8-127), (8-128), and (7-9) give [108]

$$\frac{D_h''}{D_h} = 1 - \frac{\bar{\kappa}_0}{\bar{\kappa}} \tag{8-129}$$

The specific flow resistance is not a membrane constant, but depends on the composition of the solutions (see Sec. 7-4). In the usual ion-exchanger membranes the specific flow resistance is of the order of 10^{12} to 10^{14} g cm^{-3} sec^{-1}. A typical ion-exchanger membrane ($X \approx 2$ N $= 2 \cdot 10^{-3}$ mole/cm^3; $d \approx 0.1$ cm; $\rho_0 \approx 10^{13}$ g cm^{-3} sec^{-1}; $\bar{\kappa} \approx 10^{-2}$ Ω^{-1} cm^{-1}; $\epsilon \approx 0.6$) thus has an electroosmotic permeability of the order of 10^{-2} cm^3 amp^{-1} sec^{-1} and a hydrodynamic permeability of the order of 10^{-12} g^{-1} cm^2 sec. With 1 amp/cm^2 current density (corresponding to 10 volts potential difference across the membrane) the electroosmotic transference of 1 cm^3 through 1 cm^2 membrane cross section requires about a minute. On the other hand, with 10 atm pressure difference across the membrane the hydrodynamic transfer of 1 cm^3 requires about 50 hr. The solvent transference number of water is usually of the order of 5 to 50 moles/faraday.

Electroosmosis reduces the efficiency of electrodialytic demineralization since not only ions but also solvent are removed from the solution. In order to keep electroosmotic losses low, membranes should be chosen which combine high ionic mobilities with a high flow resistance.

If the solutions in the membrane cell contain a nonelectrolyte solute in addition to the electrolyte, then the nonelectrolyte also is electroosmotically transferred together with the solvent [36]. In experiments with aqueous solutions it was observed that the mole ratio of nonelectrolyte to solvent transferred is smaller than the mole ratio in the solutions [36]. This is not surprising since water is transferred not only by electroosmotic convection but also in the form of ionic hydration shells.

The equations in this section are derived for "homogeneous" membranes. Furthermore, specific interactions between the ions and the membrane material were neglected, and the ionic distribution within the membrane was assumed to be uniform. Strong specific interactions may cause anomalous behavior (see Sec. 7-4). For example, with strongly associating counter ions such as ThO^{2+}, the solvent may even be transferred in the direction of the co-ion flux (*negative electroosmosis;* see Fig. 8-22) [89]. Nonuniform ionic distribution may become important in weakly crosslinked resins of large mesh width where the counter ions are concentrated around the matrix chains [43,69].

The available experimental results are so far not sufficient for quantitative tests of the equations. However, with the exception of systems

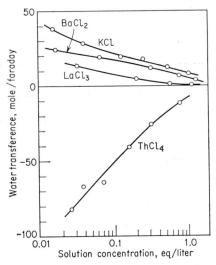

FIG. 8-22. Electroosmotic water transfer across a cation-exchanger membrane (Nepton CR-61). With ThO^{2+} as the counter ion, the membrane shows negative electroosmosis. *From N. W. Rosenberg, J. H. B. George, and W. D. Potter* [89].

with strong specific interactions, the qualitative conclusions are well confirmed [12,69,89,124,134].

c. Cells with Solutions of Different Concentrations

In cells with solutions of different concentrations there is ionic diffusion in addition to transference and convection. The calculation of the ionic fluxes, concentration profiles, and convection requires integration of the flux equations (8-2). A solution has been given by Schlögl [101]. It is restricted to one 1,1-valent electrolyte and not applicable to very low current densities. Diffusion coefficients, fixed-charge concentration, activity coefficients, and flow resistance are assumed to be constant. For the sake of simplicity it will also be assumed that the diffusion constants of the cation and anion are equal $(\bar{D}_+ = \bar{D}_- = \bar{D})$ and that the membrane is a cation exchanger. Under these conditions the system of equations given in Sec. 8-2 is

$$J_+ = -\bar{D}\left[\frac{d\bar{C}_+}{dx} + \bar{C}_+\frac{\mathfrak{F}}{RT}\frac{d\varphi}{dx}\right] + \bar{C}_+\mathfrak{v}$$

$$J_- = -\bar{D}\left[\frac{d\bar{C}_-}{dx} - \bar{C}_-\frac{\mathfrak{F}}{RT}\frac{d\varphi}{dx}\right] + \bar{C}_-\mathfrak{v}$$

$$\text{(8-130)}$$

$$\bar{C}_+ - \bar{C}_- = X \qquad \text{electroneutrality} \qquad \text{(8-131)}$$

$$I = \mathfrak{F}(J_+ - J_-) \qquad \text{charge conservation} \qquad \text{(8-132)}$$

$$J_+, J_- = \text{const.} \qquad \text{steady state} \qquad \text{(8-133)}$$

The convection rate is given by Eq. (8-101). The pressure term is usually very small as compared to the electric term (the effect of 1 volt potential difference is approximately the same as that of 1000 atm pressure difference). Thus the pressure term can be neglected unless the current density is very small:

$$\mathfrak{v} = - \frac{\bar{D}_0}{d} \frac{\mathfrak{F}}{RT} \Delta\bar{\varphi} \qquad \left(\bar{D}_0 \equiv \frac{RTX}{\epsilon\rho_0}\right) \qquad (8\text{-}134)$$

where $\bar{D}_0$ is defined by the relation above; $\Delta\bar{\varphi} \equiv \bar{\varphi}'' - \bar{\varphi}'$.

Integration of Eqs. (8-130) with these conditions yields the following relations

$$\frac{I}{\mathfrak{F}} = J_+ - J_- = - \frac{\bar{D}_0 X}{d} (1 + rs) \frac{\mathfrak{F}}{RT} \Delta\bar{\varphi} \qquad (8\text{-}135)$$

$$J_+ = - \frac{\bar{D}_0 X}{2d} (1 + r)(1 + s) \frac{\mathfrak{F}}{RT} \Delta\bar{\varphi} = \frac{I}{\mathfrak{F}} \frac{(1 + r)(1 + s)}{2(1 + rs)} \qquad (8\text{-}136)$$

where the parameters r and s are given by

$$\frac{r}{r - \bar{D}/\bar{D}_0} \log \frac{\bar{c}''/X - r}{\bar{c}'/X - r} = \frac{s}{s - \bar{D}/\bar{D}_0} \log \frac{\bar{c}''/X - s}{\bar{c}'/X - s} \qquad (8\text{-}137)$$

$$\frac{r(1 + rs)}{r - \bar{D}/\bar{D}_0} \log \frac{\bar{c}''/X - r}{\bar{c}'/X - r} = I \frac{d}{D\mathfrak{F}X} \qquad (8\text{-}138)$$

where $\bar{c} = \bar{C}_+ + \bar{C}_- =$ "anion-plus-cation concentration"; superscripts $'$ and $''$ refer to the left and right membrane boundaries, respectively.

The calculation of the fluxes, electroosmotic transference, current density, etc., is as follows. First, the parameters r and s are calculated for a given current density by use of Eqs. (8-137) and (8-138). The corresponding intramembrane potential difference $\Delta\bar{\varphi}$ is determined from Eq. (8-135). Now the cation flux is obtained from Eq. (8-136) and the electroosmotic transference from Eqs. (8-134) and (8-124). The anion flux then follows from Eq. (8-135). The electric potential difference between the solutions is obtained by adding the difference of the Donnan potentials to $\Delta\bar{\varphi}$. The quantities are then tabulated as functions of the current density.

The calculation of the concentration profiles is cumbersome, but leads to very interesting results. Only a qualitative analysis will be given. Details can be found in Schlögl's paper [101]. First, membranes with very high flow resistance ($\bar{D}/\bar{D}_0 \gg 1$) will be examined. Here, convection is negligible. With positive current flowing from the dilute to the concentrated solution, the concentration profiles have negative curvature, and with the current flowing in opposite direction they have positive curvature (see the curves for $\bar{D}/\bar{D}_0 = \infty$ in Fig. 8-23). One might say that the co-ion—which is transferred in the direction opposite to the electric current—is reluctant to change its concentration on its way across the membrane.

The situation is quite different in membranes with low flow resistance $(\bar{D}/\bar{D}_0 \approx 1)$. Here, convection is strong and carries pore liquid in the direction of the current. The convection is so fast that the pore liquid finds little time to change its concentration while being transferred across the membrane. The concentration profiles thus have curvatures which are just the opposite to those in membranes with high flow resistance (see the curves for $\bar{D}/\bar{D}_0 = 1$ in Fig. 8-23). With membranes of intermediate flow resistance, the co-ion and convection effects counteract one another. The resulting concentration profiles are S-shaped and have an inflection point at a

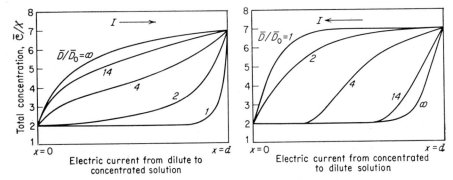

Electric current from dilute to concentrated solution

Electric current from concentrated to dilute solution

Fig. 8-23. Theoretical profiles of the anion-plus-cation concentration ("total concentration") in a cation-exchanger membrane for high current densities and fixed boundary concentrations. The various curves correspond to different values of the ratio $\bar{D}/\bar{D}_0$. *From R. Schlögl and U. Schödel [101].*

critical anion-plus-cation concentration $\bar{\mathbb{C}}_{cr} = X\bar{D}/\bar{D}_0$. All these effects become more pronounced when the electric current density is increased.

A comparison of the concentration profiles for positive and negative electric current in Fig. 8-23 reveals an unexpected membrane property. The electric conductivity of the membrane obviously parallels the average anion-plus-cation concentration within the membrane. Thus the conductivities for positive and negative current are quite different: the membrane acts as a *rectifier* [18,101,126–128]. With cation-exchanger membranes of high flow resistance $(X\bar{D}/\bar{\mathbb{C}}\bar{D}_0 \gg 1)$ the conductivity for current from the dilute to the concentrated solution is higher than for current in the opposite direction. With cation-exchanger membranes of low flow resistance $(X\bar{D}/\bar{\mathbb{C}}\bar{D}_0 \ll 1)$ the situation is reversed. Just the opposite holds for anion-exchanger membranes. The rectifier effect, however, is not instantaneous because steady-state concentration profiles must first be established.

The current efficiency in a two-compartment cell with solutions of different concentrations is readily calculated from Eqs. (8-136) and (8-135):

$$q_I = \frac{J_+\mathfrak{F}}{I} = \frac{(1+r)(1+s)}{2(1+rs)} \tag{8-139}$$

for a cation-exchanger membrane and a 1,1-valent electrolyte. The current efficiency depends on the concentrations of the solutions and the fixed membrane charges, the current density, the ionic mobilities, and the flow resistance of the membrane material.

Ionic transference in membrane cells with solutions of different concentrations is often described in terms of "integral transference numbers." These are defined as the number of moles which 1 faraday transfers across the membrane (transport by diffusion not included). Mathematically, the integral transference number of species i is

$$\bar{T}_i \equiv \frac{\int_{,}^{''} \bar{t}_i \, d \ln \bar{a}_{\pm}}{\int_{,}^{''} d \ln \bar{a}_{\pm}} \tag{8-140}$$

where $\bar{t}_i$ is the (differential) transference number which, of course, is not constant throughout the membrane. It is often overlooked that the integral transference number is a *function of the current density* [102]. The current density affects the shape of the concentration profiles (see the curvatures produced in Fig. 8-23 by high current density) and thus also the transference numbers which are functions of the relative concentrations.

The theory outlined in this section is of recent origin. Nevertheless the principal conclusions are at least qualitatively confirmed [101].

8-9. SORTING EFFECTS

In several membrane systems studied in this chapter, one property has been encountered which deserves further attention. The behavior of the system can be such that one or more mobile species migrate against the gradient of their chemical potential. The energy required is supplied by another process in the system. The following phenomena may serve as typical examples. Negative osmosis is solvent migration from the concentrated to the dilute solution; the energy stems from simultaneous electrolyte diffusion (Sec. 8-6). Incongruent salt flux is electrolyte migration from the dilute to the concentrated solution; the energy stems from simultaneous solvent diffusion (Sec. 8-6). In multi-ionic cells, a counter-ion species may migrate from one solution into another where its concentration is higher; the energy stems from diffusion of another counter ion in opposite direction (Sec. 8-3c).

In all these examples the solutions on either membrane side have different compositions, and no external force is applied. It is also possible to produce fluxes across membranes between solutions of identical composition by exerting a force on the system. The conditions can be arranged in such a way that two different species migrate in opposite directions. A trivial example is electrodialysis where the cation goes to the cathode and the anion to the anode. Even ions of equal sign, however, can be made to migrate in opposite directions. The theoretical basis for such "sorting" effects is the following. The flux equations for two species A and B of equal sign consist of various additive terms which may have different signs. The signs of corresponding terms in the equations for A and B are equal. The conditions, however, may well be such that one term outweighs the other in the equation for A but not in the equation for B. In this case, the net fluxes of A and B have opposite signs, i.e., opposite directions. This shows that "sorting" can occur when at least two opposing forces act on the ions. It is usually sufficient to apply one force (or create it in a different part of the system); the other may automatically arise as a reaction force to the first one. This general formulation will be illustrated by two simple examples.

Counter-ion sorting can be achieved by pressure (see page 394). Consider an ideally permselective membrane between solutions of identical composition containing two counter-ion species. Pressure applied to one solution causes convection across the membrane. This convection carries both species toward the solution of lower pressure. Simultaneously, convection builds up a counteracting streaming potential which drives the counter ions back toward the solution of higher pressure. With the smaller and more mobile ion the rate of transference is higher and outweighs convection. With the larger and less mobile ion convection outweighs transference. The solution under higher pressure thus accumulates the faster ion. This result is not astonishing. The only possibility (except for solvent transfer) of reducing the volume of the solution under higher pressure without net charge transfer is replacement of large counter ions by an equivalent number of small counter ions (Fig. 8-24).

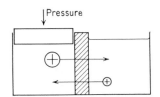

FIG. 8-24. Sorting of counter ions by pressure (*schematic*).

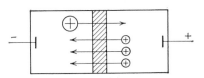

FIG. 8-25. Sorting of counter ions by an electric field in a cell with closed compartments of constant volume (*schematic*).

Another example is electrodialysis in a cell with closed compartments of constant volume, an ideally permselective membrane, reversible electrodes, and solutions containing two counter-ion species. The electric field drives both counter ions across the membrane. The faster species is transferred at the higher rate. The transference produces a pressure difference between the solutions. Pressure counteracts transference and drives the counter ions back. Again, the smaller and faster ion is more strongly affected by the electric field, and the larger and slower one by the pressure difference. The result is accumulation of the faster cation in the cathode compartment (or anion in the anode compartment). Again, it is readily seen that the only possibility (except for solvent transfer) to carry net charge from one compartment to the other without volume changes is the exchange of one large counter ion for several smaller ones (Fig. 8-25).

Quite a number of similar systems can be built.

Migration of a species against its chemical potential gradient and sorting effects resemble "active transport" in physiological membrane systems. The considerations in this section show that such phenomena are not at all miraculous and can occur even in very simple systems. Schlögl [103] has used the principle outlined here to build a much more elaborate model which actually simulates active transport under physiological conditions.

8-10. EXPERIMENTAL METHODS

a. Measurement of Ionic Fluxes and Concentration Profiles

The measurement of self-diffusion fluxes across membranes by use of isotopes has already been described (Sec. 6-9c). Diffusion and interdiffusion fluxes are usually determined in the same way, i.e., by measuring the concentration changes of the species under consideration in one or both solutions. The analytical methods must be sensitive enough to permit the flux to be calculated from small concentration changes, since large changes would reduce the flux.

The effect of concentration changes in the solutions is particularly critical in bi-ionic and multi-ionic systems with counter ions of different valences. The appearance of even very small amounts of a multivalent ion on the other membrane side may reduce

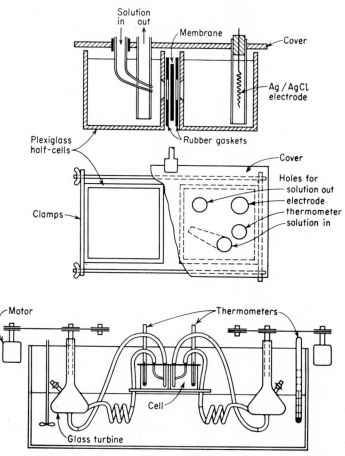

FIG. 8-26. Apparatus for measuring membrane potentials. *Top:* the actual cell in front and top view; *bottom:* the whole assembly. The membrane is clamped between two plexiglass half-cells. The solutions are agitated by circulation through thermostated glass turbines and nozzles in the half-cells in such a way that a violent jet sweeps across the membrane surface. (In the front view the solution inlet and outlet are shown only on the left, the electrode only on the right.) *From G. Scatchard and F. Helfferich* [93].

the flux considerably (see page 362). A very convenient means for keeping concentration changes in the solutions at a low level is "buffering" with added granular ion-exchange material. The ion exchanger scavenges foreign ions diffusing into the solution and replaces them by the ionic species initially present [28,68].

Efficient agitation must be provided. This is particularly important in interdiffusion of counter ions because of possible film diffusion control [28,93,123]. A suitable setup is shown in Fig. 8-26. The membranes should not overlap the openings in the solution compartments. This can be achieved by using a membrane which has been cast in an inert frame [101] (see Fig. 8-27) or by placing the membrane in a tightly fitting rubber tube which connects the compartments [28].

Concentration profiles are measured by using a tightly packed stack of several membranes (Fig. 8-27). After attainment of the steady state, the apparatus is disassembled and the individual membranes are analyzed separately for one or several ionic species [28,101]. Special care must be taken to prevent formation of liquid films or air bubbles between the membranes.

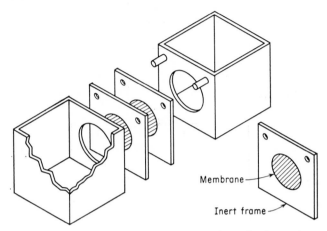

Membrane

Inert frame

FIG. 8-27. Cell for measuring concentration profiles. A stack of membranes is clamped between the solution compartments. The membranes are cast in inert plastic frames. The membrane cross section is smaller than the openings in the solution compartments. The cell is inserted into the apparatus shown in Fig. 8-26.

As a rule, it is intended to measure fluxes and concentration profiles in the steady (or quasi-stationary) state. The time required for attainment of the steady state can be estimated by use of Eq. (8-11).

b. Measurement of Membrane Potentials

A large variety of cells for membrane potential measurements have been described [3,6,9,19,21,30,39,46,52,58,63,70,79,93,94,98,104,119,127,136,139]. A convenient setup is shown in Fig. 8-26. Efficient agitation must be provided, particularly in bi-ionic and multi-ionic systems.

The emf of the cell is measured with a potentiometer (Fig. 8-28). A sensitive galvanometer or an amplifier in combination with a microamperemeter can be used as the zero instrument.

The choice of the electrodes depends on the nature of the electrolytes. Calomel electrodes are almost universally applicable. The most convenient "direct" reversible electrodes are Ag/AgCl and Ag/AgBr electrodes.

The membrane potential is calculated by subtracting the difference of the electrode potentials from the emf of the cell (see Sec. 8-4a). The difference between calomel-electrode potentials is usually assumed to be zero. With direct reversible electrodes, the difference in the electrode potentials may be of the same order as the membrane potential itself. For example, the concentration cell

$$\text{Ag|AgCl} \quad \left| \begin{array}{c} \text{KCl} \\ a' \end{array} \right. \left| \begin{array}{c} \text{membrane} \\ \text{ideally permselective for K}^+ \end{array} \right| \left. \begin{array}{c} \text{KCl} \\ a'' \end{array} \right| \text{AgCl|Ag} \qquad (8\text{-}141)$$

gives the emf

$$E = E_m + \Delta E_{el} = \frac{RT}{\mathfrak{F}} \ln \frac{a'_K}{a''_K} + \frac{RT}{\mathfrak{F}} \ln \frac{a'_{Cl}}{a''_{Cl}} = \frac{2RT}{\mathfrak{F}} \ln \left(\frac{a'_\pm}{a''_\pm} \right)_{KCl} \qquad (8\text{-}142)$$

The emf thus is twice as large as the membrane potential (assuming $f_{Na} = f_{Cl} = f_\pm$). The same cell with a membrane which is ideally permselective for Cl^- gives zero emf.

In concentration cells, ionic diffusion across the membrane is usually negligible. In bi-ionic and multi-ionic cells, however, there is rapid interdiffusion of counter ions which may cause concentration changes in the solutions. Remedies are: small membrane

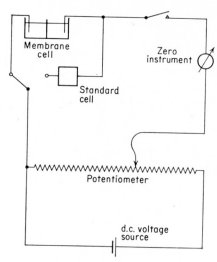

Fig. 8-28. Electric circuit for potential measurements.

cross section, large solution volumes, or "buffering" of the solutions with granular ion exchangers (see page 410).

In membrane systems with only two permeating species, the membrane potential reaches the steady-state value for membrane diffusion control when equilibrium between the membrane surfaces and the adjacent bulk solutions is attained (see page 370). As a rule, this occurs long before the steady state within the membrane is reached.* Use can be made of this fact in measurements of bi-ionic potentials; film diffusion effects and contamination of the solutions by diffusion can be avoided by making the measurements with a stack of two membranes, one in A form facing the solution AY, and one in B form facing the solution BY. The potential for complete membrane diffusion control is almost immediately attained and remains undisturbed until significant amounts of A and B reach the membrane surfaces on the BY and AY sides, respectively [79,93].

c. Measurement of Transference Numbers, Electroosmosis, and Permeabilities

Transference numbers can be determined in cells of the type (8-113). The electrode compartments are filled with known volumes of the solution. The amount of electricity

---

* Glass electrodes seem to behave similarly. Here, the steady state is practically never attained.

passed through the cell is measured coulometrically.   With electrodes which are reversible with respect to the co-ion, the electrolyte increase (in equivalents per faraday) in one
electrode compartment (or the decrease in the other) gives directly the counter-ion
transference number.   With electrodes which are reversible with respect to the counter
ion, the co-ion transference number is obtained.   The current also transfers solvent.
Hence the number of ions transferred should be determined directly by analyzing the
whole content of the electrode compartment rather than from concentration changes

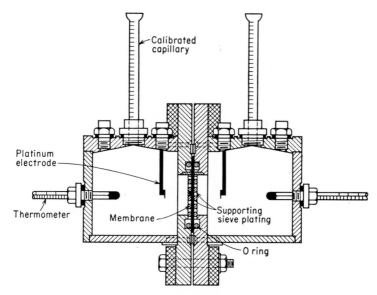

FIG. 8-29. Cell for measuring transference numbers and electroosmotic water transfer.
The cell is equipped with platinum electrodes, calibrated capillaries, magnetic stirrers,
and thermometers. *From J. G. McKelvey, K. S. Spiegler, and M. R. J. Wyllie* [68].

found by analyzing aliquots.   Efficient agitation and a current density well below the
critical should be used to prevent electrolyte depletion at the membrane surface.   In
order to prevent errors caused by electrolyte diffusion, the membrane should not be too
thin and the concentration changes should be kept as small as the analytical accuracy
permits.
   Alternatively, the solution in one compartment can be tagged with a radioactive
tracer.   The transference of the tracer is now measured.   This procedure is very convenient and circumvents the need of determining small concentration changes [68].
Isotopic interdiffusion, however, may cause serious errors unless the membrane thickness
and current density are chosen in such a way that the diffusion rate is much smaller
than the transference rate.
   Electroosmosis can be measured in a similar cell with closed compartments carrying
calibrated capillaries (Fig. 8-29).   The electroosmotic volume transfer (in milliliters per
faraday) is calculated from the change in level height in the capillaries [68].   Note that
the observed volume change also includes the changes caused by the electrode reactions.
   The *hydrodynamic permeability* D_h'' can be measured in a simple apparatus (Fig. 8-30)
[101].   The solution is pressed through the membrane.   The volume increase on the
low-pressure side of the cell is measured in a calibrated capillary.   The solution must be
carefully ultrafiltered prior to use because the membrane is easily clogged by even very

small amounts of colloidal impurities.   The reproducibility of the measurements has often been poor; there is some indication that prolonged exposure to high pressure may affect the membrane properties.

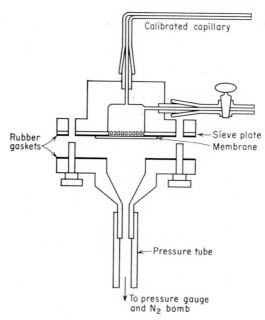

Fig. 8-30. Apparatus for measuring hydrodynamic permeabilities.   The permeability is calculated from the rate of motion of the meniscus in the calibrated capillary.   *From R. Schlögl and U. Schödel* [101].

SUMMARY

This chapter deals with systems in which an ion-exchanger membrane is between two solutions.   The processes taking place depend on the nature of the membrane.   Ion-exchanger membranes have two unique properties: permselectivity (i.e., a permeability which is much higher for counter ions than for co-ions) and high electric conductivity.   Most membrane phenomena are direct consequences of these properties.

The causes of permselectivity are obvious.   Donnan exclusion prevents co-ions from entering and penetrating the membrane.   Counter ions, in contrast, are freely admitted to the membrane and thus have little difficulty in passing through it.   The Donnan effect and, hence, the permselectivity gradually disappear when the solution concentrations are increased and approach the concentration of fixed ionic groups in the membrane.

Permselectivity explains the characteristic diffusion behavior of ion-exchanger membranes.   Interdiffusion of counter ions is very fast, and interdiffusion of co-ions is extremely slow.   Nonelectrolytes diffuse at an intermediate rate.   The rate of electrolyte diffusion across the membrane from a concentrated into a dilute solution is controlled by the slowest process involved, namely, diffusion of the co-ion. The rate falls far short of that of nonelectrolyte diffusion.

In so-called multi-ionic systems with various counter-ion species in both solutions, a species can migrate into the solution in which its (absolute) concentration is higher. The relative permeability for the various competing counter ions is also affected by the selectivity of the membrane material.

Interdiffusion (and self-diffusion) of counter ions across the membrane itself can be so fast that diffusion across adherent Nernst "films" at the membrane surfaces becomes rate-controlling (film diffusion control). As in ion exchange with beads, film-diffusion control is favored by high capacity, small thickness, and weak crosslinking of the membrane, and by low concentration and inefficient agitation of the solutions.

The solutions on both membrane sides differ in their electric potential. The potential difference between the (bulk) solutions is called membrane potential. It is by means of the electric potential differences that the system manages to meet the electroneutrality condition; the electric field regulates the various ionic fluxes in such a way that no net transfer of electric charge occurs. The membrane potential consists of the diffusion potential within the membrane, the Donnan potentials at the membrane/solution interfaces, and (in the case of film diffusion control) the diffusion potentials in the films. Membrane potentials between electrolyte solutions of different concentrations are called concentration potentials. With ideally permselective membranes there is no (irreversible) electrolyte diffusion, and the concentration potential reaches the thermodynamic limiting value. Concentration-potential measurements can be used for determining ionic activities ("membrane electrodes"). Membrane potentials between solutions which contain two or more counter-ion species are called bi-ionic and multi-ionic potentials, respectively. The interpretation of these potentials is somewhat complex. The solution concentrations, ionic valences, and the selectivity of the membrane material determine the Donnan potentials while the relative ionic mobilities determine the diffusion potentials in the membrane and the films. The systems are very sensitive to film effects. With counter ions of different valences, a change from membrane to film diffusion control may cause a spectacular change and even a reversal of sign of the membrane potential.

Solvent diffusion (osmosis) across ion-exchanger membranes between electrolyte solution is, as a rule, anomalous, i.e., not proportional to the osmotic pressure difference between the solutions. The pore liquid in the membrane carries a net electric charge and, hence, is affected by the electric potential gradient which arises from ionic diffusion. Diffusing electrolytes may even carry solvent from the concentrated to the dilute solution (negative osmosis). On the other hand, solvent may carry electrolyte from the concentrated to the dilute solution (incongruent salt flux).

Application of excess hydrostatic pressure to one solution forces liquid through the membrane. The displacement of the electrically charged pore liquid causes a counteracting electric potential difference, the streaming potential. Solvent passes the membrane at a higher rate than electrolytes ("electrolyte filtration").

An electric current generated by an external source and passed through a membrane cell transfers many more counter ions than co-ions across the membrane. This is an obvious consequence of permselectivity. Two-compartment cells with one membrane and with electrodes which are reversible with respect to the co-ion can be used for electrodialytic demineralization of solutions. Multicompartment cells with alternating cation- and anion-exchanger membranes in series are more practical, however. The current efficiency of these processes depends on the counter-ion transport numbers. The electric potential gradient within the membrane also causes a transference of solvent (electroosmosis). The electric conductivity of ion-exchanger membranes for positive and negative current is not the same. The sign and magnitude of this "rectifier effect" depend on experimental conditions and membrane properties, particularly on the flow resistance.

In quite a number of membrane systems, a mobile species can migrate against the gradient of its chemical potential. The required energy is supplied by diffusion of other species. "Sorting" of counter ions can take place when an external force (pressure, electric field) is applied; different species are accumulated in the two solutions. Sorting can occur even when the solutions have identical initial composition. These phenomena are related to "active transport" in physiological membrane systems.

Several theoretical approaches can be used for describing membrane phenomena. In the past, most of the theoretical work on membrane potentials and electric transference has been based on quasi-thermodynamics. Alternatively, thermodynamics of irreversible processes can be applied. This approach also gives the ionic fluxes and concentration profiles. The theoretical treatment in this chapter is based on a refined form of the Nernst-Planck flux equations and may be considered as a simplification of thermodynamics of irreversible processes. Only the steady (or quasi-stationary) state is considered. General analytical solutions have been found for systems with one 1,1-valent electrolyte and convection, and with arbitrary electrolyte mixtures in the absence of convection. These general solutions are rather complex. In a number of simpler systems with negligible convection (isotopic redistribution, only two mobile species in the membrane, solutions of identical composition, etc.) the treatment is much more straightforward. Here, even minor effects such as the concentration dependence of activity coefficients, ionic mobilities, etc., are readily included. The theories give a comprehensive picture of all membrane phenomena and are, at least qualitatively, well confirmed. In no other field of ion exchange has theory advanced as far as here.

REFERENCES

1. Barrer, R. M., "Diffusion in and through Solids," pp. 14–19, Cambridge University Press, New York, 1941.
2. Behn, U., *Ann. Phys. u. Chem.*, **62**, 54 (1897).
3. Bergsma, F., and A. J. Staverman, *Discussions Faraday Soc.*, **21**, 61 (1956).
*4. Bergsma, F., and C. A. Kruissink, *Advances in Polymer Sci.*, **2**, 307 (1961).
5. Boer-Nieveld, D. Y., and D. Pauli, *Rept.* T.A.270, *Gen. Tech. Dept. T.N.O., Central Natl. Council Appl. Sci. Research, Netherlands*, 1952.
6. Bonhoeffer, K. F., L. Miller, and U. Schindewolf, *Z. physik. Chem.*, **198**, 270, 281 (1951).
7. Carr, C. W., and L. Topol, *J. Phys. Chem.*, **54**, 176 (1950).
8. Chandler, R. C., and J. W. McBain, *J. Phys. Chem.*, **53**, 930 (1949).
9. Clarke, J. T., J. A. Marinsky, W. Juda, N. W. Rosenberg, and S. Alexander, *J. Phys. Chem.*, **56**, 100 (1952).
*10. Crank, J., "The Mathematics of Diffusion," p. 48, Oxford University Press, New York, 1956.
*11. Davson, H., and J. F. Danielli, "The Permability of Natural Membranes," chap. 21 and appendix A, Cambridge University Press, New York, 1943.
12. Despić, A., and G. J. Hills, *Discussions Faraday Soc.*, **21**, 150 (1956); see also discussion remarks pp. 202, 203.
13. Donnan, F. G., *Z. Elektrochem.*, **17**, 572 (1911).
14. Dray, S., and K. Sollner, *Biochim. et Biophys. Acta*, **18**, 341 (1955).
15. Dray, S., and K. Sollner, *Biochim. et Biophys. Acta*, **21**, 126; **22**, 213, 220 (1956).
16. Erikson, E., *Kgl. Lantbruks Högskol. Ann.*, **16**, 420 (1949); *Chem. Abstr.*, **44**, 903 (1950).
17. Frisch, H. L., *J. Phys. Chem.*, **61**, 93 (1957).
18. Goldman, D. E., *J. Gen. Physiol.*, **27**, 37 (1943).
19. Graydon, W. F., and R. J. Stewart, *J. Phys. Chem.*, **59**, 86 (1955).
20. Gregor, H. P., and K. Sollner, *J. Phys. Chem.*, **58**, 409 (1954).
21. Gregor, H. P., and D. M. Wetstone, *Discussions Faraday Soc.*, **21**, 162 (1956).
22. Groot, S. R. de, "Thermodynamics of Irreversible Processes," Amsterdam, North Holland Publ. Co., 1951.
23. Guggenheim, E. A., *J. Phys. Chem.*, **34**, 1758 (1930).
24. Hale, D. K., and D. J. McCauley, *Trans. Faraday Soc.*, **57**, 135 (1961).
25. Helfferich, F., *Z. physik. Chem. (Frankfurt)*, **4**, 386 (1955).
26. Helfferich, F., *Discussions Faraday Soc.*, **21**, 83 (1956).
27. Helfferich, F., and R. Schlögl, *Discussions Faraday Soc.*, **21**, 133 (1956).
28. Helfferich, F., and H. D. Ocker, *Z. physik. Chem. (Frankfurt)*, **10**, 213 (1957).
29. Henderson, P., *Z. physik. Chem.*, **59**, 118 (1907); **63**, 325 (1908).
30. Hills, G. J., J. A. Kitchener, and P. J. Ovenden, *Trans. Faraday Soc.*, **51**, 719 (1955).
31. Hills, G. J., P. W. M. Jacobs, and N. Lakshminarayanaiah, *Nature*, **179**, 96 (1957); *Proc. Roy. Soc. (London)*, **A262**, 246 (1961).
32. Hirsch, P., *Chem. Weekblad*, **47**, 1025 (1951).
33. Hirsch, P., *Rec. trav. chim.*, **70**, 567 (1951); **71**, 354, 525 (1952).
34. Hodgkin, A. L., and B. Katz, *J. Physiol.*, **108**, 37 (1949).
35. Ikeda, T., *J. Chem. Phys.*, **28**, 166 (1958).
36. Jarvis, J. W., and F. L. Tye, *J. Chem. Soc.*, **1960**, 620; **1961**, 4483.
37. Juda, W., N. W. Rosenberg, J. A. Marinsky, and A. A. Kasper, *J. Am. Chem. Soc.*, **74**, 3736 (1952).
*38. Juda, W., J. A. Marinsky, and N. W. Rosenberg, *Ann. Rev. Phys. Chem.*, **4**, 373 (1953).

* Review articles are marked with asterisks.

39. Kahlweit, M., *Z. physik. Chem. (Frankfurt)*, **6**, 45 (1956).
40. Katz, W. E., and N. W. Rosenberg (Ionics Inc.), U.S. Patent 2,694,680, 1954.
41. Keynes, R. D., *J. Physiol.*, **114**, 119 (1951).
42. Kirkwood, J. G., in "Ion Transport Across Membranes," H. T. Clarke (ed.), p. 119, Academic Press, Inc., New York, 1954.
43. Kitchener, J. A., *Discussions Faraday Soc.*, **21**, 207 (1956).
44. Kobatake, Y., *Busseiron Kenkyu*, **84**, 35; **87**, 58 (1955); *Chem. Abstr.*, **49**, 12918 (1955); *J. Chem. Soc. Japan, Pure Chem. Sec.*, **77**, 878, 882 (1956).
45. Kobatake, Y., *Busseiron Kenkyu*, **95**, 124 (1956); *Chem. Abstr.*, **51**, 5597 (1956).
46. Kressman, T. R. E., *J. Appl. Chem.*, **4**, 123 (1954).
47. Kressman, T. R. E., *Ind. Chemist*, **30**, 99 (1954).
48. Kressman, T. R. E., and F. L. Tye, *Discussions Faraday Soc.*, **21**, 185 (1956).
49. Laidler, K. J., and K. E. Shuler, *J. Chem. Phys.*, **17**, 851 (1949).
50. Lightfoot, E. N., and I. J. Friedman, *Ind. Eng. Chem.*, **46**, 1579 (1954).
51. Lorenz, P. B., *J. Phys. Chem.*, **56**, 775 (1952).
52. Lorimer, J. W., E. I. Boterenbrood, and J. J. Hermans, *Discussions Faraday Soc.*, **21**, 141 (1956).
53. Mackay, D., and P. Meares, *Kolloid Z.*, **167**, 37 (1959).
54. Mackay, D., and P. Meares, *Trans. Faraday Soc.*, **55**, 1221 (1959).
55. Mackay, D., and P. Meares, *Kolloid Z.*, **171**, 139 (1960).
55a. Mackay, D., and P. Meares, *Kolloid Z.*, **176**, 23 (1961).
56. Mackie, J. S., and P. Meares, *Proc. Roy. Soc. (London)*, **A232**, 498, 510 (1955).
57. Mackie, J. S., and P. Meares, *Discussions Faraday Soc.*, **21**, 111 (1956); see also discussion remark p. 128.
58. Manecke, G., and K. F. Bonhoeffer, *Z. Elektrochem.*, **55**, 475 (1951).
59. Manecke, G., *Z. Elektrochem.*, **56**, 672 (1952).
60. Manecke, G., *Z. physik. Chem.*, **201**, 1 (1952).
61. Manecke, G., *Z. physik. Chem.*, **201**, 193 (1952).
62. Manecke, G., and H. Heller, *Discussions Faraday Soc.*, **21**, 101 (1956); *Z. Elektrochem.*, **61**, 150 (1957).
63. Marshall, C. E., *J. Phys. Chem.*, **43**, 1155 (1939); **48**, 67 (1944).
64. Marshall, C. E., and W. E. Bergman, *J. Phys. Chem.*, **46**, 325 (1942).
65. Marshall, C. E., and C. A. Krinbill, *J. Am. Chem. Soc.*, **64**, 1814 (1942).
66. Mazur, P., and J. T. G. Overbeek, *Rec. trav. chim.*, **70**, 83 (1951).
67. McKelvey, J. G., Jr., K. S. Spiegler, and M. R. J. Wyllie, *J. Phys. Chem.*, **61**, 174 (1957).
68. McKelvey, J. G., Jr., K. S. Spiegler, and M. R. J. Wyllie, *J. Electrochem. Soc.*, **104**, 387 (1957).
69. Meares, P., and H. H. Ussing, *Trans. Faraday Soc.*, **55**, 142 (1959).
70. Meyer, K. H., and J. F. Sievers, *Helv. chim. Acta*, **19**, 649, 665 (1936).
71. Meyer, K. H., and W. Straus, *Helv. chim. Acta*, **23**, 795 (1940).
72. Meyer, K. H., and P. Bernfeld, *Helv. chim. Acta*, **28**, 962 (1945).
*73. Meyer, K. H., and H. Mark, "Makromolekulare Chemie," 3d ed., p. 894, Akademische Verlagsanstalt Geest and Portig, Leipzig, 1953.
74. Michaelis, L., *Kolloid Z.*, **62**, 2 (1933).
75. Mindick, M., and R. Oda, *Nalco Reprint No. 77*, National Aluminate Corp., 1958.
76. Neihof, R., and K. Sollner, *Discussions Faraday Soc.*, **21**, 94 (1956); see also discussion remark p. 133. *J. Phys. Chem.*, **61**, 159 (1957).
77. Nernst, W., *Z. physik. Chem.*, **2**, 613 (1888); **4**, 129 (1889).

* Review articles are marked with asterisks.

78. Oel, H. J., *Z. physik. Chem. (Frankfurt)*, **10**, 165 (1957).
79. Oppen, D., and H. Staude, *Z. Elektrochem.*, **64**, 834 (1960).
80. Overbeek, J. T. G., *J. Colloid Sci.*, **8**, 420 (1953).
81. Overbeek, J. T. G., *J. Colloid Sci.*, **8**, 593 (1953).
81a. Partridge, S. M., and A. M. Peers, *J. Appl. Chem.*, **8**, 49 (1958).
82. Pattle, R. E., *Nature*, **174**, 660 (1954).
83. Peers, A. M., *Discussions Faraday Soc.*, **21**, 124 (1956).
84. Peterson, M. A., and H. P. Gregor, *J. Electrochem. Soc.*, **106**, 1051 (1959).
85. Planck, M., *Ann. Phys. u. Chem.*, **39**, 161 (1890).
86. Pleijel, H., *Z. physik. Chem.*, **72**, 1 (1910).
87. Richter, G., and K. F. Bonhoeffer, *Z. physik. Chem. (Frankfurt)*, **5**, 294 (1955).
88. Rosenberg, N. W., and C. E. Tirrell, *Ind. Eng. Chem.*, **49**, 780 (1957).
89. Rosenberg, N. W., J. H. B. George, and W. D. Potter, *J. Electrochem. Soc.*, **104**, 111 (1957).
90. Scatchard, G., *J. Am. Chem. Soc.*, **75**, 2883 (1953).
91. Scatchard, G., in "Ion Transport Across Membranes," H. T. Clarke (ed.), p. 128, Academic Press, Inc., New York, 1954.
92. Scatchard, G., *Discussions Faraday Soc.*, **21**, 27 (1956).
93. Scatchard, G., and F. Helfferich, *Discussions Faraday Soc.*, **21**, 70 (1956).
94. Scatchard, G., J. S. Coleman, and A. L. Shen, *J. Am. Chem. Soc.*, **79**, 12 (1957).
95. Schindewolf, U., and K. F. Bonhoeffer, *Z. Elektrochem.*, **57**, 216 (1953).
96. Schlögl, R., Thesis, Göttingen, 1952.
97. Schlögl, R., and F. Helfferich, *Z. Elektrochem.*, **56**, 644 (1952).
98. Schlögl, R., *Z. Elektrochem.*, **57**, 195 (1953).
99. Schlögl, R., *Z. physik. Chem. (Frankfurt)*, **1**, 305 (1954).
100. Schlögl, R., *Z. physik. Chem. (Frankfurt)*, **3**, 73 (1955).
101. Schlögl, R., and U. Schödel, *Z. physik. Chem. (Frankfurt)*, **5**, 372 (1955).
102. Schlögl, R., *Discussions Faraday Soc.*, **21**, 46 (1956).
103. Schlögl, R., Habilitation Thesis, Göttingen, 1957.
104. Schmid, G., *Z. Elektrochem.*, **54**, 424 (1950).
105. Schmid, G., *Z. Elektrochem.*, **55**, 229 (1951).
106. Schmid, G., and H. Schwarz, *Z. Elektrochem.*, **55**, 684 (1951).
107. Schmid, G., and H. Schwarz, *Z. Elektrochem.*, **56**, 35 (1952).
108. Schmid, G., *Z. Elektrochem.*, **56**, 181 (1952).
109. Shafertshtein, I. Ya., and A. M. Bulgakova, *Uchenye Zapiski, Kharkov Univ.*, **47**; *Trudy Nauch.-Issledovotel. Khim. Inst.*, **10**, 169 (1953); *Chem. Abstr.*, **49**, 10554 (1955).
110. Söllner, K., *Z. Elektrochem.*, **36**, 36, 234 (1930).
111. Söllner, K., and A. Grollman, *Z. Elektrochem.*, **38**, 274 (1932).
112. Söllner, K., *J. Am. Chem. Soc.*, **65**, 2260 (1943).
113. Söllner, K., and H. P. Gregor, *J. Phys. Chem.*, **51**, 299 (1947); **54**, 330 (1950).
114. Söllner, K., *J. Phys. Chem.*, **53**, 1211, 1226 (1949).
*115. Söllner, K., *J. Electrochem. Soc.*, **97**, 139 C (1950); *Ann. N.Y. Acad. Sci.*, **57**, 177 (1953).
*116. Söllner, K., S. Dray, E. Grim, and R. Neihof, in "Ion Transport Across Membranes," H. T. Clarke (ed.), p. 144, Academic Press, Inc., New York, 1954.
117. Söllner, K., and R. Neihof, *Arch. Biochem. Biophys.*, **62**, 507 (1956).
*118. Spiegler, K. S., *J. Electrochem. Soc.*, **100**, 303 C (1953).
*119. Spiegler, K. S., in "Ion Exchange Technology," F. C. Nachod and J. Schubert (eds.), p. 118, Academic Press, Inc., New York, 1956.

---

* Review articles are marked with asterisks.

*120. Spiegler, K. S., and M. R. J. Wyllie, in "Physical Techniques in Biological Research," G. Oster and A. W. Pollister (eds.), vol. 2, p. 301, Academic Press, Inc., New York, 1956.

121. Spiegler, K. S., *Trans. Faraday Soc.*, **54**, 1409 (1958).

122. Staverman, A. J., *Trans. Faraday Soc.*, **48**, 176 (1952); *Chem. Weekblad*, **48**, 334 (1952).

123. Stewart, R. J., and W. F. Graydon, *J. Phys. Chem.*, **60**, 750 (1956).

124. Stewart, R. J., and W. F. Graydon, *J. Phys. Chem.*, **61**, 164 (1957).

125. Teorell, T., *Proc. Soc. Exptl. Biol.*, **33**, 282 (1935).

126. Teorell, T., *Nature*, **162**, 961 (1948).

127. Teorell, T., *Z. Elektrochem.*, **55**, 460 (1951).

*128. Teorell, T., *Progr. Biophys.*, **3**, 305 (1953).

*129. Teorell, T., *Discussions Faraday Soc.*, **21**, 9 (1956).

130. Toman, M., *Chem. zvesti*, **7**, 7 (1953); *Chem. Abstr.*, **48**, 13343 (1954).

131. Wiebenga, E. H., *Rec. trav. chim.*, **65**, 273 (1946).

131a. Wilson, J. R. (ed.), "Demineralization by Electrolysis," Butterworth & Co. (Publishers), Ltd., London, 1960.

132. Winger, A. G., G. W. Bodamer, and R. Kunin, *J. Electrochem. Soc.*, **100**, 178 (1953).

133. Winger, A. G., G. W. Bodamer, R. Kunin, C. J. Prizer, and G. W. Harmon, *Ind. Eng. Chem.*, **47**, 50 (1955).

134. Winger, A. G., R. Ferguson, and R. Kunin, *J. Phys. Chem.*, **60**, 556 (1956).

135. Woermann, D., K. F. Bonhoeffer, and F. Helfferich, *Z. physik. Chem. (Frankfurt)*, **8**, 265 (1956).

136. Wright, M. L., *Trans. Faraday Soc.*, **49**, 95 (1953); **50**, 89 (1954); *J. Phys. Chem.*, **58**, 50 (1954).

137. Wyllie, M. R. J., and H. W. Patnode, *J. Phys. Chem.*, **54**, 204 (1950).

138. Wyllie, M. R. J., *J. Phys. Chem.*, **58**, 67 (1954).

139. Wyllie, M. R. J., and S. L. Kanaan, *J. Phys. Chem.*, **58**, 73 (1954).

140. Zwolinski, B. J., H. Eyring, and C. E. Reese, *J. Phys. Chem.*, **53**, 1426 (1949).

* Review articles are marked with asterisks.

9

Ion-exchange Columns

Most ion-exchange operations, whether in the laboratory or in plant-scale processes, are carried out in columns. A solution is passed through a bed of ion-exchanger beads where its composition is changed by ion exchange or sorption. The composition of the effluent and its change with time depend on the properties of the ion exchanger (ionic form, capacity, degree of crosslinking, etc.), the composition of the feed, and the operating conditions (flow rate, temperature, etc.). An elucidation of this dependence is the chief aim of the discussion in this chapter.

The kinetics of column processes is complex. The discussion of ion-exchange kinetics in batch operations (Sec. 6-3c) has shown that even this much simpler problem has been solved for only a few ideal limiting cases. Contrary to occasional claims, a general and rigorous quantitative theory of ion exchange in columns does not yet exist. It even seems that such a general theory is hardly feasible at all. The conventional mathematical methods at least fail. This, however, has not deterred the physical chemists and chemical engineers. Theories in surprising numbers have been developed. These theories are based on various drastic simplifications or semiempirical approaches. Nevertheless, they can be used to predict the approximate performance of a given column and to find the probable range of optimum operating conditions for an envisaged process. The key to success is the choice of the theory which is the most appropriate for the particular problem. This choice requires judgment and experience; the chemist or engineer must have a sound understanding of the decisive factors in his process, in order to select a theory in which these factors are adequately taken into account.

The qualitative discussion in this chapter is intended to serve as a guide in recognizing the fundamental features and decisive factors in the most important column operations. The subsequent quantitative treatment is restricted to only the simpler calculation methods. Actual design calculations must be adapted in detail to the specific purpose and are beyond the scope of this book.   Electrochemical phenomena are discussed separately.

9-1. ION EXCHANGE IN COLUMNS

Ion exchange is often used for removing a certain ion from a solution or for replacing it by another ion.   Typical examples are the removal of phosphate ions which interfere with standard qualitative inorganic analysis [90,186,192] and, for quantitative determinations, the replacement of alkali metal ions by H^+ which is readily titrated [186,192].   Industrial applications of this kind are, for example, water softening [30,131], metal recovery from

Feed

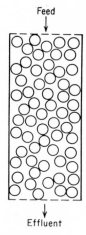

Effluent

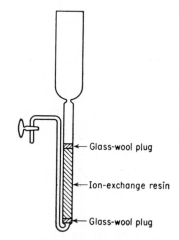

Glass-wool plug

Ion-exchange resin

Glass-wool plug

FIG. 9-1. Schematic picture of a packed column.

FIG. 9-2. Simple ion-exchange column for laboratory use. *From   O.   Samuelson* [186].

wastes [65,159], treatment of radioactive wastes [224], and regeneration of plating solutions [159,162].

Let us assume that the ion B in an electrolyte BY should be replaced by another ion A.*   In principle, ion exchange of B for A can be carried out in a batch process by equilibrating the solution with an ion exchanger in A form.   However, ion-exchange equilibrium is attained before B is completely removed from the solution.   Complete removal of B requires either an extremely large excess of the ion exchanger or a series of repeated equilibrations with fresh portions of the ion exchanger.   In a column, the conditions are much more favorable.   On its way through the bed, the solution comes in contact over and over again with layers of ion-exchanger

---

* For ion exchange with solutions which contain several counter ion species, see Sec. 9-7c.

particles which are still completely in A form (see Fig. 9-3). One might say that, in the column, the solution goes automatically through a series of (not necessarily complete) batch equilibrations. Thus all ions B are eventually replaced by A before the solution appears in the effluent.

When the solution is first fed to the column, it will exchange all its ions B for A in a comparatively narrow zone at the top of the bed. The solution, now containing the electrolyte AY, passes through the lower part of the column without further change in composition. As the feed is continued, the top layers of the bed are constantly exposed to fresh solution BY. Eventually, they are completely converted to B form and lose their effi-

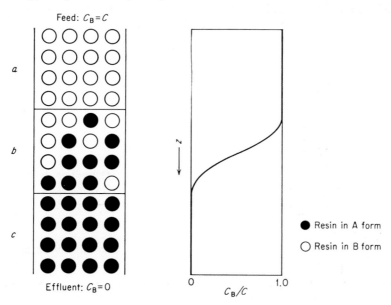

FIG. 9-3. Performance of an ion-exchange column (*schematic*). The exhausted zone, the ion-exchange zone, and the still unconverted zone are marked *a*, *b*, and *c*. The axial concentration profile ("exchange isochrone") of the counter ion from the feed is shown on the right. *From O. Samuelson* [186].

ciency; they become "exhausted." The zone in which the ion exchange occurs is thus displaced downstream. In due course, this zone reaches the bottom of the column. This is the "breakthrough" of B; now, ions B first appear in the effluent.* The operation is usually discontinued at or before breakthrough, and the column is "regenerated" with a solution of AY. Continuation beyond breakthrough results in complete displacement of A by B in the column. Thereafter, the whole bed is in equilibrium with the

---

* The concept of breakthrough is useful, but is not an absolute one. Microscopic leakage, although it may not be detectable, occurs always once the holdup liquid in the bed has been displaced.

feed BY which then passes through without change in composition (see Fig. 9-4).

At breakthrough, the bottom layers of the bed are not yet completely converted to B form. The *breakthrough capacity* (i.e., the amount of ions B taken up prior to the breakthrough) thus is less than the over-all ion-exchange capacity of the column (see also Sec. 4-1). The breakthrough and over-all capacities of a column are readily determined from the effluent history (Fig. 9-4). The over-all capacity is, of course, given by the volume capacity of the ion exchanger and the size of the bed. The breakthrough capacity, in contrast, depends on the nature of the process and the operating conditions and is a meaningless figure unless these are specified.

As a rule, one attempts to use the ion exchanger as efficiently as practicable. The *degree of column utilization*—defined as the fraction of ion-exchange material which is effective—is obviously given by the ratio of the

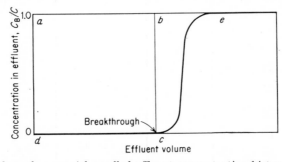

FIG. 9-4. Breakthrough curve (also called effluent concentration history, "exchange iso-plane") of the counter ion from the feed (*schematic*). The breakthrough capacity is proportional to the area *abcd*, the over-all capacity is proportional to the area *aecd*.

breakthrough and the over-all capacities. The factors which determine the degree of utilization will now be examined.

Evidently the degree of utilization is high when the breakthrough is sharp, i.e., when the overlap of the zones of A and B remains small. The sharpness of the boundary between A and B depends on the equilibrium and rate of ion exchange and on the operating conditions.

Ion-exchange equilibrium is "favorable" when B (the counter ion from the feed) is preferred by the ion exchanger, and "unfavorable" when A (the counter ion initially in the bed) is preferred. It is obvious that in repeated batch equilibrations fewer stages are necessary to remove B from the solution if B is strongly preferred. Likewise, in the column, fewer layers are required. *The stronger the preference of the ion exchanger for the counter ion from the feed, the sharper is the boundary.* (Note that the preference also depends on the nature of the co-ion; see pages 164 and 202.)

The effect of equilibrium on the behavior of the boundary is not only a matter of degree. Favorable and unfavorable equilibria result in quite different patterns. If equilibrium is favorable, any ions A behind the boundary are displaced preferentially by B and will soon catch up with the boundary. Similarly, any ions B ahead of the boundary are preferentially retained by the ion exchanger until the boundary reaches them again. Favorable equilibrium thus counteracts any perturbations which tend to level out the boundary. The boundary is said to be *self-sharpening*. It attains a steady-state shape when the sharpening effect of equilibrium and the leveling effect of the perturbations balance one another (see page 475). This shape remains unchanged as the boundary travels farther down the column. The stronger the preference for B, the sooner this "constant pattern" is attained. A process which involves a self-sharpening boundary is often called a *displacement*.

On the other hand, if equilibrium is unfavorable, the situation is reversed. Ions A behind the boundary are preferentially retained and fall still farther behind, and ions B ahead of the boundary are less strongly held than their competitors and increase their lead. Unfavorable equilibrium thus promotes spreading of the boundary. The boundary is *nonsharpening* and becomes more and more diffuse on its way through the column. It can be shown that, eventually, the spread of the boundary increases in proportion to the distance traveled. The stronger the preference for A, the sooner this "proportionate pattern" is attained. Most elution techniques involve non-sharpening boundaries.

The importance of these effects cannot be overemphasized. They are the key to an understanding of all column operations. It is worthwhile to view the migration of the counter ions through the bed in even more detail. The ions of a species are partly in the moving liquid and partly in the stationary ion exchanger. It is obvious that the (average) rate of migration of a species depends on the distribution between the moving and the stationary phase. The retardation is stronger when the stationary fraction is larger. The distribution coefficient $\lambda_i' \equiv \bar{C}_i/C_i$ thus determines the migration rate. Now, let us examine the migration in a column in which two zones containing the counter ions B and A, respectively, follow one another with a certain overlap. Ion exchange, as a stoichiometric process, does not change the total concentration in either the ion exchanger or the solution (provided that electrolyte sorption is insignificant). The total solution concentration C thus is constant throughout the column and equal to the feed concentration, and the total concentration in the ion exchanger $\bar{C}$ is also constant and equal to the concentration of the fixed ionic groups. It follows that the distribution coefficients of B and A in their respective zones (where the other counter ion is absent) are equal, independent of the nature of the counter ion, and given by the ratio $\bar{C}/C$. Hence B and A, in their own zones, move at equal rates. The migration rate increases with increasing feed concentration, decreases with increasing concentration of fixed ionic groups, and is, of course, proportional to the flow rate. In the overlap, however, the situation is different. Here, both counter ions compete, and the preferred species has the higher distribution coefficient and thus moves at the lower rate. This is always true in zones in which more than one counter ion is present. The sharpening effect of favorable equilibrium and the spreading effect of unfavorable equilibrium are necessary consequences of this fact.

These considerations show that the degree of column utilization can be improved by choosing the ion exchanger and the operating conditions in such a way that the counter ion from the feed is strongly preferred. An undesired consequence, however, is that, now, the conditions for regeneration of the bed become more unfavorable, at least if the selectivity cannot be reversed in the regeneration step.

The *rate of ion exchange* and the *operating conditions* also affect the sharpness of the boundary. Any volume element of the solution is in contact with a given layer of the bed for only a limited time. This time is usually insufficient for attainment of local equilibrium. In other words, ion exchange is usually not fast enough to keep pace with the change in solution composition while the boundary passes through the layer. It is evident that the failure of attaining local equilibrium tends to spread the boundary. Local equilibrium is more closely approached when the rate of ion exchange is high and when the rate of motion of the boundary is low, so that more time is left for ion exchange to keep pace. Hence, *the boundary is sharpened by any measure which increases the ion-exchange rate and decreases the rate of motion of the boundary.* Sharp boundaries are most strongly affected by low rates of ion exchange because, here, the solution composition in the layers changes most rapidly when the boundary passes through.

High rates of ion exchange can be achieved by using ion exchangers of small *particle size* and (if particle diffusion is rate-controlling) of low *crosslinking*, and by operating at an elevated *temperature* (see Table 6-1). The following disadvantages must be considered, however. Small particle size results in high flow resistance of the column. Low crosslinking gives rise to more strongly pronounced changes in swelling which favor channeling (see Sec. 9-10a); furthermore, the volume capacity of the ion exchanger is lower (see Sec. 4-2) and the rate of motion of the boundary thus is higher. High temperature may decrease the selectivity or promote undesired chemical reactions. Moreover, an increase in ion-exchange rate remains without effect if a proportionate pattern has been attained.

The rate of motion of the boundary can be reduced by decreasing the flow rate and the concentration of the feed and increasing the volume capacity of the ion exchanger. Here, the chief disadvantage is that any reduction in migration rate necessarily entails a loss of time. Moreover, the measures mentioned above are ineffective when film diffusion is rate-controlling because they also reduce the rate of film-diffusion controlled ion exchange (see Table 6-1). They are also ineffective if a proportionate pattern has been attained.

A very low migration rate of the boundary may give rise to another undesired effect. The boundary is spread by counter-ion diffusion in the direction of the column axis. The spreading by this so-called *longitudinal diffusion* is proportional to the residence time and to the counter-ion mobilities. Again, sharp boundaries are more strongly affected since they involve larger longitudinal concentration gradients. In ion-exchange operations, however, longitudinal diffusion can become noticeable only at very low flow rates (see page 454).

The effect of *column size and shape* on the degree of utilization is now readily recognized. An increase in column length (the cross section being kept constant) increases both the breakthrough and the over-all capacity. If equilibrium is favorable, the boundary attains the "constant pattern," and both capacities are increased by the same additive amount. The breakthrough curve in Fig. 9-4 is shifted to the right without change in shape. The degree of utilization thus increases with column length and approaches unity. On the other hand, if equilibrium is unfavorable, the boundary attains the "proportionate pattern," and both capacities are increased by the same factor. The breakthrough curve in Fig. 9-4 is shifted to the right and spread proportionally. Hence an increase in column length (beyond a certain limit) does not increase the degree of utilization which remains well below unity. Disadvantages of longer columns are that more ion exchanger is needed and that the flow resistance is higher.

Another variable is the *aspect ratio* of the column (ratio of length and diameter). A high aspect ratio (at constant bed volume and flow rate) improves the utilization if equilibrium is favorable and has little effect if equilibrium is unfavorable. Disadvantages of high aspect ratios are high flow resistance and either low throughput or high flow rate. Moreover, columns of very small diameter tend to suffer from flow maldistribution because of wall effects (see Sec. 9-10a).

Last but not least, the boundary can be distorted by irregularities in the packing and hydrodynamic phenomena (flow maldistribution, channeling, fingering; see Sec. 9-10a). Careful packing and uniform particle size are essential for achieving sharp boundaries.

The results of this purely qualitative study can be summarized as follows. Within certain limits, a high degree of column utilization is favored by:

Strong preference of the ion exchanger for the counter ion from the feed
Small and uniform particle size
High volume capacity
Low degree of crosslinking
Elevated temperature

Low flow rate
Low concentration of counter ions in the feed
High column length or aspect ratio

The gain in column efficiency may be offset by undesired side effects, however.

The effects of ion-exchange equilibrium [16,23,79,176,247], particle size [79,186,212,219], temperature [33,59,113,219], flow rate [79,156,183,186,210, 212,219], feed concentration [79,210,212,219], and column size and shape [79,156,183,186,239,247] on the breakthrough capacity, as discussed in this section, are in agreement with experimental observations.

9-2. CONVENTIONAL COLUMN OPERATION

In conventional single-stage ion-exchange operations, a liquid feed is passed through the column with the intent of replacing the counter ions by another counter-ion species which is initially in the ion exchanger. Generally speaking, counter ions B in the feed are exchanged for counter ions A by an ion exchanger in A form. At breakthrough of species B the feed is discontinued. The column must now be reconverted to the A form for the next ion-exchange cycle. Reconversion is usually carried out with a solution of an electrolyte AY which removes B from the column by exchange for A. This reconversion is commonly called *regeneration* if the ion-exchanged solution is the desired product, and *recovery* if species B is the desired product.

The preceding section has shown that a high breakthrough capacity for B can be attained by chosing conditions in such a way that the ion exchanger prefers B to A, so that a self-sharpening boundary arises. As a rule, however, preference for species B leads to unfavorable equilibrium and a nonsharpening boundary in the regeneration or recovery step and, hence, to a much higher than the stoichiometric regenerant requirement. In most cases, an only moderate preference of the ion exchanger for species B is the best compromise.

In a few cases, the selectivity of the ion exchanger can be reversed in such a way that equilibrium is favorable in both the sorption and the regeneration or recovery steps. A classical example is water softening where small quantities of Ca^{2+}, Mg^{2+}, and other polyvalent cations are replaced by Na^+. From dilute solutions (hard water) the polyvalent ions are preferentially taken up because of the electroselectivity effect (see page 156), but in equilibria with highly concentrated solutions Na^+ is preferred. Thus the ion exchanger can be regenerated with only little more than the stoichiometric amount of concentrated brine, although equilibrium in the sorption step is highly favorable. Much of the success of ion exchange in water softening is due to this fortunate coincidence.

In water softening and many other applications, several counter-ion species are simultaneously removed. The species with the strongest affinity for the ion exchanger is accumulated in the first layers of the column near the inlet. As a rule, this species also is most obstinately retained by the resin in the regeneration step. In such cases, "countercurrent" regeneration is advantageous [16]. Sorption can be performed with downflow and regeneration with upflow, or vice versa. In this way one can avoid having to force the most strongly preferred ion through the whole column. Countercurrent regeneration has another advantage. As a rule, it is not economical to carry regeneration to completion. With cocurrent regeneration, remaining small quantities of species B are left near the outlet of the column and thus cause early contamination of the effluent in the next sorption step. With countercurrent regeneration, the outlet in regeneration becomes the inlet in sorption, and remaining B ions in this part of the column can do little harm.

Highly selective ion exchangers are occasionally needed, for example, for efficient removal of small quantities of a counter-ion species from a large excess of competing counter ions. Straightforward regeneration of such resins usually requires excessive amounts of regenerant. Here, regeneration in two steps with favorable equilibria is often more advantageous than regeneration in one step with unfavorable equilibrium [253a]. For example, one-step reconversion of chelating resins such as Dowex A-1 (iminodiacetic acid groups) from the Cu^{2+} or Ni^{2+} form to the Na^+ form with, say, NaCl is impractical because of the great preference of the resins for the transition-group metal ions. The latter, however, are readily displaced by strong acids which spring the chelate bonds. The resin, now in H^+ form, is then easily converted to the desired Na^+ form by treatment with NaOH; neutralization of H^+ by OH^- in the external solution provides so strong a "driving force" that equilibrium is highly favorable for this conversion also (see also page 164).

Economic considerations in plant-scale applications often lead to rather intricate regeneration schemes which are beyond the scope of this book. The interested reader is referred to the technical literature [16,30,50,98a,131, 156,248].

In plant operation, ion exchange is usually carried out with two columns, one on stream and one on regeneration, to provide an uninterrupted product flow. A larger number of columns in parallel on stream are occasionally used to avoid idling if regeneration requires much less time than exhaustion.

With at least three columns, a very high degree of column utilization can be attained by operating with two or more columns in series on stream and one column on regeneration. After regeneration, this latter column is added as the last column to the series of columns on stream. By this time, the first of the columns on stream is almost or completely exhausted and is switched to regeneration. By always adding a freshly regenerated column downstream and regenerating the exhausted column that was highest upstream one can achieve practically complete utilization of ion-exchange capacity. Such a "merry-go-round" operation has been used, for example, in uranium-ore processing where regeneration costs depend little on the degree of exhaustion of the columns [132].

Another way of achieving a high utilization of the ion exchanger is by continuous countercurrent operation where the ion exchanger and the solutions are moved in opposite directions at such relative rates that the exchange zone remains stationary. A great variety of countercurrent contactors has been designed, but so far none of them has been entirely satisfactory.

9-3. TWO-STAGE, MULTISTAGE, AND MIXED-BED DEIONIZATION

Ion exchange can be used not only for replacing one ion by another, but also for complete removal of electrolytes from solutions (*deionization, demineralization*). A typical and very important practical application is the deionization of boiler feed water.

Complete removal of electrolytes—unless they are acids or bases—requires the use of both a cation and an anion exchanger. The cation exchanger replaces the cations A, B, . . . by H^+

$$A + B + \cdots + \overline{H^+} \rightarrow H^+ + \overline{A} + \overline{B} + \cdots \tag{9-1}$$

and the anion exchanger replaces the anions Y, Z, . . . by OH^-

$$Y + Z + \cdots + \overline{OH^-} \rightarrow OH^- + \overline{Y} + \overline{Z} + \cdots \tag{9-2}$$

H^+ and OH^- combine, forming H_2O.

Deionization can be carried out as a *two-stage* process [16,30,89,131]. The solution is first passed through a cation-exchange bed in H^+ form and then through an anion-exchange bed in OH^- form. The cations are removed in the first bed. While passing through the bed, however, the solution becomes more and more acidic. The accumulation of H^+ ions in the solution discourages the process (9-1). Thus the efficiency of removal of the last traces of metal cations becomes rather poor. Besides, the pH change may have other objectionable consequences (for example, sucrose inversion when solutions containing sucrose are demineralized).

These considerations have led to the design of *multistage* units [16,89,177, 252]. Here, the solution is passed through a series of columns with cation and anion exchangers alternating. The bulk of the cations is replaced by H^+ in the first column (which can now be run to a higher breakthrough concentration), and the remaining traces are taken up by later cation-exchange columns after the solution has been neutralized by anion exchange. Up to seven columns are used in standard installations.

The first bed in two-stage and multistage deionizers is usually a strong-acid resin which prefers metal cations to H^+. This guarantees a self-sharpening boundary and thus a high utilization. In the following anion-exchange cycle the boundary is automatically self-sharpening because the presence of H^+ in the solution guarantees favorable equilibrium. The last bed is, as a rule, a weak-acid (or weak-base) resin which is more apt to give a neutral final product.

The highest deionization efficiency is obtained with a so-called *mixed bed* (or *monobed*), a single column containing an intimate mixture of cation- and anion-exchanger particles [28a,30,105,130,149,173,234]. Here, both processes (9-1) and (9-2) occur simultaneously at neighboring beads, and the solution thus remains neutral. The H^+ and OH^- ions from the ion exchangers disappear instantaneously by reacting with one another. This guarantees extremely favorable equilibria of cation and anion exchange throughout the column and thus a very high degree of utilization and a very clean product.

Mixed-bed deionizers have one serious disadvantage, namely, their regeneration is difficult. As a rule, the two exchangers are separated, individually regenerated, and mixed for further use. The separation is usually achieved by "backwashing" (passing water upward through the column); the heavier cation exchanger then settles below the lighter anion exchanger [130,149,234].

An interesting alternative which, however, has found little use is the following. First, the anion exchanger is regenerated by caustic; then the cation exchanger, now in Na^+ form, is regenerated by a polymeric acid (ligninsulfonic acid) [242]. The polymeric anion is excluded by sieve action; the anion exchanger thus remains in OH^- form.

Mixed-bed units have also been used for final "clean-up" in multistage demineralization schemes [222].

9-4. ION EXCLUSION

Ion exclusion* is an elegant method for separating strong electrolytes from weak electrolytes and nonelectrolytes [7,14,204,253]. No actual ion exchange occurs. The ion exchanger acts merely as a sorbent.

The pronounced difference in sorption behavior of strong electrolytes and nonelectrolytes has been discussed in a previous chapter (Sec. 5-3). Strong electrolytes are efficiently excluded by the Donnan effect. There is no such exclusion of nonelectrolytes. The ion exclusion technique is based on this difference.

An electrolyte, say, AY can be separated from a nonelectrolyte in a column with a resin in A form (or Y form). The nonelectrolyte is more

---

* Actually, "electrolyte exclusion" would be a more appropriate name.

strongly sorbed and, hence, more strongly retained. After sorption in the upper part of the column, both solutes are eluted with pure solvent. The electrolyte appears first in the effluent. After elution, the column is ready for the next sorption cycle. No regeneration is required since no ion exchange has occurred.

An overlap of the bands of the electrolyte and the nonelectrolyte in the effluent can be avoided only at considerable sacrifices in flow rate and product concentrations. As a rule, recycling of the intermediate mixed fraction is more economical. Much higher product concentrations can be obtained by an attractive, semicontinuous technique [14,204]. Here, only comparatively small but concentrated fractions of the pure components are taken as product cuts from the effluent which is otherwise recycled. A

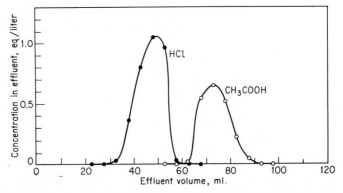

Fig. 9-5. Experimental effluent concentration history in separation of hydrochloric acid from acetic acid by ion exclusion. Feed: 15 ml 1.17 M HCl + 0.66 M CH₃COOH; resin: 100 ml Dowex 50-X8. *From R. M. Wheaton and W. C. Bauman* [253].

fresh amount of the initial mixture is added to the recycle stream at the point of maximum overlap. This procedure is illustrated in Fig. 9-6.

Ion exclusion can also be used for separating electrolytes from one another, provided that they differ sufficiently in their degree of dissociation or their ionic valences.

The separation is obviously favored by strong (but reversible) sorption of the nonelectrolyte (or weaker electrolyte) and by efficient Donnan exclusion of the strong electrolyte. Donnan exclusion is favored by high valence of the co-ion and low valence of the counter ion (see Sec. 5-3c and e). For example, a 2,1-valent electrolyte is usually more efficiently removed by an anion exchanger than by a cation exchanger of comparable capacity. High capacity of the ion exchanger and low electrolyte concentration of the solution also promote efficient ion exclusion. The nonelectrolyte concentration has little effect. The separation efficiency also depends on how well local equilibrium in the layers of the bed is approached (see page 426).

For example, the separation is usually improved by decreasing the particle size of the resin and the flow rate. Special attention should be devoted to the degree of crosslinking of the resin. High crosslinking gives a high ion-exchange capacity (per unit volume) of the resin and thus efficient Donnan exclusion. On the other hand, the sorption rate is low. The optimum degree of crosslinking depends somewhat on the molecular size of the non-electrolyte; the technique must fail when sieve action prevents the non-electrolyte molecules from entering the resin.

The basic principle of ion exclusion is the same as that of conventional chromatography on a nonionic sorbent. In both cases, the separation is

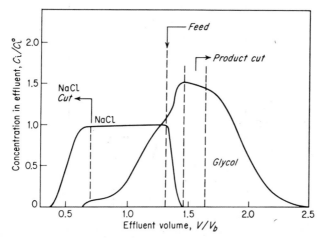

Fig. 9-6. Semicontinuous ion-exclusion process for separation of glycol from NaCl. Only the concentrated effluent fractions are taken as product cuts in every cycle. The other cuts are returned to the column in the same order, and new feed is inserted at the point of maximum cross-contamination. After a few cycles, the effluent history attains a steady state which is shown in the diagram. The concentration of glycol in the product cuts is higher than in the original mixture. Feed: NaCl 10% wt + ethylene-glycol 10% wt, 0.26 bed volumes; resin: Dowex 50-X8. *From W. C. Bauman, R. M. Wheaton, and D. W. Simpson* [14].

effected by the difference in sorption strength of the solutes. The unique feature of ion exclusion is the mechanism which causes this difference.

9-5. ION RETARDATION

An alternative and rather similar technique for separating strong electrolytes from weak electrolytes or nonelectrolytes is *ion retardation* [95]. Here too, the resin acts only as a sorbent, and the separation is effected by the difference in sorption strength.

Ion retardation makes use of "snake-cage" polyelectrolytes. These are resins which contain both acid and base groups and sorb electrolytes.

more strongly than either weak or nonelectrolytes (see Sec. 3-4 and Fig. 5-22). A snake-cage bed resembles a mixed bed (Sec. 9-3), except that sorbed electrolytes can be eluted from the snake-cage bed by washing with pure solvent. The mixed bed, in contrast, requires regeneration but gives a much sharper separation.

Ion retardation is carried out in the same way as ion exclusion. The only difference is that, here, the nonelectrolyte appears first in the effluent (Fig. 9-7). No regeneration is required.

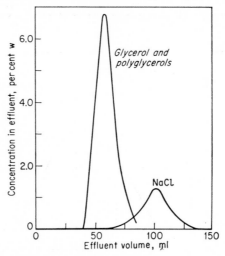

FIG. 9-7. Experimental effluent concentration history in separation of NaCl from glycerol and polyglycerols by ion retardation. Feed: 12.5% wt glycerol, 6.2% wt polyglycerols, 6% wt NaCl; temperature 70°C; resin: Retardion 11 A 8. *From M. J. Hatch, J. A. Dillon, and H. B. Smith* [95].

Ion exclusion and ion retardation supplement one another in a fortunate way. In ion retardation, nonelectrolyte sorption should be small. The isolation of macromolecular nonelectrolytes thus becomes feasible. Here, of course, ion exclusion would fail. On the other hand, macromolecular electrolytes can be separated from nonelectrolytes by ion exclusion, but not by ion retardation.

Electrolyte sorption by snake-cage polyelectrolytes seems to be chiefly determined by the affinities of the acid groups for the cation and of the base groups for the anion. The resins can distinguish somewhat between different electrolytes. This effect can be used for separating electrolytes from one another [95].

9-6. SEPARATION BY SELECTIVE DISPLACEMENT

Ion exchange is an excellent tool for separating mixtures of various counter ions. Even very delicate separations can be achieved by ion-exchange chromatography which will be discussed in the next section. A much simpler technique is *selective displacement* [57,61b,144,154,174,180,186,192]. It can be used when the ions differ strongly in their affinity for the ion exchanger. The principle of selective displacement will be illustrated by a simple example.

Two counter ions B and C can be separated in the following way. A small amount of the mixture which contains B and C is introduced into a column which contains an ion exchanger in, say, A form. The affinity of the ion exchanger for A should be intermediate. Suppose the selectivity sequence is $B \ll A \ll C$. Species B is only weakly held by the ion exchanger and is

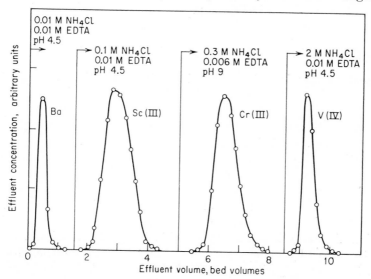

FIG. 9-8. Separation of barium, scandium, chromium, and vanadium on a strong-base anion exchanger by selective displacement with complexing buffers. *From K. A. Kraus and F. Nelson* [127].

readily displaced from the column by a solution AY. Species C, which is more strongly held than A, remains in the column and can be eluted subsequently with another, more efficient eluent.

Selective displacement requires high selectivities. These can often be obtained by the use of complexing agents. As a rule, the affinity of a counter ion for the ion exchanger is reduced by complexing with the co-ion (see Secs. 5-6b and 9-7d). Thus species B can be selectively displaced by a complexing agent which forms complexes with B, but not with C. Species C may then be eluted with another complexing agent.

In a modification of this technique, anion exchangers are used for separating cations [6a,108,126,127,185,187,192,257,258,262a]. Cations forming anionic complexes are taken up by anion exchangers whereas noncomplexing cations are excluded by the Donnan effect. Thus a cation which forms no (or only a weak) anionic complex is readily displaced by the complexing agent, while its companion is complexed and remains in the column. The complexing cation can then be eluted under conditions which favor breakup of the complex. The affinities of various complexing cations for anion exchangers depend strongly on the concentration of the complexing anion (see Sec. 5-6c). Such cations can be separated when the anion concentration is properly adjusted to give maximum selectivity. Excellent resolutions have been obtained with HCl [126], HBr [98], HF [257], and HCl-HF mixtures [124,125,164] as complexing agents. The pioneer work of K. A. Kraus [124–126] has shown that almost any pair of bivalent or polyvalent cations can be separated in this way.

9-7. PRINCIPLES OF ION-EXCHANGE CHROMATOGRAPHY

Chromatography is a technique in which resolution of a mixture is achieved by virtue of differences in migration rates of the components in a packed column. Chromatography was first applied to colored substances where "bands" of different colors can be seen while they move down the column. This is how the technique got its name.

Conventional chromatography on alumina, kieselguhr, activated carbon, etc., has proved to be an excellent tool, particularly for separations of organic compounds. More recently, ion exchangers have been introduced as separating agents. Within only a few years, ion-exchange chromatography has become one of the most important techniques for delicate separations in analytical and preparative inorganic chemistry. Perhaps its most spectacular achievement was the separation of the rare earths in hitherto unknown purity [113,209–211,219,237,240]. Ion-exchange chromatography has played an important role in the isolation and identification of the new transuranium elements [45,73,150,221,235,260] and has even been used for enrichment of isotopes [46,78,141,141a,218,228]. Organic substances such as amino acids [92–94,158,160,161,171,172,225], peptides [18a,158,193], proteins [158,208], nucleic acids [250], alcohols [146,158,190], glycols [146,188,189], carbonyl compounds [24,146,158,199], carbohydrates and derivatives [117,118,142,158,184,263], ethers [190,199], amines [97,158, 190,250a], hydrocarbons [199,229], and phenols [196,199] have also been separated in ion-exchange columns.*

The mode of operation in conventional chromatography with nonionic sorbents and ion-exchange chromatography is rather similar. There is one characteristic difference in mechanism, however. In conventional chromatography the mechanism is sorption and desorption; the components

---

* The mechanism in separations of organic molecules, however, is usually sorption (partition) rather than ion exchange; see also Secs. 9-7e and 9-8.

of the mixture are reversibly sorbed by the solid sorbent* and can be eluted with pure solvent.   In ion-exchange chromatography the mechanism is stoichiometric exchange of counter ions; the counter ions of the mixture, when taken up by the ion exchanger, liberate the original counter ion and can be eluted only by an electrolyte since other counter ions are needed to take their place in the resin.   In practice, however, a clear-cut distinction between these two types of chromatography can hardly be made since most of the conventional sorbents are not strictly nonionic and most ion-exchange processes are accompanied, to a greater or lesser degree, by sorption or hydrolysis.

Chromatographic columns can be operated in different ways.   The most important techniques are *elution development, displacement development,* and *frontal analysis.*   In the development techniques, a certain amount of the mixture is introduced at the top of the column and is then "developed" by a suitable agent.   On their way down the column the components of the mixture separate into individual "bands" which emerge one after the other.   In frontal analysis, the mixture is continuously fed to the column; the front boundaries of the various components emerge at different times, but a separation into pure fractions is not achieved.   The principles of these techniques will now be illustrated.

a. Displacement Development

Suppose that three counter ions, B, C, and D, should be separated by displacement development.   An ion exchanger is chosen which can distinguish between these counter ions, i.e., which has at least some selectivity. The ion-exchange bed is converted to, say, the A form, where A is a counter ion which has less affinity for the resin than the counter ions of the mixture. A substantial amount of the mixture is now introduced at the top of the column.   Development is carried out with a counter ion, say, E which the resin prefers to the counter ions of the mixture (selectivity sequence $A < B < C < D < E$).

The development agent EY, when fed to the column, displaces the counter ions of the mixture with a self-sharpening boundary.   These, in turn, displace the original counter ion A with a self-sharpening boundary. Within the zone which is occupied by the mixture, the ion exchanger retains the ion D most strongly and the ion B least strongly.   Thus D is accumulated in the upper part and B in the lower part of the zone.   On its way through the bed the zone separates into individual bands of counter ions in the sequence of selectivity.   Between these bands self-sharpening boundaries arise.   The bands follow one another without intervals and move at equal rates.   The migration rate is determined by the flow rate,

---

* In *partition chromatography,* the solid is merely the carrier of a stationary liquid phase. Ion exchangers can also be used in partition chromatography; see Sec. 9-7e.

the feed concentration, and the volume capacity of the ion exchanger and is independent of the nature of the counter ions (see page 425). In the effluent the bands appear in the sequence of selectivity: A, B, C, D, E. Of course, the boundaries are not ideally sharp. A certain overlap of neighboring bands cannot be avoided (see Figs. 9-9 and 9-10).

Displacement development thus yields pure fractions BY, CY, and DY and small overlaps which, if required, can be resolved by renewed displacement development in a smaller column. The technique is primarily suited for preparative separations.

The various factors which determine the separation efficiency are readily understood. The overlap of neighboring fractions should be as small as practicable. Hence the column should be long enough for the boundaries to attain the steady-state shape. A further increase in column length (at constant column diameter) does not improve the separation. A high

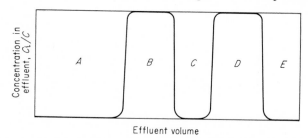

Effluent volume

Fig. 9-9. Effluent concentration history in displacement development (*schematic*). The counter ions B, C, and D are separated on a resin in A form by development with the counter ion E. (The concentrations of A, C, and E are plotted from the top of the diagram.)

aspect ratio (at constant bed volume and flow rate) is favorable since it gives long bands and thus less relative overlap. However, the separation now requires more time unless a higher flow rate is used which may offset the gain. High selectivity, high volume capacity, and small particle size of the resin, low flow rate, low feed concentration, and elevated temperature are favorable since they give sharp boundaries. These effects and the disadvantages they entail have been discussed in detail in Sec. 9-1.

The effluent concentration histories of ion-exchange and conventional (nonionic) displacement development [99,114] are very similar. The only essential difference is that in ion-exchange displacement the total (equivalent) concentration in the effluent remains constant and equal to the feed concentration, whereas in nonionic displacement it usually increases stepwise with every breakthrough of a new component. This difference is due to the fact that ion exchange is stoichiometric whereas nonionic exchange adsorption is not.

b. Elution Development

Suppose that the same counter ions, B, C, and D, should now be separated by elution development. The same resin in A form can be used (selectivity sequence A < B < C < D). A small amount of the mixture is introduced at the top of the column and is developed with a solution AY, i.e., with a counter ion which has *less* affinity for the resin than the counter ions of the mixture.

In elution development, the boundary between eluent and mixture is nonsharpening. The counter ion A soon bypasses the counter ions of the mixture, which are more strongly held. The species B, C, and D now migrate in the presence of A. All three are slower than A, and the species which is most strongly preferred by the resin is the slowest. The mixture thus separates into individual bands which travel at, *different* rates and,

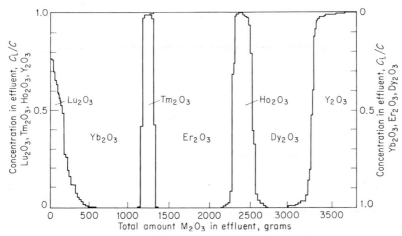

Fig. 9-10. Plant-scale separation of heavy rare earths by displacement development. Displacement agent: citrate buffer of pH 8.0 prepared from 0.1% wt citric acid and concentrated NH_3; resin: Nalcite HCR in H^+ form. *From F. H. Spedding and J. E. Powell* [219].

hence, come farther and farther apart when moving down the column. The bands have nonsharpening boundaries* and flatten out more and more on their way downstream. In the effluent, individual bands containing B, C, and D in low concentration appear on a background of A (Fig. 9-11). Complete resolution of B, C, and D can be obtained. The technique is quite similar to conventional elution development on nonionic adsorbents [99] and to gas chromatography [114] and is primarily suited for quantitative analysis.

The various factors which determine the column performance are readily explained. The sample size should be kept small to avoid "overloading" which results in mutual interference of the peaks (see also page 478).

---

* It is true that, initially, the front boundaries are self-sharpening [182a]. The sharpening effect, however, is lost when the peak concentrations become much smaller than the total concentration.

High selectivity of the ion exchanger guarantees large differences in the migration rates of the various "peaks" and thus facilitates the separation. The sharpness of the peaks depends on how well local equilibrium in the layers of the bed is approached.* Sharp peaks are obtained when the ion-exchange rates are high and the migration rates are low. Small particle size and high volume capacity of the resin, low flow rate, low eluent concentration, and elevated temperature thus favor clean separations (see page 426). An increase in column length increases the distance between the peaks and thus the separation efficiency; at the same time, however, the bands are flattened. As far as possible the operating conditions are chosen in such a way that essentially no overlap of neighboring bands occurs. On the other hand, unnecessary intervals between the bands should be

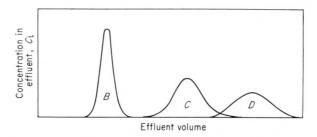

Effluent volume

Fig. 9-11. Effluent concentration history in elution development (*schematic*). The counter ions B, C, and D are separated by elution with the counter ion A. Resolution of C and D in the diagram is incomplete.

avoided and the latter should be kept as sharp as possible in order to save time and reagents. In special cases a stepwise or continuous change in eluent composition (similar to selective displacement, see Sec. 9-6) is advantageous (*gradient elution*) [19,32,60,145,160,161,165,170,261]. The calculation of optimum operating conditions is not simple. This problem will be discussed in more detail in a later section (see page 460).

c. Frontal Analysis

Frontal analysis differs from the development techniques in that the mixture which is investigated is continuously fed to the column rather than being developed by a displacing or eluting agent.

Suppose that the mixture consists of the electrolytes BY, CY, and DY, and that the ion exchanger is in A form. The counter ion A should be least strongly held by the resin. (Selectivity sequence A < B < C < D.) The mixture then displaces species A with a

---

* Occasionally, differences in ion-exchange rates rather than selectivities are used as the basis for separations [129]. In this case, local equilibrium is consciously avoided. The ion which is taken up by the resin at the lowest rate is then the first to appear in the effluent. However, this technique is seldom used because sharp separations cannot be achieved.

self-sharpening boundary.   In the mixture, species B is least preferred by the resin and thus migrates at the highest rate.   Behind the rear boundary of A a zone develops which contains B only.   Species C migrates more rapidly than D and is thus accumulated behind the band of B.   In the effluent, the displaced ion A is followed by B, then by a mixture of B and C, and eventually—when the column has attained equilibrium

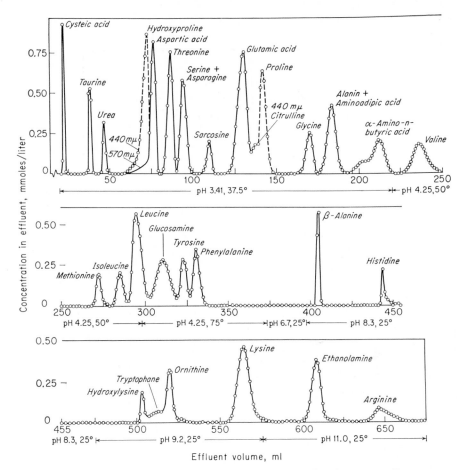

FIG. 9-12. Analytical separation of amino acids by elution development.   Temperature and pH of the eluent are changed stepwise.   The effluent is recorded spectrophotometrically at 440 and 570 mμ after reaction with ninhydrin.   Eluent: sodium citrate buffer for pH 3.41 to 6.7, sodium carbonate-bicarbonate buffer for pH 6.7 to 11.0; resin: Dowex 50-X8 in Na⁺ form.   *From S. Moore and W. H. Stein* [161].

with the feed—by a mixture of B, C, and D (see Fig. 9-13).   The boundaries of the various pure and mixed bands are all self-sharpening.

Frontal analysis is comparatively simple to handle.   Only one component, however, of the mixture (the counter ion which is least preferred by the resin) is actually isolated.   The components can only be recognized by the occurrence of the "fronts" in the effluent.   The relative amounts of the species cannot be calculated from the distances between the fronts unless the selectivity of the resin is known.   These are serious limitations which impair the value of the technique.

The effluent histories of ion-exchange and conventional (nonionic) frontal analysis [35,99,114] are very similar.   The only essential difference is that the total effluent concentration remains constant in ion-exchange frontal analysis, and usually rises stepwise with every new boundary in conventional frontal analysis.   This effect has already been discussed in the description of displacement development (see Sec. 9-7a).

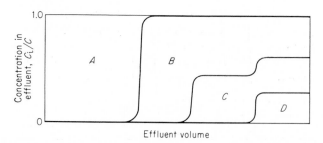

Fig. 9-13. Effluent concentration history in frontal analysis (*schematic*).   The concentrations of B and C are plotted from the curves for C and D, respectively.

d. Use of Complexing Agents

Separations by ion-exchange chromatography are based on the selectivity of the ion exchanger.   A separation is possible only when the ion exchanger can distinguish between the various counter ions.   The most delicate and challenging problems are, of course, separations of counter ions such as the rare-earth cations which are almost identical in their behavior.   Unfortunately, little ion-exchange selectivity can be expected in such cases, and straightforward ion-exchange chromatography is bound to fail.   Nevertheless, separations can be achieved if the selectivity can be enhanced by special means.   An efficient and convenient way of improving and adjusting ion-exchange selectivities is by use of complexing agents [18,22,27,73,116,127, 137,163,192,206,261].   Complexes even of very similar ions such as the rare-earth cations may differ considerably in their strengths.   In the presence of a complexing anion, a cation exchanger usually prefers the cation which forms the weaker complex (see Sec. 5-6b).   Differences in the strengths of the citrate [153,209–213,215,237,238,240,241], lactate [41,59, 151,153,165,260], ethylenediaminetetraacetate [147,153,214,217,254], nitrilotriacetate [58,143], and α-hydroxyisobutyrate complexes [33,207] of the rare-earth cations have been used for achieving complete separations of traces and of gram and even kilogram quantities.

The effect of complex formation on ion-exchange equilibria has been discussed in more detail in Sec. 5-6.   Here, it may suffice to stress the two most important points.   First, the extent of complex formation by a given cation is determined by the complex strength (i.e., the stability constants) and the concentration of the (free) complexing anion.   Second, the separation factor of two given cations depends on the free-anion concentration; the optimum separation factor can be attained by proper adjustment of this concentration. In chromatographic separations the complexing anion is introduced as the development agent. The free-anion concentration in the column thus depends on the composition of this agent. Note that the free-anion concentration is a function of the pH if the anion forms a weak acid.

Wherever possible, the free-anion concentration should be adjusted in such a way that the optimum separation factor is attained. This can be done only within certain limits, however, because the free-anion concentration also determines whether displacement development or elution development takes place. This important point will be illustrated by a typical example.

> *Example.* The rare-earth cations can be separated on a cation-exchange bed in H^+ form by development with citrate buffers. In one technique, an ammonium citrate buffer of pH 7.5 to 8.0 (prepared from 0.1 per cent citric acid and ammonia) is used [213]. The high citrate-ion concentration in the slightly alkaline buffer causes extensive complex formation and thus reduces the affinity of the rare-earth cations for the ion exchanger so much that, now, NH_4^+ is preferred. Hence, development is by *displacement*.
>
> In another technique an ammonium citrate buffer of pH 2.5 to 3.0 (prepared from 5 per cent citric acid and ammonia) is used [209,210]. Here, the concentration of free citrate ions is much lower because citric acid is only weakly dissociated. Hence the rare-earth cations are less extensively complexed and are preferred by the ion exchanger, even though citrate is present. Thus development is by *elution*.

This example shows that, for every separation, there is a critical concentration of free complexing anions in the development agent. Displacement development occurs when the free-anion concentration is higher than the critical one, and elution development occurs when the free anion concentration is lower.

In elution development of traces, the concentration and pH of the development agent remain essentially unchanged while the latter passes through the column. The optimum free-anion concentration can thus be adjusted directly (provided it does not exceed the critical concentration) by a suitable choice of the composition of the development agent. In displacement development the situation is different. Here, the counter ion of the agent (NH_4^+ in the example above) is retained by the ion exchanger at the rear boundary of the mixture. The free-anion concentration in the zone occupied by the mixture depends on the extent of complex formation. In every band an individual, stationary concentration of free complexing anions and a corresponding pH are attained [216]. Both, of course, are affected by the composition of the development agent. They can be calculated from the equations given in Sec. 5-6.

e. Partition Chromatography with Ion Exchangers

In partition chromatography, a granular solid is used as the carrier for a stationary liquid phase. Chromatographic separations are achieved by virtue of differences in the distribution coefficients of the components of a mixture between the stationary liquid and the percolating solution. Upon development with a suitable solvent or agent, the components emerge in the sequence of increasing distribution coefficients. As a rule, the elution-development technique is used.

Ion exchangers can be used as the stationary phase in partition chromatography of nonelectrolytes and even of electrolytes. In such operations, the ion exchanger acts merely as a sorbent, and no ion exchange takes place. The use of ion exchangers is advantageous if they can distinguish more sharply than nonionic sorbents between the components of the mixture, i.e., if the differences between the distribution coefficients of the components are greater. Ion exclusion, which is based on the pronounced dependence of the sorption strength on the degree of dissociation of the sorbate, is an extreme example of partition chromatography with ion exchangers (see Sec. 9-4). Elution chromatography of amino acids on cation exchangers is essentially based on similar, but more delicate, differences (see Fig. 9-12).

The sorption characteristics of ion exchangers depend on the ionic form of the resin and the composition of the external solution (see the detailed discussion in Sec. 5-3). If the mixture contains no electrolytes, one is free to choose the most suitable ionic form of the resin. Also, the resolution can often be enhanced by the use of particular development agents. For example, in nonelectrolyte separations, addition of an electrolyte may reduce the solubilities of the nonelectrolytes and thus promote sorption and separation ("salting-out chromatography") [24,146,177a,190]. The opposite case is also found; if sorption of the nonelectrolytes is stronger than desired, addition of agents such as acetic acid may increase the solubility in the external aqueous phase and thus facilitate elution ("solubilization chromatography") [199]. Particular effects can be achieved by addition of water-miscible organic solvents (alcohol, acetone, etc.) which may profoundly affect the distribution of both electrolytes and nonelectrolytes (see Sec. 10-4) [42,196,250a,258].

In the techniques mentioned so far, only one solvent or mixtures of miscible solvents are used, and the differences in the distribution coefficients of the species arise merely from various interactions with the matrix, the fixed ionic groups, or the counter ions of the ion exchanger. More recently, however, ion exchangers have also been used for "true" partition chromatography with a stationary and a moving solvent that are *immiscible* with one another. For example, metals have been separated with partially or completely water-swollen ion exchangers as the stationary phase and kerosene solutions of alkylphosphoric acids or phosphine oxides as the moving phase [205]. Such "gel-liquid extraction" can be carried out with a wide variety of combinations of immiscible solvent pairs and with stationary solid as well as moving liquid ion exchangers [205].

Partition chromatography with ion exchangers has so far been developed by only a few investigators. One may hope for further progress in this promising field.

9-8. "LIGAND EXCHANGE" AND OTHER TECHNIQUES BASED ON CHEMICAL REACTIONS

"Ligand exchange" is a recently developed technique for isolating or separating anions or neutral molecules which can form complexes with metal ions [70,96,97,229]. An ion exchanger is used as a solid carrier for the complexing metal ion. Usually, the metal ion is the counter ion in a cation exchanger. An exchange of ligands for others (or for solvent molecules) takes place between the external solution and the coordination shells of the metal ions in the resin. Displacement of the metal ion from the resin by ion exchange must be avoided. A more detailed discussion of ligand-exchange equilibria has been given in Sec. 5-7.

Ligand exchange is an efficient means of separating ligands from non-ligands [96,229]. The solution containing the ligand is passed through a ligand-exchange column, i.e., a column with an ion exchanger in the complexing metal-ion form. The ligand is preferentially sorbed, while non-ligands pass through relatively unhindered. The advantage over other, more conventional techniques is that complex formation is a very strong interaction if the proper metal is chosen. Because of the strong tendency of the ligand to form complexes with the metal in the resin, ligand sorption is highly selective, and almost the full ligand-exchange capacity is utilized even if the ligand concentration in the external solution is very low (see, for example, Fig. 5-27). The ligand can be recovered from the column by displacement with another, more strongly complexing ligand. Alternatively, displacement can be carried out with an acid which removes both the ligand and the metal by ion exchange. If a resin is used which holds the metal ion firmly by complexing with the fixed ionic groups, the ligand can also be displaced with a buffer of a pH such that the metal-ligand bonds are broken but the metal-resin bonds are not.

Ligands can be separated from one another by ligand-exchange chromatography [96]. The standard chromatographic techniques—displacement development, elution development, gradient elution, frontal analysis, etc.— can be used. Displacement development of a ligand mixture is carried out with a ligand that complexes more strongly, and elution development with one that complexes less strongly than the ligands of the mixture. If the complexes formed by the latter are sufficiently weak, a solvent alone can be used for elution development. The physical mechanism of the separations is the same as in ion-exchange chromatography (see Sec. 9-7), with the only difference that ligands instead of counter ions are exchanged. The

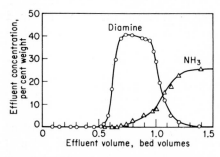

FIG. 9-14. Ligand-exchange displacement of a diamine (1,3-diaminopropanol-2) with concentrated aqueous ammonia. Resin: Amberlite IRC-50 in Ni^{2+} form. The diamine was selectively sorbed from a *dilute* solution by the resin in nickel-ammonia-complex form and is recovered in high concentration by displacement with *concentrated* ammonia. *From F. Helfferich* [97].

advantage of ligand exchange over other chromatographic techniques is that complex formation is, as a rule, a more specific interaction than ordinary physical sorption or ion exchange. The complexes of various even rather similar ligands with a properly chosen metal ion usually differ considerably in their strengths. Accordingly, high selectivities can be attained. In this respect, ligand exchange can be compared with the separation of metals such as the rare earths by ion-exchange chromatography with complexing agents (see Sec. 9-7d). In that technique, differences in the strength of complexes of various metal ions with a ligand are used for separating the metals; in ligand exchange, differences in the strength of complexes of a metal ion with various ligands are used for separating the latter.

Ligand exchange is a particularly useful technique for separating ligands of different coordinative valences [96,97]. Here, the selectivity of the ligand exchanger depends on the total ligand concentration of the solution. Low concentration favors preference of the ligand exchanger for the ligand of the higher coordinative valence, and vice versa (see Sec. 5-7, Fig. 5-43). The selectivity can thus be adjusted and even reversed at will by changing the solution concentration. By a reversal of the selectivity, favorable equilibrium can be attained in both the sorption and the regeneration or recovery steps. For example, from a *dilute* solution of a monodentate and a bidentate ligand the latter is efficiently removed by selective sorption onto a ligand exchanger. The bidentate ligand can then be recovered in high concentration by selective displacement from the resin with a *concentrated* solution of the monodentate ligand (see Fig. 9-14). The situation is quite similar to that in water softening where the electroselectivity effect permits the selectivity for Na^+ and polyvalent cations to be reversed, so that equilibrium is also favorable in both the sorption and the regeneration steps (see Sec. 9-2).

A serious limitation of ligand exchange is that displacement of the complexing metal ion from the resin by ion exchange with other cations in the solution cannot be tolerated.   Therefore the technique is mainly suited for separations of nonionic ligands such as ammonia, alkyl amines, polyhydric alcohols, etc., in solutions of low ionic strength.   In the presence of strong electrolytes and in separations of anionic ligands, protection against metal-ion loss—at a sacrifice in ligand-exchange capacity—can be obtained by using resins which hold the metal firmly by partial complexing with the fixed ionic groups (see Sec. 5-7).

Ligand exchange, in contrast to ion exchange, is not restricted to liquid-phase operations.   For example, the principle of ligand exchange has recently been used in gas-liquid chromatography.   The complexing metal ion, in partially complexed form, is dissolved in the stationary liquid phase.   Compounds in the gas stream which form complexes with the metal are selectively retarded [31].

A number of similar techniques have been developed which involve chemical reactions other than complex formation with metal counter ions. For example, silica has been removed from water by anion exchange after addition of F^- ions which complex the silica, forming $[SiF_6]^{2-}$ [13,255a]. Carbohydrates and related compounds have been removed from solutions and have been chromatographically separated from one another with anion exchangers in borate [117,118,142,189,263] or bisulfite form [184,186]. These latter techniques are based on the addition of the organic compounds to the borate or bisulfite anion.

The possibilities of exploiting chemical reactions in chromatographic and other separations with ion exchangers have certainly not yet been exhausted.   This interesting field deserves further attention.

9-9. QUANTITATIVE TREATMENT

The mathematical treatment of column processes is a complex problem. Rigorous solutions seem hardly feasible, even in comparatively simple cases.   The current theories of column performance are based on drastically simplifying assumptions and thus give only approximate results.   There is a large number of such theories which differ in their assumptions and their degree of complexity.   They all have their merits and disadvantages. In this section, only a brief survey of the various approaches can be given. Emphasis is on crude and relatively simple approximation methods which can be handled without excessive effort by chemists who have no special mathematical training.   The application of these methods will be illustrated by practical examples.

The mathematical theories are sufficiently general to be applicable with minor, if any, obvious modifications to sorption, ion exclusion, ligand exchange, etc., as well as to ion exchange.   In fact, most of them have been developed originally for sorption rather than ion-exchange processes.   The applicability of a simplified theory hinges on the mode of operation rather than on the particular mechanism of solute uptake. For example, the mathematics of elution development and displacement development are quite different, whereas those of ion-exchange and nonionic elution development are the same. The presentation in this section is arranged accordingly.

In view of the great variety of column operations, a complete quantitative treatment is beyond the scope of this book. The mathematically inclined reader, however, will have little difficulty in adapting one or the other theory to a problem not covered here. In any such attempt, the choice of the proper theory is crucial since even seemingly harmless and plausible assumptions may lead to grave errors. A guide pointing out the most common pitfalls is given at the end of this section (Sec. 9-9d).

a. Theoretical Approaches, Models, and Assumptions

The various theories of column performance can be divided into two groups, the equilibrium theories and the rate theories.

In the *equilibrium theories* it is assumed that local equilibrium between liquid and sorbent in the layers of the bed is attained. In practice this condition is usually not met. Deviations from local equilibrium can be accounted for in a semiempirical way by introducing the concept of "effective plates."* The basic idea is that the actual continuous column process can be represented in good approximation by a fictitious discontinuous process in which equilibrium is attained in a plate of finite height before the solution moves from this plate to the next. In this model a discrete, finite solution volume is subjected to a series of equilibrations, one in each effective plate. The plate height of a column must be determined experimentally. These theories have the advantage of being relatively simple. Their disadvantage is that the plate height is an empirical quantity which cannot be predicted.

In another group of equilibrium theories, the flow through the column is treated as continuous, but it is assumed that local equilibrium in the layers is actually attained. This latter assumption greatly restricts the range of validity.

In the *rate theories* no assumptions concerning local equilibrium in the layers are made. The calculations are based on continuous flow through the column and finite rates of ion exchange or sorption. This line of approach is, of course, more realistic. Unfortunately it calls for a considerable mathematical effort. The chief advantage of the rate theories is that column performance can be predicted from fundamental data without the use of empirical quantities. Such calculations bring out the effect of the operating variables such as flow rate, feed concentration, particle

---

* This concept must be applied with care. Considerable confusion may arise from inconsistent definitions and improper generalizations, see pages 481 and 484.

size, etc., and thus permit optimum operating conditions to be predicted. The discussion in this section deals chiefly with such calculations.

The various rate theories differ in their assumptions about ion-exchange (or sorption) rates and equilibria. The rigorous differential rate equations of ion exchange (see Sec. 6-3c) are too complex to be solved analytically. Instead, various simplified rate laws have been used (see Sec. 6-4). An even more serious limitation of most theories is that simplifying assumptions about equilibria are made. Many approaches are based on linear ion-exchange (or sorption) isotherms. Such theories fail to bring out the self-sharpening and broadening effects of favorable and unfavorable equilibria, respectively, and are only applicable to elution development of traces and to the rare case of ion exchange without selectivity (which, of course, is of little other than academic interest). Other, more useful rate theories include the effect of selectivity but assume constant separation factors. More general cases can be handled only by rather complex and lengthy approximation methods. An excellent survey of these various approaches has been given by Vermeulen [247,248].

The usual theories of column performance involve a number of further idealizations. Most calculations are made for ideal "plug flow," i.e., they neglect the effects of eddy mixing and flow maldistribution. The less serious effects of changes in swelling and temperature are also disregarded. These perturbations will be examined in Sec. 9-10.

The main object of the following discussion is to show quantitatively the dependence of column performance on the operating conditions and to outline simple means by which optimum operating conditions can be calculated from fundamental data. This requires the use of rate theories.

b. Rate Theories

The calculation of column performance under nonequilibrium conditions requires solutions of the following simultaneous equations:

The rate laws of intraparticle and film diffusion
The ion-exchange equilibrium condition at the particle surface
The material balances for the various species in a horizontal layer of the bed

The general rate laws are nonlinear differential equations, and the equilibrium condition introduces a nonlinear boundary condition. Analytical solutions can be obtained only when simplifications are made. In the following, the rate laws are approximated by simple linear relations. This still leaves the difficulty of nonlinear ion-exchange equilibrium. Fortunately, the two most important cases—elution development of small quantities, and self-sharpening boundaries in displacement processes—are comparatively simple to handle. In elution development of small quantities the assumption of a linear isotherm is a reasonable approximation, and the calculation of self-sharpening boundaries is facilitated by the fact that a stationary (i.e., time-independent) shape is attained. Other cases are more complex and will be discussed in less detail.

The treatment given in the following is largely based on Glueckauf's approach [77,79,80]. Glueckauf uses the concept of "effective plates" which originated from the theory of distillation and was first applied to chromatography by Martin and Synge [148]. This concept is the basis of the equilibrium theories in which the plate height is an empirical quantity. In Glueckauf's rate theory, however, the plate height is calculated from fundamental data and is merely a convenient, but by no means indispensable, auxiliary.

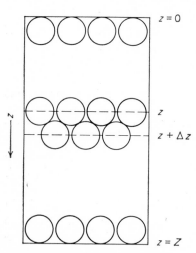

Fig. 9-15. Schematic representation of a packed bed. The material balance is set up for the "plate" between z and $z + \Delta z$. From E. Glueckauf [79].

The material balances. The material balances for the various species are set up for an arbitrary horizontal layer of the bed. The content of the layer changes with time as a result of solution flow and longitudinal diffusion. The material balance expresses that, for any species, the increase in the amount present in the layer equals influx minus outflux.

The material balances are usually formulated for an infinitesimal layer. The treatment given here, however, follows Glueckauf [79,80] who emphasizes that a layer cannot be reduced to a thickness of less than approximately one sorbent-particle diameter without losing its geometrical and mechanical characteristics*

(see Fig. 9-15). Accordingly, the material balance is set up for a layer of a thickness $\Delta z = 1.64r_0$ (Glueckauf uses the interlayer distance in closest packing of spheres). The material balance for an arbitrary species i is

$$q\left(\frac{\partial X_i}{\partial V}\right)_z + \left(\frac{\partial C_i}{\partial z}\right)_V - \frac{\Delta z}{2}\left(\frac{\partial^2 C_i}{\partial z^2}\right)_V - \frac{D\beta}{v\sqrt{2}}\left(\frac{\partial^2 C_i}{\partial z^2}\right)_V = 0 \qquad (9\text{-}3)$$

where q = column cross section; X_i = amount of species i (in sorbent *and* solution) per unit volume of bed; C_i = concentration of species i in interstitial solution; V = solution volume which has passed the layer since operation was started;

* This argument of Glueckauf is largely intuitive and may seem artificial. His conclusion, however, is supported by more sophisticated treatments of hydrodynamics in fixed beds (see Sec. 9-10a) according to which eddy dispersion has, indeed, such an effect.

z = space coordinate downstream = distance from column inlet; D = effective diffusion coefficient in interstitial liquid; β = fractional void volume of bed; v = linear flow rate = solution volume which passes through unit cross section of bed in unit time.

The third and fourth terms in Eq. (9-3) are correction terms which arise from finite particle size and longitudinal diffusion, respectively.

Derivation. The material balance can be derived in the following way. Consider the change which occurs in a layer between z and $z + \Delta z$ while an infinitesimal solution volume dV passes through, a volume V having passed previously. Prior to the passage of the solution volume dV, the plate contained the amount $q \Delta z X_i(V)$ of species i, and afterward it contains the amount $q \Delta z X_i(V + dV)$. Thus the change in content is

$$dX_i = q \Delta z [X_i(V + dV) - X_i(V)] \tag{9-4}$$

The solution enters the plate with the concentration $C_i(z)$ of species i and leaves it with the concentration $C_i(z + \Delta z)$. Inflow minus outflow thus is

$$(\delta X_i)_{\text{flow}} = dV[C_i(z) - C_i(z + \Delta z)] \cong -dV\left[\left(\frac{\partial C_i}{\partial z}\right)_V \Delta z - \frac{1}{2}\left(\frac{\partial^2 C_i}{\partial z^2}\right)_V \Delta z^2\right] \tag{9-5}$$

(the first two terms of a Taylor expansion are used for approximating the finite difference in C_i). The diffusion flux of species i in the direction of the column axis is

$$J_i = -D\left(\frac{\partial C_i}{\partial z}\right)_V \tag{9-6}$$

The amount of species i which diffuses into the plate at the location z in the time dt required for the solution volume dV to pass thus is [77]

$$\frac{J_i(z)q\beta \, dt}{\sqrt{2}} = -\frac{Dq\beta \, dt}{\sqrt{2}}\left(\frac{\partial C_i(z)}{\partial z}\right)_V \tag{9-7}$$

(The factor $1/\sqrt{2}$ takes care of the obstruction of the diffusion path by the sorbent particles.) An analogous relation, with z replaced by $z + \Delta z$, holds for the amount which diffuses out of the plate at the location $z + \Delta z$. Substituting dt by use of

$$v = \frac{1}{q}\left(\frac{\partial V}{\partial t}\right)_z \tag{9-8}$$

and neglecting third and higher-order differential quotients, one obtains for the change in the content of the layer by longitudinal diffusion

$$(\delta X_i)_{\text{diff}} = \frac{D\beta \, dV \, \Delta z}{\sqrt{2}}\left(\frac{\partial^2 C_i}{\partial z^2}\right)_V \tag{9-9}$$

The material balance is

$$dX_i = (\delta X_i)_{\text{flow}} + (\delta X_i)_{\text{diff}} \tag{9-10}$$

Equation (9-3) is obtained by substituting Eqs. (9-4), (9-5), and (9-9) in Eq. (9-10).

The material balance (9-3) is still quite general since no assumptions about local equilibrium and ion-exchange (or sorption) isotherms have been made. Local equilibrium is a limiting case in which X_i is a function of C_i only. This function is given by the isotherm. For nonequilibrium conditions the functional relationship between X_i and C_i must be obtained by combining Eq. (9-3) and the isotherm with the rate equation of ion exchange (or sorption). Here, approximations must be made. Various lines of approach can be chosen. It depends on the nature of the column process which of these approaches is the most practical. In the following, elution development of traces, self-sharpening boundaries in displacement operations, and nonsharpening boundaries will be examined.

Elution development of trace quantities. In elution development, a mixture of several counter ions is separated on an ion exchanger in A form by elution with an agent AY (see Sec. 9-7b). The bands of the components overlap, at least in the earlier stages of the development. A rigorous and general treatment thus requires the use of multicomponent isotherms. A simpler approach can be used, however, if the separation involves trace quantities only. The uptake of a trace component i by the ion exchanger (or sorbent) is usually not affected by the presence of other trace components. Furthermore, the developing counter ion A is present in much larger concentration so that only a short section of the isotherm of the exchange of i for A near the origin is needed. This short section is, as a rule, almost linear (see Sec. 5-5). Thus the isotherm can be written as

$$\bar{X}_i^* = \lambda_i'' C_i \qquad \text{or} \qquad X_i^* = (\beta + \lambda_i'') C_i \qquad (\lambda_i'' = \text{const.}) \qquad (9\text{-}11)$$

where $\bar{X}_i$ = amount of species i in the ion exchanger per unit volume of bed; asterisks are used to indicate equilibrium; λ_i'' = column distribution ratio.†

Under nonequilibrium conditions, the actual amount $\bar{X}_i$ in the resin deviates from $\bar{X}_i^*$, which is the amount the resin would contain when being in equilibrium with the interstitial solution of concentration C_i. The extent of this deviation depends on the ion-exchange rate. The rates of particle- and film-diffusion controlled ion exchange (or sorption) may be approximated by simple "linear-driving-force" relations [see Eq. (6-63)]. This approximation is crude, but very convenient. For particle diffusion control, the relation is [79]

$$\left(\frac{\partial \bar{X}_i}{\partial t}\right)_z = \frac{\bar{D}}{0.071 r_0^2} (\bar{X}_i^* - \bar{X}_i) \qquad (9\text{-}12)$$

and for film diffusion control [79]

$$\left(\frac{\partial \bar{X}_i}{\partial t}\right)_z = \frac{3D}{2\delta r_0} (C_i - C_i^*) \qquad (9\text{-}13)$$

---

† The column distribution ratio λ_i'' is not identical with the molar distribution coefficient λ_i' since $\bar{X}_i^*$ is the equilibrium amount in the ion exchanger per unit volume of the bed (*including* interstitital volume) rather than per unit volume of the swollen ion exchanger alone; see definition of λ_i' in Eq. (5-29). The interrelation is $\lambda_i'' = \lambda_i'(1 - \beta)$.

where r_0 = particle radius; δ = film thickness; $\bar{D}$ = interdiffusion coefficient in the ion exchanger; C_i^* = interstitial solution concentration in equilibrium with $\bar{X}_i$ (here, $C_i^* = \bar{X}_i / \lambda_i''$).

Both relations imply that, at any time, the rate is proportional to the distance from equilibrium. The proportionality factors are obtained by curve fitting with more rigorous rate laws (Sec. 6-3). The film thickness δ can be approximated by the empirical relation [79]*

$$\delta = \frac{0.2 r_0}{1 + 70 v r_0} \tag{9-14}$$

Combination of Eqs. (9-12) to (9-14) with the material balance (9-3) gives after minor simplifications [79]

$$\left(\frac{\partial C_i}{\partial z}\right)_V + q(\lambda_i'' + \beta)\left(\frac{\partial C_i}{\partial V}\right)_z - \frac{H}{2}\left(\frac{\partial^2 C_i}{\partial z^2}\right)_V = 0 \tag{9-15}$$

Here, the quantity H is the height of an "effective plate" (EHTP = effective height of theoretical plate in Glueckauf's publications). Under the assumptions mentioned, the plate height is [79]

$$H = 1.64 r_0 + \frac{\lambda_i''}{(\lambda_i'' + \beta)^2}\frac{0.14 r_0^2 v}{\bar{D}} + \left(\frac{\lambda_i''}{\lambda_i'' + \beta}\right)^2\frac{0.266 r_0^2 v}{D(1 + 70 r_0 v)} + \frac{D\beta\sqrt{2}}{v} \tag{9-16}$$

The four terms on the right-hand side reflect the various perturbations in the column. The first term is due to finite particle size, the second to slow particle diffusion, the third to slow film diffusion, and the fourth to longitudinal diffusion.†

Derivation. Equations (9-15) and (9-16) are readily derived in the following way. First, the material balance without the correction terms for finite particle size and longitudinal diffusion is combined with the rate law (9-12) for particle diffusion, the isotherm (9-11), and Eq. (9-8). Differentiation of the rate law (9-12) with respect to V serves to substitute $\partial X_i / \partial V$ in the material balance. With minor simplifications, an equation of the form of Eq. (9-15) is obtained in which H is given by the second term of Eq. (9-16). Then, the same procedure is repeated with the rate law (9-13) for film diffusion. This time, H is given by the third term in Eq. (9-16). It can be shown that, with a linear isotherm, the perturbing effects of slow particle diffusion, slow film diffusion, finite particle size, and longitudinal diffusion are additive when correction terms of higher order are disregarded [121,243,247]. Thus the total plate height is given by Eq. (9-16).

---

* For relations between the film thickness and the dimensionless Sherwood (or modified Nusselt), Reynolds, and Schmidt (or Prandtl) numbers, see footnote to page 253.

† Except for inclusion of the film-diffusion term and minor differences in the coefficients, Eq. (9-16) is identical to the well-known VanDeemter equation for the plate height in gas chromatography [114,243].

Equation (9-16) shows that the effective plate height depends on the distribution coefficient of the species. Thus, in a separation, the plate height is different for the different species. This point is often overlooked. The smaller the distribution coefficient, the faster the respective band moves, and the larger is the plate height (at least if $\lambda_i'' > 1$, which is usually true). This is reasonable since it is more difficult for ion exchange to keep pace with the migration of a faster band.

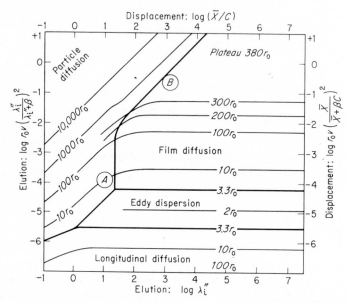

FIG. 9-16. Effective plate height as a function of the operating conditions (calculated from Eqs. (9-16) and (9-30) with $D = 10^{-5}$ cm²/sec and $\bar{D} = 3 \cdot 10^{-7}$ cm²/sec). The plate heights are given as contour lines. The coordinates left and below are for elution development, those right and above for displacement with self-sharpening boundaries. The diagram is divided into several regions, showing which phenomenon gives the greatest contribution to the plate height. The operating conditions which correspond to the numerical examples on pages 460 and 470 are indicated by A and B, respectively. *From E. Glueckauf* [79].

The longitudinal-diffusion term in Eq. (9-16) involves the flow rate v in the denominator. The diffusion coefficients D in the aqueous phase are usually of the order of 10^{-5} cm²/sec, and the particle radius is rarely smaller than 0.01 cm. The longitudinal-diffusion term thus contributes little to the total plate height unless the flow rate is extremely low. In the following, this term will be neglected.

The plate height as a function of the operating conditions is shown in Fig. 9-16. Note, however, that this diagram is not universal. Its form depends on the magnitude of the diffusion coefficients. The diagram is very convenient for illustrating the prediction of optimum operating conditions and will be discussed in this connection (see pages 459 and 469).

A necessary consequence of the assumption of linear isotherms for all species [Eq. (9-11)] is that the various bands migrate independently. The migration rates of the "peaks" (band maxima) are given by

$$\frac{dz_{max}}{dt} = \frac{v}{\lambda_i'' + \beta} \tag{9-17}$$

More convenient for evaluation is the equivalent relation

$$\frac{V_i}{V_b} = \lambda_i'' + \beta \tag{9-18}$$

where V_i is the feed volume ("retention volume") required to elute the peak from a column of length Z, and $V_b = qZ$ is the over-all bed volume (including void). These relations become obvious when it is considered that the amount of species i per unit bed volume is larger by the factor $\lambda_i'' + \beta$ than the amount per unit volume of solution, and that any perturbation spreads the band symmetrically about its peak and thus has no effect on the migration rate of the peak. In Eqs. (9-17) and (9-18) the concentration of the eluent does not appear explicitly. Its effect, however, is reflected in the distribution ratio; the higher the eluent concentration, the smaller is the distribution ratio and the faster the band will move.

The height and number of effective plates do not affect the migration rates of the peaks, but they determine the sharpness of the bands and thus the efficiency of the separation. In the early part of their travel down the column, the shape of the bands, though accurately calculable, is given by a rather complex expression [see Eq. (9-60)]. But after having passed through about 25 plates the bands attain simpler shapes. Now, the peak concentration in the effluent is given by [79,114]

$$(C_i)_{max} = \frac{Q_i}{V_i}\left(\frac{N}{2\pi}\right)^{1/2} \tag{9-19}$$

where Q_i = total amount (in moles) of species i; $N = Z/H$ = number of effective plates.

The shape of the band is given by [79,114]

$$C_i(V) = (C_i)_{max}\exp\left[-\frac{N(V_i - V)^2}{2V_iV}\right] \tag{9-20}$$

The higher the number of effective plates in a column of given length, the sharper are the bands. The bands are symmetrical. The band of the ion which is least preferred (smallest value of V_i) comes out as the sharpest in the effluent.

Equations (9-19) and (9-20) can be obtained as asymptotic solutions of Eq. (9-15) under the appropriate initial and boundary conditions. The derivation is somewhat lengthy and will be omitted. The interested reader is referred to the literature [80,114, 243,247] and the discussion on page 477.

The number of effective plates N can be determined experimentally by use of Eq. (9-19). The quantity Q_i in this equation, if not known beforehand, can be obtained by graphical integration of the effluent history. A more convenient way of determining the number of effective plates is by measuring the bandwidth. The bandwidth ΔV_i of species i is defined as the number of solution-volume units in the effluent between the intercepts of the tangents to the front and rear flanks of the peak with the abscissa (see Fig. 9-17). The relation between the bandwidth and the number of effective plates is

$$N = 16 \left(\frac{V_i}{\Delta V_i} \right)^2 \tag{9-21}$$

where V_i is the peak retention volume of species i.

In the derivation of Eqs. (9-17) to (9-20) it has been assumed that the species of the mixture are sorbed, prior to development, from a sample of very small size. Large sample size results in loading of an appreciable fraction of the column prior to development

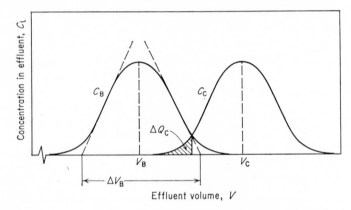

Fig. 9-17. Bandshape, bandwidth, and overlap of neighboring bands in elution development (schematic).

and thus affects the retention volumes and peak shapes (see Fig. 9-26). The equations are applicable when

$$V_s < \frac{V_b(\lambda_i'' + \beta)}{2 \sqrt{N}} \tag{9-22}$$

where V_s is the volume of the introduced sample [80,114,243]. In the following it will be assumed that this condition is met.

The *sharpness of separation* depends on the overlap of neighboring bands and can be calculated in the following way. The amount ΔQ_i of a species in a section of the elution band is obtained by integration of Eq. (9-20) [79,80]:

$$\Delta Q_i(V) = Q_i[\tfrac{1}{2} - A(y_i)] \tag{9-23}$$

where

$$y_i \equiv (V_i - V) \left(\frac{N}{V_i V} \right)^{\tfrac{1}{2}} \quad \text{and} \quad A(y_i) \equiv \left(\frac{1}{2\pi} \right)^{\tfrac{1}{2}} \int_{x=0}^{x=y_i} \exp\left(-\frac{x^2}{2} \right) dx$$

The function $A(y_i)$ is the area under the normal curve of error and is tabulated in the "Handbook of Chemistry and Physics" [264]; a brief table is given in the Appendix (page 590). Equation (9-23) gives the amount eluted by a feed volume $V < V_i$. Since the bands are symmetrical, it also gives the amount remaining in the column after elution with $V > V_i$ (see Fig. 9-17).

The purity of the fractions of successive species in the effluent depends on the effluent volume at which the cut is made. In Fig. 9-17 the minor cutoff ΔQ_C is the amount of C in the effluent fraction of B, and ΔQ_B is the amount of B in the fraction of C. As a rule, the best way of making the cut is that in which the fractional impurities, ξ, in both bands are equal, so that

$$\xi_B \equiv \frac{\Delta Q_B}{Q_C - \Delta Q_C} = \xi_C \equiv \frac{\Delta Q_C}{Q_B - \Delta Q_B} \tag{9-24}$$

or, since a reasonable sharpness of separation requires $\Delta Q_i \ll Q_i$:

$$\xi \equiv \xi_B = \xi_C = \frac{\Delta Q_B}{Q_C} = \frac{\Delta Q_C}{Q_B} \tag{9-25}$$

If the total amounts of B and C are approximately equal ($Q_B \approx Q_C$), the cut should be made at the effluent volume $(V_B V_C)^{1/2}$.

Combination of Eqs. (9-23) and (9-25) gives [79]

$$\xi = \frac{2Q_B Q_C}{Q_B^2 + Q_C^2} [\tfrac{1}{2} - A(y')] \tag{9-26}$$

where

$$y' \equiv \left[\left(\frac{V_C}{V_B} \right)^{1/4} - \left(\frac{V_B}{V_C} \right)^{1/4} \right] N^{1/2}$$

According to Eq. (9-18), the ratio of the peak retention volumes, V_C/V_B, is related by the distribution coefficients by

$$\alpha' \equiv \frac{V_C}{V_B} = \frac{\lambda_C'' + \beta}{\lambda_B'' + \beta} \tag{9-27}*$$

The relative cross contamination ξ thus depends on the ratio of the peak retention volumes α', the number of effective plates N, and the relative amounts Q_B and Q_C. This interrelation is shown in Fig. 9-18 where a log probability scale has been used to obtain straight lines. This graph can be used for determining the number of effective plates required for attaining the desired purity of the products.

Example. Suppose that two species B and C are present in a mole ratio 10:1 ($Q_B/Q_C = 10$), that their peak retention-volume ratio α' is 1.5, and that the maxi-

---

* Note that the peak retention-volume ratio α' is *not* identical with the separation factor α_B^C which, by definition, is $\alpha_B^C = \lambda_C''/\lambda_B''$.

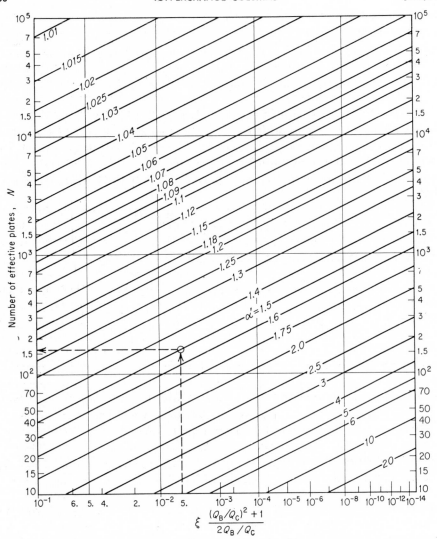

FIG. 9-18. Interrelation of product purity, peak retention-volume ratio, and number of effective plates in elution development. The determination of the required number of plates in the numerical example is indicated by arrows. *From E. Glueckauf* [80].

mum permissible contamination is 0.1% ($\xi = 10^{-3}$). In this case,

$$\xi[(Q_B/Q_C)^2 + 1]/(2Q_B/Q_C) = 5 \cdot 10^{-3}$$

which gives the abscissa value in Fig. 9-18. On the line for $\alpha' = 1.5$, the corresponding point is found at a plate number of about 160. For $Q_B/Q_C = 1$, the abscissa value would be 10^{-3} and the number of required plates about 240.

Prediction of Optimum Operating Conditions. In principle, any desired purity can be attained in a chromatographic separation, provided that the ion exchanger has at least some selectivity.   Of course, higher purity of the products requires more effort, time, and reagents.   As a rule, a certain purity of the products is desired, and one wishes to carry out the separation in as short a time as possible.   The calculation of optimum operating conditions which give the desired purity in a minimum of time will be illustrated below.   For this purpose the diagram 9-16 is very convenient.

The sharpness of separation is improved when the number of effective plates is increased (see Fig. 9-18).   An obvious way to accomplish this is to lengthen the column.   This, however, increases the separation time (at least when the other conditions are kept constant).   Therefore any possibilities for increasing the number of plates without adding to the separation time should first be exhausted.

First, the diagram 9-16 shows that at any given point on the graph the plate height is proportional to the particle radius.   In a column of given length the number of effective plates can thus be increased by reducing the particle size.   This even allows the flow rate to be increased (saving separation time) since the ordinate in the diagram involves the product vr_0 of flow rate and particle size.   The flow resistance of the column is also increased, however.   The minimum permissible particle size is reached when a further increase in flow resistance would prevent attainment of the desired flow rate.

For a given particle size, the plate height as well as the separation time depends on the operating conditions.   In the diagram 9-16, any point on the curved surface corresponds to a specific set of conditions.   Any change in conditions which moves the corresponding point to the right or straight down decreases the migration rate of the peaks since either the distribution coefficients are increased or the flow rate is decreased.   The resulting loss of time is worthwhile if, and only if, a more than equivalent gain in effective plates is obtained.   This is only the case in the upper left of the diagram. The best operating conditions are thus found near the border line between the regions of particle diffusion and film diffusion.   Analytical separations usually require a high degree of purity and thus a large number of effective plates.   Here, the plate height should be kept as small as possible, so that columns of reasonable size and flow resistance can be used.   Hence, optimum conditions for such operations are usually found near the "triple point" where the regions of particle diffusion, film diffusion, and eddy dispersion touch.   In the triple point, the first three terms in Eq. (9-16) are equal and the fourth is negligible.

The general character of the diagram 9-16 is universal, but the numerical values of the plate heights and the position of the border lines of the different regions depend on the values of the diffusion coefficients.   For example, if the diffusion coefficient in the ion exchanger is very low, the contribution of particle diffusion to the plate height is correspondingly high [see Eq. (9-16)].   The plate heights in the region of particle diffusion become larger, and the border line of this region is displaced to the lower right.   Similarly, lower diffusion coefficients in the aqueous phase raise and broaden the region of film diffusion and reduce the region of longitudinal diffusion. A rise in temperature increases the diffusion coefficients in both the ion exchanger and the solution and decreases the plate heights throughout the diagram, except in the region of longitudinal diffusion which now becomes more important. Hence the use of the diagram is no substitute for numerical calculations.

The calculation of optimum operating conditions will now be illustrated by a practical example [79].

Example. Find optimum operating conditions for the separation of trace quantities of Na^+ and K^+ by elution development with HCl. The ions are present in approximately equal amounts. The desired purity is 99.9 per cent. The following data are given:

Particle radius of ion exchanger............	$r_0 \cong 0.025$ cm (35 mesh)
Volume capacity.........................	$\bar{X} = 1.2$ meq/cm³ bed
Fractional void volume of bed.............	$\beta = 0.4$
Interdiffusion coefficient in resin...........	$\bar{D} \cong 2 \cdot 10^{-6}$ cm²/sec
Diffusion coefficient in aqueous phase.......	$D \cong 2 \cdot 10^{-5}$ cm²/sec
Separation factors......................	$\alpha_H^{Na} = 1.4$
	$\alpha_H^K = 2.8$
Column cross section....................	$q = 1.1$ cm²

Solution. Excessive column length can be avoided when operating conditions near the triple point in Fig. 9-16 are chosen. Thus the first three terms in Eq. (9-16) are equated to one another, and the fourth term is neglected. It is wise to double the first term since packing irregularities can hardly be avoided. In this way one obtains the effective plate height $H \approx 10r_0 = 0.25$ cm (average for Na^+ and K^+). The optimum distribution ratio (average for Na^+ and K^+) is obtained by equating the second term in Eq. (9-16) with the third

$$\lambda_i'' = \frac{0.14D}{0.266\bar{D}} = 5.3$$

(The required flow rate is so low that $70r_0 v \ll 1$.) Since both Na^+ and K^+ are present in traces only, $\lambda_i'' \equiv \bar{X}_i / C_i \approx \bar{X}\alpha_H^i / C$, where α_H^i is the average separation factor and C is the solution concentration in the column. Hence the average distribution ratio 5.3 is attained with the HCl eluent concentration

$$C = \frac{\bar{X}\alpha_H^i}{\lambda_i''} \cong \frac{1.2 \cdot 2}{5.3} \cong 0.45 \text{ M}$$

Now the individual distribution ratios can be calculated:

$$\lambda_K'' = \frac{\bar{X}\alpha_H^K}{C} = \frac{1.2 \cdot 2.8}{0.45} = 7.5$$

$$\lambda_{Na}'' = \frac{\bar{X}\alpha_H^{Na}}{C} = \frac{1.2 \cdot 1.4}{0.45} = 3.75$$

The optimum flow rate is obtained by equating the first (doubled) term in Eq. (9-16) with the third:

$$v \approx \frac{3.28(\lambda_i'' + \beta)^2 D}{0.266\lambda_i''^2 r_0} = 0.012 \text{ cm/sec}$$

With a column cross section of 1.1 cm² this corresponds to a throughput of 0.78 cm³/min.

The ratio of the peak retention volumes is, according to Eq. (9-27),

$$\alpha' = \frac{V_K}{V_{Na}} = \frac{\lambda_K'' + \beta}{\lambda_{Na}'' + \beta} = 1.9$$

the ratio Q_K/Q_{Na} is approximately unity, and the maximum permissible contamination is $\xi = 10^{-3}$. With these values, Fig. 9-18 gives the number of required effective plates $N = 85$. Thus the optimum bed length and bed volume are

$$Z = NH = 21 \text{ cm}$$
$$V_b = Zq = 23 \text{ cm}^3$$

The Na⁺ peak will emerge at the effluent volume $V_{Na} = qZ(\lambda_{Na}'' + \beta) = 96$ cm³, and the K⁺ peak at 182 cm³. The cut should be made at $\sqrt{V_K V_{Na}} = 131$ cm³. Elution of K⁺ is 99.9 per cent complete at about 235 cm³. The separation time can be calculated from the throughput (0.78 cm³/min) and is about 5 hr. The time can be somewhat reduced by raising the flow rate or the eluent concentration after the cut has been made.

In practice, it is wise not to rely too much on the accuracy of such calculations. Rather, one should "overdesign," for example, by using a somewhat longer column. It is true that, under operating conditions as above, deviations from local equilibrium are minor so that the approximate rate equations do not introduce serious errors. Plate heights as low as $10r_0$, however, can only be achieved with very carefully and uniformly packed beds.

The equations are quite general and can be applied equally well to separations of other than univalent counter ions, to elution with complexing agents, and to all other types of elution development.* The only essential assumptions are that the distribution ratios are constant (i.e., independent of concentration and of one another) and that the column is sufficiently long for the bands to attain the eventual shape given in Eq. (9-20). The particular mechanism of solute uptake or exchange affects the distribution coefficients, separation factors, and diffusion ratios, but not the validity of the equations. Note, however, that in separations involving counter ions of different valences and in elution with complexing agents the distribution ratios and separation factors depend strongly on the solution concentration and, in some cases, also on the pH (see pages 157, 210 and 211). Here, it may be advantageous to operate not at the triple point in Fig. 9-16, but, rather, at a point where the retention-volume ratios are most favorable.

Displacement processes. The treatment in the preceding section is based on linear ion-exchange isotherms and thus is not applicable to dis-

---

* For gas chromatography, a somewhat different procedure has recently been suggested by Giddings [69] who minimizes the "separation function" $F \equiv (V_C - V_B)^2 / 8(\Delta V_C^2 + \Delta V_B^2)$, in order to find the minimum permissible column size and the according operating conditions.

placement processes involving self-sharpening boundaries. The self-sharpening character of a boundary between two counter ions is due to the "favorable equilibrium," i.e., to the preference of the resin for the displacing counter ion (see Sec. 9-1). The exchange isotherm of the two counter ions thus is necessarily nonlinear (see Sec. 5-4a). Elution development of traces, which was treated above, involves only fractional conversion of the ion exchanger, and the corresponding short section of the exchange isotherm can be approximated by linear relations such as Eq. (9-11). This is not possible in displacement since, here, the resin is completely converted from one ionic form to another, so that the (nonlinear) isotherm is needed in its full length. In fact, it is just the curvature of the isotherm which produces the self-sharpening effect.

The calculation of the early stages of a displacement process is very difficult (see page 475). Fortunately, the bands and boundaries soon attain a steady-state shape which is much simpler to calculate. In the following, this steady state, the column efficiency, and the separation requirements will be discussed for cases in which the resin is completely converted from one ionic form to the other. Incomplete conversion (partially presaturated bed, mixed feed, frontal analysis) is discussed later (see page 476).

Migration Rate. The steady-state migration rate of the bands and boundaries is equal for all species and is readily derived. Consider a horizontal layer of thickness Δz in the bed. This layer contains $q\,\Delta z(\bar{X} + \beta C)$ equivalents of counter ions. Per unit time, qvC equivalents pass into the next layer downstream. The time required for all the counter ions from the layer to pass into the next, i.e., to move the distance Δz, thus is

$$\Delta t = \frac{\Delta z(\bar{X} + \beta C)}{vC}$$

Hence the migration rate is

$$v_{\mathrm{b}} = \frac{\Delta z}{\Delta t} = \frac{v}{\bar{X}/C + \beta} \tag{9-28}$$

This is the rate with which a plane of any given solution composition travels downstream. The rate is a function of the volume capacity of the ion exchanger, the fractional void volume of the bed, the flow rate, and the total concentration of the feed and is independent of the nature of the individual ions.

Steady-state Shape of Self-sharpening Boundaries. The sharpness of a boundary between two counter ions, B displacing A, depends on their separation factor $\alpha_{\mathrm{A}}^{\mathrm{B}}$ * and on the operating conditions. When the steady

---

* The separation factor, according to the definition in Eq. (5-70), is $\alpha_{\mathrm{A}}^{\mathrm{B}} = \bar{X}_{\mathrm{B}}^{*}C_{\mathrm{A}}/\bar{X}_{\mathrm{A}}^{*}C_{\mathrm{B}}$.

state has been attained, the spread of the boundary becomes independent of the traveled distance and is given by [79]

$$z'(x_B) = \frac{H_p + H_0}{2}\left(\frac{1}{\alpha_A^B - 1}\ln\frac{1}{x_B} - \frac{\alpha_A^B}{\alpha_A^B - 1}\ln\frac{1}{1 - x_B} + 1\right)$$
$$+ \frac{H_f + H_0}{2}\left(\frac{\alpha_A^B}{\alpha_A^B - 1}\ln\frac{1}{x_B} - \frac{1}{\alpha_A^B - 1}\ln\frac{1}{1 - x_B} - 1\right) \quad (9\text{-}29)$$

where $x_B \equiv z_B C_B/(z_A C_A + z_B C_B)$ = equivalent ionic fraction of B.

Here, $z'(x_B)$ is the distance of the plane with concentration x_B from the "center of gravity" of the boundary (see Fig. 9-19), and

$$H_p = \frac{\bar{X}/C}{(\bar{X}/C + \beta)^2}\frac{0.142 r_0^2 v}{\bar{D}} \qquad H_0 = 1.64 r_0$$

$$H_f = \left(\frac{\bar{X}/C}{\bar{X}/C + \beta}\right)^2\frac{0.266 r_0^2 v}{D(1 + 70 r_0 v)} \qquad (9\text{-}30)$$

are the plate-height contributions due to particle diffusion, finite particle size, and film diffusion. It is assumed in the derivation that the separation

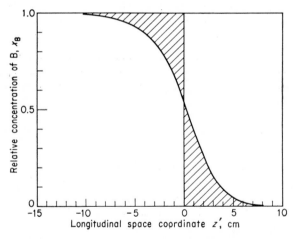

FIG. 9-19. Shape of a self-sharpening boundary, calculated from Eq. (9-29) with $H_p + H_0 = 4$ cm, $H_f + H_0 = 2$ cm, $\alpha_A^B = 10$. The normalization of the z' axis is such that $z' = 0$ coincides with the center of gravity of the boundary (i.e., the shaded areas are equal).

factor is constant, that the linear-driving-force rate laws of ion exchange are valid, and that the spreads caused by particle and film diffusion are additive. (This latter assumption is only an approximation; see page 476, where also calculations with nonconstant separation factors are discussed.) Furthermore, longitudinal diffusion has been disregarded as unimportant

in the usual range of operating conditions.*   A table facilitating the evaluation of Eq. (9-29) is given in the Appendix (page 586).

Derivation.   It is convenient to choose the boundary itself as the frame of reference.
The concentrations in the resin and the solution, $\bar{X}_i$ and C_i, thus become independent of
t and V and are functions of the space coordinate
z' only.   Relative to this frame of reference the
resin moves upstream with the rate $-v_b$, and the
solution downstream with the rate $v - v_b$ (see Fig.
9-20).   A material balance can be set up at an arbitrary plane z' by equating the amount of species i
transferred upstream by the resin to the amount
transferred downstream by the solution:

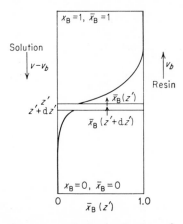

$$q\bar{X}_i v_b = q C_i (v - v_b) \qquad (9\text{-}31)$$

or

$$\frac{\bar{X}_i}{C_i} = \frac{v - v_b}{v_b} = \text{const.} \qquad (9\text{-}32)$$

At sufficient distances on either side of the boundary
one has

$$x_i = 0, \ \bar{x}_i = 0,$$
and
$$x_i = 1, \ \bar{x}_i = 1, \text{ respectively} \qquad (9\text{-}33)$$

Fig. 9-20. Self-sharpening boundary and motion of the solution
and the resin with the center of
gravity of the boundary as the
frame of reference (*schematic*).

Combination of the conditions (9-33) with Eq. (9-32)
and the definitions $x_i \equiv z_i C_i / C$ and $\bar{x}_i \equiv z_i \bar{X}_i / \bar{X}$
shows that, by necessity,

$$\bar{x}_i = x_i \qquad (9\text{-}34)$$

In other words, the equivalent ionic fractions of i in the resin and the solution are equal.
The "operating line" in the exchange-isotherm diagram is the diagonal (see Fig. 9-21).†
    A material balance for the displacing species B in the resin is now set up in a layer
between z' and $z' + dz'$.   The resin enters the layer from below with the concentration
$\bar{X}_B(z' + dz')$ and leaves it with the concentration $\bar{X}_B(z')$.   The difference between the
ingoing and outgoing amounts of B per unit time is equal to the amount of B exchanged
in the layer per unit time:

$$q v_b [\bar{X}_B(z' + dz') - \bar{X}_B(z')] = -q \, dz' \left(\frac{\partial \bar{X}_B}{\partial t}\right)_z \qquad (9\text{-}35)$$

Hence

$$\frac{d\bar{X}_B}{dz'} v_b = -\left(\frac{\partial \bar{X}_B}{\partial t}\right)_z \qquad (9\text{-}36)$$

With particle diffusion rate controlling, the right-hand side of Eq. (9-36) is substituted by
use of the rate law (9-12).   The definition (5-70) of the separation factor gives

$$z_B \bar{X}_B^* = \frac{z_B C_B \alpha_A^B}{C + z_B C_B (\alpha_A^B - 1)} \qquad (9\text{-}37)$$

---

* For the effect of longitudinal diffusion on boundaries, see Wicke [256], Ledoux [136b],
Lapidus [11,135], Lightfoot [139], Vermeulen [247], and particularly Acrivos [3], who has
given the most adequate treatment for self-sharpening boundaries.
    † An analogous situation is found in distillation columns operating under total reflux.

and Eq. (9-34) gives with the definitions of x_B and $\bar{x}_B$

$$C_B = \frac{\bar{X}_B C}{\bar{X}} \qquad (9\text{-}38)$$

With these substitutions, Eq. (9-36) can be integrated. With film diffusion rate controlling, the procedure is the same, except that the rate law (9-13) is applied and that Eq. (5-70) is used for substituting C_B^*. Equation (9-29) is now obtained with the assumption that the perturbations resulting from particle diffusion and film diffusion are additive. The (usually unimportant) plate height contribution due to finite particle size (see page 450) is somewhat arbitrarily added to H_p and H_f.* The integration constants, $+1$ and -1, in Eq. (9-29) stem from the normalization of the z' axis such that $z' = 0$ coincides with the center of gravity of the boundary, i.e., $\int_0^1 z' \, dx_B = 0$ (note that $\int_0^1 \ln x \, dx = -1$).

Figure 9-21 illustrates the action of ion exchange. In an arbitrary plane z' with a solution composition $x_B(z')$, the actual composition of the resin is $\bar{x}_B(z') = x_B(z')$. This point lies on the diagonal. With particle diffusion control, the driving force of ion exchange is proportional to the difference $\bar{x}_B^*(z') - \bar{x}_B(z')$; with film diffusion control proportional to $x_B(z') - x_B^*(z')$. It is obvious that a boundary can only be stable when the differences are positive, i.e., when equilibrium is favorable.

The boundaries are, as a rule, not symmetrical. Their shape depends on the relative plate-height contributions from particle and film diffusion. Film diffusion control results in significant "leakage" of small quantities of B ahead of the main boundary, whereas particle diffusion control results in "tailing" of A. This is apparent from Fig. 9-21 which shows that with film diffusion control the driving force is particularly small at low conversion

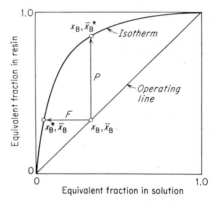

FIG. 9-21. Isotherm and operating line for a self-sharpening boundary in displacement with complete conversion from A form to B form. With particle diffusion control the driving force for ion exchange is proportional to P, with film diffusion control proportional to F.

to B form (i.e., at the "foot" of the boundary), and with particle diffusion control at high conversion (i.e., at the "tail" of the boundary).

Displacement of a Single Species. The mathematically simplest displacement operation is displacement of a counter ion A from the bed by another counter ion B which is preferred by the resin. The effluent volume

---

* Glueckauf adds H_0 only to H_p [79].

at which a given concentration x_B emerges from the column is [79]

$$V(x_B) = q \left(\frac{\bar{X}}{C} + \beta \right) [Z - z'(x_B)] \tag{9-39}$$

where $z'(x_B)$ is given by Eq. (9-29). This relation is obtained from Eq. (9-29) by equating the over-all column capacity*

$$Q_{total} = qZ(\bar{X} + \beta C) \tag{9-40}$$

to the amount of B fed until the center of gravity ($z' = 0$) of the boundary emerges from the column. Equation (9-39) can be used for computing the effluent history.

For the calculation of the *breakthrough capacity* and the *degree of column utilization*, Eq. (9-39) can be simplified [79]. As a rule, the permissible breakthrough concentration is much smaller than the feed concentration ($x_B \ll 1$). The breakthrough capacity is defined as the amount of B (in equivalents) taken up by the bed until breakthrough is reached.* With $x_B \ll 1$, the breakthrough capacity is

$$Q_b(x_B) \cong Q_{total} \left[1 - \frac{H_p + H_0}{2Z} \left(\frac{1}{\alpha_A^B - 1} \ln \frac{1}{x_B} + 1 \right) \right. $$
$$\left. - \frac{H_f + H_0}{2Z} \left(\frac{\alpha_A^B}{\alpha_A^B - 1} \ln \frac{1}{x_B} - 1 \right) \right] \tag{9-41}$$

For $\alpha_A^B \gg 1$, this expression reduces to

$$Q_b(x_B) \cong Q_{total} \left[1 - \frac{H_p + H_0}{2Z} - \frac{H_f + H_0}{2Z} \left(\ln \frac{1}{x_B} - 1 \right) \right] \tag{9-42}$$

From Eq. (9-41) or (9-42), the degree of column utilization

$$\eta \equiv \frac{Q_b}{Q_{total}} \tag{9-43}$$

is readily obtained.

The derivation of the equations is based on the assumption that the steady-state shape of the boundary has been attained. This limitation is not serious since the steady state is reached after the boundary has passed through only a few effective plates. The number of plates required is somewhat larger when the separation factor is small (for $\alpha_A^B = 5$, about 5 plates are needed, and for $\alpha_A^B = 1.2$, about 35 plates). This can be shown by use of Eq. (9-51).

The breakthrough capacity and the degree of column utilization depend, as the equations show, on the concentration x_B that can be tolerated in

---

* According to these definitions, the over-all and breakthrough capacities include the counter-ion content of the interstitial solution.

the effluent. Furthermore, Eq. (9-42) leads to the interesting conclusion that, with very strongly favorable equilibrium, the breakthrough capacity and thus the degree of column utilization do not depend on the value of the separation factor, but only on the ion-exchange rate, particularly on the rate of film diffusion. The limiting case of negligible resistance to particle diffusion—which is a good approximation for the effluent history up to breakthrough, where the effect of slow particle diffusion is small— had been derived before by Michaels [156], and the still simpler limiting case of irreversible sorption or ion exchange with film diffusion control [Eq. (9-42) without the correction for particle diffusion] even earlier by Drew (quoted by Klotz [121a]).

Displacement Development of Mixtures. In displacement development, a mixture of counter ions is introduced at the top of the column and is then separated by development with a counter ion which is preferred by the resin. The counter ions of the mixture arrange themselves in bands with self-sharpening front and rear boundaries (see Sec. 9-7a). The shapes of the various boundaries can be calculated from Eq. (9-29). The length of the band of an arbitrary species i (i.e., the distance between the centers of gravity of its front and rear boundaries) is given by

$$Z_i = \frac{|z_i| Q_i}{q(\bar{X} + \beta C)} \tag{9-44}$$

where Q_i = total amount of i in moles; z_i = valence of species i; C = concentration (in equivalents) of the displacement agent.

The fractional impurities in the bands can be calculated from Eqs. (9-29) and (9-44). Note that the band length depends on the column cross section q, whereas the spread of the boundaries does not. The desired purity can thus be attained by choosing a column with a sufficiently small cross section.

In displacement development, the mixed band must travel a certain distance in order to be resolved into individual bands of the components. Thereafter, the sharpness of separation is not improved by further displacement downstream. For a two-component mixture of, say, B and C the distance required for resolution is approximately [175,218]

$$Z_{sep} \cong Z_{B+C} \frac{z_C Q_C + \alpha_B^C z_B Q_B}{(z_B Q_B + z_C Q_C)(\alpha_B^C - 1)} \tag{9-45}$$

where Z_{B+C} = length of zone being displaced.

For example, the resolution of approximately equal amounts of B and C with $\alpha_B^C = 2$ requires displacement of the zone by about 1.5 times its own length, and with $\alpha_B^C = 1.2$ by about six times its own length. It is assumed in the derivation that the band lengths are much larger than the effective plate height and that $C_i \ll \bar{X}_i$.

Derivation. Equation (9-45) is readily derived in the following way. Resolution occurs because, in the presence of C, B is less strongly taken up by the resin and thus migrates faster than C. The calculation is made with a frame of reference which moves at the migration rate of the zone. Complete resolution requires interchange of equivalent amounts ΔQ_B (shaded area in Fig. 9-22) and ΔQ_C across the plane at z' which becomes the eventual boundary. The rate at which B moves downstream, and C upstream, across this (moving) plane is readily calculated from the distribution coefficients of B and C

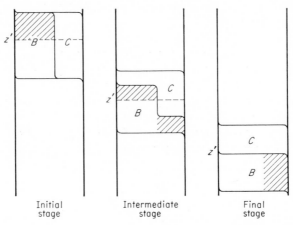

| Initial
stage | Intermediate
stage | Final
stage |

Fig. 9-22. Resolution of a two-component mixture in displacement development (*schematic*).

in the presence of one another and from Eq. (9-28). With the condition $C_i \ll \bar{X}_i$, Eq. (9-45) is obtained.

Similar, more lengthy calculations can be made for multicomponent displacement development and frontal analysis. For multicomponent displacement development, a simple, conservative estimate can be made by applying Eq. (9-45) to the pair of adjacent components, say, M and N with the smallest mutual separation factor, α_M^N:

$$Z_{sep} = Z_{\Sigma i,j} \frac{\sum_j z_j Q_j + \alpha_M^N \sum_i z_i Q_i}{\left(\sum_i z_i Q_i + \sum_j z_j Q_j\right)(\alpha_M^N - 1)} \qquad (9\text{-}46)$$

where $Z_{\Sigma i,j}$ = total length of zone being displaced; summation over i comprises M and all species with lower affinity for the resin than M, and that over j comprises N and all species with higher affinity than N.

Mixed-bed and Multistage Demineralization. The treatment is readily adapted to *mixed-bed demineralization.* The actual mixture of a cation and an anion exchanger can be regarded as one single "salt-removing resin."

The salt-removal equilibrium in the bed is very favorable (see Sec. 9-3), so that the limiting equation (9-42) applies for the breakthrough capacity. In most applications, the salt content of the feed is low. Then the rate-controlling step of ion exchange is film diffusion, and the correction for particle diffusion can be omitted. A more detailed discussion has recently been given by Frisch [61a].

The calculation of column performance in *two-stage* and *multistage demineralization* is more difficult. Consider, for example, an anion-exchange column which forms the second stage. The feed, coming from the first cation-exchange column, is acidic. Anion-exchange equilibrium thus is highly favorable. With progressing anion exchange and concomitant neutralization of H^+, however, anion-exchange equilibrium becomes less favorable and may even become unfavorable when the pH has substantially risen. In other words, the separation factor decreases sharply with progressing anion removal from the feed. Analogous considerations apply to any further stages. Equations (9-29), (9-39), and (9-41), which are derived with a constant separation factor, are inapplicable. For calculations with nonconstant separation factors, see page 478. A detailed theory for such operations has so far not been developed.

Prediction of Optimum Operating Conditions. The effect of operating conditions on the sharpness of separation or column efficiency is similar to that in elution development (see page 458). The diagram 9-16, which gives the effective plate height as a function of the operating conditions, can also be applied to displacement processes when the coordinates are chosen in a slightly different way. Thus most of the conclusions which were discussed earlier are equally valid in displacement processes.

Two special features of displacement, however, should be stressed as being important in plant operations in which the composition of the feed is given and a breakthrough concentration is specified.

In contrast to elution development, the shapes of the boundaries depend on the individual plate-height contributions due to particle diffusion and film diffusion rather than on the total plate height alone. Film diffusion control results in "leakage" of the displacing ion ahead of the main front. This leakage may seriously reduce the breakthrough capacity if high product purity is required. In comparison, the "tailing" caused by particle diffusion control is less harmful [see Eq. (9-42) in which H_f is weighted by a large factor when $x_B \ll 1$].

The second feature becomes important when very dilute solutions are processed ($C \ll \bar{X}$). The corresponding operating points are far on the right in the diagram 9-16. On the "plateau" in the upper right, the flow rate can be considerably increased without significant loss in effective plates, provided that the sloping region of particle diffusion control is not reentered [79]. The reason is that, here, an increase in flow rate reduces the film thickness and thus accelerates the (film-diffusion controlled) ion exchange about as much as it accelerates the migration of the boundary. This is reflected in Eq. (9-30) which shows that H_f becomes independent of v when $v \gg 1/70r_0$.

The calculation of optimum operating conditions will be illustrated by a practical example.

Example. Find optimum operating conditions and minimum dimensions for a water-softening column which meets the following requirements:

Maximum permissible hardness in effluent............	$C_B = 10^{-4}$ g CaO/liter
Throughput................................	$qv = 60$ m³/hr
Water capacity per cycle..........................	1,200 m³
Desired degree of column utilization.................	$\eta \geq 75\%$

The following data are given:

Hardness of raw water............................	$C_B^0 = 0.1$ g CaO/liter
Particle radius of resin...........................	$r_0 \cong 0.05$ cm (18 mesh)
Volume capacity of resin..........................	$\bar{X} = 50$ kg CaO/m³ bed
Separation factor at raw-water concentration.........	$\alpha_{Na}^{Ca} = 10^3$
Interdiffusion coefficient in resin....................	$\bar{D} = 3 \cdot 10^{-7}$ cm²/sec
Interdiffusion coefficient in solution.................	$D = 10^{-5}$ cm²/sec
Fractional void volume of bed......................	$\beta = 0.4$

[margin note: $1 \text{ m}^3 = 264 \text{ Gallons.}$]

With the available pressure head, the maximum attainable flow rate is 3 cm/sec in a bed of 1 m length and is inversely proportional to the bed length.

Solution. The required breakthrough capacity is calculated from the water capacity per cycle and the hardness of the raw water:

$$Q_b(C_B^0) = 1,200 \text{ m}^3 \cdot 0.1 \text{ kg CaO/m}^3 = 120 \text{ kg CaO}$$

The required effective bed volume thus is 120 kg CaO/50 kg CaO m⁻³ = 2.4 m³. The total bed volume is 2.4 m³/η = 3.2 m³. With bed volume and throughput given, flow rate and bed length are proportional to one another. On the other hand, the plate height and particularly the harmful contribution H_f increase less than proportionally with the flow rate [see Eq. (9-30)]. Hence the aspect ratio of the column should be as high as compatible with the desired throughput. From

$$v = \frac{0.03 \text{ m}^2/\text{sec}}{Z} \qquad qv = 60 \text{ m}^3/\text{hr} = 1.7 \cdot 10^{-2} \text{ m}^3/\text{sec} \qquad qZ = 3.2 \text{ m}^3$$

one obtains

Flow rate...................	$v = 1.2$ cm/sec
Column cross section........	$q = 1.4$ m²
Bed length.................	$Z = 2.3$ m

It remains to be checked whether the column can attain the desired degree of utilization. Omitting unimportant terms one obtains from Eqs. (9-30)

$$H_p = \frac{0.142 r_0^2 v C_{Ca}^0}{\bar{D}\bar{X}} \approx 3 \text{ cm}$$

$$H_f = \frac{0.266 r_0^2 v}{D(1 + 70 r_0 v)} \approx 16 \text{ cm}$$

and after substituting in Eqs. (9-42) and (9-43)

$$\eta = 1 - \frac{H_f}{2Z}\left(\ln \frac{C_{Ca}^0}{C_{Ca}} - 1\right) - \frac{H_p}{2Z} \approx 0.79$$

The degree of column utilization thus is slightly higher than required.

The accuracy of the results should not be overestimated. At best, the calculation gives a rough approximation. Moreover, in plant operation a number of further factors must be considered [16,50,98a,156,248]. For example, it is usually not economical to regenerate the bed completely. Besides, technical units often fail to attain the calculated degree of column utilization because flow maldistribution resulting from packing irregularities can hardly be avoided. Nevertheless, the equations and especially the diagram 9-16 provide valuable information as to how a change in operating conditions will affect the column performance.

The equations in this part of the section are derived specifically for ion-exchange processes; it is implied that the total counter-ion concentrations $\bar{X}$ and C in the resin and the solution are constant, i.e., that the exchange is stoichiometric. Application of the treatment to sorption and exchange sorption processes, which are usually non-stoichiometric, requires modifications. These, however, are minor as long as the concentrations of the two components on either side of the boundary are unequivocal functions of one another so that the calculations can be made, as in ion exchange, with only one concentration variable.

Nonsharpening boundaries and general solutions. The derivation of more general solutions which include nonsharpening boundaries and also cover the time interval before the constant or proportionate pattern is attained is rather difficult. Several solutions based on various ion-exchange rate laws have been derived (see also next section). The most useful solutions are given in the following.

Elution with a Linear Ion-exchange Isotherm. Let us consider elution of a counter ion A from the bed by another counter ion B under nonequilibrium conditions, but with a linear exchange isotherm ($\alpha_B^A = 1$). The boundary between B and A is nonsharpening because the sharpening effect of favorable equilibrium is absent.

The analogous heat-transfer problem has first been solved by Anzelius [6], Schumann [194], and Furnas [63]. Furnas [15] recognized the applicability of the solution to mass-transfer processes. The effluent concentration history can be expressed as

$$x_B(\mathfrak{T},\mathfrak{N}) = \mathfrak{g}(\mathfrak{N},\mathfrak{T}\mathfrak{N}) \qquad (9\text{-}47)$$

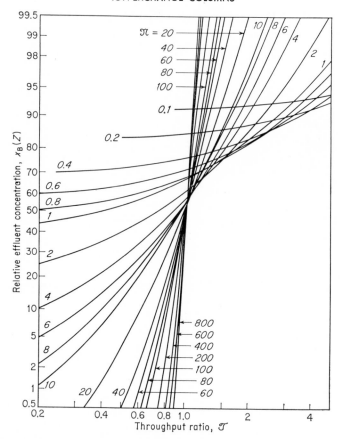

FIG. 9-23. The $\mathcal{J}$ function in dimensionless representation. The diagram gives the relative effluent concentration as a function of the throughput ratio with the number of transfer units as the parameter. *From T. Vermeulen* [247].

where the function $\mathcal{J}$ and its arguments are defined by

$$\mathcal{J}(x,y) \equiv 1 - \int_0^x \exp\left(-y - \xi\right) I_0(2\sqrt{y\xi})\, d\xi$$

$$\mathfrak{T} \equiv \frac{(V - V_b\beta)C}{V_b\bar{X}} = \text{throughput ratio*}$$

$$\mathfrak{N} = \frac{kZ}{v} = \text{number of effective transfer units (ETU) or reaction units}$$

---

* The throughput ratio $\mathfrak{T}$ is a very useful parameter. It is linear in the feed (or effluent) volume and is defined in such a way that it is zero when one void volume has passed the column, and reaches unity when the solution volume which has passed through the bed is stoichiometrically equivalent to the ion-exchange capacity of the bed.

and I_0 is a modified Bessel function of the first kind; the constant k in the definition of $\mathfrak{N}$ is the rate constant in the linear-driving-force rate law

$$\frac{\partial \bar{X}_i}{\partial t} = k(C_i - C_i^*) = k\,\frac{C}{\bar{X}}\,(\bar{X}_i^* - \bar{X}_i)$$

By comparison with the rate laws (9-12) and (9-13), the $\mathcal{J}$ function can thus be correlated with the effective-plate-height concept [Eq. (9-16)]:

$$\mathfrak{N} = 2N \left(\frac{\lambda_i''}{\lambda_i'' + \beta}\right)^2 \cong 2N \qquad (9\text{-}48)$$

where N is the number of effective plates. The transfer units (or reaction units) thus are *not* identical with the effective plates in Eq. (9-15) but, rather, have only about half the height of the latter.

The behavior of the $\mathcal{J}$ function is shown in Fig. 9-23. The effluent concentration histories, normally S-shaped, come out as almost straight lines in this diagram with logarithmic-probability coordinates. The function has been discussed in detail by Klinkenberg [120]. Tables and graphical representations are available [15,63,85,104,120]. The most extensive table is that of Brinkley for the function $g(x,y) \equiv 1 - \mathcal{J}(x,y)$ [24a]. An extract of this table is given in the Appendix (pages 587 to 589).

A more rigorous solution of the same problem has been given by Rosen [178] who used rate laws based on diffusion equations rather than on approximations such as Eq. (6-54), (9-12), or (9-13). Rosen's solution is*

$$x_B(\xi,\theta) = \frac{1}{2} + \frac{2}{\pi} \int_0^\infty \exp\left[-\epsilon\xi H_1(\mu,\nu)\right] \sin\left[\sigma\theta\mu^2 - \epsilon\xi H_2(\mu,\nu)\right] \mathrm{d} \ln \mu \qquad (9\text{-}49)$$

where

$$\xi \equiv \frac{z(1 - \beta)}{v} \qquad \theta \equiv t - \frac{\beta z}{v}$$

$$H_1(\mu,\nu) \equiv \frac{H_a + \nu(H_a^2 + H_b^2)}{(1 + \nu H_a)^2 + (\nu H_b)^2}$$

$$H_2(\mu,\nu) \equiv \frac{H_b}{(1 + \nu H_a)^2 + (\nu H_b)^2}$$

$$H_a(\mu) \equiv \frac{\mu(\sinh 2\mu + \sin 2\mu)}{(\cosh 2\mu - \cos 2\mu)} - 1$$

$$H_b(\mu) \equiv \frac{\mu(\sinh 2\mu + \sin 2\mu)}{\cosh 2\mu - \cos 2\mu}$$

$$\epsilon \equiv \frac{3\bar{D}\bar{C}}{Cr_2^0} \qquad \nu \equiv \epsilon R_f \qquad \sigma \equiv \frac{2\bar{D}}{r_0^2}$$

$$R_f = \text{film resistance} \left(= \frac{r_0\delta}{3D}\right)$$

Equation (9-49) is derived with the rate laws for particle diffusion [Eqs. (6-3) and (6-4)] and film diffusion [Eqs. (6-16) and (6-17)], assuming constant diffusion coefficients. The

---

* The solution, originally derived for sorption processes, is given here in a form adapted to ion exchange.

effects of longitudinal diffusion and finite particle size are not included, but otherwise Rosen's solution is rigorous for isotopic exchange and exchange of trace components. The solution (9-49) has been numerically integrated by machine computation and has been tabulated for various parameter values [179].

The relative concentration of B, x_B, can be given as a function of the three dimensionless parameters $\eta \equiv 3\bar{D}\bar{C}R_f/Cr_0^2$, $\zeta \equiv \epsilon\xi = 3\bar{D}\bar{C}z(1-\beta)/Cvr_0^2$, and $\vartheta \equiv \sigma\theta = (2\bar{D}/r_0^2)(t - \beta z/v)$.* Figure 9-24 shows the behavior of the function (9-49) and illustrates the effects of the parameters on the sharpness of the boundary. The boundary can be sharpened by decreasing the flow rate (larger value of ζ), decreasing the film resistance (smaller value of η), decreasing the particle size (since $\eta \propto 1/r_0$ and $\vartheta \propto 1/r_0^2$), and, with large particles, by increasing the diffusion constant in the resin.

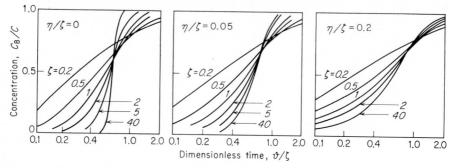

Fig. 9-24. Graphical representation of Rosen's solution for the effluent in elution with a linear isotherm. The relative effluent concentration is given as a function of the dimensionless parameters. *From J. B. Rosen* [179].

In addition to the exact solution (9-49), Rosen gives a simpler approximation [178]. Moreover, Eq. (9-49) reduces to

$$x_B(\xi,\theta) \cong \frac{1}{2}\left[1 + \text{erf}\left(\frac{3\sigma\theta/2 - \epsilon\xi}{2(\epsilon\xi/5)^{1/2}} \right) \right] \qquad (9\text{-}50)*$$

when $\eta \leq 0.01$ and $\epsilon\xi \geq 50$, i.e., for the effluent of long columns with small particle size, low flow rate, and complete particle diffusion control. This limiting solution was derived as early as 1939 by Wicke [256].

The solutions (9-47) and (9-49) can also be extended to partial presaturation of the bed and to operations with mixed feed (see page 476).

The most serious shortcoming of these solutions is that they are restricted to linear ion-exchange isotherms. This makes them inapplicable to most practical operations since, whenever possible, use is made of the selectivity of the ion exchanger. An exception is the uptake of a trace component from a feed containing a large excess of competing species (see page 202). Note also that Eq. (9-49) is not quite as general as has been claimed. In the derivation, a constant interdiffusion coefficient in the resin is assumed.

* The following relations exist between Rosen's parameters and those used in other parts of this section: $\vartheta/\zeta = 2\mathfrak{T}/3$; $\zeta = \mathfrak{N}_p/5$; $\xi/\nu = \mathfrak{N}_f$, where $\mathfrak{N}_p$ and $\mathfrak{N}_f$ are the particle-diffusion and film-diffusion transfer-unit numbers [247].

This assumption only holds for exchange of trace quantities or of counter ions of equal mobilities (see Sec. 6-3). Thus isotopic exchange and trace exchange are almost the only cases in which the solution is rigorous.

General Solution Covering Unfavorable Equilibrium. A mathematical solution for the general case of elution of a counter ion A from a bed completely in A form by another counter ion B with arbitrary (but constant) separation factor α_B^A was first derived by H. C. Thomas [230]. The solution covers unfavorable equilibrium ($\alpha_B^A > 1$) as well as favorable equilibrium ($\alpha_B^A < 1$) and also describes the development of the shape of the boundary in the time interval before attainment of the proportionate or constant pattern. Thomas' solution is derived with the rate law (6-54) [second-order reversible reaction] and can be written as [101,247]

$$x_B(\alpha_B^A, \mathfrak{T}, \mathfrak{N}) = \frac{\mathcal{J}(\alpha_B^A \mathfrak{N}, \mathfrak{T}\mathfrak{N})}{\mathcal{J}(\alpha_B^A \mathfrak{N}, \mathfrak{T}\mathfrak{N}) + \exp\left[(\alpha_B^A - 1)\mathfrak{N}(\mathfrak{T} - 1)\right]\left[1 - \mathcal{J}(\mathfrak{N}, \alpha_B^A \mathfrak{T}\mathfrak{N})\right]} \tag{9-51}$$

where $\mathcal{J}(x,y)$ is the function defined in Eq. (9-47), and

$$\mathfrak{N} \equiv \frac{k\bar{X}Z}{v}$$

where k is the second-order rate constant in the rate law.

Thomas' solution has correctly been called the most general result in the theory of column performance. By reference to his equation, all other solutions can be classified in terms of their α_B^A and $\mathfrak{N}$ values. This has been recognized and demonstrated by Vermeulen [101,247] and Goldstein [85,86].

In the limiting case of a linear isotherm ($\alpha_B^A = 1$), Eq. (9-51) reduces to Eq. (9-47). It has also been shown [101,247] that for favorable equilibrium and long columns ($\alpha_B^A < 1$, $\mathfrak{N} \gg 1$), Eq. (9-51) approaches the "constant-pattern" result

$$x_B = \frac{1}{1 + \exp\left[(\alpha_B^A - 1)\mathfrak{N}(\mathfrak{T} - 1)\right]} \tag{9-52}$$

and for unfavorable equilibrium ($\alpha_B^A > 1$, $\mathfrak{N} \gg 1$) the "proportionate-pattern" result

$$x_B = \frac{(\alpha_B^A/\mathfrak{T})^{1/2} - \alpha_B^A}{1 - \alpha_B^A} \tag{9-53}$$

Both these results had been derived before [52,202,249].* Equation (9-51) can also be used for establishing the ranges of validity of solutions for limiting cases such as the constant-pattern cases (9-29), (9-41), and (9-52) and

---

* The limiting case of Eq. (9-52) for irreversible sorption or exchange ($\alpha_B^A = 0$) was derived by Bohart and Adams [20a] as early as 1920.

the proportionate-pattern case (9-53). With $\alpha_B^A = 2$, the attainment of the proportionate pattern requires about 500 transfer units, with $\alpha_B^A = 10$ only about 10 units. Numbers for the constant pattern have already been given (see page 466).

Extensive graphical representations and numerical tables of Eq. (9-51) are available [101,102,168]. They are very valuable for design purposes.

The main shortcoming of Thomas' solution (9-51) is the fact that its derivation is based on a second-order reaction rate law which is not obeyed by ion exchange. To adapt Thomas' solution to diffusion-controlled ion exchange, Gilliland [71] and others [8,9,85,86,197,223] have correlated the second-order rate constant k with "mass-transfer coefficients" in the particles and films (see page 287). Such a procedure implies that the resistances to diffusion in the two phases are constant and additive. Unfortunately, the concept of constant and additive resistances does not hold for nonlinear isotherms. For example, the discussion of Eq. (9-29) has shown that self-sharpening boundaries display leaking or tailing, depending on whether film diffusion or particle diffusion is the slower process; in contrast, the second-order reaction rate law leads always to a symmetrical shape of the boundary. The error is most serious in the calculation of breakthrough capacities, since leakage resulting from slow film diffusion can lead to a much earlier breakthrough than one would expect on the basis of Thomas' or Gilliland's treatment.

A more adequate, but also more complex, correlation of Thomas' solution (9-51) with diffusion-controlled ion exchange has been established by Vermeulen and Hiester [101, 244,247]. These authors have shown that Eq. (9-51) can also be obtained with the linear-driving-force rate laws (9-12) and (9-13); now, however, the parameter $\mathfrak{N}$ is no longer constant, but varies with the local composition of the bed. For particle diffusion control:

$$\mathfrak{N} = \frac{\mathfrak{N}_p}{\alpha_B^A - (\alpha_B^A - 1)\bar{x}_B} \tag{9-54}$$

and for film diffusion control:

$$\mathfrak{N} = \frac{\mathfrak{N}_f}{1 + (\alpha_B^A - 1)x_B} \tag{9-55}$$

where $\mathfrak{N}_p$ and $\mathfrak{N}_f$ obey Eq. (9-48) and can thus be obtained from the corresponding terms in Eq. (9-16). This procedure reflects more adequately the effects of particle and film diffusion. Calculations with variable $\mathfrak{N}$ values are discussed later. With combined particle and film diffusion control, the boundary spreads caused by the two processes are not strictly additive; for higher accuracy a correction factor must be introduced [102,119a].

Partial Presaturation of the Bed, and Mixed Feed. The solutions (9-29), (9-41), (9-47), (9-49), and (9-51) for self-sharpening and nonsharpening boundaries were derived for beds which are initially completely in the A form and for a feed containing B as the only counter ion. These solutions, however, are readily extended to systems in which the bed is partially presaturated with B and the feed contains A in addition to B, provided that the initial bed composition is uniform and that the feed composition and the flow rate are constant [86,246,247].

Suppose that the bed is partially presaturated with B to the degree $\bar{x}_B^0$, and that the feed contains the equivalent fraction x_B^∞ of B. A solution-saturation fraction μ is defined by

$$\mu \equiv \frac{x_B - x_B^0}{x_B^\infty - x_B^0} \tag{9-56}$$

where $x_B^0 = \bar{x}_B^0/[\bar{x}_B^0 + \alpha_B^A(1 - \bar{x}_B^0)]$ is the equivalent fraction of B which a solution would have if it were in equilibrium with the presaturated resin. It can be shown that μ obeys Eq. (9-51) and its limiting cases if the arguments are substituted in the following way:

$$\text{Replace} \quad \alpha_B^A \quad \text{by} \quad \frac{(1/\alpha_B^A - 1)x_B^0 + 1}{(1/\alpha_B^A - 1)x_B^\infty + 1} \tag{9-57}$$

$$\mathfrak{N} \quad \text{by} \quad \frac{\mathfrak{N}}{(1/\alpha_B^A - 1)x_B^0 + 1} \tag{9-58}$$

$$\mathfrak{X} \quad \text{by} \quad [(1/\alpha_B^A - 1)x_B^\infty + 1][(1/\alpha_B^A - 1)x_B^0 + 1]\alpha_B^A\mathfrak{X} \tag{9-59}$$

Similarly, with an analogous substitution for α_A^B, replacement of C by $C(x_B^\infty - x_B^0)$ and of $\bar{X}$ by $\bar{X}(\bar{x}_B^\infty - \bar{x}_B^0)$, Eqs. (9-28), (9-29), and (9-41) now hold when x_B is replaced by μ.

The substitution (9-57) shows that the parameter which replaces α_B^A (or α_A^B) approaches unity when the difference between x_B^∞ and x_B^0 becomes small. This is particularly true when B is a trace component ($x_B^\infty \ll 1$, $x_B^0 \ll 1$). With the equilibrium parameter approaching unity, the self-sharpening and spreading effects of favorable and unfavorable equilibrium, respectively, disappear. Hence, with partial presaturation and mixed feed, self-sharpening boundaries are less sharp and nonsharpening boundaries sharper than with beds completely in A form and feed containing B only. This is reasonable since the operation extends over a shorter isotherm section which is more nearly linear. Figure 9-25 illustrates the case of a self-sharpening boundary. Again, the "operating line" is a straight line, but no longer the diagonal $\bar{x}_B = x_B$ as in Fig. 9-21. Comparison with Fig. 9-21 shows that in Fig. 9-25 the driving forces are smaller and, hence, the boundary is more diffuse.

Calculations with nonuniform initial bed composition and variable feed are more complex. General analytical solutions have not been found

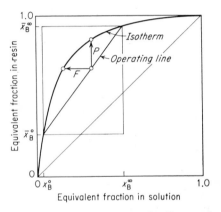

FIG. 9-25. Isotherm, operating line, and driving forces for ion exchange in displacement with partial presaturation of the bed and mixed feed (*schematic*).

Amundson [5] has extended Thomas' method to obtain an algebraic framework for numerical integrations of binary cases (only two counter-ion species in the system). Cornaz [40,248] has worked out equations which can be applied to cyclic operations with incomplete saturation (discontinued at breakthrough) followed by incomplete regeneration; however, the evaluation is somewhat cumbersome. Also, such calculations for cyclic operations which involve interruptions between the saturation, regeneration, and washing steps suffer more seriously than others from the fact that the actual rate of particle-diffusion controlled ion exchange or sorption depends on the history of the particles and not only, as assumed, on the momentary average concentration in the particle (see page 482). In other words, the relaxation of the intraparticle concentration profiles during the interruptions and the washing step is not included.

An important limiting case of variable feed is the following. The bed is initially in the A form. For a period of partial or complete saturation corresponding to the throughput ratio $\mathfrak{X}_{\text{sat}}$ feed containing B is introduced. At the end of this period, elution with feed containing A only is started. It has been shown [100,244,247] that with a linear isotherm the effluent concentration history can be given as the difference between the history for saturation starting with $\mathfrak{T} = 0$ and continuing throughout the elution period, and a second history representing elution from the uniformly presaturated bed and starting with $\mathfrak{T}' = \mathfrak{T} - \mathfrak{T}_{\text{sat}}$. Accordingly:

$$x_{\text{B}}(\mathfrak{N},\mathfrak{T}) = \mathcal{J}(\mathfrak{N},\mathfrak{T}\mathfrak{N}) - \mathcal{J}(\mathfrak{N},\mathfrak{T}'\mathfrak{N}) \qquad (9\text{-}60)$$

Somewhat more complex relations are obtained for nonlinear isotherms and for mixed feed [247]. These relations can be used in elution development to calculate the dependence of band shapes and retention volumes on the sample size (see Fig. 9-26). Also, the shapes of asymmetric bands under nonlinear equilibrium conditions can be calculated.

Calculations with Nonconstant Separation Factors and Transfer-unit Heights. The general solution (9-51) can still be used when the parameters $\alpha_{\text{B}}^{\text{A}}$ and $\mathfrak{N}$ vary. Hiester

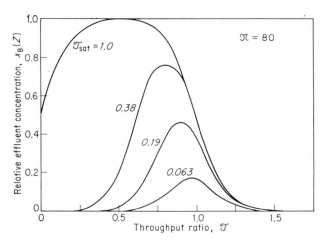

FIG. 9-26. Effect of sample size in elution with a linear isotherm. The curves are calculated for a column with 80 transfer units. *From T. Vermeulen and N. K. Hiester* [244].

and Vermeulen [101,247] have developed the following procedure. The effluent concentration history is divided into a number of segments, each of which is small enough for $\alpha_{\text{B}}^{\text{A}}$ and $\mathfrak{N}$ to be essentially constant. The values of $\alpha_{\text{B}}^{\text{A}}$ and $\mathfrak{N}$ in each segment are calculated from the average x_{B}. The various segments can now be constructed by curve matching with master curves having the appropriate $\alpha_{\text{B}}^{\text{A}}$ and $\mathfrak{N}$ values. The "length" $\Delta\mathfrak{T}$ of a segment is obtained from the difference in the $\mathfrak{T}$ values at either end of the range in x_{B} covered by the segment. Now the segments can be pieced together consecutively to give the complete effluent concentration history. The $\mathfrak{T}$ coordinate of the curve is established by graphical integration which permits $\mathfrak{T} = 1$ to be located.

This procedure has been used, for example, for obtaining effluent concentration histories based on the linear-driving-force rate laws (9-12) and (9-13) which, in the framework of Eq. (9-51), lead to nonconstant $\mathfrak{N}$ values [see Eqs. (9-54) and (9-55)].

Other rate theories. The survey of rate theories in the preceding part of this section is by no means complete. Many other solutions based on various assumed rate laws of ion exchange or sorption and various kinds of isotherms have been derived.

In most approaches, reversible or irreversible first- or second-order reaction rate laws are postulated [4,5,23,100,201,202,233,246,249]; see Eqs. (6-53) to (6-59). A detailed theory of this type, based on a first-order reversible reaction rate law, has recently been developed by Giddings [66,67] for gas chromatography (elution development); this author also discussed consecutive reactions on the sorbent, sorbents with sites having different affinities, etc. Alternatively, constant "mass-transfer coefficients" (see page 287) have been used and correlated to variables such as the particle size and the Reynolds and Schmidt numbers of the bed (see also page 476).

More appealing are the approaches in which diffusion rate laws or close approximations to these are used [20,55,76,81,111,136,155,231,232,245,256]. An example is Vermeulen's "quadratic-driving-force" approximation [Eq. (6-11)] for particle-diffusion controlled exchange [245]. Several limiting cases have been solved. More rigorous numerical calculations which extend Rosen's treatment [Eq. (9-49)] to Freundlich-type isotherms have recently been made on electronic computers [236]. However, in all these approaches a constant effective interdiffusion coefficient is assumed. In ion exchange, this assumption is unrealistic (see Sec. 6-3c) and makes the superiority of such theories over the simpler linear-driving-force and reaction-rate theories questionable.

Other solutions have been derived for partial or complete rate control by "pore diffusion," i.e., interdiffusion in wide pores of the solid which are freely accessible to the bulk fluid outside and in which the composition of the fluid does not differ from that outside when equilibrium is attained [2,247]. These solutions are of potential value for coarse and highly porous ion exchangers.

An excellent and comprehensive survey of the various approaches and their correlations with the solution (9-51) has been given by Vermeulen [247].

c. Equilibrium Theories

The most common equilibrium theories [60,152,182,188] are based on a model which was first suggested and used by Martin and Synge [148]. In this "discontinuous" model, the solution in an effective plate of the bed attains equilibrium with the ion exchanger (or sorbent) before it moves on into the next plate. The effluent thus consists of a sequence of finite solution volumes, each of which is so large as to fill an effective plate. On their way through the column, these volumes are subjected to a series of equilibrations, one in each effective plate. It is assumed that deviations from local equilibrium in the actual continuous column process can be accounted for in the model by choosing a corresponding effective plate height. One might say that these equilibrium theories substitute mixing in the plates for nonequilibrium as the cause of boundary spreading. The plate height is an empirical quantity and must be determined by fitting theoretical elution curves to the results of elution experiments.

A simple and typical example is the treatment given by Mayer and Tompkins [152] for elution development of traces. A linear isotherm [Eq. (9-11)] is assumed. The calculation leads to Gaussian-shaped bands with a peak concentration of

$$(C_i)_{max} = \frac{Q_i}{V_i} \left[\frac{N}{2\pi} \frac{(\lambda_i'' + \beta)}{\lambda_i''} \right]^{1/2} \tag{9-61}*$$

The migration rate of the peaks is the same as in the rate theories [see Eqs. (9-17) and (9-18)]. When expressed as a function of the number of effective plates, the sharpness of

---

* The relation is rewritten in terms of the quantities used in this section.

the bands in the equilibrium theory is slightly greater than in the rate theories.   The proper plate height for the equilibrium theory thus is somewhat greater than that given by Eq. (9-16).   A theoretical effluent history fitted to experimental data is shown in Fig. 9-27.

The Mayer-Tompkins theory has been refined by making the calculations with a continuous rather than discontinuous flow of solution, but maintaining the empirical plate concept [182].   The theory has also been applied to gradient elution [60].

Recently, the Mayer-Tompkins theory has been applied to the interesting case of chromatography of a labile species which reacts while being developed.   Kallen [110] has treated the case in which a species A forms, in an irreversible first-order reaction, another species B having a different distribution coefficient:

$$A \rightarrow B \qquad\qquad -\frac{dC_A}{dt} = kC_A \qquad\qquad \lambda_A'' \neq \lambda_B'' \qquad\qquad (9\text{-}62)$$

The reaction reduces the concentration of species A throughout its band by the factor $\exp(-kV/qv)$, while the bandwidth and the peak retention volume remain essentially

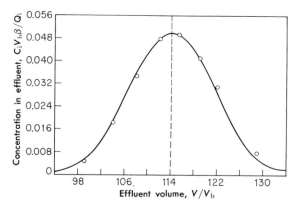

Fig. 9-27.   Effluent history of a band in elution development.   *Circles:* experimental values for praseodymium in a praseodymium/cerium separation on Dowex 50 with citrate buffer of pH 3.0.   *Solid line:* calculated from the Mayer-Tompkins theory and fitted to the experimental points by choice of $N = 240$.   *From S. W. Mayer and E. R. Tompkins* [152].

unchanged.   Simultaneously, the reaction generates a band of species B.   This latter band is broad and strongly asymmetrical since new B molecules are constantly produced in the band of A which increase its distance from that of B.   A typical case calculated by Kallen is shown in Fig. 9-28.   Similar situations may arise in ion-exchange chromatography with complexing agents if complex formation or rearrangement is slow.

The most obvious shortcoming of these equilibrium theories is their inability to predict the plate height and to provide information as to how a change in operating conditions will affect the column performance.   Consequences are that the plate height must be experimentally determined before any calculations can be made, and that optimum operating conditions can only be found experimentally by trial and error.   This is even more unfortunate than it may seem at first glance.   The rate theories, which are based on a more accurate model, have shown that the plate height is *not the same* for the various species in a separation [see Eq. (9-16)]. This fact is often overlooked, and yet it greatly impairs the successful application of equilibrium theories. Note also that the equilibrium theories are applicable only in special cases such as linear isotherms or constant-pattern displacement. Like many approximations, equilibrium theories are often derived and applied without exact knowledge of the limitations of the model.

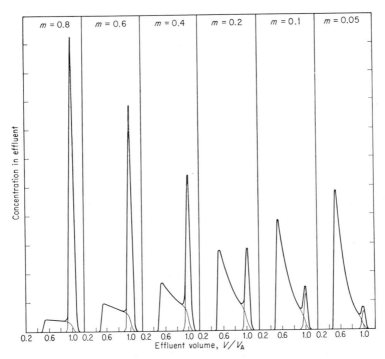

Fig. 9-28. Chromatography of a labile substance. Effluent concentration histories for elution development of a substance A forming another substance B by a first-order reaction. The curves are calculated with the Mayer-Tompkins model for a column with 1,000 effective plates, a peak retention-volume ratio $V_A/V_B = 2$, and various values of the parameter $m \equiv \exp(-V_A k/qv)$. *From J. Kallen and E. Heilbronner* [110].

In other equilibrium theories [37,43,64,166,176,202,251,259] it is assumed that local equilibrium in the column is actually attained. The effective-plate concept is not used. These theories are inadequate for favorable and linear equilibria because, here, the spreading effect of the finite ion-exchange rate persists even after the boundary has traveled long distances. For unfavorable equilibria, however, the theories give rather good approximations since, here, the boundary rapidly becomes diffuse and approaches the proportionate pattern in which local equilibrium prevails (for example, the limiting equation (9-53) is independent of the transfer-unit number

$\mathfrak{N}$ and is readily derived with the assumption of local equilibrium). Of particular interest are calculations of multicomponent systems [43,74,166] and for complex isotherms that are partly favorable and partly unfavorable [75,241a].

The only advantage of the equilibrium theories over the rate theories is their much greater simplicity. In cases in which the mathematics of even a simple rate theory gets out of hand, an equilibrium theory may still be formulated without too much effort and may be able to give significant answers. The use of equilibrium theories, however, should be restricted to such cases and to operations in which local equilibrium is indeed attained.

d. General Comments

The discussion in this section has shown that the combined efforts of many investigators have succeeded in constructing a general theoretical framework of column performance. The core of this framework is Thomas' solution (9-51). With the appropriate modifications and extensions, this solution and its limiting cases cover almost the entire range of process conditions from elution development of traces to displacement and regeneration in plant operations.

However, this truly remarkable success should not distract attention from the fact that it was achieved with rather serious idealizations. It is worthwhile to study the most important idealizations and their consequences critically, since a theory is useful only when applied judiciously and with accurate knowledge of its limitations.

Perhaps the most serious idealization in the rate theories is the use of simplified rate laws for ion exchange. The discussion of ion-exchange kinetics in Sec. 6-3c has shown that the actual rate laws are far more complex than any of the approximations which have been used in column-performance calculations. The difficulty of incorporating accurate ion-exchange laws into the developed framework is fundamental rather than only a matter of sufficiently close approximations. Usual rate theories of column performance are based on the assumption that the rate of ion exchange (or sorption) can be given as some function

$$\frac{\partial \bar{X}_i}{\partial t} = f(\bar{X}_i, \bar{X}_i^*, C_i, C_i^*) \tag{9-63}$$

With particle diffusion control this assumption is not valid. The rate is not an unequivocal function of the momentary average compositions of the solid and liquid in contact with one another, but depends on the shape of the concentration profiles in the particles and thus on the particle history. This is clearly borne out by the "interruption test" (see page 256) in which relaxation of the intraparticle concentration gradients during an interruption period leads to a higher exchange rate after reestablishment of the contact with the liquid, though the average compositions of the solid and liquid have not been changed. Any function of the form (9-63) can thus be valid only for a specific set of initial and boundary conditions. Even the best approximation of the type (9-63) may be seriously in error when the boundary conditions are changed, and in column operations the boundary conditions for ion exchange inherently vary from case to case.

Theories for mixed and nonuniform bed and feed compositions are most strongly affected. For example, water-softening columns are known to "recover" when left standing after breakthrough, so that additional feed can be softened. The regeneration efficiency in an incompletely saturated bed may depend markedly on the length of time the column was left standing (or was backwashed) between saturation and regeneration. These effects are due to relaxation of intraparticle concentration gradients. Moreover, the shape of the internal concentration profiles depends strongly on the mobility ratio of the exchanging ions (see Fig. 6-7). All these effects are not covered by the theories.

The only way to overcome this difficulty is by using, as in Rosen's treatment, the continuity condition within the particle to keep track of the internal concentration profiles instead of using an equation of the type (9-63). This, however, breaks up the framework built around Eq. (9-51) and adds greatly to the already considerable mathematical complexity of the treatment. Accurate and general analytical solutions of the actual rate laws have not been found even with the much simpler boundary conditions in batch exchange (see Sec. 6-3c). Therefore there is hardly any hope of finding such solutions for columns.

Other simplifications which may impair the validity of even the most elaborate rate theories which have been developed so far are the omission of hydrodynamic effects such as flow maldistribution (see Sec. 9-10), of swelling and shrinking of the ion exchanger, specific interactions, and their effects on the ion-exchange rate. A further shortcoming of the present theories is their inability to handle variations in flow rate and multiple feed with any degree of accuracy, except in a few limiting cases.

These critical observations spotlight the somewhat unsatisfactory present status of the theory. Even the most refined solutions now available may be seriously in error. In view of this lack of accuracy, the effort in applying one of the theories is justified only if the required answers can be obtained without excessive difficulties. In complicated systems, the use of even a simple equilibrium theory may be preferable to lengthy calculations which give only slightly more accurate results. It is for this reason that the major part of this section has been devoted to crude and simple approximation methods. Really accurate calculations can be made numerically, but they are so complex that electronic computers become indispensable. Numerical computing methods have been discussed by Acrivos [1], Amundson [5], Funk [62], Lapidus [49], Opler [167,169], and Tien [236]. Recently, the possibility of using memory analog computers for calculations of this type has also been discussed [109a].

Advocating the use of simple theories, however, makes it necessary to point out the pitfalls which are encountered in their application. A theory is completely useless unless it reflects the most important properties of the system to which it is applied. Any theory must first be checked as to whether it meets this criterion. For example, self-sharpening boundaries arise because equilibrium is favorable, and theories which assume a linear isotherm are thus inapplicable. Attempts to calculate an "effective plate height" from the shape of a self-sharpening boundary by the use of a linear-isotherm theory lead to a value which has no physical significance. The following simple rules may be helpful:

1. In elution development of small quantities, linear isotherms are a reasonable approximation. The width of a band depends critically on the over-all ion-exchange rate, but only little on the nature of the rate-controlling mechanism and the specific form of the rate laws. The width also depends somewhat on the distribution coefficient.

2. In displacement processes, the shape of a (self-sharpening) boundary depends on the shape of the exchange isotherm, the exchange rate, and the nature of the rate-controlling mechanism. As a rule, the "constant pattern" is a reasonable approximation.

3. The shape of a self-sharpening boundary depends not only on the over-all ion-exchange rate, but also on the relative contributions of particle and film diffusion. The widely used concept of constant and additive mass-transfer resistances in the particle and the film fails to bring out this feature and thus is inadequate for most applications.

4. In elution under unfavorable-equilibrium conditions, the shape of a (nonsharpening) boundary depends critically on the shape of the isotherm, but only little on the exchange rate. For strongly unfavorable equilibria, the "proportionate pattern" and local equilibrium are reasonable approximations.

In (2) and (3), the use of a constant (average) separation factor is a reasonable approximation if the actual factor varies little, if the over-all spread rather than the specific shape of the boundary is sought, and, in displacement only, if the separation factor is very large.

Most theories operate with the concept of effective plates, transfer units, reaction units, or mixing stages. These concepts are very convenient, but must be applied with care. Much confusion may arise from the different definitions which are in use. Note that mixing stages are defined for spread by longitudinal diffusion and are applicable to linear-isotherm theories only, that effective plates in equilibrium theories and Glueckauf's rate theory are about twice as high as the transfer or reaction units in the framework built around Thomas' equation (9-51), and that the plate height under identical conditions in the same operation is different for different species.

One last warning concerns the interpretation of effluent histories. The discussion in this section has dealt with methods of calculating effluent histories from fundamental data, namely, from ion-exchange equilibria and rates. Frequently this procedure is reversed, i.e., it is attempted to derive such data from experimental effluent histories by the use of one theory or the other. Here, the investigator finds himself on dangerous ground indeed. The theories must postulate simple forms of the rate laws and isotherms. The validity of these assumptions in the special case cannot be checked directly. Moreover, all bands and boundaries under any conditions are more or less bell-shaped or S-shaped, respectively, and the evaluation must thus be based on often minor deviations from the standard shape. For example, it is not easy to discern whether strong "tailing" of a boundary is due to slow particle diffusion or to the particular shape of the isotherm. The task of interpreting an effluent history may be compared to that of a physician when diagnosing a patient's illness. In both cases a correct interpretation of the symptoms requires much skill and experience, and in both cases it may happen that the conclusions are more characteristic of the theory than of the actual conditions.

e. Experimental Evidence

The wealth of experimental results on chromatographic and other separations with ion exchangers and other sorbents is almost overwhelming; however, in only relatively few investigations have conscious efforts been made to conduct critical tests of the various theories by comparison with independent measurements of equilibrium isotherms and diffusion coefficients. The most extensive work has been done on elution development. In particular, the excellent work of Hamilton [94] on ion-exchange chromatography of amino acids has shown that the dependence of column performance on the operating variables is correctly represented by the simple theory of elution development and is consistent with the assumption of intraparticle diffusion coefficients of the expected order of 10^{-7} cm²/sec. With respect to the more elaborate theories for other operations, there is still a certain gap between the admirable, but purely theoretical and appallingly complex studies of mathematicians and the empirical or semiempirical interpretations of experimental results by practical chemists. In general, one might say that the relatively simple theories and calculation methods outlined in this section have proved to be reasonably successful when applied judiciously. In particular, all qualitative features are in excellent agreement with experimental observations. Complete quantitative confirmation must await the results of further studies designed for this purpose.

9-10. HYDRODYNAMIC AND THERMOCHEMICAL EFFECTS

Several interesting aspects of column processes are not adequately covered by the treatment in the preceding section. This is particularly true for the hydrodynamics of packed beds and for thermochemical effects. A brief discussion of these is given in the following sections.

a. Hydrodynamic Aspects

In the preceding section it was assumed that motion of the liquid down the column is uniform (ideal "plug flow"), i.e., that all volume elements migrate at the same rate and, consequently, that the bulk-solution concentration is only a function $C_i(z,t)$ and is uniform in any horizontal plane in the column. This, of course, is an oversimplification. In the actual bed any horizontal solution layer is continuously distorted because the liquid has to bypass the solid particles. This gives rise to eddy dispersion and flow maldistribution. *Eddy dispersion* (also called *eddy mixing* or *eddy diffusion*)* is a longitudinal spread of solute resulting from the meandering paths and continuous changes in velocity imposed upon the volume elements of the liquid. It occurs even in completely regularly packed beds. *Flow maldistribution* (also called *channeling*) is nonuniformity of velocity caused by packing irregularities. It results from the fact that the liquid moves at a higher rate in the more loosely packed regions of the bed where it finds less flow resistance. Channeling thus distorts bands and boundaries. Even in completely uniformly packed beds, density and viscosity differences between adjacent bands can result, under certain conditions, in a peculiar distortion of the boundary ("fingering").

Eddy dispersion. Eddy dispersion occurs with both laminar and turbulent flow.

With *laminar flow*, a solution element following a streamline is forced to change its velocity continuously because the available cross section along its path is nonuniform. Also, neighboring stream paths separate and join, so that a molecule can cross over to another path, thereby changing its flow velocity. The resulting spread of solute from an originally sharp horizontal zone obeys, like diffusion, the laws of statistics and can be characterized by an "eddy-diffusion constant."

The situation is well illustrated by a simple "random walk" approach which has recently been given by Giddings [68]. The following assumptions are made. The velocity along a stream path persists on the average for a distance $2ar_0$ (measured in axial direction), where $a \approx 1$ is a characteristic packing constant. After that, a new velocity differing on the average by $\bar{v}$ ($= v/\beta =$ average velocity in axial direction) is acquired. As in random walk, the molecules step back and forward with respect to the average velocity. In order to cross over into a neighboring stream path with a different velocity, a molecule must diffuse the average distance $2br_0$, where $b \approx 1$ is another packing constant. The average number of velocity changes per unit time thus is

$$n = \frac{\bar{v}}{2ar_0} + \frac{D}{2b^2 r_0^2} \tag{9-64}$$

where $D =$ effective diffusion coefficient in the liquid.

According to H. A. Einstein's theory of random walk [51] the random-walk diffusion constant (or eddy-dispersion constant) is

$$E = \frac{\bar{v}^2}{2n} = \frac{a\bar{v}r_0}{1 + Da/b^2 r_0 \bar{v}} \tag{9-65}$$

---

* None of these terms is well chosen. The effect arises even with laminar flow in the absence of eddies and is not a diffusion phenomenon. However, within certain limits there is a formal mathematical analogy with eddy formation and with diffusion. Golay [84] has recently suggested the term "multi-path" instead of "eddy" dispersion.

and the plate height associated with eddy dispersion (in accordance with Eq. (9-15)) is

$$H_e = \frac{2E}{\bar{v}} = \frac{2ar_0}{1 + D\beta a/b^2 v r_0} \tag{9-66}$$

Equation (9-66) shows that H_e is proportional to the flow rate at very low flow rates and reaches a constant final value at moderate flow rates:

$$H_e = 2ar_0 \qquad \left(v \gg \frac{D}{r_0}\right) \tag{9-67}$$

This is in accordance with experimental observations [68,82,115]. As a rule, the constants a and b are found in the range $1 \leq a, b < 6$.

A more elegant statistical treatment given by Beran [17] also leads to a spread corresponding to Eq. (9-67). Similar results have been obtained by others [29,121,123,243].

Calculations for *turbulent flow* have been made by Baron [10] who finds that Eq. (9-67) also holds under these conditions, this time with $a \approx 6$. A similar result is obtained when Taylor's calculations [227] for (empty) pipes are adapted to granular beds.

In Glueckauf's version of the rate theories, eddy dispersion is somewhat intuitively accounted for by setting up the material balance for a layer of about one particle diameter thickness (see page 450) rather than for an infinitesimal layer. Actually, the first term in his equation (9-16) should be replaced by the right-hand side of Eq. (9-66) or (9-67). Under the usual conditions ($D \approx 10^{-5}$ cm²/sec; $r_0 \geq 0.01$ cm) Eq. (9-67) applies except when the flow rate is extremely low. The close resemblance with Glueckauf's term justifies the use of Eq. (9-16) in the form given on page 453.

Flow maldistribution. Flow maldistribution is caused by packing irregularities. In irregularly packed beds, the mean fractional void volume (averaged over a volume which is large in comparison to the particle volume) is not uniform throughout the bed. The more loosely packed regions ("channels") offer less flow resistance. Here, the flow rate is correspondingly higher, and bands and boundaries advance more rapidly. The resulting distortion of the bands and boundaries is counteracted by molecular diffusion in radial direction and radial eddy dispersion.

No complete theoretical treatment of flow maldistribution and its consequences has so far been given. The following effects, however, are established.

The packing density is necessarily lower in the immediate neighborhood of the (rigid) column wall which imposes a restriction on the arrangement of the particles. At the wall itself the density is zero, but the flow rate is also very small because of friction with the wall. It has been found that the flow rate in carefully packed columns is at its maximum at a distance of about one particle diameter from the column wall [195]. The flow rate at this location may be more than twice as high as in the center of the column. The consequences of this "channeling" at the wall are more serious when the column cross section is small and the particle size is large because the region of low flow resistance then constitutes a larger portion of the total bed. The effect becomes significant when the bed diameter is less than thirty times the particle diameter [195,198]. Mathematical analyses of this effect have been given by Schwartz [195], Fahien [47,54], and Liles [139a].

Flow maldistribution is strongly affected by swelling and shrinking of the resin. Expansion of the resin during the operation reduces flow maldistribution since it tends to close any existing channels. Shrinking has the opposite effect and favors particularly channeling at the column wall [28].

Flow maldistribution is especially harmful in displacement development. An efficient remedy is the use of "coupled columns" [36,88]. The effluent of the first column is passed through a narrow capillary which transforms the sharp, but distorted boundary into a diffuse, but horizontal one. This diffuse front is then resharpened in a second column, usually of smaller diameter.

Both flow maldistribution and eddy dispersion are at their minimum when the packing is regular and the particle size and shape are uniform. This stresses the need for careful selection of the particles (see Sec. 6-9a) and good packing techniques when delicate separations are attempted.

"Fingering." In displacement processes with highly concentrated solutions, the liquids in adjacent bands may differ significantly in their densities and viscosities. Here, the boundary between the bands can become distorted in a peculiar manner; long, uniform-sized "fingers" of the displacing liquid can intrude deeply into the liquid being displaced. Such "fingering" can occur even in quite uniformly packed beds [103].

It is obvious that a boundary between two liquids tends to be unstable if the upper liquid has the higher density, and vice versa. In displacement in porous media, however, this gravity effect may be partially offset or even outweighed by a viscosity effect; displacement by the more viscous liquid favors stability of the boundary, and displacement by the less viscous one favors instability. With the less viscous liquid displacing, the flow resistance of the bed is smallest where, through an accidental disturbance, the displacing liquid has bulged out the boundary. Because of the faster flow through the area of less flow resistance, the bulge tends to grow. With the more viscous liquid displacing, the flow resistance is highest at the bulge, and the latter thus tends to disappear. High over-all flow rate accentuates these viscosity effects. The hydrodynamic stability criterion is [34,103,181]

$$(\mu_1 - \mu_2)pv{\downarrow} + (\rho_2 - \rho_1)g > 0 \qquad \text{stable}$$
$$(\mu_1 - \mu_2)pv{\downarrow} + (\rho_2 - \rho_1)g < 0 \qquad \text{unstable} \qquad (9\text{-}68)$$

where μ = absolute viscosity, ρ = specific gravity, subscripts 1 and 2 refer to the upper and lower liquid, respectively; p = permeability coefficient of bed (= pressure gradient required for producing unit flow rate of liquid of unit viscosity); $v{\downarrow}$ = average linear flow rate, positive for downflow and negative for upflow operation; g = gravity constant.

Instability may result in the characteristic finger pattern, since a particular finger diameter and spacing are favored [34,133,226].

b. Thermochemical Effects

The heat of ion-exchange processes is usually rather small (see page 166); however, ion exchange may be followed by strongly exothermic reactions. For example, the heat of neutralization (13.7 kcal/mole) is liberated when an acid passes over an anion exchanger in OH^- form or when a base passes over a cation exchanger in H^+ form. The same is true in mixed-bed deionization. The heat of reaction gives rise to a "hot-spot" which accompanies the (self-sharpening) boundary on its way through the column.

A simple mathematical treatment of this effect has been given by Short [200]. Heat transfer by conduction and diffusion is neglected. The peak temperature and the temperature profile are calculated from the heat of reaction and the reactant concentrations and heat capacities of the resin and the solution. A remarkable result of this crude calculation is that the peak temperature keeps rising indefinitely with traveled distance when the following condition holds:

$$C_{\mathrm{B}}^0 = \frac{\bar{C}_{\mathrm{A}}^0 K}{\bar{K}} \tag{9-69}$$

where C_{B}^0 and $\bar{C}_{\mathrm{A}}^0$ are the initial concentrations of the two reactants in the feed and in the resin, respectively, and K and $\bar{K}$ are the heat capacities of the solution and the resin, respectively. Of course, a steady-state peak temperature will eventually be reached when heat conduction balances heat production. Feed concentrations near the critical value (9-69) should nevertheless be avoided in large-scale operations where the surface-to-volume ratio of the column is unfavorable for heat conduction to the outside.

A more rigorous treatment, tailored to "burn-off" of molecular sieves for removing carbonaceous deposits, is found in a manual distributed by the Linde Company [140].

A special situation is encountered in chromatography of highly radioactive substances where radiation in a band produces a significant temperature rise. This interesting case has been treated by Glueckauf [83].

9-11. ELECTROCHEMICAL PROPERTIES

The electrochemical behavior of ion-exchange beds has so far received comparatively little attention. It is likely that this field offers many still unknown possibilities. For example, observations of the electric conductivity or the streaming potential [53,157] of a column may give valuable information and even provide means for process control [56]; however, little use has been made of such methods. This is at least partly due to the fact that the theory is still in an early stage of development. For the same reason, the discussion in this section is rather fragmentary. Only electric conductivities and potential differences in the absence of flow will be studied.

a. Models

Accurate calculations of electric conductivities and potential differences in ion-exchange beds are complex problems. The bed is a mixture consisting of two phases of different properties, namely, the resin and the interstitial liquid. It is true that quite a number of theories have been worked out for transport phenomena—such as conduction of heat or electric current—in mixtures [21,25,26,61,87,122,134]; see also Sec. 7-5. However, most of these theories are based on the assumptions of either a regular lattice-type arrangement or a completely random distribution of the components. Both premises are unrealistic in the case of ion-exchange beds where the distribution of the resin particles is irregular but not random, and where the resin constitutes an essentially discontinuous phase and the liquid a continuous one.

The treatment which comes nearest to the conditions in an ion-exchange bed has been presented by Baron [10], who used a statistical cage model. He obtained the following relation

$$\frac{\kappa_{\mathrm{b}} - \bar{\kappa}}{(\kappa_{\mathrm{b}}/\kappa)^{1/3}(\kappa - \bar{\kappa})} = \beta \tag{9-70}$$

where κ_{b} = over-all specific conductivity of the packing; $\bar{\kappa}$ = specific conductivity of the solid (discontinuous phase); κ = specific conductivity of the liquid (continuous phase); β = fractional void volume of the bed.

This relation is derived for a strictly discontinuous solid phase and predicts zero bed conductivity when the liquid-phase conductivity is zero. In actual beds the resin phase is not strictly discontinuous since the particles are in contact with one another, though with only a very small contact area. The bed conductivity thus remains finite even when the

liquid-phase conductivity becomes zero (see also page 491). Hence Baron's model and
Eq. (9-70) are not applicable when the solution conductivity is very low.

A quite different approach has been chosen by Wyllie [191,262]. Here, a simple model
is used for calculating electrochemical properties from empirical geometrical parameters.
This "porous-plug" model is based on the idea that, in principle, the electric current can
take three different paths through the bed. The first path leads through alternating layers
of particles and interstitial solution, the second exclusively through particles which are in
contact with one another, and the third exclusively through the interstitial solution.
In the model, the bed is represented by three conductance elements in parallel which correspond to the three possible paths (Fig. 9-29). The fractional cross-section equivalents
a, b, and c of the three elements and the contributions d and e of the particles and the solution, respectively, to the first element are empirical constants which must be determined
experimentally.

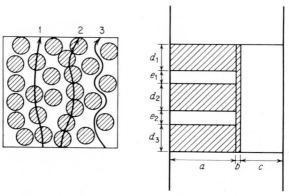

FIG. 9-29. The "porous-plug" model. *Left:* schematic representation of the three paths
which the current can take. *Right:* the simplified model consisting of three conductance
elements in parallel. The geometrical parameters d and e are given by $d_1 + d_2 + d_3 = d$,
and $e_1 + e_2 = e$. *From K. S. Spiegler, R. L. Yoest, and M. R. J. Wyllie* [220].

The application of this model to electric conductivities of uniform beds, to "concentration potentials" across beds in the absence of liquid flow, and to "leaky" membranes is
described in the following sections. Other cases have so far not been calculated.

b. Electric Conductivity

The specific conductivity of a bed which is filled with, and is in equilibrium with, a
solution of given specific conductivity may be written as the sum of the contributions
κ_1, κ_2, and κ_3 of the three conductance elements:

$$\kappa_b = \kappa_1 + \kappa_2 + \kappa_3 \tag{9-71}$$

The contributions, when defined according to this relation, are given by

$$\kappa_1 = \frac{a\kappa\bar{\kappa}}{d\kappa + e\bar{\kappa}} \qquad \kappa_2 = b\bar{\kappa} \qquad \kappa_3 = c\kappa \tag{9-72}$$

With strong-acid, spherical cation-exchange resins of moderate crosslinking (Dowex
50-X8, Amberlite IR-120) and aqueous solutions the following values for the empirical
parameters were obtained:

$$a = 0.63 \qquad b = 0.01 \qquad c = 0.34 \qquad d = 0.95 \qquad e = 0.05 \tag{9-73}$$

The values depend little on the particle size and the nature of the electrolyte. They are likely to hold rather well for other spherical resins also. The determination of the parameters is described below. The specific conductivity of the bed can be calculated from the parameters by use of Eqs. (9-71) and (9-72), provided that the specific conductivities of the resin and the solution are known.

The bed conductivity as a function of the solution conductivity is shown in Fig. 9-30. At zero solution conductivity, the current takes its way exclusively through the second conductance element. The bed conductivity is finite, though small because of the small contact area of the particles (low value of b). With increasing solution conductivity the first and second conductance elements gain importance. At the equiconductance point ($\kappa = \bar{\kappa}$) the curves for the bed conductivity and the solution conductivity intersect. Beyond this point the bed conductivity is lower than the solution conductivity. At high solution conductivities the contribution from the third element is predominant. The curve for the bed conductivity has an inflection point above the equiconductance point;

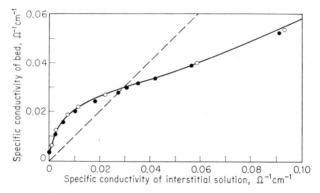

FIG. 9-30. Specific conductivity of a bed as a function of the specific conductivity of the interstitial solution (NaCl). ○ experimental values for Dowex 50-X8; ● experimental values for Amberlite IR 120. The curve is fitted to the points by choice of the parameters according to Eq. (9-73). The concentration dependence of $\bar{\kappa}$ is taken into account. *From K. S. Spiegler, R. L. Yoest, and M. R. J. Wyllie* [220].

the slope is steeper at higher conductivities because, here, the specific conductivity of the resin increases significantly with increasing solution conductivity (see Fig. 7-1).

Determination of the Geometrical Parameters. The geometrical parameters of a packing can be determined from conductivity data obtained with an arbitrary electrolyte and plotted as in Fig. 9-30. Often the resin conductivity as a function of the solution conductivity is known. Otherwise its value at the equiconductance point is obtained from the graph. In this case, however, assumptions about the concentration dependence of $\bar{\kappa}$ must be made. (This dependence affects primarily the upper part of the curve.) With $\bar{\kappa}$ known or determined, the parameters can be calculated from the bed conductivity at $\kappa = 0$ and from the slopes of the κ_b curve at $\kappa = 0$ and $\kappa = \bar{\kappa}$ by use of

$$\left(\frac{\kappa_b}{\bar{\kappa}}\right)_{(\kappa=0)} = b \qquad \left(\frac{d\kappa_b}{d\kappa}\right)_{(\kappa=0)} = \frac{a}{e} + c \qquad \left(\frac{d\kappa_b}{d\kappa}\right)_{(\kappa=\bar{\kappa})} = ae + c \quad (9\text{-}74)$$

These relations are obtained from Eq. (9-72) and by differentiation of Eq. (9-71), disregarding the concentration dependence of $\bar{\kappa}$ and making use of the fact that, by definition,

$$a + b + c = 1 \qquad\qquad d + e = 1 \qquad\qquad (9\text{-}75)$$

Equations (9-74) and (9-75) provide five relations for calculating the five unknown parameters. Alternatively, a conductivity measurement can be made with a packing of nonconducting particles of equal size and shape. In this case, $\bar{\kappa} = 0$, so that c can be calculated directly from Eq. (9-72). This determination makes one of the relations (9-74) superfluous.

c. Concentration Potentials

Wyllie's model has also been applied to "concentration potentials" across ion-exchange beds in the absence of liquid flow [220]. The concentration potential is defined as the electric potential difference between two solutions which contain the same electrolyte but differ in their concentrations; the solutions are on either side of the bed. With a 1,1-valent electrolyte the concentration potential is

$$\Delta\varphi \equiv \varphi'' - \varphi' = \frac{RT}{\mathfrak{F}}\left[\omega \ln \frac{a_\pm''}{a_\pm'} - t_Y \ln \frac{cy\alpha^2(a_\pm'')^2 + \bar{\kappa}\alpha A a_\pm'' + b\kappa\bar{\kappa}^2}{cy\alpha^2(a_\pm')^2 + \bar{\kappa}\alpha A a_\pm' + b\kappa\bar{\kappa}^2}\right.$$
$$\left. + \frac{A t_Y}{B} \ln \frac{[2cy\alpha a_\pm'' + \bar{\kappa}(A - B)][2cy\alpha a_\pm' + \bar{\kappa}(A + B)]}{[2cy\alpha a_\pm'' + \bar{\kappa}(A + B)][2cy\alpha a_\pm' + \bar{\kappa}(A - B)]}\right] \quad (9\text{-}76)$$

where $x \equiv e/a$; $y \equiv d/a$; $A \equiv 1 + by + cx$; $B \equiv (A^2 - 4bcxy)^{1/2}$; $\alpha \equiv \kappa/a_\pm$; φ = electric potential; ω = sign of fixed charges; $a_\pm$ = mean solution activity; t_Y = transference number of co-ion in the liquid phase; subscripts '' and ' refer to the two solutions on either side of the bed.

It is assumed in the derivation that the single activities a_+ and a_- can be equated to the mean activity, that the presence of co-ions in the resin can be disregarded, and that the specific conductivity of the solution is proportional to the mean solution activity.

Equation (9-76) reduces to

$$\Delta\varphi = \frac{RT}{\mathfrak{F}} \omega \ln \frac{a_\pm''}{a_\pm'} \qquad \text{for } \alpha a_\pm \ll \bar{\kappa} \qquad (9\text{-}77)$$

$$\Delta\varphi = (\omega - 2t_Y)\frac{RT}{\mathfrak{F}} \ln \frac{a_\pm''}{a_\pm'} \qquad \text{for } \alpha a_\pm \gg \bar{\kappa} \qquad (9\text{-}78)$$

The limiting case (9-77) is reached when both solutions are very dilute. The concentration potential across the bed then is the same as across an ideally permselective membrane [see Eq. (8-78)]. The limiting case (9-78) is reached when both solutions are very concentrated. Now, the concentration potential across the bed becomes equal to the liquid-junction potential between the solutions in the absence of an ion exchanger.

A comparison of observed and calculated concentration potentials is shown in Fig. 9-31. The geometrical parameters from which the thoeretical values are calculated were determined independently by conductivity measurements. The agreement is good; however, the comparison shown in Fig. 9-31 is the only one which has so far been made.

d. Application of the Model to Leaky Membranes

"Leaky" membranes have cracks or channels which provide unobstructed liquid junctions between the solutions on either membrane side. Of course, the difference between a pore and a leak is only a matter of degree. A membrane may be called leaky when the channels are so wide that the composition of the bulk liquid inside is not significantly affected by the ion-exchange properties of the walls. Many heterogeneous membranes are leaky. Here, leaking takes place through the liquid films which surround the ion-exchanger particles (see Fig. 8-2).

Leaky membranes resemble ion-exchange beds in that both provide unobstructed liquid junctions. The "porous-plug" model can thus be applied to leaky membranes also [220]. Of course, the values of the geometrical parameters will differ greatly from

Eq. (9-73). A fourth, nonconducting element representing the inert binder may be included in the model instead of, or in addition to, the third conductance element.

The porous-plug model may serve to illustrate one interesting feature of leaky membranes, namely, their limiting behavior at great dilution of the solutions. Any electric potential difference across beds and leaky membranes in the absence of flow necessarily approaches the corresponding membrane potential across ideally permselective membranes when the solutions are sufficiently diluted. An example was given in Eq. (9-77). The reason is that, for $\kappa = 0$, transport of ions and electric current can occur through the second conductance element only. Leaks and channels thus do not contribute. Similarly, interdiffusion and transference of counter ions approach the limiting laws

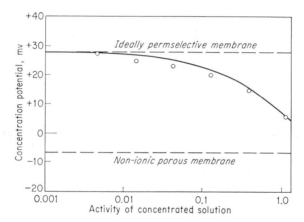

Fig. (9-31). Concentration potentials across a bed. *Circles:* experimental points obtained with Dowex 50-X8 and NaCl solutions of an activity ratio $a'_{\pm}/a''_{\pm} = 3:1$. *Solid line:* theoretical curve is calculated from Eq. (9-76). *Broken lines:* limiting cases of the potentials across ideally permselective and nonionic porous membranes. *From K. S. Spiegler, R. L. Yoest, and M. R. J. Wyllie* [220].

for permselective membranes. In contrast, interdiffusion of co-ions, electrolyte and nonelectrolyte diffusion, and transfer of solvent take place only via the third element of the model (i.e., the channels) when the solutions are very dilute. Hence these phenomena approach, at great dilution of the solutions, the limiting law for nonionic porous membranes.

9-12. EXPERIMENTAL METHODS

Detailed prescriptions for design and operation of ion-exchange columns are beyond the scope of this book. The reader is referred to the extensive literature in this field. Only a few hints for setting up simple laboratory columns and a brief description of methods for determining effluent concentration histories and electrochemical properties will be given.

a. Simple Laboratory Columns

Ion exchange in columns can be carried out with very simple equipment. An ordinary glass tube or burette can be used as the column. The resin is held in place by a glass-wool plug or a glass sinter disk at the bottom of the column. The feed can be introduced by means of a separatory funnel [91,182a,186,265].

The following hints may be helpful.

The liquid volume below the bed should be kept as small as possible, so that mixing of consecutive portions of the effluent is at its minimum. This is particularly important when the flow rate is low.*

In order to obtain a reasonably regular packing and to remove any air bubbles from the bed, the column should be "backwashed," prior to use, with solvent in upflow. Avoid stepwise settling of the resin while backwashing since this leads to alternating strata of smaller and larger particles. Keep the column strictly vertical; otherwise flow patterns develop with upflow on one side and downflow on the other side of the column, and the smaller particles accumulate on the downflow side.

The bed should never fall dry. A foolproof column design which prevents this is shown in Fig. 9-2.

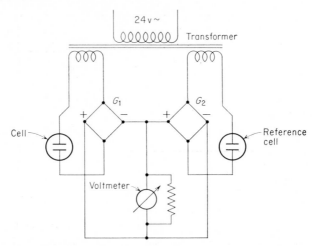

FIG. 9-32. Circuit for recording electric conductivities in column effluents. The effluent cell and the reference cell containing feed are balanced in a bridge circuit with two two-way rectifiers G_1 and G_2. The reading of the recording voltmeter is proportional to the difference of the cell conductivities. *From R. Wickbold* [255].

Care must be taken when introducing a feed which causes expansion of the resin, for example, when the feed is switched from an organic solvent to water or from a concentrated to a dilute solution. Expansion of the resin may clog or even rupture the column. In such cases it is recommended to change the feed composition gradually rather than abruptly and to introduce the feed with upflow.

For operation at an elevated temperature, jacketed columns are used. A column design for operation under pressure and at elevated temperature has been described by Kraus [128]. Special ion-exchange columns for microscale separations have been developed by Lawson [136a] and Schnitger [192a].

b. Determination of Effluent Concentration Histories

The most primitive means for determining an effluent concentration history is to collect the effluent in fractions which are subsequently analyzed by standard methods. In chromatographic separations a large number of fractions may have to be taken. Here,

---

* A quantitative treatment of the "dead-volume" effect in elution development has recently been given by Johnson and Stross [109]. See also Kieselbach [119].

automatic fraction collectors are a great help.   The collector can be triggered by a detecting device in the effluent in such a way that fractions of equal composition are automatically combined and that effluent which contains no products is discarded.

Alternatively, the effluent can be passed through a detecting device which continuously records a characteristic physical property, for example:

Electric conductivity (in regeneration with H$^+$ or OH$^-$, ion exclusion and ion retardation, chromatography of amino acids, etc.) [12,44,48,72,106,203,255].

pH *value* (in regeneration with H$^+$ or OH$^-$, displacement development of acids and bases, etc.) [107,172].

Refractive index (in separations of organic substances, etc.) [95].

Polarographic half-step potential (in separations of inorganic ions) [138].

Radioactivity (in separations of fission products, trans-uranium elements, etc.) [23,39].

Visible- or UV-light absorption (in separations of organic substances) [160,161].

A very sensitive control by conductivity measurement can be obtained by using two cells [12,255].   The second cell contains feed and is balanced in a bridge circuit with the cell in the effluent (see Fig. 9-32).   Unbalance of the bridge indicates the appearance of a band or boundary.   Radioactivity measurements are not restricted to separations of radioactive materials.   Most inorganic and organic compounds can be tagged with radioactive tracers and can thus be detected and recorded.   Ultraviolet absorption is often measured in elution development of organic substances.   A suitable wavelength must be chosen.   It is often difficult to see whether an absorption peak on the chart is due to a single or to several incompletely resolved components.   A very elegant procedure is to measure at two different wavelengths; as long as the ratio of the absorption coefficients

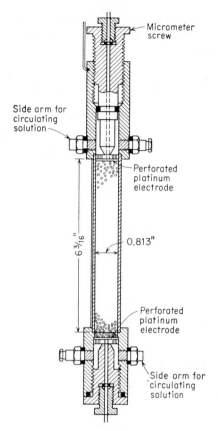

FIG. 9-33. Apparatus for measuring electric conductivities of ion-exchange beds. *From M. C. Sauer, Jr., P. F. Southwick, K. S. Spiegler, and M. R. J. Wyllie* [191].

at the two wavelengths remains constant, the effluent may be presumed to contain a single component only [38,161].

Columns can be equipped with detecting devices ("feelers") at various places within the bed.   In this way the migration of bands and boundaries in the column can be observed [30a,112,260].

The various methods can be used for automatic process control, for example, for cutting fractions or discontinuing the feed at breakthrough.

c. Electrochemical Measurements

An apparatus for measuring the *electric conductivity* of a bed is shown in Fig. 9-33.   As a rule, the conductivity varies somewhat with the pressure which is exerted on the bed by the electrodes. The variation becomes much stronger beyond a certain characteristic pressure. Reproducible values are obtained when the reading is always taken at this characteristic point [191]. Electric circuits for conductivity measurements have been described in Sec. 7-5.

Electric potential differences across ion-exchange beds are measured in the same way as in membrane systems (see Secs. 8-4 and 8-10b).

SUMMARY

Most ion-exchange operations are carried out in columns. Ion-exchange columns can be used for replacement, removal, and separation of ions and nonelectrolytes.

The simplest column operation is the replacement of a counter ion in the feed by another counter ion which is initially in the resin. The counter ion from the feed is removed by ion exchange and is absent in the effluent until breakthrough occurs. The sharpness of the boundary between the zones of the two counter ions and thus the breakthrough capacity and the degree of column efficiency depend primarily on the ion-exchange equilibrium. Equilibrium is "favorable" when the counter ion from the feed is preferred by the resin, and "unfavorable" in the opposite case. With favorable equilibrium, the boundary is "self-sharpening" and attains a steady-state shape ("constant pattern") which does not change when the boundary travels farther down the column. In the steady state, the sharpening effect of favorable equilibrium and the broadening effects of finite ion-exchange rate, longitudinal diffusion, and other disturbances balance one another. With unfavorable equilibrium there is no sharpening effect, and the boundary becomes more and more diffuse on its way through the column. Eventually, a "proportionate pattern" is reached in which the spread of the boundary is proportional to the traveled distance. The chief reason (other than unfavorable equilibrium) for broadening of boundaries is that ion exchange occurs at a finite rate and thus fails to keep pace with the migration of the boundary. Hence the boundary becomes sharper when the ion-exchange rate is increased and the migration rate of the boundary is decreased. This is particularly true for self-sharpening boundaries. A small particle size of the resin, elevated temperature, low flow rate, and low feed concentration are favorable.

Dissolved electrolytes can be completely removed from aqueous solutions by exchange of all cations for H^+ and all anions for OH^-. This can be achieved in two-stage and multistage installations consisting of cation- and anion-exchange columns in series. Mixed-bed deionization is more efficient. Here, a single column containing an intimate mixture of cation- and anion-exchanger particles is used. Cation and anion exchange thus occur simultaneously at neighboring particles.

Electrolytes can be separated from nonelectrolytes by "ion exclusion" and "ion retardation." Ion exclusion is based on the fact that ion exchangers sorb nonelectrolytes more strongly than electrolytes, which are excluded by the Donnan effect. Hence electrolytes are less strongly retained by the resin and are first to emerge in the effluent upon elution with solvent. In ion retardation, a snake-cage polyelectrolyte is used as the sorbent. These resins sorb electrolytes more strongly than nonelectrolytes. Here, the nonelectrolyte emerges first from the column. Both methods can also be used for separations of weak from strong electrolytes.

Counter ions can be separated conveniently from one another by selective displacement, provided that an ion exchanger with sufficiently pronounced selectivity can be found. After sorption of the mixture, the ion with less affinity for the resin is displaced from the bed by a suitable agent, while the ion which is more strongly held remains in the bed and can be displaced later by another agent. The required high selectivity is often attained by using complexing agents. This method has been particularly successful in the separation of cations in the form of their anionic complexes in anion-exchange columns.

Counter ions which differ little in their properties can be separated by ion-exchange chromatography. The separation is based on the selectivity of the resin. The most important chromatographic techniques are elution development and displacement development. In both cases, the mixture containing the counter ions is introduced at the top of the column and is then "developed" by a suitable agent. In displacement development the agent is a counter ion which is preferred by the resin to the counter ions of the mixture. The mixture is resolved into individual bands between which self-sharpening boundaries arise. The bands follow one another without intervals and all migrate at the same rate. In elution development, the development agent is a counter ion which has less affinity for the resin than the counter ions of the mixture. The mixture is resolved into individual bands which migrate at different rates and thus increase their distance from one another; the bands flatten out more and more on their way through the column and are increasingly diluted with the development agent. The sharpness of chromatographic separations depends greatly on the selectivity of the ion exchanger. Complexing agents are often used for increasing the selectivity.

Anions and molecules which form complexes with metal ions can be isolated and separated from one another by "ligand exchange." In this technique, an ion exchanger is used as a solid carrier for a complexing metal ion. Ligands with stronger complexing tendency are more strongly retained by complex formation in the resin. Thus, upon elution or development, the ligands emerge from the bed in the sequence of increasing complexing tendency. An advantage of ligand exchange over other, more conventional chromatographic techniques is the high specificity of complex formation.

Ligand exchange is particularly useful for separating ligands which differ in their coordinative valences since, here, the selectivity can be adjusted and even reversed at will by varying the solution concentration.

Chemical reactions other than complex formation, for example, the association of sugar with borate counter ions in anion exchangers, can be exploited in a similar way for chromatographic and other separations.

The theories of column performance can be classified into equilibrium theories and rate theories. In the equilibrium theories, the ion-exchange column is treated as an analogue to a distillation column with a certain number of effective plates. It is implied that local equilibrium between resin and solution is attained in every plate before the solution moves on to the next plate. In the actual column, local equilibrium is usually not attained. Deviations from local equilibrium and all other disturbances are accounted for in the theory by choice of a corresponding plate height. The plate height is an empirical quantity and cannot be predicted on a theoretical basis. The only advantage of the equilibrium theories is their simplicity. The rate theories are more satisfactory but also more complex. No assumptions about local equilibrium are made. Column performance is calculated with due respect to the finite rate of ion exchange which may give rise to deviations from local equilibrium. The concept of effective plates (or transfer units) may be used as a convenient, but by no means indispensable, auxiliary. The plate height can be calculated from the operating conditions. Simple solutions can only be obtained with drastic idealizations. Nevertheless, the various rate theories are very useful approximations, especially since they provide quantitative information about the effect of the operating conditions on column performance. However, the choice of the appropriate theory for any particular case requires judgment and a sound qualitative understanding of the relevant factors. Also, the accuracy of the results should not be overestimated and usually does not warrant lengthy and complex calculations when simpler approximations can be used. Many solutions are available in the form of tables and graphical representations. Greater accuracy can be obtained by numerical calculations on electronic computers.

The theory of electrochemical properties of ion-exchange columns is still in an early stage of development. A simple semiempirical model has proved to be useful when applied to conductivities and concentration potentials in the absence of liquid flow. The model consists of three conductance elements in parallel which represent the three possible paths of the electric current, namely, through alternating layers of particles and solution, through particles only, and through the interstitial solution only. The equations involve empirical geometrical parameters which are characteristic of the packing. The model can also be applied to leaky membranes.

REFERENCES

1. Acrivos, A., *Ind. Eng. Chem.*, **48**, 703 (1956).
2. Acrivos, A., and T. Vermeulen, unpublished, 1958.
3. Acrivos, A., *Chem. Eng. Sci.*, **13**, 1 (1960).
4. Amundson, N. R., *J. Phys. Chem.*, **52**, 1153 (1948).
5. Amundson, N. R., *J. Phys. Chem.*, **54**, 812 (1950).
6. Anzelius, A., *Z. angew. Math. Mech.*, **6**, 291 (1926).
6a. Ariel, M., and E. Kirowa, *Talanta*, **8**, 214 (1961).
7. Asher, D. R., and D. W. Simpson, *J. Phys. Chem.*, **60**, 518 (1956).
8. Baddour, R. F., D. J. Goldstein, and P. Epstein, *Ind. Eng. Chem.*, **46**, 2192 (1954).
9. Baddour, R. F., and R. D. Hawthorn, *Ind. Eng. Chem.*, **47**, 2517 (1955).
10. Baron, T., unpublished, 1954.
11. Bastian, W. C., and L. Lapidus, *J. Phys. Chem.*, **60**, 816 (1956).
12. Baticle, A. M., *Compt. rend.*, **236**, 2055 (1953).
13. Bauman, W. C., J. Eichhorn, and L. F. Wirth, *Ind. Eng. Chem.*, **39**, 1453 (1947).
*14. Bauman, W. C., R. M. Wheaton, and D. W. Simpson, in "Ion Exchange Technology," F. C. Nachod and J. Schubert (eds.), p. 182, Academic Press, Inc., New York, 1956.
15. Beaton, R. H., and C. C. Furnas, *Ind. Eng. Chem.*, **33**, 1500 (1941).
*16. Becker-Boost, E. H., *Chem. Ing. Technik*, **27**, 579 (1955); **28**, 411 and 532 (1956); in "Ullmann's Encyklopädie der technischen Chemie," 3d ed., vol. 8, p. 823, Urban & Schwarzenberg, Munich-Berlin, 1957.
17. Beran, M. J., *J. Chem. Phys.*, **27**, 270 (1957).
18. Blaedel, W. J., E. D. Olsen, and R. F. Buchanan, *Anal. Chem.*, **32**, 1866 (1960).
18a. Boardman, N. K., and S. M. Partridge, *Nature*, **171**, 208 (1953).
19. Bock, R. M., and Nan-Sing Ling, *Anal. Chem.*, **26**, 1543 (1954).
20. Bogue, D. C., *Anal. Chem.*, **32**, 1777 (1960).
20a. Bohart, G. S., and E. Q. Adams, *J. Am. Chem. Soc.*, **42**, 523 (1920).
21. Böttcher, C. J. F., "Theory of Electric Polarization," Elsevier Press, New York, 1952.
22. Bovy, R., and G. Duyckaerts, *Anal. Chim. Acta*, **11**, 134 (1954).
23. Boyd, G. E., L. S. Myers, Jr., and A. W. Adamson, *J. Am. Chem. Soc.*, **69**, 2849 (1947).
24. Breyer, A., and W. Rieman III, *Anal. Chim. Acta*, **18**, 204 (1958).
24a. Brinkley, S. R., Jr., U.S. Dept. Interior, U.S. Bureau of Mines, Explosives and Physical Sciences Div., Report 3172, 1951.
25. Brown, W. F., Jr., *J. Chem. Phys.*, **23**, 1514 (1955).
26. Bruggeman, D. A. G., *Ann. Physik*, **24**, 636 (1935); **25**, 645 (1936).
27. Buser, W., *Helv. chim. Acta*, **34**, 1635 (1951).
28. Byrne, E. B., and L. Lapidus, *J. Am. Chem. Soc.*, **77**, 6506 (1955).
28a. Caddell, J. R., and R. L. Moison, *Chem. Eng. Progr. Symp. Ser.*, **50**, No. 14, 1 (1954).
29. Cairns, E. J., and J. M. Prausnitz, *Chem. Eng. Sci.*, **12**, 20 (1960).
*30. Calmon, C., and A. W. Kingsbury, in "Ion Exchange Technology," F. C. Nachod and J. Schubert (eds.), p. 231, Academic Press, Inc., New York, 1956.
30a. Carmody, D. R. (Standard Oil Co. Indiana), U.S. Patent 2,954,338, 1960.
31. Cartoni, G. P., R. S. Lowrie, C. S. G. Phillips, and L. M. Venanzi, in "Gas Chromatography 1960," R. P. W. Scott (ed.), p. 273, Butterworth & Co. (Publishers), Ltd., London, 1960.

* Review articles are marked with asterisks.

32. Cherkin, A., F. E. Martinez, and M. S. Dunn, *J. Am. Chem. Soc.*, **75**, 1244 (1953).

33. Choppin, G. R., and R. J. Silva, *J. Inorg. & Nuclear Chem.*, **3**, 153 (1956).

34. Chuoke, R. L., P. van Meurs, and C. van der Poel, *Petroleum Trans. AIME*, **216**, 188 (1959).

35. Claesson, S., *Arkiv Kemi Mineral. Geol.*, **A20**, No. 3 (1945); **A24**, No. 7 (1946); *Ann. N.Y. Acad. Sci.*, **49**, 183 (1948); *Discussions Faraday Soc.*, **7**, 34 (1949).

36. Claesson, S., *Arkiv Kemi Mineral. Geol.*, **A24**, No. 16 (1947).

37. Coates, J. I., and E. Glueckauf, *J. Chem. Soc.*, **1947**, 1308.

38. Cohn, W. E., and C. E. Carter, *J. Am. Chem. Soc.*, **72**, 2606 (1950).

39. Cook, G. B., and J. F. Duncan, "Modern Radiochemical Practice," Oxford University Press, New York, 1952.

40. Cornaz, J. P., and N. K. Hiester, unpublished, 1957.

41. Cuninghame, J. G., J. Eakins, E. R. Mercer, M. L. Sizeland, and H. H. Willis, *J. Inorg. & Nuclear Chem.*, **1**, 163 (1955).

42. Davies, C. W., and B. D. R. Owen, *J. Chem. Soc.*, **1956**, 1676, 1681.

43. DeVault, D., *J. Am. Chem. Soc.*, **65**, 532 (1943).

44. DeVerdier, C. H., and C. I. Sjöberg, *Acta Chem. Scand.*, **8**, 1161 (1954).

45. Diamond, R. M., K. Street, Jr., and G. T. Seaborg, *J. Am. Chem. Soc.*, **76**, 1461 (1954).

46. Dickel, G., *Z. Elektrochem.*, **54**, 353 (1950).

47. Dorweiler, V. P., and R. W. Fahien, *A. I. Ch. E. Journal*, **5**, 139 (1959).

48. Drake, B., *Arkiv Kemi*, **4**, 401, 469 (1952); **8**, 159, 189 (1955).

49. Dranoff, J. S., and L. Lapidus, *Ind. Eng. Chem.*, **50**, 1648 (1958); **53**, 71 (1961).

50. DuDomaine, J., R. L. Swain, and O. A. Hougen, *Ind. Eng. Chem.*, **35**, 546 (1943).

51. Einstein, H. A., Thesis, E. T. H. Zürich, 1937.

52. Ekedahl, E., E. Högfeldt, and L. G. Sillén, *Nature*, **166**, 722 (1950).

53. Epshtein, Y. A., *Issled. Oblasti Khromatog., Trudy Vses. Soveshchan. Khromatog., Acad. Nauk SSSR, Otdel. Khim. Nauk*, **1950**, 211; *Chem. Abstr.*, **48**, 2443 (1954).

54. Fahien, R. W., and J. M. Smith, *A. I. Ch. E. Journal*, **1**, 28 (1955).

55. Faucher, J. A., Jr., R. W. Southworth, and H. C. Thomas, *J. Chem. Phys.*, **20**, 157 (1952).

56. Fawcett, S. (The Permutit Co. Ltd.), Brit. Patent 714,642, 1954.

57. Fisher, S., and R. Kunin, *Anal. Chem.*, **29**, 400 (1957).

58. Fitch, F. T., and D. S. Russell, *Can. J. Chem.*, **29**, 363 (1951).

59. Freiling, E. C., and L. R. Bunney, *J. Am. Chem. Soc.*, **76**, 1021 (1954).

60. Freiling, E. C., *J. Am. Chem. Soc.*, **77**, 2067 (1955).

61. Frey, G. S. son, *Z. Elektrochem.*, **38**, 260 (1932).

61a. Frisch, N. W., and R. Kunin, *A. I. Ch. E. Journal*, **6**, 640 (1960).

61b. Fritz, J. S., B. B. Garralda, and S. K. Karraker, *Anal. Chem.*, **33**, 882 (1961).

62. Funk, J. E., and G. Houghton, *Nature*, **188**, 389 (1960).

63. Furnas, C. C., *Trans. Am. Inst. Chem. Engrs.*, **24**, 142 (1930).

64. Gapon, E. N., and T. B. Gapon, *Zhur. Priklad. Khim.*, **21**, 937 (1948); *Chem. Abstr.*, **44**, 9210 (1950).

65. Gerstner, F., *Z. Elektrochem.*, **57**, 221 (1953); *Chem. Ing. Technik*, **26**, 264 (1954); in "Ion Exchange and Its Applications," p. 64, Society of Chemical Industry, London, 1955.

66. Giddings, J. C., and H. Eyring, *J. Phys. Chem.*, **59**, 416 (1955).

67. Giddings, J. C., *J. Chem. Phys.*, **26**, 169 (1957); **31**, 1462 (1959); *J. Chromatog.*, **2**, 44 (1959); **3**, 443 (1960); *Nature*, **188**, 847 (1960); *Anal. Chem.*, **33**, 962 (1961).

68. Giddings, J. C., *Nature*, **184**, 357 (1959).

69. Giddings, J. C., *Anal. Chem.*, **32**, 1707 (1960).

70. Giesen, J., and F. Müller (Inventa A. G.), U.S. Patent 2,916,525, 1959.

71. Gilliland, E. R., and R. F. Baddour, *Ind. Eng. Chem.*, **45**, 330 (1953).

72. Gilwood, M. E., *Instr. and Automation*, **27**, 1633 (1954).

73. Glass, R. A., *J. Am. Chem. Soc.*, **77**, 807 (1955).

74. Glückauf, E., *Nature*, **156**, 748 (1945); *Proc. Roy. Soc. (London)*, **A186**, 35 (1946).

75. Glueckauf, E., *J. Chem. Soc.*, **1947**, 1302, 1321.

76. Glueckauf, E., and J. I. Coates, *J. Chem. Soc.*, **1947**, 1315.

77. Glueckauf, E., *Discussions Faraday Soc.*, **7**, 12 (1949).

78. Glueckauf, E., K. H. Barker, and G. P. Kitt, *Discussions Faraday Soc.*, **7**, 199 (1949).

*79. Glueckauf, E., in "Ion Exchange and Its Applications," p. 34, Society of Chemical Industry, London, 1955.

80. Glueckauf, E., *Trans. Faraday Soc.*, **51**, 34 (1955).

81. Glueckauf, E., *Trans. Faraday Soc.*, **51**, 1540 (1955).

82. Glueckauf, E., in "Vapor Phase Chromatography," D. H. Desty and C. L. A. Harbourn (eds.), p. 29, Academic Press, Inc., New York, 1957.

83. Glueckauf, E., in "Gas Chromatography," D. H. Desty (ed.), p. 69, Academic Press, Inc., New York, 1958.

*84. Golay, M. J. E., in "Gas Chromatography 1960," R. P. W. Scott (ed.), p. 139, Butterworth & Co. (Publishers), Ltd., London, 1960.

85. Goldstein, S., *Proc. Roy. Soc. (London)*, **A219**, 151, 171 (1953).

86. Goldstein, S., and J. D. Murray, *Proc. Roy. Soc. (London)*, **A252**, 334, 348, 360 (1959).

*87. Gorring, R. L., and S. W. Churchill, *Chem. Eng. Progr.*, **57**, July 1961, p. 53.

88. Hagdahl, L., *Acta Chem. Scand.*, **2**, 574 (1948).

*89. Hagge, W., in "Ion Exchange and Its Applications," p. 49, Society of Chemical Industry, London, 1955.

90. Hahn, R. B., C. Backer, and R. Backer, *Anal. Chim. Acta*, **9**, 223 (1953).

91. Hale, D. K., in "Ion Exchangers in Organic and Biochemistry," C. Calmon and T. R. E. Kressman (eds.), pp. 130, 157, Interscience Publishers, Inc., New York, 1957.

*92. Hamilton, P. B., in "Ion Exchangers in Organic and Biochemistry," C. Calmon and T. R. E. Kressman (eds.), p. 255, Interscience Publishers, Inc., New York, 1957.

93. Hamilton, P. B., *Anal. Chem.*, **32**, 1779 (1960).

94. Hamilton, P. B., D. C. Bogue, and R. A. Anderson, *Anal. Chem.*, **32**, 1782 (1960).

95. Hatch, M. J., J. A. Dillon, and H. B. Smith, *Ind. Eng. Chem.*, **49**, 1812 (1957).

96. Helfferich, F., *Nature*, **189**, 1001 (1961).

97. Helfferich, F., *J. Am. Chem. Soc.*, **84**, 3237, 3242 (1962).

98. Herber, R. H., and J. W. Irvine, Jr., *J. Am. Chem. Soc.*, **76**, 987 (1954).

98a. Herrmann, E., *Chem. Ing. Technik*, **27**, 573 (1955).

*99. Hesse, G., *Angew. Chem.*, **67**, 9 (1955).

100. Hiester, N. K., and T. Vermeulen, *J. Chem. Phys.*, **16**, 1087 (1948).

101. Hiester, N. K., and T. Vermeulen, *Chem. Eng. Progr.*, **48**, 505 (1952).

102. Hiester, N. K., S. B. Radding, R. L. Nelson, Jr., and T. Vermeulen, *A. I. Ch. E. Journal*, **2**, 404 (1956).

103. Hill, S., *Chem. Eng. Sci.*, **1**, 247 (1952).

104. Hougen, O. A., and W. R. Marshall, *Chem. Eng. Progr.*, **43**, 197 (1947).

105. Jacobs, S., *Chem. & Ind. (London)*, **1955**, 944.

106. James, A. T., A. J. P. Martin, and S. S. Randall, *Biochem. J.*, **49**, 293 (1951).

107. Jeffrey, R. N., *Anal. Chem.*, **23**, 936 (1951).

108. Jentzsch, D., *Z. anal. Chem.*, **152**, 134 (1956).

109. Johnson, H. W., Jr., and F. H. Stross, *Anal. Chem.*, **31**, 357 (1959).

* Review articles are marked with asterisks.

109a. Jury, S. H., and J. M. Andrews, *Ind. Eng. Chem.*, **53**, 883 (1961).
110. Kallen, J., and E. Heilbronner, *Helv. chim. Acta*, **43**, 489 (1960).
111. Kasten, P. R., L. Lapidus, and N. R. Amundson, *J. Phys. Chem.*, **56**, 683 (1952).
112. Kayas, G., *J. chim. phys.*, **47**, 408 (1950).
113. Ketelle, B. H., and G. E. Boyd, *J. Am. Chem. Soc.*, **69**, 2800 (1947).
*114. Keulemans, A. I. M., "Gas Chromatography," 2d ed., Chap. 4, Reinhold Publishing Corp., New York, 1959.
115. Keulemans, A. I. M., and A. Kwantes, in "Vapor Phase Chromatography," D. H. Desty and C. L. A. Harbourn (eds.), p. 15, Academic Press, Inc., New York, 1957.
116. Khopkar, S. M., and A. K. De, *Anal. Chim. Acta*, **23**, 441 (1960).
117. Khym, J. X., and L. P. Zill, *J. Am. Chem. Soc.*, **73**, 2399 (1951); **74**, 2090 (1952).
*118. Khym, J. X., L. P. Zill, and W. E. Cohn, in "Ion Exchangers in Organic and Biochemistry," C. Calmon and T. R. E. Kressman (eds.), p. 392, Interscience Publishers, Inc., New York, 1957.
119. Kieselbach, R., *Anal. Chem.*, **33**, 806 (1961).
119a. Klamer, K., C. van Heerden, J. C. H. Linssen, and D. W. van Krevelen, *Chem. Eng. Sci.*, **9**, 1, 10, 20 (1958).
120. Klinkenberg, A., *Ind. Eng. Chem.*, **46**, 2285 (1954).
121. Klinkenberg, A., and F. Sjenitzer, *Chem. Eng. Sci.*, **5**, 258 (1956).
*121a. Klotz, I. M., *Chem. Reviews*, **39**, 241 (1946).
122. Kondorskii, E., *Doklady Akad. Nauk SSSR*, **80**, 197 (1951).
123. Kramers, H., and G. Alberda, *Chem. Eng. Sci.*, **2**, 173 (1953).
124. Kraus, K. A., and G. E. Moore, *J. Am. Chem. Soc.*, **71**, 3263, 3855 (1949); **73**, 9, 13, 2900 (1951); **77**, 1383 (1955).
125. Kraus, K. A., F. Nelson, and G. E. Moore, *J. Am. Chem. Soc.*, **77**, 3972 (1955); **78**, 2692 (1956).
*126. Kraus, K. A., and F. Nelson, *Proc. Intern. Conf. Peaceful Uses of Atomic Energy, Geneva*, **7**, 113 (1956).
127. Kraus, K. A., and F. Nelson, in "Symposium on Ion Exchange and Chromatography in Analytical Chemistry," Special Technical Publication No. 195, American Society for Testing Materials, 1958.
128. Kraus, K. A., R. J. Raridon, and D. L. Holcomb, *J. Chromatog.*, **3**, 178 (1960).
129. Kressman, T. R. E., *J. Phys. Chem.*, **56**, 118 (1952).
130. Kunin, R., and F. X. McGarvey, *Ind. Eng. Chem.*, **43**, 734 (1951); U.S. Patent 2,578,837, 1951.
*131. Kunin, R., and F. X. McGarvey, in "Ion Exchange Technology," F. C. Nachod and J. Schubert (eds.), p. 95, Academic Press, Inc., New York, 1956.
*132. Kunin R., "Elements of Ion Exchange," p. 105, Reinhold Publishing Corporation, New York, 1960.
*133. Lamb, H., "Hydrodynamics," 6th ed., Chaps. IX, XI, Cambridge University Press, New York, 1932.
134. Landauer, R., *J. Appl. Phys.*, **23**, 779 (1952).
135. Lapidus, L., and N. R. Amundson, *J. Phys. Chem.*, **56**, 984 (1952).
136. Lapidus, L., and J. B. Rosen, *Chem. Eng. Progr. Symp. Ser.*, **50**, No. 14, 97 (1954).
136a. Lawson, G. J., and J. W. Purdie, *Microchim. Acta*, **1961**, 415.
136b. Ledoux, E., *J. Phys. Chem.*, **53**, 960 (1949).
137. Lerner, M., and W. Rieman III, *Anal. Chem.*, **26**, 610 (1954).
138. Lewis, J. A., and K. C. Overton, *Analyst.*, **79**, 293 (1954).
139. Lightfoot, E. N., Jr., *J. Phys. Chem.*, **61**, 1686 (1957).

---

* Review articles are marked with asterisks.

139a. Liles, A. W., and C. J. Geankoplis, *A. I. Ch. E. Journal*, **6**, 591 (1960).

*140. Linde Company, "Design Manual for Octane Improvement," Book II, p. D-74, 1959.

141. Lindner, R., *Z. Naturforschung*, **9a**, 798 (1954).

141a. Lindner, R., and T. Bergdahl, *Z. Elektrochem.*, **64**, 919 (1960).

142. Lock, M. V., and G. N. Richards, *J. Chem. Soc.*, **1955**, 3024.

143. Loriers, J., and D. Carminati, *Compt. rend.*, **237**, 1328 (1953).

144. MacNevin, W. M., and W. B. Crummett, *Anal. Chem.*, **25**, 1628 (1953).

145. Mader, C., *Anal. Chem.*, **26**, 566 (1954).

146. Manalo, G. D., A. Breyer, J. Sherma, and W. Rieman III, *J. Phys. Chem.*, **63**, 1511 (1959).

147. Marsh, J. K., *J. Chem. Soc.*, **1957**, 978.

148. Martin, A. J. P., and R. L. M. Synge, *Biochem. J.*, **35**, 1358 (1941).

*149. Martin, O., *Ind. Chemist*, **28**, 448 (1952).

150. Martin, W. J., and G. W. Parker, *J. Tenn. Acad. Sci.*, **29**, 132 (1954).

151. Maslova, G. B., P. P. Nazarov, and K. V. Chmutov, *Zhur. Neorg. Khim.*, **5**, 359 (1960).

152. Mayer, S. W., and E. R. Tompkins, *J. Am. Chem. Soc.*, **69**, 2866 (1947).

153. Mayer, S. W., and E. C. Freiling, *J. Am. Chem. Soc.*, **75**, 5647 (1953).

154. Meloche, V. W., and A. F. Preuss, *Anal. Chem.*, **26**, 1911 (1954).

155. Merriam, C. N., Jr., R. W. Southworth, and H. C. Thomas, *J. Chem. Phys.*, **20**, 1842 (1952).

156. Michaels, A. S., *Ind. Eng. Chem.*, **44**, 1922 (1952).

157. Michaels, A. S., and C. S. Lin, *Ind. Eng. Chem.*, **47**, 1249 (1955).

158. Miller, B. S., and J. A. Johnson, *Trans. Am. Assoc. Cereal Chem.*, **12**, 29 (1954); *Chem. Abstr.*, **48**, 6307 (1954).

*159. Mindler, A. B., in "Ion Exchange Technology," F. C. Nachod and J. Schubert (eds.), p. 285, Academic Press, Inc., New York, 1956.

160. Moore, S., and W. H. Stein, *J. Biol. Chem.*, **176**, 367 (1948); **178**, 53 (1949).

161. Moore, S., and W. H. Stein, *J. Biol. Chem.*, **192**, 663 (1951).

*162. Morrison, W. S., in "Ion Exchange Technology," F. C. Nachod and J. Schubert (eds.), p. 321, Academic Press, Inc., New York, 1956.

163. Nelson, F., *J. Am. Chem. Soc.*, **77**, 813 (1955).

164. Nelson, F., R. M. Rush, and K. A. Kraus, *J. Am. Chem. Soc.*, **82**, 339 (1960).

165. Nervik, W. E., *J. Phys. Chem.*, **59**, 690 (1955).

166. Offord, A. C., and J. Weiss, *Discussions Faraday Soc.*, **7**, 26 (1949).

167. Opler, A., *Ind. Eng. Chem.*, **45**, 2621 (1953).

168. Opler, A., and N. K. Hiester, "Tables for Predicting the Performance of Fixed Bed Ion Exchange and Similar Mass Transfer Processes," *Report*, Stanford Research Institute 1954.

*169. Opler, A., in "Ion Exchange Technology," F. C. Nachod and J. Schubert (eds.), p. 219, Academic Press, Inc., New York, 1956.

170. O'Sullivan, D. G., *Analyst*, **85**, 434 (1960).

171. Partridge, S. M., and R. G. Westall, *Biochem. J.*, **44**, 418 (1949).

172. Partridge, S. M., *Biochem. J.*, **44**, 521; *Discussions Faraday Soc.*, **7**, 296 (1949).

173. Permutit Co. Ltd. (R. T. Pemberton, A. J. R. Walter, and E. L. Holmes), Brit. Patent, 553,233, 1943.

174. Povondra, P., Z. Šulcek, R. Přibil, and R. Štangl, *Talanta*, **8**, 705 (1961).

175. Powell, J. E., and F. H. Spedding, *Chem. Eng. Progr. Symp. Ser.*, **55**, No. 24, 101 (1959).

---

* Review articles are marked with asterisks.

176. Rachinskii, V. V., *Zhur. Priklad. Khim.* **27**, 831 (1954); *Chem. Abstr.*, **49**, 1376 (1955).
177. Richter, A., *Angew. Chem.*, **52**, 679 (1939).
*177a. Rieman III, W., *J. Chem. Educ.*, **38**, 338 (1961).
178. Rosen, J. B., *J. Chem. Phys.*, **20**, 387 (1952).
179. Rosen, J. B., *Ind. Eng. Chem.*, **46**, 1590 (1954).
180. Ryabchikov, D. I., P. N. Palei, and Z. K. Mikhailova, *Zhur. Anal. Khim.*, **15**, 88 (1960).
181. Saffman, P. G., and G. Taylor, *Proc. Roy. Soc.* (*London*), **A245**, 312 (1958).
182. Said, A. S., *A. I. Ch. E. Journal*, **2**, 477 (1956); **5**, 223 (1959).
*182a. Salmon, J. E., and D. K. Hale, "Ion Exchange: A Laboratory Manual," Academic Press, Inc., New York, 1959.
183. Samuelson, O., *Svensk Kem. Tidskr.*, **53**, 422 (1941); **58**, 247 (1946).
184. Samuelson, O., and E. Sjöström, *Svensk Kem. Tidskr.*, **64**, 305 (1952).
185. Samuelson, O., L. Lundén, and K. Schramm, *Z. anal. Chem.*, **140**, 330 (1953).
*186. Samuelson, O., "Ion Exchangers in Analytical Chemistry," pp. 45, 117, 136, 196, John Wiley & Sons, Inc., New York, 1953.
187. Samuelson, O., and B. Sjöberg, *Anal. Chim. Acta*, **14**, 121 (1956).
188. Sargent, R., and W. Rieman III, *J. Phys. Chem.*, **60**, 1370 (1956).
189. Sargent, R., and W. Rieman III, *Anal. Chim. Acta*, **16**, 144 (1957).
190. Sargent, R., and W. Rieman III, *J. Org. Chem.*, **21**, 594 (1956); *J. Phys. Chem.*, **61**, 354 (1957); *Anal. Chim. Acta*, **17**, 408 (1957); **18**, 197 (1958).
191. Sauer, M. C., Jr., P. F. Southwick, K. S. Spiegler, and M. R. J. Wyllie, *Ind. Eng. Chem.*, **47**, 2187 (1955).
*192. Schindewolf, U., *Angew. Chem.*, **69**, 226 (1957).
192a. Schnitger, H., K. Papenberg, E. Ganse, R. Czok, T. Büchner, and H. Adam, *Biochem. Z.*, **332**, 167 (1959).
*193. Schroeder, W. A., in "Ion Exchangers in Organic and Biochemistry," C. Calmon and T. R. E. Kressman (eds.), p. 299, Interscience Publishers, Inc., New York, 1957.
194. Schumann, T. E. W., *J. Franklin Inst.*, **208**, 405 (1929).
195. Schwartz, C. E., and J. M. Smith, *Ind. Eng. Chem.*, **45**, 1209 (1953).
196. Seki, T., *J. Chromatog.*, **4**, 6 (1960).
197. Selke, W. A., and H. Bliss, *Chem. Eng. Progr. Symp. Ser.*, **46**, No. 10, 509 (1950).
198. Sheridan, M. B., and M. B. Donald, *Ind. Chemist*, **1959**, 439, 487.
199. Sherma, J., and W. Rieman III, *Anal. Chim. Acta*, **18**, 214; **19**, 134 (1958); **20**, 357 (1959).
200. Short, J. F., P. G. Smith, and G. H. Twigg, *J. Appl. Chem.*, **3**, 198 (1953).
201. Sillén, L. G., and E. Ekedahl, *Arkiv Kemi Mineral. Geol.*, **A22**, No. 15, 16 (1946).
202. Sillén, L. G., *Arkiv Kemi*, **2**, 477 and 499 (1950); *Nature*, **166**, 722 (1950).
203. Šimánek, V., and J. Janák, *Chem. Listy*, **48**, 1623 (1954); *Chem. Abstr.*, **49**, 4331 (1955).
204. Simpson, D. W., and W. C. Bauman, *Ind. Eng. Chem.*, **46**, 1958 (1954).
205. Small, H., *J. Inorg. & Nuclear Chem.*, **19**, 160 (1961).
206. Smith, G. W., and S. A. Reynolds, *Anal. Chim. Acta*, **12**, 151 (1955).
207. Smith, H. L., and D. C. Hoffman, *J. Inorg. & Nuclear Chem.*, **3**, 243 (1956).
208. Sober, H. A., G. Kegeles, and J. Gutter, *J. Am. Chem. Soc.*, **74**, 2734 (1952).
209. Spedding, F. H., A. F. Voigt, E. M. Gladrow, and N. R. Sleight, *J. Am. Chem. Soc.*, **69**, 2777 (1947).
210. Spedding, F. H., A. F. Voigt, E. M. Gladrow, N. R. Sleight, J. E. Powell, J. M. Wright, T. A. Butler, and P. Figard, *J. Am. Chem. Soc.*, **69**, 2786 (1947).

---

* Review articles are marked with asterisks.

*211. Spedding, F. H., *Discussions Faraday Soc.*, **7**, 214 (1949).

212. Spedding, F. H., E. I. Fulmer, J. E. Powell, and T. A. Butler, *J. Am. Chem. Soc.*, **72**, 2354 (1950).

213. Spedding, F. H., E. I. Fulmer, J. E. Powell, T. A. Butler, and I. S. Yaffe, *J. Am. Chem. Soc.*, **73**, 4840 (1951).

214. Spedding, F. H., J. E. Powell, and E. J. Wheelwright, *J. Am. Chem. Soc.*, **76**, 612 (1954).

215. Spedding, F. H., and J. E. Powell, *J. Am. Chem. Soc.*, **76**, 2545 (1954).

216. Spedding, F. H., and J. E. Powell, *J. Am. Chem. Soc.*, **76**, 2550 (1954).

217. Spedding, F. H., J. E. Powell, and E. J. Wheelwright, *J. Am. Chem. Soc.*, **76**, 2557 (1954).

218. Spedding, F. H., J. E. Powell, and H. J. Svec, *J. Am. Chem. Soc.*, **77**, 1393, 6125 (1955).

*219. Spedding, F. H., and J. E. Powell, in "Ion Exchange Technology," F. C. Nachod and J. Schubert (eds.), p. 359, Academic Press, Inc., New York, 1956.

220. Spiegler, K. S., R. L. Yoest, and M. R. J. Wyllie, *Discussions Faraday Soc.*, **21**, 174 (1956).

221. Street, K., Jr., S. G. Thompson, and G. T. Seaborg, *J. Am. Chem. Soc.*, **72**, 4832 (1950).

222. Stromquist, D. M., and A. C. Reents, *Ind. Eng. Chem.*, **43**, 1065 (1951).

223. Sujata, A. D., J. T. Banchero, and R. R. White, *Ind. Eng. Chem.*, **47**, 2193 (1955).

*224. Swope, H. G., in "Ion Exchange Technology," F. C. Nachod and J. Schubert (eds.), p. 458, Academic Press, Inc., New York, 1956.

225. Talley, E. A., and W. L. Porter, *J. Chromatog.*, **3**, 434 (1960).

226. Taylor, G., *Proc. Roy. Soc. (London)*, **A201**, 192 (1950).

227. Taylor, G., *Proc. Roy. Soc. (London)*, **A219**, 186 (1953).

228. Taylor, T. I., and H. C. Urey, *J. Chem. Phys.*, **6**, 429 (1938).

229. Thomas, C. L. (Sun Oil Co.), U.S. Patent 2,865,970, 1958.

230. Thomas, H. C., *J. Am. Chem. Soc.*, **66**, 1664 (1944); *Ann. N.Y. Acad. Sci.*, **49**, 601 (1948).

231. Thomas, H. C., in "Ion Exchange," F. C. Nachod (ed.), p. 29, Academic Press, Inc., New York, 1949.

232. Thomas, H. C., *J. Chem. Phys.*, **19**, 1213 (1951).

233. Thomas, H. C., and C. N. Merriam, Jr., *J. Phys. Chem.*, **60**, 249 (1956).

234. Thompson, J., F. X. McGarvey, J. F. Wantz, S. F. Alling, M. E. Gilwood, and D. R. Babb, *Chem. Eng. Progr.*, **49**, 341, 437 (1953).

235. Thompson, S. G., B. G. Harvey, G. R. Choppin, and G. T. Seaborg, *J. Am. Chem. Soc.*, **76**, 6229 (1954).

236. Tien, C., and G. Thodos, *A. I. Ch. E. Journal*, **5**, 373 (1959).

237. Tompkins, E. R., J. X. Khym, and W. E. Cohn, *J. Am. Chem. Soc.*, **69**, 2769 (1947).

238. Tompkins, E. R., and S. W. Mayer, *J. Am. Chem. Soc.*, **69**, 2859 (1947).

239. Tompkins, E. R., D. H. Harris, and J. X. Khym, *J. Am. Chem. Soc.*, **71**, 2504 (1949).

*240. Tompkins, E. R., *Discussions Faraday Soc.*, **7**, 232 (1949).

241. Trombe, F., and J. Loriers, *Compt. rend.*, **236**, 1567 (1953).

241a. Tudge, A. P., *Can. J. Phys.*, **39**, 1600, 1611 (1961).

242. Turvolgyi, B. L., L. Anyas-Weisz, and W. F. Graydon, *Can. J. Technol.*, **31**, 168 (1953).

243. VanDeemter, J. J., F. J. Zuiderweg, and A. Klinkenberg, *Chem. Eng. Sci.*, **5**, 271 (1956).

* Review articles are marked with asterisks.

244. Vermeulen, T., and N. K. Hiester, *Ind. Eng. Chem.*, **44**, 636 (1952).
245. Vermeulen, T., and E. H. Huffman, *Ind. Eng. Chem.*, **45**, 1658, 1664 (1953).
246. Vermeulen, T., and N. K. Hiester, *J. Chem. Phys.*, **22**, 96 (1954).
*247. Vermeulen, T., *Advances in Chem. Eng.*, **2**, 147 (1958).
*248. Vermeulen, T., and N. K. Hiester, *Chem. Eng. Progr. Symp. Ser.*, **55**, No. 24, 61 (1959).
249. Walter, J. E., *J. Chem. Phys.*, **13**, 332 (1945).
250. Ward, D. N., and J. D. Putch, *Makromol. Chem.*, **38**, 230 (1960).
250a. Watkins, S. R., and H. F. Walton, *Anal. Chim. Acta*, **24**, 334 (1961).
251. Weiss, J., *J. Chem. Soc.*, **1943**, 297.
252. Wesly, W., *Bull. Centre Belge Étude Doc. Eavx*, **19**, 24 (1953); *Chem. Abstr.*, **47**, 11611 (1953).
253. Wheaton, R. M., and W. C. Bauman, *Ind. Eng. Chem.*, **45**, 228 (1953); *Ann. N.Y. Acad. Sci.*, **57**, 159 (1953).
253a. Wheaton, R. M., *Chem. Eng. Progr. Symp. Ser.*, **50**, No. 14, 43 (1954).
254. Wheelwright, E. J., and F. H. Spedding, *J. Am. Chem. Soc.*, **75**, 2529 (1953).
255. Wickbold, R., *Z. anal. Chem.*, **132**, 401 (1951).
255a. Wickbold, R., *Z. anal. Chem.*, **171**, 81 (1959).
256. Wicke, E., *Kolloid Z.*, **86**, 295 (1939).
257. Wilkins, D. H., *Talanta*, **2**, 355 (1959).
258. Wilkins, D. H., G. E. Smith, J. S. Fritz, and D. J. Pietrzyk, *Talanta*, **2**, 392 (1959).
259. Wilson, J. N., *J. Am. Chem. Soc.*, **62**, 1583 (1940).
260. Wish, L., E. C. Freiling, and L. R. Bunney, *J. Am. Chem. Soc.*, **76**, 3444 (1954).
261. Wish, L., *Anal. Chem.*, **33**, 53 (1961).
262. Wyllie, M. R. J., and P. F. Southwick, *Gulf Research Dev. Comp., Tech. Rept.* 3750, 1953.
262a. Wynne, E. A., R. D. Burdick, and L. H. Fine, *Anal. Chem.*, **33**, 807 (1961).
263. Zill, L. P., J. X. Khym, and G. M. Cheniae, *J. Am. Chem. Soc.*, **75**, 1339 (1953).
264. "Handbook of Chemistry and Physics," Chemical Rubber Publishing Co., 42d ed., p. 211, Cleveland, Ohio, 1960–61.
265. "Dowex: ION Exchange," p. 43, The Dow Chemical Company, Midland, Mich., 1959.

* Review articles are marked with asterisks.

10

Behavior in Nonaqueous and Mixed Solvents

Ion exchange between a solid and a solution can only occur if certain requirements are met. A solvent must be used in which the exchanging species are soluble. There must be ions in both the solution and the solid, i.e., the solute and the functional groups of the solid must be at least partially dissociated. The ions must be free to move and to exchange places with one another. This requires a porous structure of the solid which should have either an open and rigid crystalline lattice or an elastic matrix which is expanded by swelling in the solvent. Last but not least, no destruction or dissolution of the solid ion exchanger in the solvent should occur.

With water as the solvent and with the solids which qualify as ion exchangers, these conditions are usually met. Water, because of its high dielectric constant, is an excellent solvent for most inorganic and quite a number of organic acids, bases, and salts. Strong electrolytes, by definition, dissociate largely or completely when dissolved in water, and aqueous solutions even of weak electrolytes and strong complexes contain ions in measurable concentrations. The development of our present ion-exchange resins was aimed chiefly at achieving absolute stability and high ion-exchange rates in aqueous systems.

Water, however, is by no means the only solvent which allows ion exchange to take place. There are other solvents with high dielectric constants in which electrolytes can dissolve and dissociate and in which most of the common ion exchangers are stable. Such solvents are formamide (dielectric constant $\epsilon = 126$), anhydrous ammonia ($\epsilon = 22$), ethylene glycol ($\epsilon = 41$), methanol ($\epsilon = 32$), ethanol ($\epsilon = 26$), and acetone ($\epsilon = 27$). The last three solvents, in particular, have practical importance in ion exchange. They can be used with or without addition of water. Certain substances, for example, many organic acids, are more readily dissolved in these solvents than in water. In quite a number of cases, organic solvents can be used for achieving effects which cannot be obtained with water.

In certain applications of ion exchangers, no exchange of counter ions is intended. For example, the ion exchanger may be used merely as a sorbent or catalyst. In such cases, solvents can be used in which no significant ionization occurs.

The theory of ion exchange, as outlined in the preceding chapters, applies in principle to any solvent. Of course, the nature of the solvents affects the solubility, dissociation, and solvation of the solutes and the behavior of the ion exchanger, and certain peculiarities and side effects are more pronounced with organic solvents than with water. These peculiarities will be discussed in a qualitative manner. No quantitative treatment is attempted since, at present, neither the experimental evidence nor the theoretical foundations are adequate. It is even impossible to decide whether the qualitative picture is essentially complete or will have to be refined by inclusion of further effects.

10-1. ION EXCHANGE IN NONAQUEOUS SYSTEMS

From a theoretical point of view, the solvents can be divided into two groups. Solvents of the first group, which includes water, dissociate partially and form anions and cations which may participate in ion exchange. Solvents of the second group do not form ions.

A typical nonaqueous solvent of the first group is anhydrous ammonia. Its analogy to water is obvious:

$$2H_2O \rightleftharpoons H_3O^+ + OH^-$$
$$2NH_3 \rightleftharpoons NH_4^+ + NH_2^- \tag{10-1}$$

The NH_4^+ ion in anhydrous ammonia plays the same role as the H^+ ion (more accurately, the H_3O^+ ion) in water, and the NH_2^- ion that of the OH^- ion. For example, a cation exchanger in anhydrous NH_4^+ form can be used for removing potassium amide, KNH_2, from anhydrous ammonia:

$$K^+ + NH_2^- + \overline{NH_4^+} \rightarrow 2NH_3 + \overline{K^+} \tag{10-2}$$

The resin can be regenerated with an "acid," say, NH_4Cl:

$$NH_4^+ + \overline{K^+} \rightarrow K^+ + \overline{NH_4^+} \tag{10-3}$$

The processes (10-2) and (10-3) correspond exactly to the removal of a base, say, KOH from an aqueous solution by cation exchange with a resin in H^+ form and to regeneration of the resin by an acid, say, HCl [20].

Many other examples could be given [3]. The use of ion exchangers for such purposes offers possibilities of which little use has so far been made.

A typical solvent of the second group is acetone. Quite a number of electrolytes are soluble and at least partly dissociated in acetone. Ordinary ion exchange can thus take place with acetone as the solvent. Such ion-exchange processes obey essentially the same rules as those in aqueous media when no acids or bases are involved. The following peculiarities are observed, however:

1. Electrolytes are less strongly dissociated in acetone than in water because the dielectric constant of acetone is lower. As a consequence, Donnan exclusion is less efficient, and hence ion exchange is accompanied by pronounced electrolyte sorption. Ion exchange with acetone solutions thus resembles exchange of weak aqueous electrolytes with weakly dissociated resins.

2. Acetone is catalytically decomposed by strong-base resins in OH⁻ form. Certain other resins are decomposed by acetone. No such resins can be used in acetone solutions.

3. Equilibria and rates in systems with acetone as the solvent are strongly affected by the presence of water which may be formed in the course of the process (for example, by reaction of a dissolved base with a resin in H⁺ form). Water is accumulated by the resin, and even small quantities may have a profound effect on the behavior of the system.

With other solvents of the second group the situation is similar.

Complications may arise when mixed solvents such as alcohol-water, acetone-water, or dioxane-water mixtures are used. These will be discussed in the next section (Sec. 10-2b).

10-2. SWELLING

a. Swelling in Pure Solvents

Swelling of an ion-exchange resin in water is chiefly caused by the hydration tendency of the fixed ionic groups and counter ions, the osmotic activity of the counter ions, and the electrostatic repulsion between neighboring fixed ionic groups. The elastic matrix expands until swelling equilibrium is attained. Swelling equilibrium is a balance of forces; the osmotic and electrostatic forces are balanced by the tendency of the expanded matrix to contract (see Sec. 5-2).

Swelling in *polar* nonaqueous solvents is quite similar. The solvation tendency of the ions, the osmotic pressure difference, and the electrostatic repulsion between fixed charges are the most important factors. The less polar the solvent, the weaker is the solvation tendency of the ions. The lower the dielectric constant of the solvent, the stronger are the electrostatic interactions between ions of opposite charges, so that ion-pair formation and association are favored [23] and the osmotic activity of the ions in the resin is reduced. These effects tend to reduce swelling of the resin. However, electrostatic repulsion between fixed charges becomes stronger when the dielectric constant is lower [29], at least as long as the charges are not neutralized by association with counter ions. This effect tends to increase swelling of the resin.

Because of these opposing effects, theoretical predictions of the dependence of swelling on the polarity and dielectric constant of the solvent are difficult to make. Experimental evidence indicates that *most resins swell more strongly in polar than in less polar solvents*, and that swelling in water ($\epsilon = 81$) is more pronounced than in solvents with lower dielectric constants [4,5,8,10,11,15,16,25,35]. Several exceptions to these rules have been found, for example, with weak-acid resins in H^+ form and with anion exchangers (see below). Even with strong-acid resins, particularly when in H^+ form, it is often found that swelling in solvents with dielectric constants between 40 and 50 (ethylene glycol and aqueous alcohols) is stronger than in pure water [4,5]. The polarity of the solvent cannot be the cause since the dipole moments of water (1.84 Debye), methanol (1.68 Debye), and ethanol (1.70 Debye) are quite similar. (The dipole moment of ethylene glycol is 3.49 Debye.) It is likely that the stronger electrostatic repulsion between fixed charges in solvents of intermediate dielectric constants produces stronger swelling as long as the dielectric constant is high enough to guarantee essentially complete ionic dissociation. In pure methanol ($\epsilon = 32$) and ethanol ($\epsilon = 26$) the resins usually swell less than in water [4,5,8,15,16] and in nonpolar solvents such as benzene and kerosene most resins swell hardly at all [4,35]. Exceptions are discussed below.

The solvation tendency of the counter ions depends on the nature of the solvent. Several effects can be explained in this way. For example, in water the Li^+ form of cation exchangers usually swells more strongly than the other alkali-ion forms since Li^+, the ion with the smallest crystalline radius, has the strongest solvation tendency (see Sec. 5-2). This situation may be reversed in alcohols, in which solvation is less pronounced [25]. The present knowledge of ionic solvation and association in various solvents is insufficient for making reliable predictions about swelling of ion-exchange resins in different ionic forms. As a rule, the procedure is reversed, i.e., the swelling behavior of the resins is used as evidence for deducing the extent of solvation and association in the resins [15,16].

The osmotic pressure difference, the electrostatic repulsion, and the solvation tendency are not the only forces which may result in swelling of the resin. *Nonpolar* solvents such as benzene may produce or enhance swelling by London interactions with organic constituents of the resin matrix or with organic counter ions. According to the old rule of thumb *similia similibus solvuntur* one may expect that *structural similarity of the solvent molecules and the organic constituents of the resins favors swelling*. This is indeed so.

For example, weak-acid resins in H^+ form swell more strongly in methanol than in water [4,10]. Here, the electrostatic and osmotic forces contribute little because of incomplete dissociation, and are outweighed by the strong affinity of the carboxylic acid groups for the alcohols. In contrast, the alkali-ion forms of the resins swell more strongly in water than in alcohols [4,8] since, here, dissociation is more complete and the osmotic and electrostatic forces are more important. It has also been found that, as a rule, strong-base resins swell more strongly in alcohols than in water [4,10]. Here, the ionic form has little effect. These resins carry fixed ionic groups with organic substituents, such as

$$
\begin{array}{ccc}
CH_3 & & CH_3 \\
| & & | \\
-N^+-CH_3 & \text{or} & -N^+-C_2H_4OH \\
| & & | \\
CH_3 & & CH_3
\end{array}
$$

The affinity of such groups for organic solvents is, of course, relatively strong. At the same time, the bulky substituents guarantee a considerable minimum distance between the center of the fixed charge and the counter ion and thus favor dissociation even in solvents of relatively low dielectric constant. Resins of this type also swell in benzene and kerosene [4].

b. Selective Swelling in Mixed Solvents

When a dry resin is brought into a mixed solvent such as aqueous acetone, it takes up both components of the solvent. As a rule, however, one component is preferred by the resin and is taken up more strongly. One component may arbitrarily be called the "solvent," and the other the "solute"; the rules for nonelectrolyte sorption (see Sec. 5-3b) thus become applicable. In the case of aqueous acetone, most resins strongly prefer water.

The resin prefers the component for which it has the greater affinity. The affinity may be due to electrostatic interactions between the ions or polar groups in the resin and the (polar) solvent molecules, or to London interactions which usually are much weaker [28]. A fairly reliable measure for the affinity is the extent of swelling of the resin in the pure solvent. *The resin usually prefers the more polar component of a mixed solvent* [11,16]. Most resins make little distinction between water, methanol, and ethanol since the dipole moments of these substances are rather similar [5] (exceptions have been mentioned in the previous section); however, they prefer water to less polar substances such as acetone (see Fig. 10-1) and dioxane [5,11,16]. This effect is most strongly pronounced with resins of a high degree of crosslinking and correspondingly high internal ionic concentrations and with solutions of low water content. The obvious cause is the strong tendency of the ions in the resin to form hydration shells [11].

Water is so strongly preferred to nonpolar organic solvents such as benzene which are immiscible with water, that wet resins do not lose water when being rinsed with these solvents [4,10,14,33a]. This effect has considerable practical importance (see Sec. 10-5).

Experimental data on swelling in organic and mixed solvents are still rather scanty. Moreover, their value for theoretical considerations is impaired by the fact that most investigations were carried out with incompletely dehydrated resins [4,10].

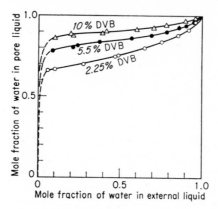

FIG. 10-1. Preferential uptake of water from aqueous acetone. Resins: sulfonated polystyrenes with 2.25, 5.5, and 10 per cent DVB, in H$^+$ form. *From results by C. W. Davies and B. D. R. Owen* [11].

10-3. CAPACITY

The rules which hold for the capacity of ion exchangers in aqueous systems can also be applied to nonaqueous systems. Only a few peculiarities will be mentioned.

The capacity in contact with a solvent of the first group depends on the relative acidity of the solution in the same way as the capacity of weak-acid and weak-base ion exchangers in aqueous media depends on the pH of the solution (see Sec. 4-2). For example, the capacity in anhydrous ammonia usually is a function of the pNH$_4$ value.

With solvents of the second group, one might expect that all functional groups of the resin are operative and that the weight capacity (per "specific amount" of the resin) thus is the same as the maximum capacity in aqueous systems. However, in solvents which produce little swelling, attainment of ion-exchange equilibrium may be so slow that, under the usual experimental conditions, large portions of the resin remain inaccessible for counter ions from the solution. The observed operative capacity may thus be smaller than the theoretical one.

In organic solvents, ion exchange is often overshadowed by strong electrolyte sorption. For example, it has been found that incompletely dehydrated resins sorb, per fixed ionic group, up to four molecules of acetic acid from benzene-oil mixtures [4], and up to one and a half equivalents of electrolytes such as $CoCl_2$ from acetone [19]. The sorption capacity thus is often much higher than in aqueous systems. Deceivingly high values may thus be found when ion-exchange capacity measurements are not corrected for electrolyte sorption.

These effects are readily understood in a qualitative way; however, quantitative predictions can so far not be made.

10-4. ION-EXCHANGE AND SORPTION EQUILIBRIA

Ion-exchange and sorption equilibria are strongly affected by the solvent. Equilibrium depends on the degree of dissociation in the resin and the solution, ionic solvation, swelling pressure, complex formation, and other specific interactions. All these phenomena are profoundly influenced by the nature of the solvent. With mixed solvents, the nonuniform distribution of the solvent components introduces an additional factor which affects equilibrium.

Ion-exchange equilibria in nonaqueous and mixed solvents have been measured by many investigators [1,5,6,13,14a,15,17a,18,23,24,27,31,32,33b, 34a,36a]. At present, however, the theory is still far from being able to predict equilibria under given conditions. The interplay of the various and often opposing factors is too complex, and too little is so far known about the factors themselves. Experimental results can thus be explained in only a tentative way. In the following, only a few striking peculiarities will be mentioned.

Equilibrium is most strongly affected by a change in solvent if specific interactions such as complex formation are involved [7,22,33b]. The strengths and solubilities of complexes greatly depend on the nature of the solvent. The behavior of the cyano complexes of silver and gold may be given as a typical example. With aqueous electrolytes, it is next to impossible to elute these complexes from strong-base anion-exchange resins, but with HCl in aqueous acetone the noble metals are readily displaced [7]. Another, more perspicuous example is the effect that addition of aliphatic alcohols has on anion-exchange equilibria of chloro complexes. Presence of alcohols enhances the formation of chloro complexes and thus favors uptake of the complexed metal by anion exchangers (see also Sec. 5-6c). With addition of alcohols, the technique of separating metals by anion exchange of their chloro complexes can thus be extended to a number of further metals of which the complexes in purely aqueous media are too weak [14a,17a,36,36a]; see also Sec. 9-6.

Sorption of electrolytes is, as a rule, much stronger with organic and mixed solvents than with water as the solvent [19]. With purely organic solvents, the presence of a solvent of low dielectric constant in the resin favors association and ion-pair formation and thus reduces the Donnan potential and

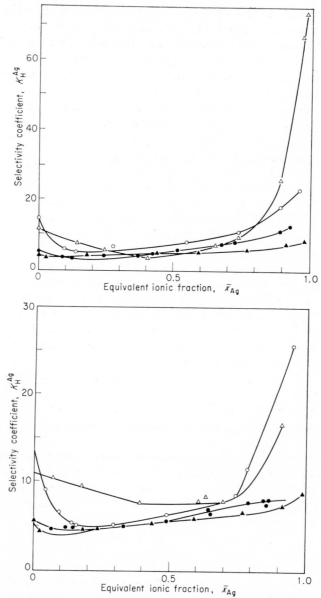

FIG. 10-2. Ion-exchange equilibria Ag^+/H^+ with a strong-acid cation exchanger (Dowex 50-X8) in water-ethanol (*upper diagram*) and water-dioxane mixtures (*lower diagram*). The selectivity coefficient is shown as a function of the ionic composition of the resin. The various curves are for different solvent compositions.

△   25 per cent water, 75 per cent ethanol or dioxane
○   50 per cent water, 50 per cent ethanol or dioxane
●   75 per cent water, 25 per cent ethanol or dioxane
▲   100 per cent water

From O. D. Bonner and J. C. Moorefield [5].

Donnan exclusion of electrolytes (see Sec. 5-3c). With mixed aqueous-organic solvents such as aqueous acetone or aqueous dioxane, water is accumulated in the resin, and the hydrophilic electrolytes prefer the more aqueous pore liquid to the more organic liquid phase outside [11,12].

In systems with purely organic solvents, the strength of electrolyte sorption is closely related to the solubility and solvation of the solute in the respective solvent. For example, the higher the solubility of an organic acid in ethanol, the more readily is the acid eluted from resins by ethanol [9]. Differences in sorption strength can be used for quantitative separations of inorganic electrolytes. For example, $CoSO_4$ and $NiSO_4$ have been separated with an anion exchanger and molten urea as the solvent [33].

In systems with mixed solvents, sorption equilibrium can be considered as a distribution of the solute between two liquid phases, namely, between the pore liquid and the external liquid phase. The resin acts as the solid carrier for the pore liquid and, at the same time, is responsible for the difference in solvent composition of the two phases. The distribution of the dissolved electrolyte depends primarily on differences in solvation and dissociation in the two phases and, of course, on interactions with other constituents of the resin. For example, aqueous acetone can be used for enhancing the selectivity of strong-acid resins. K^+, which is preferred in aqueous systems, has less tendency than the other alkali ions to form ion pairs with anions in acetone. Sorption of, say, KCl from aqueous acetone thus is stronger than that of the other alkali chlorides. Consequently, the selectivity of the resin for K^+ is increased by addition of acetone [11,27].

Water-swollen ion exchangers can also be used in combination with water-immiscible solvents to which complexing agents may be added [33a]. The principle of such relatively new "gel-liquid extraction" techniques has been outlined in Sec. 9-7e.

The possibilities of enhancing and reversing selectivities of ion-exchange resins by addition or exclusive use of organic solvents is receiving increasing attention [9,11,12,17,21,33,36,36a]. Even in isotopic separations, the resolution can be improved by addition of organic solvents [26,26a]. The same is true for separations of organic compounds [30,34a].

10-5. KINETICS

The rates and rate laws of ion exchange in nonaqueous media differ considerably from those in aqueous systems. Nevertheless, it seems safe to assume that the fundamental mechanism of ion exchange is the same in both cases. The differences in behavior are necessary consequences of the general rules which are well established in aqueous systems (see Chap. 6).

The *rate-determining step* in ion exchange is, as a rule, interdiffusion of the counter ions either in the resin itself or across an adherent liquid "film" (see Sec. 6-2). The slower of these two processes controls the over-all rate. In systems with organic solvents, the mobilities of the counter ions in the resin are usually lower than in aqueous systems because swelling is less pronounced and electrostatic interactions with fixed charges are stronger. Particle diffusion thus is relatively slow and usually is the rate-controlling mechanism [37].

It has so far not been established whether the actual exchange reaction at the fixed ionic groups may be rate-controlling in certain special cases, particularly when the degree of dissociation is low. Also, diffusion across the interface resin/solution cannot be conclusively ruled out as a possible rate-determining step when water-wet resins are used in solvents which are immiscible with water.

The *rate of ion exchange* in systems with organic solvents is nearly always considerably lower than in comparable aqueous systems [4,10,25,34,37] because particle diffusion, as a rule, is so much slower. The rate is particularly low when swelling is insignificant and when the solvent is very viscous. In such cases, equilibrium may not be attained even in days or weeks. The choice of the proper solvent thus is very important for achieving reasonable ion-exchange rates. As a rule, good swelling agents guarantee relatively high rates. Accordingly, polar solvents with reasonably high dielectric constants usually are preferable.

Ion exchange in organic media is usually accompanied by considerable electrolyte sorption. The rates of electrolyte sorption and desorption depend on the solution concentration even if particle diffusion is rate-controlling (see Sec. 6-6a). Pronounced deviations from the ideal limiting rate laws for strong aqueous electrolytes, in which electrolyte sorption is neglected, thus are the rule.

A special situation is encountered when ion exchange is carried out with mixed aqueous-organic solvents. As a rule, the resin accumulates water in its pores (see Sec. 10-2b). Electrolyte sorption may be particularly strong. At the same time, the mobilities of the counter ions in the resin remain relatively high because the presence of water guarantees at least moderate swelling and ionic dissociation. This shows that, in many cases, ion-exchange rates can be considerably increased by addition of water to the organic solvent [4,10,25]. In organic solvents which are immiscible with water, high exchange rates can be attained by using water-wet resins. The water remains in the resin where its presence is beneficial [10,14,33a].

Experimental evidence on ion-exchange kinetics with nonaqueous and mixed solvents is still rather scanty. So far, however, the experimental results are in qualitative agreement with the theoretical considerations.

10-6. ELECTROCHEMICAL PROPERTIES

Electrochemical measurements with ion exchangers can also be carried out in nonaqueous systems. For example, concentration potentials across ion-exchanger membranes have been measured with anhydrous ammonia and ethanol as solvents [2]. The results can be used for estimating integral transference numbers and activity-coefficient ratios of the counter ions. In principle, ion-exchanger membranes can be used as "membrane electrodes" for determining unknown activities in nonaqueous solutions (see Sec. 8-4c), provided that the membranes are permselective and that suitable electrodes for potential measurements in the solutions are available.

SUMMARY

Ion exchange can occur in systems with nonaqueous or mixed solvents, provided that certain conditions are met. As a rule, ion exchange is accompanied by a pronounced sorption of electrolytes.

Swelling of ion-exchange resins strongly depends on the nature of the solvent. Because of the polar character of the fixed charges and counter ions the resins usually swell more strongly in polar than in nonpolar solvents. London interactions between solvent molecules and structurally similar constituents of the resin may produce or enhance swelling in nonpolar solvents. When mixed solvents are used, the resins usually accumulate the more polar component of the solvent. Under certain conditions resins may swell more strongly in solvents of moderately high dielectric constants (40 to 50) than in pure water.

The useful ion-exchange capacity in systems with organic solvents may be considerably lower than in aqueous media because attainment of ion-exchange equilibrium is often so slow that only a fraction of the fixed ionic groups becomes operative. In contrast, the sorption capacity for electrolytes may be considerably higher than in aqueous systems.

Ion-exchange and sorption equilibria depend strongly on the nature of the solvent. The most important factors which determine equilibria and selectivities are dissociation and solvation in the solvent and specific interactions such as complex formation. A change of solvent may result in striking changes in selectivity, particularly if specific interactions are involved.

Interdiffusion of counter ions in the resin in systems with organic solvents is, as a rule, rather slow because the solvents usually produce little swelling and favor ionic association. Hence the rate of ion exchange is often very low, and particle diffusion usually is the rate-determining step. Ion exchange is often accompanied by strong sorption of electrolytes. This impairs the validity of the ideal limiting rate laws which hold for strong electrolytes in aqueous systems.

Electrochemical measurements such as determination of concentration potentials across ion-exchanger membranes can also be carried out in nonaqueous systems.

REFERENCES

1. Bafna, S. L., *J. Sci. Ind. Research* (*India*), **B12**, 613 (1953); *Chem. Abstr.*, **48**, 8610 (1954).

2. Bergin, M. J., and A. H. A. Heyn, *J. Am. Chem. Soc.*, **76**, 4765 (1954).

3. Blasius, E., and F. Wolf, *Z. anal. Chem.*, **171**, 88 (1959).

4. Bodamer, G. W., and R. Kunin, *Ind. Eng. Chem.*, **45**, 2577 (1953).

5. Bonner, O. D., and J. C. Moorefield, *J. Phys. Chem.*, **58**, 555 (1954).

6. Brusset, H., and M. Kikindai, *Chim. anal.*, **34**, 192 (1952); *Chem. Abstr.*, **46**, 10778 (1952).

7. Burstall, F. H., P. J. Forrest, N. F. Kember, and R. A. Wells, *Ind. Eng. Chem.*, **45**, 1648 (1953); U.S. Patent 2,753,258, 1956.

8. Calmon, C., and M. A. Wilich, 1952, unpublished.

9. Carroll, K. K., *Nature*, **176**, 398 (1955).

10. Chance, F. S., Jr., G. E. Boyd, and H. J. Garber, *Ind. Eng. Chem.*, **45**, 1671 (1953).

11. Davies, C. W., and B. D. R. Owen, *J. Chem. Soc.*, **1956**, 1676.

12. Davies, C. W., and B. D. R. Owen, *J. Chem. Soc.*, **1956**, 1681.

13. Davydov, A. T., and R. F. Skoblionok, *Trudy Nauch.-Issled. Khim. Inst. Kharkov Univ.*, **10**, 195 and 205 (1953); *Chem. Abstr.*, **49**, 10003 (1955).

14. Eaves, A., and W. A. Munday, *J. Appl. Chem.*, **9**, 145 (1959).

14a. Fritz, J. S., and D. J. Pietrzyk, *Talanta*, **8**, 143 (1961).

15. Gable, R. W., and H. A. Strobel, *J. Phys. Chem.*, **60**, 513 (1956).

16. Gregor, H. P., D. Nobel, and M. H. Gottlieb, *J. Phys. Chem.*, **59**, 10 (1955).

17. Grubhofer, N., and L. Schleith, *Naturwissenschaften*, **42**, 580 (1955).

17a. Janauer, G. E., and J. Korkisch, *Talanta*, **8**, 569 (1961).

18. Kakihana, H., and K. Sekiguchi, *J. Pharm. Soc. Japan*, **75**, 111 (1955); *Chem. Abstr.*, **49**, 5923 (1955).

19. Katzin, L. I., and E. Gebert, *J. Am. Chem. Soc.*, **75**, 801 (1953).

20. Keenan, C. W., and W. J. McDowell, *J. Am. Chem. Soc.*, **75**, 6348 (1953).

21. Kember, N. F., P. J. MacDonald, and R. A. Wells, *J. Chem. Soc.*, **1955**, 2273.

22. Korkisch, J., and F. Tera, *J. Inorg. & Nuclear Chem.*, **15**, 177 (1960).

23. Kressman, T. R. E., and J. A. Kitchener, *J. Chem. Soc.*, **1949**, 1211.

24. Materova, E. A., Zh. L. Vert, and G. P. Grinberg, *Zhur. Obshchei Khim.*, **24**, 953 (1954); *Chem. Abstr.*, **49**, 33 (1955).

25. Mattisson, M., and O. Samuelson, *Acta Chem. Scand.*, **12**, 1395 (1958).

26. Ohtaki, H., H. Kakihana, and K. Yamasaki, *Z. physik. Chem. (Frankfurt)*, **21**, 224 (1959).

26a. Ohtaki, H., *Z. physik. Chem. (Frankfurt)*, **27**, 209 (1961).

27. Panchenkov, G. M., V. I. Gorshkov, and M. V. Kulanova, *Zhur. Fiz. Khim.*, **32**, 361, 616 (1958); *Chem. Abstr.*, **52**, 14279, 14280 (1958).

28. Reichenberg, D., and W. F. Wall, *J. Chem. Soc.*, **1956**, 3364.

29. Rice, S. A., and F. E. Harris, *Z. physik. Chem. (Frankfurt)*, **8**, 207 (1956).

30. Rückert, H., and O. Samuelson, *Svensk Kem. Tidskr.*, **66**, 337 (1954); *Chem. Abstr.*, **49**, 8658 (1955).

31. Sakaki, T., and H. Kakihana, *Kagaku*, **23**, 471 (1953); *Chem. Abstr.*, **47**, 10951 (1953).

32. Sakaki, T., *Bull. Chem. Soc. Japan*, **28**, 217, 220 (1958); *Chem. Abstr.*, **52**, 16004 (1958).

33. Sansoni, B., *Z. Naturforsch.*, **11b**, 117 (1956).

33a. Small, H., *J. Inorg. & Nuclear Chem.*, **19**, 160 (1961).

33b. Van Erkelens, P. C., *Anal. Chim. Acta*, **25**, 42 (1961).

34. Vermeulen, T., and E. H. Huffman, *Ind. Eng. Chem.*, **45**, 1658, 1664 (1953).

34a. Watkins, S. R., and H. F. Walton, *Anal. Chim. Acta*, **24**, 334 (1961).

35. Westermark, T., *Acta Chem. Scand.*, **14**, 1857 (1960).

36. Wilkins, D. H., G. E. Smith, J. S. Fritz, and D. J. Pietrzyk, *Talanta*, **2**, 392 (1959).

36a. Wilkins, D. H., and G. E. Smith, *Talanta*, **8**, 138 (1961).

37. Wilson, S., and L. Lapidus, *Ind. Eng. Chem.*, **48**, 992 (1956).

11

Catalysis by Ion Exchangers

Many chemical reactions, both inorganic and organic, can be catalyzed by ion exchangers. This is true for reactions of gases and of liquids and solutes. Typical catalyzed gas reactions are the synthesis of ammonia, cracking of olefins, hydrogenations, reductions such as preparation of aniline from nitrobenzene, oxidations such as preparation of sulfur trioxide from sulfur dioxide, and other technically important processes. Reactions of liquids and solutes include esterification, ester hydrolysis, sucrose inversion, dehydration of alcohols, hydration of acetylene derivatives, and aldol, acyloin, and Knoevenagel condensations. Much has been published on ion exchangers as catalysts;* however, most investigations have dealt with practical applications rather than with theoretical problems. A firmly established theory of catalysis by ion exchangers does not yet exist.

Catalysis of reactions of liquids and solutes by ion exchangers can usually be explained in terms of the catalytic activity of the counter ions and is analogous to homogeneous-phase catalysis by dissolved electrolytes. The catalytic activity of the ion exchanger thus is directly related to the ion-exchange properties. Catalysis of reactions of gases by ion exchangers has no such close analogue in homogeneous catalysis, and its relation to the ion-exchange properties of the catalyst is less distinct. In this chapter, emphasis is on the correlations between ion-exchange and catalytic properties. Liquid-phase reactions thus are discussed in more detail.

11-1. REACTIONS OF GASES AND VAPORS

Heterogeneous catalysis of gas-phase reactions by solids is a very interesting field which has received much attention for more than half a century. The reaction occurs at the external and internal surface of the porous catalyst

---

* See reviews, Refs. 4, 19, 21, 33.

where the reactants are activated by being sorbed. Many theories have been advanced, but details of the mechanisms of most reactions have not been firmly established. As a rule, catalysts are developed by trial and error, and heterogeneous catalysis is still an art as much as it is a science.

Quite a number of the catalysts are zeolites or other materials with ion-exchange properties; however, in many cases it is not at all clear whether the catalytic activity is related to the ability of the catalyst to act, under quite different conditions, as an ion exchanger. Apparently it is impossible to make a sharp distinction between the catalytic activities of ion exchangers and of other catalysts which have no ion-exchange properties. A discussion of the various theories of heterogeneous catalysis is beyond the scope of this book [14,15,42]. In the following, only a few interpretations are mentioned in which the ion-exchange properties of the catalyst play an essential part.

In many cases the catalytically active species is a metal. The reaction occurs at the surface of the metal. Thus, the larger the surface area, the higher is the catalytic activity. Platinum black and Raney nickel are typical examples of metal catalysts with very large surface areas. High dispersion—and thus a large surface—of a metal on a carrier can be achieved by using an ion exchanger as the solid support, introducing the active metal as the counter ion, and reducing the ion *in situ* [42a]. Of course, the procedure of reducing a component of the catalyst to the metal is an old one and is not restricted to ion exchangers.

Other catalytic reactions such as cracking of hydrocarbons and hydration of olefins over zeolitic materials do not involve metal surfaces. One reaction mechanism, which involves formation of carbonium ions as reaction intermediates, is directly related to the ion-exchange properties of the catalyst. (The question whether, in any particular case, carbonium ions are actually formed or whether only a polarization at the catalyst surface occurs is more a matter of definition than a genuine difference in the reaction mechanism.) For example, C. L. Thomas [47] assumed the following reaction path for cracking of di-isobutylene

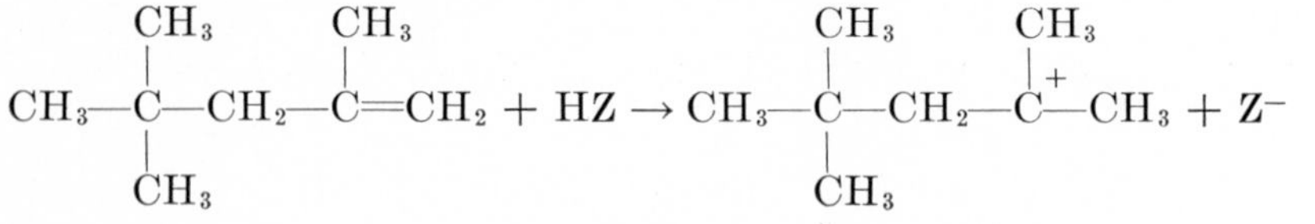

$$CH_3-\underset{\underset{CH_3}{|}}{\overset{\overset{CH_3}{|}}{C}}-CH_2-\overset{\overset{CH_3}{|}}{C}=CH_2 + HZ \rightarrow CH_3-\underset{\underset{CH_3}{|}}{\overset{\overset{CH_3}{|}}{C}}-CH_2-\overset{\overset{CH_3}{|}}{\overset{+}{C}}-CH_3 + Z^- \quad (11\text{-}1)$$

followed by

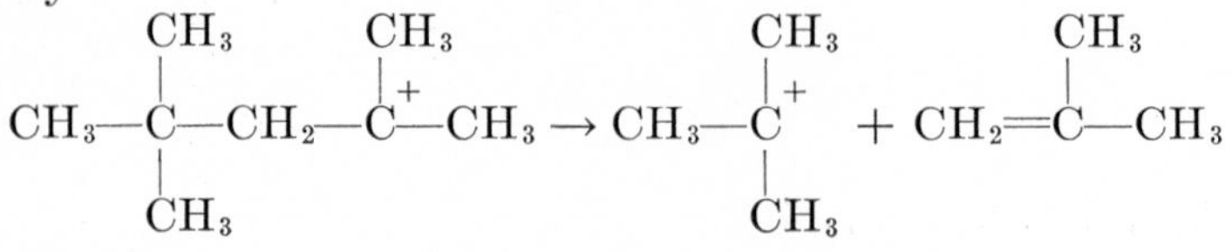

$$CH_3-\underset{\underset{CH_3}{|}}{\overset{\overset{CH_3}{|}}{C}}-CH_2-\overset{\overset{CH_3}{|}}{\overset{+}{C}}-CH_3 \rightarrow CH_3-\underset{\underset{CH_3}{|}}{\overset{\overset{CH_3}{|}}{\overset{+}{C}}} + CH_2=\overset{\overset{CH_3}{|}}{C}-CH_3 \quad (11\text{-}2)$$

and

$$
\begin{array}{c}
\underset{\displaystyle \overset{|}{CH_3}}{\overset{\displaystyle \overset{CH_3}{|}}{CH_3-C}}-CH_2-\underset{}{\overset{\displaystyle \overset{CH_3}{|}}{C}}=CH_2 + CH_3-\overset{\displaystyle \overset{CH_3}{|}}{\underset{\displaystyle \overset{|}{CH_3}}{C}}{}^{+} \rightarrow
\end{array}
$$

$$
\underset{\displaystyle \overset{|}{CH_3}}{\overset{\displaystyle \overset{CH_3}{|}}{CH_3-C}}-CH_2-\overset{\displaystyle \overset{CH_3}{|}}{C}{}^{+}-CH_3 + CH_2=\overset{\displaystyle \overset{CH_3}{|}}{C}-CH_3 \quad (11\text{-}3)
$$

Here Z is a matrix element of the alumosilicate catalyst. The steps (11-2) and (11-3) constitute a chain reaction. The chain is terminated by

$$
CH_3-\overset{\displaystyle \overset{CH_3}{|}}{\underset{\displaystyle \overset{|}{CH_3}}{C}}{}^{+} + Z^{-} \rightarrow CH_2=\overset{\displaystyle \overset{CH_3}{|}}{\underset{\displaystyle \overset{|}{CH_3}}{C}} + HZ \quad (11\text{-}4)
$$

This step also regenerates the catalyst.

Hydration of isoolefins is explained by Nachod [37] by the analogous mechanism

$$
\underset{H_3C}{\overset{H_3C}{\diagdown}}C=CH_2 + HZ \rightarrow \underset{H_3C}{\overset{H_3C}{\diagdown}}\overset{+}{C}-CH_3 + Z^{-} \quad (11\text{-}5)
$$

$$
\underset{H_3C}{\overset{H_3C}{\diagdown}}\overset{+}{C}-CH_3 + H_2O + Z^{-} \rightarrow \underset{H_3C}{\overset{H_3C}{\diagdown}}COH-CH_3 + HZ \quad (11\text{-}6)
$$

These mechanisms involve proton transfer from the catalyst, which should be acidic, to the reactant. A certain parallelism of catalytic activity and ion-exchange capacity of acidic catalysts has indeed been found [17,18,28, 34,35]. On the other hand, the catalytic activity is by no means restricted to acidic materials. Rather, vanadium zeolites [25] and sodium, copper, and lead alumosilicates [36] also have catalytic activity for cracking.

Efficient catalysis of gas reactions requires a large surface area of the catalyst. Crystalline inorganic ion exchangers, particularly zeolites, are used because their open and rigid pore structure guarantees accessibility of the internal surface. Ion-exchange resins, in contrast, are of little use since their elastic matrix contracts and closes the pores when the resin is not in contact with a solvent. Also, their thermal stability is inferior.

11-2. REACTIONS OF LIQUIDS AND SOLUTES

A large number of reactions of liquids and solutes are subject to homogeneous catalysis by dissolved electrolytes. In many of these cases, the electrolyte is an acid or a base. The catalytically active species are the H^+ ion or the OH^- ion. Sucrose inversion and ester hydrolysis are well-known examples. Other ions may be catalytically active. For example, Hg^{2+} catalyzes the hydration of acetylene derivatives, and CN^- catalyzes benzoin condensation.

It has been found that the dissolved electrolyte can be replaced by an ion exchanger which contains the catalytically active ion as the counter ion. The reaction now occurs in the pores of the ion exchanger where the active species is present.* Sucrose inversion [9a,10,24,29,44,45,58], ester hydrolysis [7–9,12,13,20,24,30,39,40,43,44,48], hydration of acetylene derivatives [38], benzoin condensation [41], and many other reactions [21] can thus be catalyzed by ion exchangers in the H^+, OH^-, Hg^{2+}, CN^-, and other ionic forms.

The ability of ion exchangers to catalyze liquid-phase reactions was first observed by Tacke and Süchting [45], who found that sucrose in aqueous solution is inverted by acidic zeolites. Practical applications and plant-scale processes were first developed by the I. G. Farbenindustrie during World War II [23,24].

The use of solid ion exchangers has the following advantages over homogeneous catalysis by dissolved electrolytes:

1. The catalyst is readily removed from the reaction products by, say, decantation or filtration.

2. Continuous operation in columns is possible [23,40].

3. Often the purity of the products is superior since side reactions are less significant [26,32,44]. In some cases it is possible to isolate reaction intermediates which cannot be obtained by homogeneous catalysis [49]. Also, the greater selectivity of the ion-exchanger catalyst (see next section) may be advantageous [13,31,55].

On the other hand, the applicability of the method is restricted by the chemical and thermal stability of the ion exchangers. Also, ion-exchanger catalysts are much more expensive than dissolved electrolytes.

As a rule, organic ion-exchange resins rather than other ion-exchange materials are used for catalysis of liquid-phase reactions. The resins are superior to the inorganic ion exchangers because of the higher mobilities of the reactants and products in the pores of the (swollen) catalyst. Also, the chemical stability of the resins, particularly against acids, is usually higher. Serious disadvantages of the organic resins are their limited thermal

---

* It is conceivable, though not yet conclusively established, that in certain cases the fixed ionic groups rather than the counter ions can act as the catalytically active species.

stability and, in reactions involving strong oxidation agents, their insufficient resistance to oxidative decrosslinking. For reactions at higher temperatures (above 100°C) and in the presence of oxidation agents such as H_2O_2, the newly developed inorganic ion-exchange gels (see Sec. 2-2) are likely to be more satisfactory [5].

A well-established quantitative theory of catalysis by ion exchangers does not yet exist. It is surprising how little effort has been made in the past to develop such a theory. In particular, only very few investigators [40,43] have attempted to apply the wealth of theoretical knowledge about diffusion phenomena in heterogeneous catalysis [11,46,50–54,56,57,59] to liquid-phase catalysis by ion exchangers. The theoretical picture presented in the following sections thus is, by necessity, partly hypothetical.

a. Mechanism

The pores of an ion exchanger which is in contact with a solution contain solvent, solutes, and counter ions. The counter ions are mobile and solvated and thus in a condition which is, in principle, not different from that in a corresponding homogeneous solution. It can therefore be expected that counter ions which display catalytic activity in homogeneous solutions are equally active in the pores of a resin, and that the reaction mechanism in homogeneous catalysis by a dissolved electrolyte and heterogeneous catalysis by a resin is essentially the same. These conclusions are reasonably well confirmed by experimental observations which show that the order of the actual chemical reaction is the same in both cases and that the activation energy is similar.* Catalysis of liquid-phase reactions by ion-exchange resins thus is not a true case of heterogeneous catalysis, but may be described more adequately as homogeneous catalysis in the pore liquid [22]. The principal differences between catalysis by dissolved electrolytes and by resins are, first, with resins as catalysts the reaction occurs in the pore liquid only so that the reactants must diffuse into the reaction zone and the products must diffuse out, and, second, the matrix and the fixed ionic groups may affect the reaction. The discussion in the following sections deals chiefly with these differences and glosses over the details of the mechanisms of the various chemical reactions.

b. Catalyst Selectivity

Almost every chemical reaction is accompanied to a greater or lesser degree by side reactions. Many reactions proceed in consecutive steps. In some cases a reaction mixture may undergo different reactions which lead to different products. All this, of course, is true for catalytic as well

---

* This is true for the actual chemical reaction, but not necessarily for the observed over-all process which may be diffusion-limited (see Sec. 11-3c).

as for other reactions. In all these cases an ion-exchanger catalyst may produce other results than a dissolved electrolyte. As a rule, the ion exchanger is more selective, i.e., it distinguishes more sharply between the various reactant molecules. One might say that ion exchangers as catalysts are about halfway between the nonselective dissolved electrolytes and the extremely selective enzymes.

The selectivity of the ion-exchanger catalyst may have different causes. Some of these are obvious; others are as yet less well understood. A few practical examples are discussed in the following.

Ion exchangers can discriminate between large and small molecules. Small molecules have free access to the interior of the resin where the catalytically active counter ions are located, while large molecules are excluded by sieve action (see Sec. 5-3b) and thus have little contact with the catalytically active species. For example, an ion-exchange resin, when added to a mixture of a monomeric and a polymeric ester (say, ethylacetate and polyvinylacetate) hydrolyzes the monomer without significantly attacking the polymer [13]. A dissolved acid, in contrast, hydrolyzes both the monomer and the polymer with comparable rates. Similarly, Linde Molecular Sieves Type 5A, which sorb straight-chain molecules but exclude branched-chain ones, catalyze dehydration of n-butanol without significantly attacking isobutanol [55].

Other specific effects cannot be explained in terms of molecular sizes and sieve action. For example, anion exchangers can be used for catalyzing the condensation of furfural with aldehydes [31], whereas dissolved bases under otherwise identical conditions produce almost exclusively self-crotonization of the aldehyde. Such effects can be tentatively explained with differences in sorption of the various reactants. Accumulation in the resin of one reactant by preferential sorption may favor a reaction which is insignificant in catalysis by dissolved electrolytes.

The selectivity of ion-exchanger catalysts often leads to yields which are considerably higher than those obtained with catalysis by dissolved electrolytes. Also, the ease with which the catalyst can be separated from the liquid reaction mixture facilitates the isolation of reaction intermediates and helps avoid yield losses by the subsequent reactions of the products, particularly if the desired products are not very stable in the presence of the catalyst.

11-3. KINETICS

To avoid confusion, a clear distinction should be made between the kinetics of the actual chemical reaction at the catalytically active site and the kinetics of the over-all process which includes diffusion of the reactants and products to and from the active site. The kinetics of the chemical reaction depends, of course, on the reaction mechanism and varies from case to case. A discussion of reaction mechanisms is beyond the scope of this book. In the following sections, the kinetics of the chemical reaction will be taken for granted and the kinetics of the over-all process will be discussed on this basis. The mathematics developed for heterogeneous catalysis [11,46,50,51,54,56,57,59] can be used for catalysis by ion exchangers with only minor modifications. The treatment given below is for liquid-phase reactions but can be adapted, by a few obvious changes, to gas reactions. An interesting aspect of the theory of liquid-phase reactions is the comparison between catalysis by dissolved electrolytes and by ion exchangers. This still somewhat controversial point is also briefly discussed.

a. The Rate-determining Step

In order for the reaction to occur, reactant molecules must migrate from the solution into the ion exchanger and must react; the reaction products must then migrate back into the solution (see Fig. 11-1). It will be assumed that mass transfer in the bulk solution is effected by agitation or solution flow and is fast as compared with any other step, so that concentration differences in the bulk solution are instantaneously leveled out. However, the catalyst particles are surrounded by an adherent liquid Nernst diffusion layer, a so-called film, across which mass transfer can occur by diffusion only (see Sec. 6-2). Thus three phenomena can affect the rate of the over-all process:

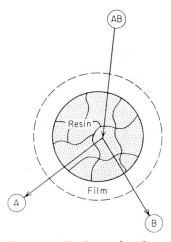

Diffusion of the reactants and products across the film

Diffusion of the reactants and products in the interior of the catalyst particle

The actual chemical reaction at the active sites

Fig. 11-1. Resin-catalyzed reaction AB → A + B (*schematic*). The reactant AB moves from the bulk solution across the film into the resin where it reacts. The products A and B move out across the film into the solution.

The old rule according to which the slowest step determines the over-all rate is, however, inapplicable in this case because the steps are not necessarily in sequence.

First, the limiting cases will be studied in which one of the three above-mentioned processes is much slower than the other two. If film diffusion is much slower than the chemical reaction, it must obviously be rate-controlling since, in this limiting case, all reactant molecules react as soon as they reach the surface of the catalyst particle (Fig. 11-2, bottom). If the chemical reaction is much slower than the diffusion processes, sorption equilibrium of the reactants is established and upheld throughout the catalyst particle since diffusion is fast enough to make up for the disappearance of reactants by chemical reaction (Fig. 11-2, top).   The over-all rate thus is controlled by the rate of the chemical reaction throughout the particle.   If intraparticle diffusion is much slower than the chemical reaction, the reactant molecules will react before they have time to penetrate into the interior of the catalyst particle.   In this latter limiting case, the reaction occurs only in a thin layer at the particle surface, and its rate is controlled by either film diffusion or chemical reaction at the surface (Fig.

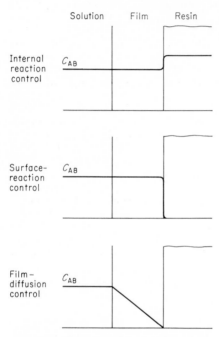

11-2, middle), whichever of these two processes is the slower one.   Intraparticle diffusion thus can affect the over-all rate, but it can never be the sole rate-determining step.   These considerations show that, in the three limiting cases, the over-all rate is controlled by:

Film diffusion
Chemical reaction throughout the particles
Chemical reaction at the particle surfaces

Intermediate cases arise if the rates of the individual steps are comparable. Often, the over-all rate is controlled by a combination of intraparticle reaction and intraparticle diffusion.

The factors which determine the rate-controlling step are readily understood.   The rate of the internal chemical reaction (with a given amount of catalyst) is independent of the resin particle size, whereas the rates of both

FIG. 11-2. Concentration profiles of the reactant in a first-order, irreversible reaction with rate control by internal reaction (*top*), surface reaction (*middle*), and film diffusion (*bottom*).

film diffusion and surface reaction are proportional to the resin surface area.   Small particle size thus favors internal reaction control.   Resins with lower degrees of crosslinking swell more strongly; accordingly, the volume capacity and thus the internal reaction rate are lower, and the intraparticle mobilities and thus the rate of intraparticle diffusion are higher.   Hence, a low degree of crosslinking favors internal reaction control.   Film diffusion obviously is rate-controlling if it is slower than the surface reaction.   This situation is exceptional and can only arise if the chemical reaction is very fast.   Favorable for film diffusion control are inefficient agitation and high viscosity of the solution (both resulting in a large film thickness).   As a rule, the activation energy of the chemical reaction is considerably higher than that of diffusion, i.e., a raise in temperature speeds up the chemical reaction more than the diffusion processes.   High temperature thus favors intraparticle diffusion limitation or film diffusion control.

Ways of predicting the rate-controlling step will be discussed in a later section (see Sec. 11-3e).

Experimental Determination of the Rate-controlling Step.   The rate-controlling step can be identified experimentally without much difficulty.   Internal reaction control is established when the over-all rate is proportional to the amount of catalyst and is independent of the particle size.   With both film diffusion and surface reaction control the rate (with a given amount of catalyst) is inversely proportional to the particle size. These two mechanisms can be distinguished by varying the agitation of the solution and the catalyst ion concentration in the resin (for example, by partial replacement of the catalytically active counter ion by an inactive one).   With film diffusion control, the over-all rate depends on agitation and is independent of the catalyst ion concentration in the resin.   With surface reaction control, the over-all rate is independent of agitation and is proportional to the catalyst-ion concentration in the resin.   Additional evidence can be obtained from determinations of the kinetic order and activation energy of the over-all process (see Sec. 11-3c).

One common pitfall should be pointed out.   The observation that the over-all rate is proportional to the resin surface area has often been taken as proof for surface reaction control.   This reasoning is inconclusive since the rate of a strongly diffusion-limited internal reaction is also proportional to the resin surface area (see pages 534 and 539). The best way of distinguishing between these two possible mechanisms is by varying the catalyst-ion concentration in the resin.   With surface reaction control the over-all rate is proportional to this concentration.   In contrast, with diffusion-limited internal reaction control this is only true for the chemical reaction but not for diffusion.   Hence, here, the over-all rate changes less than proportionally with the internal catalyst-ion concentration.

In publications of experimental results it has often been stated that the over-all rate depends on the particle size of the catalyst [7,10,27,40,44]. In some of these investigations the experimental conditions were such that diffusion processes are unlikely to have affected the over-all rate.   These results are so far unexplained.   However, the detailed investigations by Hammett and collaborators [7,20], who also carried out comparative measurements with superficially sulfonated resin particles, are strong evidence in support of the views presented in this section.   It is true that an unambiguous confirmation would require measurements not only of over-all rates but also of the diffusion coefficients of the reactants and products in the resins. No such measurements have as yet been reported.

b. Reaction Rate and Catalyst Performance

The rate of the over-all process in various systems can be computed when the rate law of the actual chemical reaction and other data such as diffusion coefficients of the reactants and products, etc., are known. The calculations are comparatively simple if the chemical reaction is first order and irreversible:

$$AB \rightarrow A + B \tag{11-7}$$

$$-\frac{dQ_{AB}}{dt} = kQ_{AB} \tag{11-8}$$

where Q_{AB} = amount of reactant in moles; t = time; k = rate constant.

This is true, for example, for sucrose inversion. Solutions for reversible reactions and reactions of higher order have only been obtained in a few simple cases. The resulting equations are more complex and are less readily interpreted and evaluated. For the sake of simplicity all calculations in this section will be made with the simple rate law (11-8). In the following, solutions of this rate law in systems with various rate-controlling mechanisms are given. Two types of systems will be studied, namely, batch operation and continuous operation in a catalyst column. A brief qualitative discussion of reactions of higher order follows in Sec. 11-3c.

Internal reaction control. With internal reaction control, sorption equilibrium of the reactant AB between the resin and the solution is rapidly established and is maintained throughout the process (see page 526). Thus

$$\bar{C}_{AB} = \lambda'_{AB} C_{AB} \tag{11-9}$$

The molar distribution coefficient λ'_{AB} of the reactant is assumed to be constant.* The chemical reaction occurs only within the resin, and the concentration of the reactant in the resin is uniform. The rate law (11-8) can thus be written

$$-\frac{d\bar{Q}_{AB}}{dt} = \bar{k}\bar{Q}_{AB} = \bar{k}\lambda'_{AB} C_{AB}\bar{V} \tag{11-10}$$

where $\bar{V}$ = total volume of catalyst; $\bar{k}$ = rate constant of the reaction in the catalyst; $\tilde{Q}_{AB}$ ($= \bar{Q}_{AB} + Q_{AB}$) = total amount of reactant; $\bar{Q}_{AB}$ = amount of reactant in catalyst; Q_{AB} = amount of reactant in solution.

This equation must be solved with the appropriate initial conditions and restrictions.

Batch Operation. The initial condition and the material balance for the reactant in a batch operation in which the initial amount of reactant is Q_{AB}^0 and the solution volume is V are

$$t = 0 \qquad \tilde{Q}_{AB}(0) = Q_{AB}^0 \tag{11-11}$$

$$t > 0 \qquad \tilde{Q}_{AB}(t) = C_{AB}(t)V + \bar{C}_{AB}(t)\bar{V} = C_{AB}(t)(V + \lambda'_{AB}\bar{V}) \tag{11-12}$$

---

* For nonconstant λ'_{AB}, see Sec. 11-3c.

Integration of Eq. (11-10) with these conditions gives

$$\tilde{Q}_{AB}(t) = Q_{AB}^0 \exp\left(-\frac{\bar{k}\lambda'_{AB}\bar{V}}{V + \lambda'_{AB}\bar{V}}t\right) \tag{11-13}$$

$$\tilde{Q}_A(t) = Q_A^0 + Q_{AB}^0 - \tilde{Q}_{AB}(t) \tag{11-14}$$

$$C_{AB}(t) = \frac{Q_{AB}^0}{V + \lambda'_{AB}\bar{V}} \exp\left(-\frac{\bar{k}\lambda'_{AB}\bar{V}}{V + \lambda'_{AB}\bar{V}}t\right) \tag{11-15}$$

$$C_A(t) = \frac{\tilde{Q}_A(t)}{V + \lambda'_{AB}\bar{V}} \tag{11-16}$$

The half time of the reaction is

$$t_{\frac{1}{2}} = 0.69\frac{V + \lambda'_{AB}\bar{V}}{\bar{k}\lambda'_{AB}\bar{V}} \tag{11-17}$$

Example. The time required for 99 per cent inversion $[\tilde{Q}_{AB}(t)/Q_{AB}^0 = 0.01]$ of 100 cm^3 of a sucrose solution by 5 cm^3 of a cation exchanger of fine particle size with $\bar{k} = 7 \cdot 10^{-3}$ sec^{-1} and $\lambda'_{AB} = 1$ is, according to Eq. (11-13),

$$t = -\ln(0.01)\frac{V + \lambda'_{AB}\bar{V}}{\bar{k}\lambda'_{AB}\bar{V}} = 1.38 \cdot 10^4 \text{ sec} \approx 4 \text{ hr}$$

Column Operation. The reaction can be carried out in a continuous operation in which the solution is passed through a fixed-bed catalyst in a column. A steady state in the bed is attained, provided that the feed composition and the flow rate are kept constant. In the steady state, the solution concentration in any layer normal to the column axis remains constant, and so does the reaction rate in the layer. A material balance in an arbitrary layer between z and $z + dz$ ($z =$ space coordinate in direction of column axis) can be set up by equating inflow minus outflow of the reactant to the amount which reacts in the layer. Neglecting longitudinal diffusion and temperature effects which are discussed later, one obtains with the use of Eq. (11-10) [see also Fig. 11-3]:

$$\underset{\text{inflow}}{qvC_{AB}(z)} - \underset{\text{outflow}}{qvC_{AB}(z + dz)} = \underset{\text{amount reacting}}{q\,dz(1 - \beta)\bar{k}\lambda'_{AB}C_{AB}} \tag{11-18}$$

where $q =$ column cross section; $v =$ linear flow rate (solution volume per unit time and unit bed cross section); $\beta =$ fractional void volume of the bed.

This gives

$$\frac{dC_{AB}}{dz} = -\bar{k}\lambda'_{AB}C_{AB}(z)\frac{1 - \beta}{v} \tag{11-19}$$

Integration of this equation with the initial condition

$$z = 0, \qquad C_{AB}(0) = C_{AB}^0 \tag{11-20}$$

gives the axial concentration profile of the reactant in the column:

$$C_{AB}(z) = C_{AB}^0 \exp\left(-\bar{k}\lambda_{AB}' \frac{1 - \beta}{v} z\right) \qquad (11\text{-}21)$$

The corresponding relation for the product A is

$$C_A(z) = C_A^0 + C_{AB}^0 \left[1 - \exp\left(-\bar{k}\lambda_{AB}' \frac{1 - \beta}{v} z\right)\right] \qquad (11\text{-}22)$$

C_A^0 = concentration of A in the feed; C_{AB}^0 = concentration of AB in the feed.

An analogous relation holds for the product B. The concentrations in the

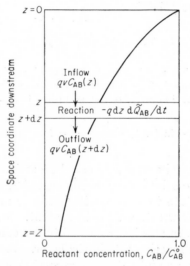

Fig. 11-3. Steady-state axial concentration profile of the reactant in continuous operation with a fixed catalyst bed, and material balance in a layer of the bed.

effluent of a column are obtained from Eqs. (11-21) and (11-22) by replacing z by the bed length Z.

> *Example.* Suppose that one liter ($V = 1,000$ cm³) of sucrose solution should be inverted to 99 per cent [$C_{AB}(Z)/C_{AB}^0 = 0.01$] in a column with internal diameter $d = 2$ cm and length $Z = 20$ cm filled with a cation exchanger of fine particle size. Assume that the rate constant, distribution coefficient, and fractional void volume of the bed are $\bar{k} = 7 \cdot 10^{-3}$ sec⁻¹, $\lambda_{AB}' = 1$, $\beta = 0.4$. The maximum permissible flow rate can be calculated from Eq. (11-21):
>
> $$v = -\ln(0.01)\bar{k}\lambda_{AB}'(1 - \beta)Z = 0.38 \text{ cm/sec}$$
>
> The operation requires
>
> $$t = \frac{V}{qv} = \frac{1,000}{3.14 \cdot 0.38} = 840 \text{ sec} = 14 \text{ min}$$
>
> This is only an approximation since the effects discussed below have been disregarded.

Longitudinal Diffusion and Temperature Effects. In the simple treatment above, longitudinal diffusion and temperature effects caused by the liberated heat of reaction were ignored. *Longitudinal diffusion* is usually unimportant. Its effect can be taken into account by including a corresponding term in the material balance (11-16). [Such a term appears, for example, in Eq. (9-3); see derivation of the latter equation on page 451.] It can be shown that the effect is negligible if $\epsilon \equiv [\bar{k}\lambda'_{AB}(1 - \beta)\beta D_{AB}]/v^2 \sqrt{2} \ll 1$, a condition which is usually met. An approximate correction for longitudinal diffusion can be made in Eqs. (11-21) and (11-22) by multiplying the exponent with $1 - \epsilon$ [14a]. A more rigorous, but much more complex solution has been given by Wehner [50b].

Temperature effects may be considerable, particularly if the reaction is highly exothermic and the column is large. In columns with small surface-to-volume ratios there is little heat exchange with the environment so that operation is essentially adiabatic. The adiabatic temperature rise is readily calculated from the heat of reaction and the concentration and heat capacity of the feed. As an approximation it can be assumed that small columns operate at the feed (or thermostat-jacket) temperature, and that large columns operate at a temperature which is higher by the adiabatic temperature rise.* At the higher temperature the rate constant $\bar{k}$ is, of course, greater. In batch operations with their much greater solution-to-resin volume ratio, temperature effects are usually negligible.

Flow maldistribution (see Sec. 9-10a) may also affect column performance. The magnitude of this effect can be determined independently by measurements of the residence-time spread [11a,22a]. To make allowance for flow maldistribution, it is wise to overdesign columns by at least 20 per cent.

Effect of intraparticle diffusion.

The optimum limiting case in which the over-all rate is exclusively controlled by the chemical reaction in the particles and which was discussed immediately above cannot always be attained. Slow intraparticle diffusion may reduce the over-all rate, especially if the reactant molecules are large and thus have a low mobility in the resin catalyst. In such cases, sorption equilibrium of the reactant is not attained since a substantial fraction of the molecules react before they can reach the center of the particle (see Fig. 11-4). The catalyst is not fully utilized since the catalytically active ions in the particle centers rarely see a reactant molecule and thus remain essentially useless. In the limiting case of extremely slow particle diffusion, the reaction occurs only in a thin layer at the particle surface (see page 526).

The mathematical derivations in the following are for spherical particles of uniform size. For nonuniform and irregularly shaped particles, the solutions are rather accurate approximations if the particle radius r_0 is taken as the radius of the "equivalent sphere"; the latter is a sphere with the same surface-to-volume ratio as the actual ion-exchange material [2].

At a given location within a particle, the concentrations change with time because of both diffusion and chemical reaction. With a first-order, irreversible reaction, the corresponding material balances for the reactant

---

* For more accurate calculations, see, for example, Refs. 2a, 22b, 42b, 50a. Note that, because of higher heat capacities and conductivities, the effect is usually much smaller with liquid-phase than with gas-phase operation.

and the product A are

$$\frac{\partial \bar{C}_{AB}}{\partial t} = \bar{D}_{AB} \operatorname{div} \operatorname{grad} \bar{C}_{AB} - k\bar{C}_{AB} = \bar{D}_{AB} \left(\frac{\partial^2 \bar{C}_{AB}}{\partial r^2} + \frac{2}{r} \frac{\partial \bar{C}_{AB}}{\partial r} \right) - k\bar{C}_{AB} \quad (11\text{-}23)$$

$$\frac{\partial \bar{C}_A}{\partial t} = \bar{D}_A \operatorname{div} \operatorname{grad} \bar{C}_A + k\bar{C}_{AB} = \bar{D}_A \left(\frac{\partial^2 \bar{C}_A}{\partial r^2} + \frac{2}{r} \frac{\partial \bar{C}_A}{\partial r} \right) + k\bar{C}_{AB} \quad (11\text{-}24)$$

An analogous relation holds for the product B, but is not required for the solutions. The boundary conditions at the interface resin/solution are

$$r = r_0 \qquad \bar{C}_{AB}(r_0,t) = \lambda'_{AB} C_{AB}(t) \qquad (11\text{-}25)$$
$$\bar{C}_A(r_0,t) = \lambda'_A C_A(t) \qquad (11\text{-}26)$$

where r_0 = particle radius.

Equations (11-23) to (11-26) must be solved with the appropriate conditions and restrictions.

Batch Operation. In batch operation, the boundary conditions (11-25) and (11-26) are not constant since the solution concentrations are functions of time. The time dependence is given by the material balances at the interface

$$-V \frac{dC_{AB}}{dt} = \frac{3\bar{V}}{r_0} \bar{D}_{AB} \left(\frac{\partial \bar{C}_{AB}}{\partial r} \right)_{r=r_0}$$
$$-V \frac{dC_A}{dt} = \frac{3\bar{V}}{r_0} \bar{D}_A \left(\frac{\partial \bar{C}_A}{\partial r} \right)_{r=r_0} \qquad (11\text{-}27)$$

The usual initial conditions (no reactant and products initially in the resin) are

$$t = 0, r \leq r_0 \qquad \bar{C}_{AB}(r,0) = 0 \qquad \bar{C}_A(r,0) = 0 \qquad (11\text{-}28)$$
$$r \geq r_0 \qquad C_{AB}(0) = C^0_{AB} \qquad C_A(0) = C^0_A$$

A simple solution can be obtained if the reaction can be treated as a quasi-stationary process, i.e., if the concentration changes in the solution are slow in comparison to the (average) residence time of a reactant molecule in the resin. This is true if the solution-to-resin volume ratio is so large that the solution constitutes an ample reservoir of reactant molecules or, more specifically, if the condition

$$\bar{Q}_{AB}(t) \ll Q_{AB}(t) \qquad (11\text{-}29)$$

is met at all times. In this case, the quasi-stationary intraparticle concentration profile of the reactant and the according rate can be calculated as a function of the solution concentration only. The time dependence is obtained subsequently by a material-balance correlation of the rate with the concentration change in the solution.

The assumption of the quasi-stationary state implies that the two terms on the right-hand side of Eqs. (11-23) and (11-24) are practically equal in magnitude and opposite in sign. With this condition, the solution of Eqs. (11-23) and (11-25) gives the quasi-stationary radial concentration profile of the reactant [11,46,50,53]

$$\bar{C}_{AB}(r,t) = C_{AB}(t)\lambda'_{AB} \frac{r_0 \sinh [r(\bar{k}/\bar{D}_{AB})^{1/2}]}{r \sinh [r_0(\bar{k}/\bar{D}_{AB})^{1/2}]} \tag{11-30}$$

This equation involves the dimensionless parameter

$$\omega \equiv r_0 \left(\frac{\bar{k}}{\bar{D}_{AB}}\right)^{1/2} \tag{11-31}$$

the so-called *Thiele modulus*.* Concentration profiles for various values of this parameter are shown in Fig. 11-4. A high value of the Thiele modulus

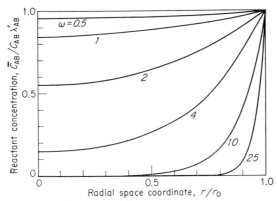

FIG. 11-4. Steady-state (or quasi-stationary) radial concentration profiles of the reactant in a catalyst particle, calculated for a first-order, irreversible reaction [Eq. (11-30)]. The various curves are for different values of the Thiele modulus ω.

results in low reactant content of the resin and, hence, in a poor utilization of the catalyst. The factors which determine the extent of diffusion limitation—particle size, rate of the chemical reaction, and reactant mobility—are reflected in the Thiele modulus (see also Sec. 11-3a).

The momentary over-all rate (i.e., the moles of reactant reacting per unit time) is obtained from Eq. (11-30) and the first-order rate law by integration over r. One obtains

$$-\frac{d\tilde{Q}_{AB}}{dt} = \bar{k}\lambda'_{AB}C_{AB}(t)\bar{V}\eta \tag{11-32}$$

where

$$\eta = \frac{3}{\omega}\left(\frac{1}{\tanh \omega} - \frac{1}{\omega}\right) \tag{11-33}$$

---

* The Thiele modulus was originally derived for reactant penetration into pores of uniform cross section (one-dimensional geometry). Equations (11-31) and (11-33) are the modifications for spherical geometry.

Comparison with the rate in the absence of diffusion limitation [Eq. (11-10)] shows that the rate in the diffusion-limited system is smaller by the factor η which may be called the "degree of catalyst utilization." This factor is a function of the Thiele modulus only. Its dependence on the Thiele modulus is shown in Fig. 11-5. The function (11-33) is tabulated in the Appendix (page 590).

For $\omega > 15$, Eq. (11-33) reduces to

$$\eta \cong \frac{3}{\omega} \tag{11-34}$$

Accordingly, the degree of utilization under otherwise identical conditions becomes

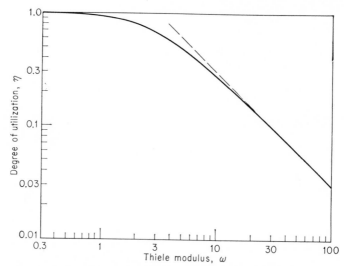

FIG. 11-5. Degree of catalyst utilization as a function of the Thiele modulus, calculated for a first-order, irreversible reaction [Eq. (11-33)]. The broken line is for the relation $\eta = 3/\omega$, which is approached at high values of the Thiele modulus.

inversely proportional to the particle radius, and hence the over-all rate becomes proportional to the resin surface area. Without invoking mathematics it is evident that this must be the case when the average depth of penetration of the reactant is much smaller than the particle radius.

Integration of Eq. (11-32) with the conditions (11-11) and (11-12) leads to relations which are identical with Eqs. (11-13) to (11-16), except that the product $\eta \cdot t$ appears instead of t:

$$\tilde{Q}_{AB}(t) = Q_{AB}^0 \exp\left(-\frac{\bar{k}\lambda'_{AB}\bar{V}}{V + \lambda'_{AB}\bar{V}}\eta t\right) \tag{11-35}$$

etc. The half time of the reaction is accordingly longer by the factor $1/\eta$:

$$t_{\frac{1}{2}} = 0.69 \frac{V + \lambda'_{AB}\bar{V}}{\bar{k}\lambda'_{AB}\bar{V}\eta} \tag{11-36}$$

Example. Suppose that the sucrose inversion discussed in the example on page 529 is carried out with a 20-mesh resin ($r_0 = 0.04$) and that the diffusion coefficient of sucrose in the resin is $\bar{D}_{AB} = 2 \cdot 10^{-6}$ cm²/sec. The Thiele modulus thus is $\omega = r_0(\bar{k}/\bar{D}_{AB})^{1/2} = 2.37$, and the degree of utilization (taken from the table in the Appendix) is $\eta = 0.75$. The time required for 99 per cent conversion is longer by the factor $1/\eta$ than that in the previous example, and is accordingly slightly more than 5 hr.

The mathematics are more complex if the condition for the quasi-stationary state [Eq. (11-29)] is not met. The solution for this more general case has been given by Smith and Amundson [43].*

$$C_A(t) = \frac{C_{AB}^0}{1 + \alpha} + 6\alpha C_{AB}^0 \Delta \left[\sum_{n=1}^{\infty} E_n \frac{Q(\bar{w}_n)}{P(\bar{w}_n)X_n} \exp(p_{n,v}t) \right.$$

$$\left. + \sum_{n=1}^{\infty} F_n \frac{w_n^2[T(w_n)\sin \bar{v}_n + S(\bar{v}_n)]}{S(\bar{v}_n)Y_n} \exp(p_{n,w}t) \right] \quad (11\text{-}37)$$

where

$$T(w_n) \equiv (w_n^2 + \Delta)(1 - \bar{D}_{AB}/\bar{D}_B) \qquad E_n \equiv [v_n^2(1 - \bar{D}_{AB}/\bar{D}_A) + \Delta]^{-1}$$
$$X_n \equiv v_n^2 + 9\alpha(1 + \alpha) \qquad F_n \equiv [w_n^2(1 - \bar{D}_{AB}/\bar{D}_A) + \Delta]^{-1}$$
$$Y_n \equiv (w_n^2 + \Delta)^2 + 9\alpha w_n^2(1 + \alpha) + 3\alpha\Delta$$
$$S(\bar{v}_n) \equiv (\bar{v}_n^2 + 3\alpha)\sin \bar{v}_n - 3\alpha\bar{v}_n \cos \bar{v}_n$$
$$P(\bar{w}_n) \equiv (-\bar{w}_n^2 - \Delta - 3\alpha)\sin \bar{w}_n + 3\alpha\bar{w}_n \cos \bar{w}_n$$
$$Q(\bar{w}_n) \equiv \left(\frac{-\bar{w}_n^2 \bar{D}_{AB}}{\bar{D}_A} - \frac{\Delta \bar{D}_{AB}}{\bar{D}_A} - 3\alpha \right)\sin \bar{w}_n + 3\alpha\bar{w}_n \cos \bar{w}_n$$
$$\alpha \equiv \frac{\bar{V}}{V} \qquad\qquad \Delta \equiv \frac{\bar{k}r_0^2}{\bar{D}_{AB}}$$
$$p_{n,w} \equiv -\frac{\bar{D}_{AB}w_n^2}{r_0^2 - \bar{k}} \qquad\qquad p_{n,v} \equiv \frac{\bar{D}_{AB}v_n^2}{r_0^2}$$

The summation extends over all v_n, w_n, $\bar{v}_n$, and $\bar{w}_n$, where v_n and w_n are the nonvanishing roots of the equations

$$(v^2 + 3\alpha)\sin v - 3\alpha \cos v = 0 \qquad (-w^2 - \Delta - 3\alpha)\sin w + 3\alpha w \cos w = 0$$

and $\quad \bar{w}_n \equiv r_0[-(p_{n,v} + \bar{k})/\bar{D}_{AB}]^{1/2} \qquad \bar{v}_n = r_0(-p_{n,w}/\bar{D}_{AB})^{1/2}$

It is assumed that the distribution coefficients, λ'_{AB} and λ'_A, are unity.

Column Operation. In a continuously operated column, a steady state is attained (see page 529). Accordingly, the intraparticle concentration profiles in any layer of the column become time-independent and can be expressed as a function of the solution concentration, $C_{AB}(z)$, in the layer. A relation identical to Eq. (11-30) is obtained, except that the variable z (distance from the column inlet) appears instead of t. The steady-state rate in each layer thus is given by a relation analogous to Eq. (11-32). The

---

* The solution given in Ref. 43 is more complex and more complete. It includes other initial conditions, chemical reaction in the solution also, and possible evaporation losses from the solution.

axial concentration profiles and the effluent concentrations can be derived in exactly the same way as in the case of internal reaction control [see Eqs. (11-18) to (11-22)]. The only difference in the calculations and results is that the product $\eta \cdot z$ appears instead of z:

$$C_{\mathrm{AB}}(z) = C_{\mathrm{AB}}^0 \exp\left(-\bar{k}\lambda'_{\mathrm{AB}}\frac{1-\beta}{v}\eta z\right) \tag{11-38}$$

$$C_{\mathrm{A}}(z) = C_{\mathrm{A}}^0 + C_{\mathrm{AB}}^0\left[1 - \exp\left(-\bar{k}\lambda'_{\mathrm{AB}}\frac{1-\beta}{v}\eta z\right)\right] \tag{11-39}$$

For attaining a specified degree of conversion, the maximum permissible flow rate is smaller by the factor η than it would be in the absence of diffusion limitation.

More complete solutions which also hold for reversible first-order reactions and include partial film diffusion control and reaction in the solution have been given by Smith and Amundson [43]. For longitudinal diffusion and flow maldistribution, see page 531.

Temperature Effects. It is tacitly assumed in the derivations that the system is isothermal, i.e., that heat conduction is fast enough to prevent temperature rise in the particles because of the evolved heat of reaction. This assumption is not necessarily valid. The temperature in the particle centers may be substantially higher than at the surfaces. The result is a higher rate for any given surface temperature. Accurate calculations which include this temperature effect are lengthy [6a]; however, simpler approximation methods have recently been developed [1,6a,40a]. This intraparticle temperature effect can be significant in both batch and column operations. In column operations one may have, in addition, the extraparticle temperature effect discussed on page 531.

Surface reaction control. The treatment in the preceding part of this section [Eqs. (11-35) and (11-37) to (11-39)] is applicable even when particle diffusion is so slow that the reactant does not penetrate more than only a thin outer layer of the catalyst particles. However, the equations fail in the limiting case in which the reactant molecules are completely excluded from the resin, for example, by sieve action. In this case ($\lambda'_{\mathrm{AB}} = 0$, or $\bar{D}_{\mathrm{AB}} = 0$) no reaction should occur according to the equations. This result is a consequence of the implicit assumption that all counter ions are *within* the resin. This is not strictly true since the particles are surrounded by a counter-ion cloud (see page 372). Reaction can occur in this cloud and also at the surface itself where fixed ionic groups are freely exposed to the solution.

The rate of the reaction at the surface and in the counter-ion cloud is proportional to the total (external) surface area F of the catalyst particles and can be characterized by a rate constant k_{s}:

$$-\frac{\mathrm{d}Q_{\mathrm{AB}}}{\mathrm{d}t} = k_{\mathrm{s}}C_{\mathrm{AB}}F = \frac{3k_{\mathrm{s}}C_{\mathrm{AB}}\bar{V}}{r_0} \tag{11-40}$$

This equation can be used instead of Eq. (11-10) for calculating the performance in batch and column operations. The derivation is the same as for Eqs. (11-13) to (11-22). One obtains for *batch operations*

$$C_{AB}(t) = C_{AB}^0 \exp\left(-\frac{3k_s \bar{V}}{r_0 V} t\right) \tag{11-41}$$

$$C_A(t) = C_A^0 + C_{AB}^0 \left[1 - \exp\left(-\frac{3k_s \bar{V}}{r_0 V} t\right)\right] \tag{11-42}$$

$$t_{1/2} = 0.23 \frac{r_0 V}{k_s \bar{V}} \tag{11-43}$$

where C_i^0 = initial concentration of species i,

and for *column operations*

$$C_{AB}(z) = C_{AB}^0 \exp\left(-3k_s \frac{1-\beta}{vr_0} z\right) \tag{11-44}$$

$$C_A(z) = C_A^0 + C_{AB}^0 \left[1 - \exp\left(-3k_s \frac{1-\beta}{vr_0} z\right)\right] \tag{11-45}$$

where C_i^0 = concentration of species i in feed.

It must be expected that the rate constant k_s is proportional to the ion-exchange capacity (per unit volume) of the catalyst and depends on the density and depth of the counter-ion cloud which is affected by the nature of the solvent, and possibly on surface adsorption of the reactant molecules.

Film diffusion control. In the limiting case of complete film diffusion control, the over-all rate is obviously given by the product of the flux of the reactant across the film and the total surface area of the catalyst particles. The reactant concentration at the surface is zero since every arriving molecule reacts at once. Treating the film as a planar layer (this is permissible if the film thickness is much smaller than the particle diameter; see page 262), one obtains for the reactant flux

$$J_{AB} = \frac{D_{AB} C_{AB}}{\delta} \tag{11-46}$$

and for the over-all rate

$$-\frac{dQ_{AB}}{dt} = J_{AB} F = \frac{3 D_{AB} C_{AB} \bar{V}}{\delta r_0} \tag{11-47}$$

where J_{AB} = flux of the reactant; δ = film thickness; F = total surface area of the catalyst particles.

Equation (11-47) can be used for calculating the performance of the catalyst in batch and column operations. The solutions are derived in the same way as in the preceding parts of this section. For *batch operations* one obtains

$$C_{AB}(t) = C_{AB}^0 \exp\left(-\frac{3 D_{AB} \bar{V}}{\delta r_0 V} t\right) \tag{11-48}$$

$$C_A(t) = C_A^0 + C_{AB}^0 \left[1 - \exp\left(-\frac{3 D_{AB} \bar{V}}{\delta r_0 V} t\right)\right] \tag{11-49}$$

$$t_{1/2} = 0.23 \frac{\delta r_0 V}{D_{AB} \bar{V}} \tag{11-50}$$

and for *column operations*

$$C_{AB}(z) = C_{AB}^0 \exp\left(-\frac{3D_{AB}(1-\beta)}{\delta r_0 v} z\right) \tag{11-51}$$

$$C_A(z) = C_A^0 + C_{AB}^0 \left[1 - \exp\left(-\frac{3D_{AB}(1-\beta)}{\delta r_0 v} z\right)\right] \tag{11-52}$$

As an example, the half time of batch reaction of a low molecular weight organic compound ($D_{AB} \approx 5 \cdot 10^{-6}$ cm^2/sec) in 100 cm^3 solution, when vigorously shaken with 5 cm^3 of a 40-mesh resin catalyst ($r_0 = 0.02$ cm; $\delta \approx 5 \cdot 10^{-3}$ cm), as calculated from Eq. (11-50), is about 1.5 min. The half times calculated for film diffusion control are rather short, i.e., film diffusion is a relatively fast process. Only in exceptional cases is the surface reaction faster still. Complete film diffusion control thus is a rare phenomenon.

Experimental evidence. Most experimental studies in which over-all reaction rates were measured had practical rather than theoretical objectives, and the dependence of the rate on the various variables was not investigated thoroughly enough for establishing the rate-controlling mechanism and the validity of the equations in this section. Also, even in the recent literature a number of attempts to interpret experimental results are marred by severe and obvious misconceptions. Moreover, results obtained by different authors can be compared only with caution since the properties of the resin catalyst may have been different. The most detailed investigation was made by Smith and Amundson [43] who studied the hydrolysis of methylformate by a commercial cation-exchange resin (Dowex 50) and obtained satisfactory agreement with Eqs. (11-37) and (11-39). The validity of Eq. (11-39) in gas reactions is well established. Unambiguous evidence for exclusive rate control by film diffusion or surface reaction has so far not been reported.

c. Order and Activation Energy of the Over-all Process

Let us consider the general case of a chemical reaction

$$M + N + \cdots \rightarrow \text{products} \tag{11-53}$$

which proceeds with the rate

$$-\frac{dC_M}{dt} = kC_M^m C_N^n \cdots \tag{11-54}$$

The kinetic order of the reaction is $m + n + \cdots$. The activation energy, E_r, which determines the temperature dependence of the rate, is given by

$$\frac{d \ln k}{dT} = \frac{E_r}{RT^2} \tag{11-55}$$

In heterogeneous catalysis, the observed over-all rate may obey a rate law such as (11-54), and an "apparent" activation energy according to Eq. (11-55) can be defined. However, the kinetic order and the activation energy of the over-all process may differ from those of the actual chemical reaction at the catalytically active sites. Possible causes for such deviations are, first, that the over-all process involves diffusion as well as the actual chemical reaction and, second, that the reactant concentrations in the reaction zone (i.e., in the pore liquid of the resin) can differ from those in the solution even if the over-all process is not diffusion-limited.

First, the simplest case of a first-order, irreversible reaction (see previous section) will be examined. Here, the over-all process is always essentially first order, regardless of the nature of the rate-controlling step. This follows from the various rate laws [Eqs. (11-10), (11-32), (11-40), and (11-47)] which all involve the reactant concentration C_{AB} in the first power.* However, the apparent activation energy differs from that of the chemical reaction if the over-all rate is affected by diffusion. With film diffusion control, the apparent activation energy is obviously that of liquid-phase diffusion (usually 2 to 5 kcal/mole in aqueous solutions) rather than that of the chemical reaction. With rate limitation by intraparticle diffusion, the apparent activation energy is a crossbreed between those of diffusion and of the chemical reaction. As a rule, the activation energy of intraparticle diffusion is of the order of 3 to 10 kcal/mole (see Sec. 6-8b) and is usually lower than that of the chemical reaction. An increase in temperature thus increases the reaction rate more than the diffusion rate. Accordingly, the Thiele modulus becomes larger and the degree of catalyst utilization smaller. Hence, the temperature increase accelerates the over-all process less than the chemical reaction. In the limiting case of strong diffusion limitation ($\omega > 15$), the apparent activation energy approaches the arithmetic means of those of reaction and diffusion:

$$E_{app} \cong \tfrac{1}{2}(E_r + E_{diff}) \qquad (\omega > 15) \qquad (11\text{-}56)$$

Contrary to widespread belief, the limit is *not* the activation energy of diffusion E_{diff}.

Equation (11-56) is readily derived in the following way. The apparent rate constant, defined in accordance with Eq. (11-54) or (11-61), is obtained from the rate law (11-32):

$$k_{app} = \frac{\bar{k}\lambda'_{AB}\bar{V}\eta}{V} \qquad (11\text{-}57)$$

Substituting η by means of Eqs. (11-34) and (11-31), one obtains

$$k_{app} \cong \frac{3\lambda'_{AB}\bar{V}}{r_0 V} (\bar{k}\bar{D}_{AB})^{1/2} \qquad (\omega > 15) \qquad (11\text{-}58)$$

and, upon differentiation,

$$\frac{d \ln k_{app}}{dT} = \frac{1}{2}\left(\frac{d \ln \bar{k}}{dT} + \frac{d \ln \bar{D}_{AB}}{dT}\right) \qquad (\omega > 15) \qquad (11\text{-}59)$$

---

* Deviations from the first-order rate law can occur with internal reaction control and intraparticle diffusion limitation because the distribution coefficient λ'_{AB} is usually somewhat concentration-dependent.

(the temperature dependence of λ'_{AB} and $\bar{V}$ is neglected as usually insignificant). By virtue of the definitions $E_{app} \equiv RT^2(\text{d ln } k_{app}/dT)$, $E_r \equiv RT^2(\text{d ln } \bar{k}/dT)$, and $E_{diff} \equiv RT^2(\text{d ln } \bar{D}/dT)$, Eqs. (11-59) and (11-56) are equivalent.

With reactions of higher than first order, diffusion limitation can affect not only the activation energy, but also the order of the over-all process. Mass transfer by diffusion is proportional to the concentration gradient. Thus, diffusion obeys essentially first-order kinetics (unless coupling of fluxes or geometrical effects are significant). With complete film diffusion control, the over-all rate is always first order, even if the reaction involves more than one reactant. In the latter case, the rate is exclusively controlled by the flux of the reactant with the lowest concentration in the solution or the lowest mobility, and is first order in this reactant and independent of the other reactant concentrations. With intraparticle diffusion-limited internal reaction control, the kinetic order of the over-all process is a cross-breed between first order and the order of the chemical reaction. It can be shown that, with strong diffusion limitation, the over-all rate approaches the order $(n + 1)/2$, where n is the order of the chemical reaction [54]. The behavior of the apparent activation energy is essentially as discussed for first-order reactions.

With intraparticle diffusion-limited reactions of higher order, the extent of diffusion limitation and thus also the order of the over-all process depend on the reactant concentration in the solution since the chemical reaction rate is proportional to a higher power of the reactant concentration than the diffusion rate. Hence, diffusion limitation is more serious at high reactant concentrations. The appropriate dimensionless parameter which takes the place of the Thiele modulus and determines the extent of diffusion limitation is

$$\omega' = r_0 \left[\frac{\bar{k}(C\lambda')^{n-1}}{\bar{D}} \right]^{1/2} \tag{11-60}$$

where n is the order of the chemical reaction, and C, λ', and $\bar{D}$ refer to the reactant (or reactants). This parameter decreases with decreasing C, i.e., with progressing conversion.

The mathematics of intraparticle diffusion-limited reactions of other than first order are rather complex, particularly if more than one reactant is involved and if the reaction proceeds in several consecutive steps. Various cases have been discussed by Wheeler [56], Wicke [57], and Weisz [51–54]. As a rule, general and accurate solutions of the set of differential equations for the chemical reaction and reactant and product diffusion can only be obtained by numerical integration with electronic computers [51].

Differences in the order and activation energy between catalysis by ion exchangers and homogeneous catalysis by dissolved electrolytes have often been reported. Differences caused by diffusion phenomena should not be confused with true differences in the actual chemical reaction. The latter will be discussed in the next section.

d. Comparison with Homogeneous Catalysis; Catalyst Efficiency

Catalysis of liquid-phase reactions by ion exchangers can be compared with homogeneous catalysis of the same reactions by dissolved electrolytes with the same catalytically active counter ions.   Such comparisons are very interesting since they help to shed light not only on the behavior of the ion exchangers as catalysts, but also on the character of the catalyzed reaction.   In this section, two interpretations which have so far emerged from such comparisons are given.   Both are still rather speculative, and much work remains to be done in this field.

Differences between homogeneous and heterogeneous catalysis caused by diffusion phenomena have been discussed in the previous section.   In the following, the rates of the actual chemical reaction in homogeneous and heterogeneous catalysis are compared.   Direct measurements of this rate in heterogeneous systems require that the chemical reaction be the sole rate-controlling mechanism.   In so far as rate equations for the over-all process in heterogeneous systems are used in the following, it will be assumed that this condition is met.

In all cases which have so far been studied and in which disturbances due to slow diffusion processes can be ruled out, the order of the chemical reaction in the particles was found to be the same as in homogeneous catalysis by a dissolved electrolyte.   This is strong evidence in support of the view that the reaction mechanism is essentially the same in both cases. However, there are differences in reaction rates, even when the amount of catalyst (in counter-ion equivalents) is the same in both cases.   Hammett has defined the *efficiency* of the ion-exchanger catalyst as the ratio of the reaction rates in the heterogeneous and the homogeneous system with equivalent amounts of catalyst.   The first order irreversible reaction

$$AB \rightarrow A + B \tag{11-7}$$

may serve as a simple example.   The rate of homogeneous catalysis by a dissolved electrolyte is

$$-\left(\frac{dQ_{AB}}{dt}\right)_{hom} = kQ_{AB} \tag{11-8}$$

The over-all rate of heterogeneous catalysis by an ion exchanger can be written as

$$\left(\frac{d\tilde{Q}_{AB}}{dt}\right)_{het} = k_{het}Q_{AB} \tag{11-61}$$

where the apparent rate constant k_{het} is independent of Q_{AB}, provided that the reaction is first order in the heterogeneous system also.   The efficiency, as defined by Hammett, then is

$$\mathfrak{q} \equiv \frac{k_{het}}{k} \tag{11-62}$$

Of course, both constants k_{het} and k are functions of the amounts of the catalyst. Equation (11-62) applies when the amounts (in counter-ion equivalents) in both systems are equal.

The efficiency can be larger [6,12,48] or smaller [7,8,20] than unity, i.e., the ion-exchanger catalyst can produce a faster or slower reaction than an equivalent amount of dissolved electrolyte.

An interesting interpretation of the efficiency has been given by Hammett [7–9,20,39]. His approach is based on Eyring's theory of rate processes [16]. This theory postulates the existence of an "activated complex" (or transition state) as an intermediate of the reaction. In terms of this theory, the first-order reaction (11-7) could be written

$$AB + C \rightarrow M^{\pm} \rightarrow A + B + C \tag{11-63}$$

The activated complex $M^{\pm}$ is in equilibrium with the reactant AB and the catalyst C:

$$\frac{m_{M^{\pm}}}{m_{AB} m_{cat}} = K^{\pm} \tag{11-64}$$

where m_i = molality of species i; $K^{\pm}$ = equilibrium constant.

The reaction rate is proportional to the concentration of the activated complex. According to the theory, the proportionality factor is universal, i.e., the same for all reactions. The efficiency of the ion-exchanger catalyst thus becomes

$$q = \frac{K^{\pm}_{het}}{K^{\pm}_{hom}} \tag{11-65}$$

At the same time, the following thermodynamic relations hold:

$$\Delta\Delta G^{\pm} \equiv \Delta G^{\pm}_{het} - \Delta G^{\pm}_{hom} = \Delta\Delta H^{\pm} - T\Delta\Delta S^{\pm} = -RT \ln q \tag{11-66}$$

$$\Delta\Delta S^{\pm} \equiv \Delta S^{\pm}_{het} - \Delta S^{\pm}_{hom} = R \frac{d(T \ln q)}{dT} \tag{11-67}$$

where $\Delta G^{\pm}$, $\Delta H^{\pm}$, and $\Delta S^{\pm}$ are the changes in standard Gibbs free energy, enthalpy, and entropy, respectively, which accompany the formation of the activated complex.

According to Hammett, the quantity $\Delta\Delta S^{\pm}$ often is an important factor in determining the efficiency. His hypothesis is that the formation of the activated complex in the ion exchanger involves some kind of a fixation to the fixed ionic groups or the matrix. Thus the reactant molecule suffers a loss of some internal degrees of freedom. Reactant molecules with many internal degrees of freedom have more entropy to lose. For these, $\Delta\Delta S^{\pm}$ becomes negative. Consequently, the efficiency in such cases is small and its temperature coefficient is negative, i.e., the activation energy of heterogeneous catalysis is less than that of homogeneous catalysis. These effects may be absent if significant interactions between reactant and solvent occur (for example, with polar reactants in a polar solvent) because such interactions are likely to reduce the internal degrees of freedom of the reactant, so that the entropy content of the latter and thus $-\Delta S^{\pm}$ are smaller

[8].   Hammett's hypothesis is in qualitative agreement with experimental observations of ester hydrolysis [8,9,39].

The practical application and quantitative confirmation of Hammett's hypothesis are somewhat difficult since the activation entropies and, in most cases, even the (absolute) entropies of the reactants cannot be measured directly.   Furthermore, this formal treatment glosses over the fact that catalysis by ion exchangers occurs in a heterogeneous system.

In other approaches [12,22,48], the heterogeneous nature of catalysis by ion exchangers has been made the starting point for interpreting the catalyst efficiency.   The basic idea is that the reaction in the heterogeneous system occurs only in the pores of the catalyst.   The pore liquid is considered as a homogeneous liquid phase in which the concentrations of the reactants and products may be different from those in the solution which is in equilibrium with the catalyst.   Heterogeneous catalysis is described by

$$-\left(\frac{\mathrm{d}\tilde{Q}_{AB}}{\mathrm{d}t}\right)_{\mathrm{het}} = \bar{k}\bar{Q}_{AB} \tag{11-10}$$

This equation differs from Eq. (11-61) in that it states explicitly the proportionality of the rate to the amount of reactant *in* the catalyst.   The rate constants in both Eqs. (11-8) and (11-10) can be assumed to be proportional to the catalyst-ion concentration in the respective phase:

$$k = k' m_{\mathrm{cat}} \qquad\qquad \bar{k} = \bar{k}' \bar{m}_{\mathrm{cat}} \tag{11-68}$$

where k' and $\bar{k}'$ are independent of the catalyst concentration and may be called "specific" rate constants.   With equivalent amounts of catalyst in the homogeneous and the heterogeneous system one obtains for the efficiency from Eqs. (11-62), (11-61), (11-8), (11-10), (11-68), and (5-28) [22]

$$q = \frac{\bar{k}'}{k'} \lambda_{AB} \tag{11-69}$$

where $\lambda_{AB} \equiv \bar{m}_{AB}/m_{AB}$ = molal distribution coefficient of the reactant.

The efficiency of the ion-exchanger catalyst thus is proportional to the distribution coefficient of the reactant.   Heterogeneous catalysis is efficient when the reactant is strongly sorbed, so that its local concentration is high in that part of the system where the catalyst ion is present.   Of course, the specific rate constants k' and $\bar{k}'$ may well differ from one another since effects other than sorption equilibrium can affect the rate.

Equation (11-69) is derived with simplifying assumptions.   The validity of Eq. (11-68) is assumed, and the effect of activity coefficients on the reaction rate is disregarded.   The second idealization is the more serious one.   This becomes apparent when a more refined theory of rate processes is applied.   When activity coefficients are included, the quotient $\bar{k}'/k'$ can be expressed by

$$\frac{\bar{k}'}{k'} = \frac{\mathcal{K}_{\mathrm{het}}^{\neq}}{\mathcal{K}_{\mathrm{hom}}^{\neq}} \left(\frac{\bar{\gamma}_{AB}\bar{\gamma}_{\mathrm{cat}}}{\bar{\gamma}_{M}^{\neq}}\right)_{\mathrm{het}} \left(\frac{\gamma_{M}^{\neq}}{\gamma_{AB}\gamma_{\mathrm{cat}}}\right)_{\mathrm{hom}} \tag{11-70}$$

where $\mathcal{K}^{\neq} \equiv a_M{}^{\neq}/a_{AB}a_{cat}$ is the "true" thermodynamic equilibrium constant of activation; a_i = activity of species i; γ_i = molal activity coefficient of species i.

The following conclusion can be drawn from this relation. The explicit correlation of the efficiency with the distribution coefficient in Eq. (11-69) is physically meaningful only if $\bar{\gamma}_{AB}/\bar{\gamma}_M{}^{\neq} \cong \gamma_{AB}/\gamma_M{}^{\neq}$, i.e., if the forces which control sorption of the reactant affect the activity coefficients of the reactant and the activated complex in the same way. In contrast, if $\bar{\gamma}_M{}^{\neq} \cong \gamma_M{}^{\neq}$ and $\bar{\gamma}_{AB} \neq \gamma_{AB}$, the quotient $\bar{k}'/k'$ becomes inversely proportional to λ_{AB}, since $\bar{a}_{AB} = a_{AB}$ and thus $\gamma_{AB}/\bar{\gamma}_{AB} = \lambda_{AB}$. Thus, in the latter case, the efficiency becomes independent of the distribution coefficient. It is likely that $\bar{\gamma}_{AB}/\bar{\gamma}_M{}^{\neq} \cong \gamma_{AB}/\gamma_M{}^{\neq}$ is a good approximation and, hence, Eq. (11-69) is meaningful if the interactions which control sorption equilibrium of the reactant involve groups of the reactant molecule which are sufficiently remote from the reactive group. In this case, the reactivity of the molecule will not be significantly changed by sorption. On the other hand, the interactions may involve the reactive group. For example, preferential sorption may result from fixation of this group to the matrix. In such cases, the reactivity will be reduced by sorption, and the effect of the higher intraparticle concentration of the reactant will be offset. Furthermore, Eq. (11-70) involves the activity coefficients, $\bar{\gamma}_{cat}$ and γ_{cat}, of the catalytically active counter ion. These coefficients represent correction factors for the relations (11-68).

Whether and how far this approach, which accounts for the heterogeneous character of the system, leads beyond Hammett's interpretation must remain an open question as long as the distribution coefficients of the reactants and products have not been determined along with the reaction rates. Nevertheless, a number of experimental observations can be qualitatively explained in terms of this approach.

Riesz and Hammett [39] have found that the efficiency in ester hydrolysis is increased when the catalytically active H^+ ions in the resin are partially replaced by quaternary ammonium ions with substituents which are structurally similar to the ester.* For example, cetyltrimethylammonium ions increase the efficiency for long-chain aliphatic esters, and methyltribenzylammonium ions, that for aromatic esters (see Table 11-1). Distribution coefficients have not been measured, but it is almost certain that the presence of a structurally similar counter ion enhances sorption of the ester (see Sec. 5-3b).

Thomas and Davies [12,48] studied hydrolysis of esters, using water as the solvent. Here, the efficiencies are larger than unity and increase with increasing molecular weight of the ester. In contrast, Bernhard and Hammett [7] measured hydrolysis of the same esters, using 70 per cent aqueous acetone as the solvent. Here, the efficiencies are smaller than unity and decrease with increasing molecular weight of the ester. It is known that sorption of organic compounds from *aqueous* solutions usually increases with molecular weight as long as sieve action is insignificant (see Sec. 5-3b). The results obtained by Thomas and Davies thus are as expected. In the second case, the unequal distribution of the components of the solvent must first be considered. The ion exchanger accumulates water (see Sec. 10-2b). It is likely that, here, the ester prefers to stay in the prevailingly organic medium, namely, in the external solution, and that this effect is stronger when the hydrocarbon character of the ester is more pronounced, i.e., when its molecular weight is higher.

---

* Note that the efficiency is defined for *equivalent amounts of the catalytically active ion* in the homogeneous and the heterogeneous system. Hence catalysis by a larger amount of resin is compared with homogeneous catalysis when H^+ in the resin is partially replaced by an inactive ion. The rate produced by an equal amount of resin is, of course, reduced when H^+ is partially replaced.

Table 11-1. Effect of partial replacement of H$^+$ by various quaternary
ammonium ions on the rate of ester hydrolysis*

Quaternary ammonium ion	Per cent H$^+$ remaining	Normalized rate constant [liter min^{-1} mole^{-1}]		
		Ethylacetate	Ethylhexanoate	Methyl-phenylacetate
	100	$10.4 \cdot 10^{-5}$	$0.925 \cdot 10^{-5}$	$2.07 \cdot 10^{-5}$
Tetramethyl...........	30.1	5.76	0.373	1.37
Tetra-n-butyl..........	31.0	4.06	0.851	1.75
Cetyltrimethyl.........	31.7	5.43	1.55	2.86
Methyltribenzyl.......	31.9	5.54	0.76	2.67

* Catalyst: Amberlite IR-112; solvent: 70 per cent aqueous acetone; temperature 40°C.
The rate constants are normalized for one equivalent of H$^+$ in the resin per liter
of solution.
From P. Riesz and L. P. Hammett [39].

This last example shows clearly how complex the situation becomes in
multicomponent systems, especially when mixed solvents are used. It
also shows how strongly the nature of the solvent can affect the reaction
rate and the efficiency of the catalyst.

e. Prediction of the Rate-determining Step and the Reaction Rate

Predictions of the rate-determining step and the reaction rate can be
made when the order of the chemical reaction, the rate constants, diffusion
coefficients, and distribution coefficients are known or can be estimated,
and when a mathematical solution of the respective rate law is available.

First, the rate-controlling mechanism must be established. This can
be done in a number of ways. One of them is illustrated in Table 11-2.
Reaction in the particles can be ruled out when the reactant molecules are
excluded from the catalyst, for example, by sieve action. Film diffusion
control can be established or ruled out by checking whether film diffusion is
slower or faster than the surface reaction. If the reactants are not excluded
and film diffusion control is ruled out, the Thiele modulus [or the corresponding parameter for other than first-order reactions, see Eq. (11-60)] is calculated. With $\omega < 0.5$, internal reaction control is established (see Fig.
11-5). It is wise to check, though, whether film diffusion is sufficiently
fast, so that it will not reduce the rate. When ω is very large, it remains to
be checked whether intraparticle diffusion is so slow that the reaction occurs
at the particle surface only. The criteria in Table 11-2 are for irreversible
first-order reactions and are readily derived from the rate laws (11-10),
(11-40), and (11-47) and Fig. 11-5. For reactions of different kinetic order,
analogous criteria can be derived from the appropriate rate laws. After
the rate-controlling step has been established, the rate can be calculated
from the respective rate law.

This procedure is only applicable when the rate constants are known or can be estimated. It can be used, for example, in scale-up calculations for

Table 11-2. Theoretical prediction of the rate-determining step

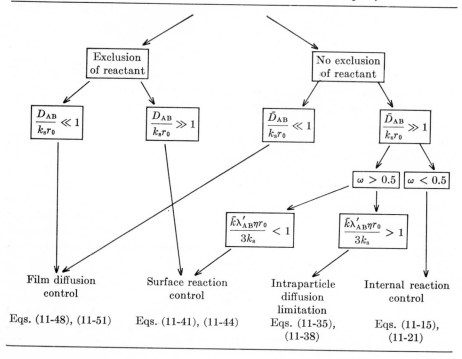

Exclusion of reactant		No exclusion of reactant	
$\dfrac{D_{AB}}{k_s r_0} \ll 1$	$\dfrac{D_{AB}}{k_s r_0} \gg 1$	$\dfrac{\bar{D}_{AB}}{k_s r_0} \ll 1$	$\dfrac{\bar{D}_{AB}}{k_s r_0} \gg 1$

$\omega > 0.5$ $\omega < 0.5$

$\dfrac{\bar{k}\lambda'_{AB}\eta r_0}{3k_s} < 1$ $\dfrac{\bar{k}\lambda'_{AB}\eta r_0}{3k_s} > 1$

Film diffusion control	Surface reaction control	Intraparticle diffusion limitation	Internal reaction control
Eqs. (11-48), (11-51)	Eqs. (11-41), (11-44)	Eqs. (11-35), (11-38)	Eqs. (11-15), (11-21)

technical processes after the basic data have been determined in laboratory-scale experiments.

Often the rate constants are not known beforehand. For liquid-phase reaction the order of magnitude of the rate constants can be estimated when the rate constant of the corresponding homogeneous reaction catalyzed by a dissolved electrolyte is known. It can be assumed that the "specific" rate constants k' and $\bar{k}'$ for homogeneous and heterogeneous catalysis, respectively, are of the same order of magnitude. The constant $\bar{k}$ can thus be estimated by use of Eqs. (11-68). The constant k_s can be estimated by assuming that the reaction occurs in a surface layer with a thickness of $d \approx 100$ A $= 10^{-6}$ cm. This gives $k_s \approx k'\bar{m}_{cat}d$. Experimental results so far are insufficient for testing the reliability of these approximations.

f. Selection of Catalysts and Operating Conditions

In most practical applications, it is desirable to obtain the highest possible reaction rate with a given amount of catalyst. This can be achieved by proper choice of the catalyst material and the operating conditions.

First of all, the type of resin and the solvent should be selected in such a way that the resin is chemically stable and swells substantially in the solvent, and that equilibrium sorption of the reactants is high. Under such conditions a high catalyst efficiency and high mobilities of reactants and products in the resin can be expected. The ion-exchange capacity of the resin should be as high as possible since the reaction rate is proportional to the amount of counter ions in the resin.

The particle size and the degree of crosslinking of the resin are important variables since they determine the rate-controlling step of the over-all process. The maximum possible rate with a given amount of catalyst is attained when the internal reaction is rate-controlling. In all other cases, the interior of the particles is not fully accessible to the reactant molecules, and the counter ions in the center of the particles are useless dead weight. This is clearly seen in Figs. 11-2 and 11-4. Any slow diffusion process decreases the over-all rate. Internal reaction control is favored by small particle size and a low degree of crosslinking which both increase the rate of intraparticle diffusion. On the other hand, a large particle size and a high degree of crosslinking have their advantages because handling is simpler and the volume capacity and mechanical stability of the resin are higher. Hence it is impractical to reduce the particle size and the degree of cross-linking to below an optimum where the over-all rate becomes independent of them and is exclusively controlled by the internal reaction. This optimum is reached when the Thiele modulus (or the corresponding parameter for other than first order reactions) has been decreased to about 0.5 (see Fig. 11-5).

Film diffusion control is comparatively rare since film diffusion is a rather fast process. If film diffusion is rate-controlling, the over-all rate can be increased by reducing the particle size, increasing the efficiency of agitation, and choosing a solvent with low viscosity. Note that, with film diffusion control, there is no optimum particle size below which the rate becomes independent of particle size.

An increase in temperature enhances the rates of both the chemical reaction and diffusion and thus gives a higher over-all rate. However, the temperature of operation is usually limited by the thermal stabilities of the resin or the compounds involved.

In certain cases, for example, in demineralization of sucrose solutions, catalytic reactions are undesired and should be suppressed as far as possible. Here, the temperature should be kept low because the activation energy of the catalytic reaction usually is much larger than that of counter-ion diffusion. Small particle size is also advantageous because the rate of ion exchange always increases with decreasing particle size, whereas the over-all rate of the catalytic process becomes independent of particle size when the Thiele modulus is sufficiently low.

11-4. EXPERIMENTAL METHODS

The experimental determination of reaction rates in heterogeneous systems is rather simple. For liquid-phase reactions, a thermostated flask which accommodates the solution and the catalyst can be used. Agitation should be provided by stirring or shaking. Reactions at higher temperature are often carried out by boiling under reflux. The reaction rate is determined from solution aliquots which are withdrawn at different times and are analyzed by standard methods [20].   Reactions of gases are more conveniently carried out by passing the gaseous reaction mixture through a thermostated catalyst bed. The degree of conversion is determined by analysis of the effluent.

The chemical and thermal stability of the catalyst must be tested.   This can be done, for example, by checking whether its weight, catalytic activity, and ion-exchange capacity remain unchanged over a number of cycles.   Stability tests are particularly important with resin catalysts because degradation products may be erroneously identified as reaction products and may thus give rise to incorrect interpretations [3,4].

Most of the rate equations involve distribution coefficients and diffusion coefficients of the reactants in the catalyst.   Their experimental determination is cumbersome since the catalytic reaction interferes with the measurements.   Diffusion coefficients can be estimated from diffusion measurements in resins in which the catalytically active counter ion has been replaced by an inactive, but similar ion which produces approximately the same swelling [58].   Distribution coefficients can be estimated in the same way.   Direct and more accurate determinations of distribution coefficients are possible if the chemical reaction is not too fast.   In this case, the use of resins of sufficiently small particle size will permit sorption equilibrium of the reactants to be attained before conversion becomes significant.   The resin is contacted with the solution for a period of time which is sufficient for establishment of sorption equilibrium, but too short for significant conversion. Reactants and products are then eluted from the resin, the reaction is completed in the eluate by addition of a soluble catalyst, and the amount of the products in the eluate is analytically determined.   This amount is stoichiometrically equivalent to the amount of reactant initially taken up by the resin [58].

SUMMARY

Ion exchangers can be used as catalysts for reactions of gases and of liquids or solutes.

Reactions of gases occur at the external and internal surface of the catalyst.   It seems that, in many cases, the catalytic activity has little direct relation to the ion-exchange properties of the catalyst.

Reactions of liquids and solutes are catalyzed by counter ions in the pores and at the surface of the ion-exchanger particles.   These reactions are analogous to homogeneous catalysis in liquid phases by dissolved electrolytes with the same counter ions.   However, ion-exchanger catalysts have, as a rule, higher selectivities than dissolved electrolytes.

Three processes can control or affect the over-all rate in heterogeneous catalysis.   These processes are the actual chemical reaction, diffusion within the catalyst particles, and diffusion across adherent "films" at the particle surfaces.   In the three possible limiting cases, the over-all rate is controlled by the chemical reaction in the catalyst, the chemical reaction at the catalyst surface, and by film diffusion.

Catalysis by ion exchangers can be carried out in batch operations or in continuous column operations.   The catalyst performance in such systems can be calculated, provided that the actual chemical reaction obeys a simple rate law.

The order and activation energy of the over-all process in heterogeneous catalysis are not necessarily those of the chemical reaction.   Differences can arise when slow diffusion processes affect the over-all rate.

The efficiency of ion exchangers as catalysts for liquid-phase reactions may be higher or lower than that of an equivalent amount of dissolved electrolyte with the same counter ion, even if the over-all rate is exclusively controlled by the chemical reaction. The causes of this difference are not yet fully established. Factors which affect the efficiency of the ion exchanger are favorable or unfavorable sorption equilibrium of the reactants, and the loss of entropy of the reactant molecules when the activated complex is formed. Both effects depend strongly on the nature of the solvent.

High degrees of efficiency and utilization of the catalyst can be attained by proper choice of the catalyst material, the solvent, and the operating conditions.

REFERENCES

 1. Akehata, T., S. Namkoong, H. Kubota, and M. Shindo, *Can. J. Chem. Eng.*, **39**, 127 (1961).
 2. Aris, R., *Chem. Eng. Sci.*, **6**, 262 (1957).
*2a. Aris, R., "The Optimal Design of Chemical Reactors," chap. 7, Academic Press, Inc., New York, 1961.
 3. Austerweil, G. V., and R. Pallaud, *Bull. soc. chim. France*, **1954**, 1164.
*4. Austerweil, G. V., "*L'échange d'ions et les échangeurs*," p. 289, Gauthiers-Villars, Paris, 1955.
 5. Austerweil, G. V., *Compt. rend.*, **247**, 1726 (1958).
 6. Bafna, S. L., *J. Phys. Chem.*, **59**, 1199 (1955).
6a. Beek, J., *A. I. Ch. E. Journal*, **7**, 337 (1961).
 7. Bernhard, S. A., and L. P. Hammett, *J. Am. Chem. Soc.*, **75**, 1798 (1953).
 8. Bernhard, S. A., and L. P. Hammett, *J. Am. Chem. Soc.*, **75**, 5834 (1953).
 9. Bernhard, S. A., E. Garfield, and L. P. Hammett, *J. Am. Chem. Soc.*, **76**, 991 (1954).
9a. Blann, W. A. (American Cyanamid Co.), U.S. Patent 2,543,694, 1950.
 10. Bodamer, G., and R. Kunin, *Ind. Eng. Chem.*, **43**, 1082 (1951).
 11. Damköhler, G., *Deut. chem. Ing.*, **3**, 430 (1937).
11a. Danckwerts, P. V., *Chem. Eng. Sci.*, **2**, 1 (1953).
 12. Davies, C. W., and G. G. Thomas, *J. Chem. Soc.*, **1952**, 1607.
 13. Deuel, H., J. Solms, L. Anyas-Weisz, and G. Huber, *Helv. chim. Acta*, **34**, 1849 (1951).
*14. Emmett, P. H. (ed.), "Catalysis," vols. I–VII, Reinhold Publishing Corporation, New York, 1954–1960.
14a. Förster, T., and K. H. Geib, *Ann. Phys.*, **20**, 250 (1934).
*15. Frankenburg, W. G., V. I. Komarewsky, E. K. Rideal, D. D. Eley, P. W. Selwood, and P. B. Weisz (eds.), "Advances in Catalysis," vols. I–XII, Academic Press, Inc., New York, 1949–1960.
*16. Glasstone, S., K. J. Laidler, and H. Eyring, "The Theory of Rate Processes," pp. 12, 195, 402, McGraw-Hill Book Company, Inc., New York, 1941.
 17. Greensfelder, B. S., H. H. Voge, and G. M. Good, *Ind. Eng. Chem.*, **41**, 2573 (1949).
 18. Grenall, A., *Ind. Eng. Chem.*, **41**, 1485 (1949).
*19. Griessbach, R., and G. Naumann, *Chem. Technik*, **5**, 187 (1953).
 20. Haskell, V. C., and L. P. Hammett, *J. Am. Chem. Soc.*, **71**, 1284 (1949).
*21. Helfferich, F., *Angew. Chem.*, **66**, 241 and 327 (1954).
 22. Helfferich, F., *J. Am. Chem. Soc.*, **76**, 5567 (1954).
22a. Hofmann, H. P., Thesis, Darmstadt (Germany), 1955.
*22b. Hougen, O. A., and K. M. Watson, "Chemical Process Principles," chap. XXI (Part III), John Wiley & Sons, New York, 1947.
 23. I. G. Farbenindustrie, Ger. Patents 877,744 and 878,348, 1953 (Appl. 1944 and 1942).

* Review articles are marked with asterisks.

24. I. G. Farbenindustrie, Ger. Patent 882,091, 1953 (Appl. 1942).
25. Jaeger, A. O., U.S. Patents 1,675,308, 1,675,309, and 1,694,123, 1928; 1,896,240, and 1,931,846, 1933.
26. Lagrange, G., P. Mastagli, and Z. Zafiriadis, *Compt. rend.*, **236,** 616 (1953).
27. Levesque, C. L., and A. M. Craig, *Ind. Eng. Chem.*, **40,** 96 (1948).
28. Mantin, I., and P. Brauman, *J. chim. phys.*, **51,** 648 (1954).
29. Mariani, E., *Ann. chim. appl.*, **39,** 283 (1949); **40,** 500 (1950).
30. Mariani, E., *Ann. chim. appl.*, **39,** 717 (1949).
31. Mastagli, P., A. Floc'h, and G. Durr, *Compt. rend.*, **235,** 1402 (1952).
32. Mastagli, P., Z. Zafiriadis, G. Durr, A. Floc'h, and G. Lagrange, *Bull. soc. chim. France*, **1953,** 693.
*33. McGarvey, F. X., and R. Kunin, in "Ion Exchange Technology," p. 272, F. C. Nachod and J. Schubert (eds.), Academic Press, Inc., New York, 1956.
34. Milliken, T. H., Jr., G. A. Mills, and A. G. Oblad, *Discussions Faraday Soc.*, **8,** 279 (1950).
35. Mills, G. A., E. R. Boedeker, and A. G. Oblad, *J. Am. Chem. Soc.*, **72,** 1554 (1950).
36. Nachod, F. C. (Atlantic Refining Co.), U.S. Patent 2,422,982, 1948.
*37. Nachod, F. C., in L. Farkas Memorial Vol., *Research Council Israel, Special Publ.* 1, Jerusalem, 1952, p. 188.
38. Newman, M. S., *J. Am. Chem. Soc.*, **75,** 4740 (1953).
39. Riesz, P., and L. P. Hammett, *J. Am. Chem. Soc.*, **76,** 992 (1954).
40. Saletan, D. I., and R. R. White, *Chem. Eng. Progr. Symposium Ser.*, **48,** No. 4, 59 (1952).
40a. Schilson, R. E., and N. R. Amundson, *Chem. Eng. Sci.*, **13,** 226, 237 (1961).
41. Schmidle, C. J., and R. C. Mansfield, *Ind. Eng. Chem.*, **44,** 1388 (1952).
*42. Schwab, G. M. (editor), "Handbuch der Katalyse," vols. I–VII, 1940–1957, Springer-Verlag OHG, Vienna.
42a. Smith, G. W., and L. H. Reyerson, *J. Am. Chem. Soc.*, **52,** 2584 (1930).
*42b. Smith, J. M., "Chemical Engineering Kinetics," chap. 10, McGraw-Hill Book Company, New York, 1956.
43. Smith, N. L., and N. R. Amundson, *Ind. Eng. Chem.*, **43,** 2156 (1951).
44. Sussman, S., *Ind. Eng. Chem.*, **38,** 1228 (1946).
45. Tacke, B., and H. Süchting, *Landwirtsch. Jahrb.*, **41,** 717 (1911).
46. Thiele, E. W., *Ind. Eng. Chem.*, **31,** 916 (1939).
47. Thomas, C. L., *Ind. Eng. Chem.*, **41,** 2564 (1949).
48. Thomas, G. G., and C. W. Davies, *Nature*, **159,** 372 (1947).
49. Wadman, W. H., *J. Chem. Soc.*, **1952,** 3051.
50. Wagner, C., *Z. physik. Chem.*, **193,** 1 (1943).
*50a. Walas, S. M., "Reaction Kinetics for Chemical Engineers," sec. 33, McGraw-Hill Book Company, New York, 1959.
50b. Wehner, J. F., and R. H. Wilhelm, *Chem. Eng. Sci.*, **6,** 89 (1956).
*51. Weisz, P. B., and C. D. Prater, in "Advances in Catalysis," vol. 6, p. 143, Academic Press, Inc., New York, 1954.
52. Weisz, P. B., and E. W. Swegler, *J. Phys. Chem.*, **59,** 823 (1955).
53. Weisz, P. B., *Z. physik. Chem. (Frankfurt)*, **11,** 1 (1957).
*54. Weisz, P. B., *Chem. Eng. Progr. Symposium Ser.*, **55,** No. 25, 29 (1959).
55. Weisz, P. B., and V. J. Frilette, *J. Phys. Chem.*, **64,** 382 (1960).
*56. Wheeler, A., in "Advances in Catalysis," vol. 3, p. 298, Academic Press, Inc., New York, 1951.
*57. Wicke, E., *Z. Elektrochem.*, **60,** 774 (1956).
58. Woliotis, L., Thesis, Göttingen, 1958.
59. Zeldovich, Ya. B., *Acta Physicochim. U.R.S.S.*, **10,** 583 (1939).

---

* Review articles are marked with asterisks.

12

Electron Exchangers and Redox Ion Exchangers

Electron exchangers are solid oxidation and reduction agents. They are insoluble, but able to swell to a limited extent. They are reversible agents, i.e., after having oxidized (or reduced) a substrate, the electron exchanger can be regenerated by a suitable oxidation (or reduction) agent. The reactivity of electron exchangers is due to built-in functional components such as quinone/hydroquinone which can be reversibly oxidized and reduced. The name "electron exchanger" is not quite appropriate, but has been generally accepted because of its elegance. Electron exchangers are, as a rule, resins with a crosslinked hydrocarbon matrix. In this respect they resemble the conventional ion-exchange resins. However, they are not ion exchangers since they carry no fixed ionic groups and no counter ions.†

Redox ion exchangers are conventional ion exchangers into which reversible oxidation-reduction couples such as Cu^{2+}/Cu, Fe^{3+}/Fe^{2+}, methylene blue/leukomethylene blue, etc., have been introduced. The oxidation-reduction couples are held in the resin either as counter ions or by sorption or complex formation. Ion exchange or desorption may cause a gradual loss of redox capacity.

Electron exchangers and redox ion exchangers behave in a way similar to the (soluble) oxidation-reduction couples to which they owe their reactivity. The redox potential of a couple is not significantly changed by incorporation of the couple into a resin. The most important difference between the soluble couples and the resins is that the latter are solid agents and thus are readily separated from the solution with which they have reacted.

---

† Phenolic OH groups which are present in most electron exchangers may act as fixed ionic groups in alkaline media. Several more recent electron exchangers contain fixed ionic groups in addition to the redox groups and thus combine the properties of electron exchangers and ion exchangers.

12-1. PREPARATION

Electron exchangers can be prepared by condensation or addition polymerization. In either case, the reactive groups can be introduced into one of the monomers or, after polymerization, into the crosslinked resin.

Condensation polymers. The first electron exchangers were condensation polymers. As early as 1944, the I. G. Farbenindustrie filed patents covering the preparation of resins by condensation of polyvalent phenols, aminophenols, and polyphenylenepolyamines with formaldehyde and their use for removing dissolved oxygen from liquids [11].

Similar condensation polymers can be prepared from a large number of organic oxidation-reduction agents with various redox potentials [17–20, 27,29,33]. Many of these agents contain phenol or naphthol units which condense readily with aldehydes. The development of these resins is chiefly due to Manecke [17–20]. One of the most stable electron exchangers of this type is a condensation product of hydroquinone, phenol, and formaldehyde (mole ratio 1:1:2). Its structure is

Particularly interesting condensation polymers have been prepared by Sansoni [27,29] from reactive dyes. Here, oxidation and reduction are accompanied by drastic changes in color. For example, the condensation product of methylene blue, resorcinol, and formaldehyde is white when reduced (leukomethylene blue) and dark blue when oxidized (methylene blue). Such resins can be used as redox indicators.

Addition polymers. Addition polymers with electron-exchange properties were first prepared in 1949 by H. G. Cassidy who, without knowledge of the previous development work by the I. G. Farbenindustrie, embarked on a systematic study of electron exchangers. His first attempts to form copolymers of vinylhydroquinone, stryrene, and divinylbenzene were, however, not very successful [3,32]. Only products of low molecular weight were obtained. Later, he recognized that the hydroquinone prevents effective polymerization by acting as a chain stopper [5,6]. This difficulty was overcome by blocking the OH groups of the hydroquinone by esterification.   The esters are then hydrolyzed after polymerization [5–7,15]:

$$(12\text{-}1)$$

Addition polymers of this type are relatively stable; however, they are even less hydrophilic than the usual condensation polymers.   Hence they swell little in aqueous solutions, and the reactive groups in their interior are not readily accessible.   As a remedy, strongly hydrophilic groups can be introduced, for example, by sulfonation [7,15].   Resins of this type combine the properties of electron exchangers and strong-acid cation exchangers.   Cation exchange does not affect the redox capacity of these resins [15,16].   This is in contrast to redox ion exchanges from which cation exchange removes the reactive oxidation-reduction couple.

Introduction of reactive groups after polymerization. Electron exchangers can be prepared from crosslinked resins by introduction of reactive groups after polymerization.

Crosslinked polystyrene is a convenient starting material. The polystyrene is nitrated, reduced, and diazotized

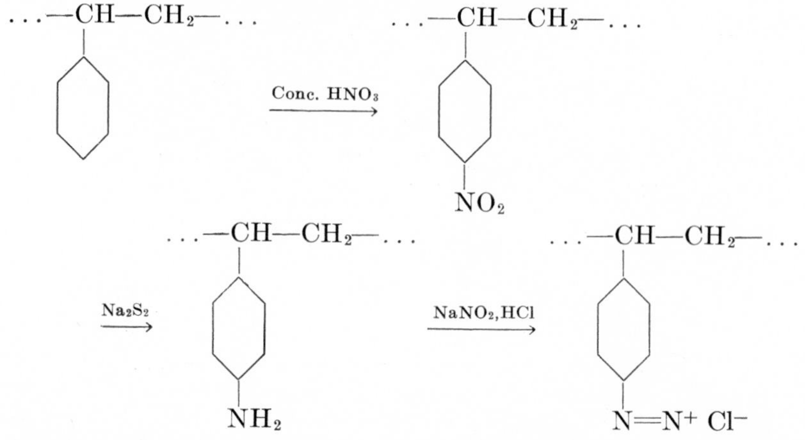

$$\ldots -CH-CH_2- \ldots \qquad \ldots -CH-CH_2- \ldots$$

Conc. HNO_3 →

NO_2

$$\ldots -CH-CH_2- \ldots \qquad \qquad \ldots -CH-CH_2- \ldots \qquad (12\text{-}2)$$

Na_2S_2 → NH_2

$NaNO_2, HCl$ → $N{=}N^+\ Cl^-$

and the diazonium chloride is coupled with reactive monomers, for example, with dyes such as methylene blue, crystal violet, or parafuchsin [29]. Coupling with methylene blue gives a particularly good electron exchanger.

Poly-thiolstyrene can be prepared from the diazonium chloride by reaction with potassium xanthogenate, followed by alkaline hydrolysis [8]:*

---

* An alternative preparation procedure which gives the same resin is [24]

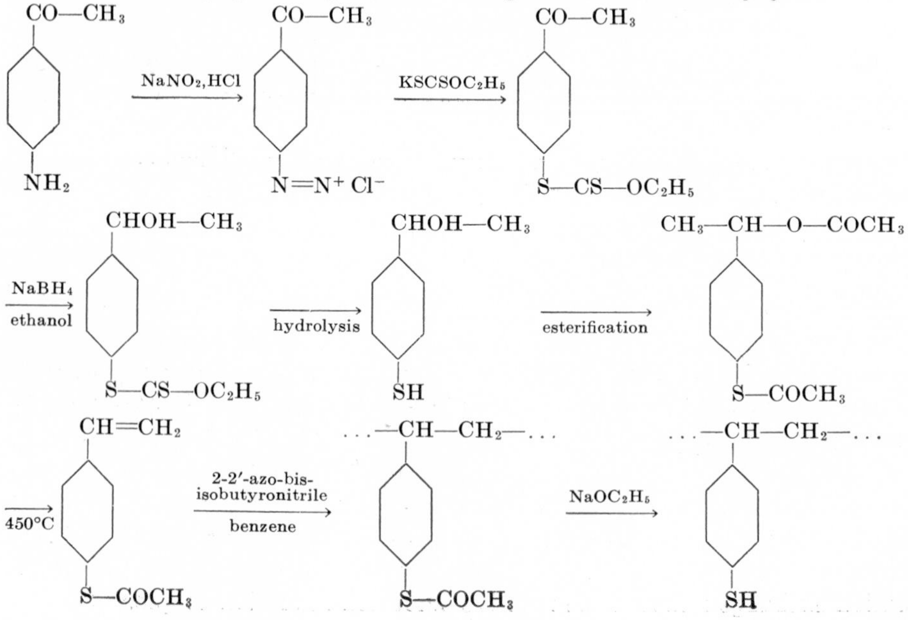

$CO-CH_3$

$NaNO_2, HCl$ → $CO-CH_3$ $N{=}N^+\ Cl^-$

$KSCSOC_2H_5$ → $CO-CH_3$ $S-CS-OC_2H_5$

$CHOH-CH_3$

$NaBH_4$ / ethanol → $S-CS-OC_2H_5$

hydrolysis → $CHOH-CH_3$ SH

esterification → $CH_3-CH-O-COCH_3$ $S-COCH_3$

$CH{=}CH_2$

450°C → $S-COCH_3$

2-2'-azo-bis-isobutyronitrile / benzene → $\ldots -CH-CH_2- \ldots$ $S-COCH_3$

$NaOC_2H_5$ → $\ldots -CH-CH_2- \ldots$ SH

$$\ldots-\text{CH}-\text{CH}_2-\ldots \quad\quad \ldots-\text{CH}-\text{CH}_2-\ldots \quad\quad \ldots-\text{CH}-\text{CH}_2-\ldots$$

$$\xrightarrow[\text{xanthogenate}]{\text{potassium}} \quad\quad\quad \xrightarrow{\text{alkali}} \quad\quad (12\text{-}3)$$

$$\text{N}{=}\text{N}^+\ \text{Cl}^- \quad\quad\quad \text{S}-\text{CS}-\text{O}-\text{C}_2\text{H}_5 \quad\quad\quad \text{SH}$$

This resin is an electron exchanger with a particularly low redox potential* (i.e., in its reduced state a very strong reduction agent).

Mercapto groups have also been introduced into polyamide resins such as nylon [2]

$$\begin{array}{c}\ldots \\ | \\ \text{NH} \\ | \\ \text{CO} \\ | \\ \ldots\end{array} \xrightarrow[\text{HCO}_2\text{H}]{\begin{array}{c}\text{H}_2\text{CO}\\\text{CH}_3\text{OH}\end{array}} \begin{array}{c}\ldots \\ | \\ \text{N}-\text{CH}_2\text{OCH}_3 \\ | \\ \text{CO} \\ | \\ \ldots\end{array} \xrightarrow[\text{CH}_3\text{C}_6\text{H}_4\text{SO}_3\text{H}]{\text{CH}_3\text{COSH}} \begin{array}{c}\ldots \\ | \\ \text{N}-\text{CH}_2\text{SCOCH}_3 \\ | \\ \text{CO} \\ | \end{array}$$

$$\xrightarrow[\text{C}_2\text{H}_5\text{OH}]{\text{KOH}} \begin{array}{c}\ldots \\ | \\ \text{N}-\text{CH}_2\text{SK} \\ | \\ \text{CO} \\ | \\ \ldots\end{array} \quad (12\text{-}4)$$

Some of the earliest electron exchangers were of this type.

Redox ion exchangers. Redox ion exchangers are easily prepared from conventional cation or anion exchangers. Either the counter ion is replaced by an ion such as Cu^{2+}, Fe^{3+}, SO_3^{2-}, etc., which can act as an oxidation (or reduction) agent [9,10,23,26,28,29,30], or an organic oxidation-reduction agent such as methylene blue is incorporated by sorption [26,29].

Duolite S-10, the only commercial redox resin so far, is a redox ion exchanger. This resin is an anion exchanger containing complexed cupric ions. It has been developed for removal of dissolved oxygen from water.

One class of synthetic redox ion exchangers deserves special mention. These are crosslinked polymers of chlorophyll or haemin derivatives containing metal-ion redox couples such as Fe^{3+}/Fe^{2+} in the form of very

---

* Throughout this chapter, the sign of the redox potential and standard redox potential is defined as recommended by the IUPAC [see *J. Am. Chem. Soc.*, **82**, 5517 (1960)]. Note that in many earlier publications by American authors the potentials are given with opposite signs.

strong complexes. Resins of this type are of little practical interest because of their high price and low redox capacity, but they are very interesting as models for biological redox systems [1,14].

12-2. REACTIONS AND APPLICATIONS

Electron exchangers react in the same way as the functional monomers which are anchored in their matrices.* An electron exchanger, in its reduced state, can reduce a dissolved substrate, provided that the redox potential of the substrate is higher than that of the electron exchanger; in other words, the electron exchanger must be a stronger reducing agent than the reduced substrate. In the course of the reaction the electron exchanger is oxidized and conveys electrons to the substrate and protons to the solution (or to the substrate). Reduction of Fe^{3+} by a hydroquinone-type electron exchanger may serve as an example

$$\ldots-CH-CH_2-\ldots \quad\quad \ldots-CH-CH_2-\ldots$$

$$HO-\langle\text{ring}\rangle-OH + 2Fe^{3+} \rightarrow O=\langle\text{ring}\rangle=O + 2Fe^{2+} + 2H^+$$

$$(12\text{-}5)$$

The reaction cannot be reversed since the redox couple Fe^{3+}/Fe^{2+} has a higher standard redox potential than the electron exchanger. In other words, Fe^{3+} is a stronger oxidizing agent than the oxidized electron exchanger and, correspondingly, Fe^{2+} is a weaker reducing agent than the reduced electron exchanger. Reduction of the resin can only be achieved by a stronger reducing agent, for example by Ti^{3+}:

$$\ldots-CH-CH_2-\ldots \quad\quad \ldots-CH-CH_2-\ldots$$

$$O=\langle\text{ring}\rangle=O \quad\rightarrow\quad HO-\langle\text{ring}\rangle-OH \quad\quad (12\text{-}6)$$

$$+ 2Ti^{3+} + 2H_2O \quad\quad\quad + 2TiO^{2+} + 2H^+$$

---

* Exceptions can arise from steric hindrance in the polymer. For example, it has been found that crosslinked methylvinylketone polymers, in contrast to analogous monomeric ketones, do not give the Meerwein-Ponndorf-Verley-Oppenauer reaction (oxidation of alcohols in the presence of aluminum alkoxide catalysts) [12]. A likely explanation is the following. According to Woodward, the reaction involves formation of a heterocyclic intermediate; polymerization of the vinyl groups makes formation of this intermediate impossible [12].

The reaction behavior of the electron exchanger can be quite generally expressed by the "electrode reaction"

$$\ldots-CH-CH_2-\ldots \qquad \ldots-CH-CH_2-\ldots$$

$$+ 2H^+ + 2e^- \quad (12\text{-}7)$$

Combination of this expression with the electrode reaction of the respective substrate couple gives the reaction equation of the system. In the example above, Eqs. (12-5) and (12-6) are obtained by combination of Eq. (12-7) with

$$Fe^{2+} \rightleftharpoons Fe^{3+} + e^- \qquad\qquad (12\text{-}8)$$

and
$$Ti^{3+} + H_2O \rightleftharpoons TiO^{2+} + 2H^+ + e^- \qquad (12\text{-}9)$$

respectively.

In electron exchangers with mercapto groups, oxidation involves reaction of two neighboring groups. The electrode reaction is*

$$\ldots-SH \qquad \ldots-S$$
$$\rightleftharpoons \qquad | + 2H^+ + 2e^- \qquad (12\text{-}10)$$
$$\ldots-SH \qquad \ldots-S$$

It is interesting to compare electron-exchange reactions with ion exchange. An ion exchanger in A form can be completely converted to the B form by treatment with a sufficient excess of a solution containing BY. (It is true that the required excess of BY may be very large if the resin prefers the ion A.) In contrast, conversion of electron exchangers from the oxidized to the reduced form, and vice versa, becomes virtually impossible if the reduction or oxidation agent is too weak, i.e., has too high or too low a redox potential. In unfavorable cases, practically no reaction occurs even when a very large excess of the agent is used. This situation is characteristic for any combination of two redox couples. For example, the reducing agent Fe^{2+} is too weak to reduce alkali ions to the metal. The oxidation and reduction abilities of an electron exchanger thus are confined to ranges which can be characterized by the standard redox potential of the resin (see also Sec. 11-3b). However, this difference between electron exchange and ion exchange is only a matter of degree. The expressions for thermodynamic equilibrium in oxidation-reduction reactions and in ion exchange are formally identical [compare Eq. (12-18) with Eq. (5-101)]. The difference in behavior is due to the difference in the free-energy changes. These are usually much greater in oxidation-reduction reactions, which are

---

* It has been claimed recently that the —SH groups are oxidized to —SO$_2^-$ groups [31a].

chemical reactions, than in ion exchange, which is merely a redistribution of counter ions by diffusion. As a result, equilibria in oxidation-reduction reactions generally are much more strongly favorable or unfavorable than in ion exchange.

The most important advantage of electron exchangers over dissolved oxidation or reduction agents is their insolubility. After oxidation or reduction of a substrate, the resin is readily removed from the solution. No contamination of the solution by redox agents or their products occurs. Equation (12-7) shows that only electrons and protons are transferred between the resin and the solution. Hence the only change in the solution—except for the oxidation state of the substrate—is an increase or decrease in pH. Even the pH remains constant if the substrate accepts or donates protons [for example, see reaction (12-14)].

Another advantage of electron exchangers is that they are readily regenerated after use.

In spite of these advantages, electron exchangers have so far not been widely used. The reason is, at least in part, that practical applications are seriously limited by the relatively low reaction rates and, in many cases, by insufficient chemical stability of the resins.

Several practical applications which illustrate the reaction behavior of electron exchangers are described below.

An application of practical importance is the *removal of dissolved oxygen* from water or aqueous solutions [10,11,20,23,29]. The reaction proceeds in two steps. The electrode reactions are

$$O_2 \ + 2H^+ + 2e^- \rightleftharpoons H_2O_2 \tag{12-11}$$
$$\underline{H_2O_2 + 2H^+ + 2e^- \rightleftharpoons 2H_2O} \tag{12-12}$$
$$O_2 \ + 4H^+ + 4e^- \rightleftharpoons 2H_2O \tag{12-13}$$

Combination of the over-all electrode reaction (12-13) with the electrode reaction of the electron exchanger gives

$$2RH_2 + O_2 \rightleftharpoons 2R + 2H_2O \tag{12-14}$$

where RH_2 is the reduced form, and R the oxidized form, of the electron exchanger.

Oxygen, when being reduced, accepts the protons which are released by the electron exchanger. Hence there is no pH change in the solution. The standard redox potential of the first step [reaction (12-11)] is +0.682 volt, and that of the second step [reaction (12-12)] is +1.77 volts. An electron exchanger with a standard redox potential which is lower than about +0.7 volt can thus accomplish both reactions. The second reaction can be made to proceed more slowly than the first one, though equilibrium is more favorable in the second reaction. In this way it is possible to isolate the intermediate product, H_2O_2 [21].

In analytical chemistry, electron exchangers can be used as an auxiliary in oxidimetric titrations, for example, for *reduction of* Fe^{3+} prior to iron determination by titration with permanganate [29]. The advantage of electron exchangers over the conventional Jones reductor is that the solution is not contaminated by metal ions. The standard redox potential of most electron exchangers is lower than that of the couple Fe^{3+}/Fe^{2+} (+0.771 volt) and thus is high enough for accomplishing the reduction.

Another application is *removal of dissolved halogen* from aqueous solutions, say,

$$RH_2 + Cl_2 \rightarrow R + 2H^+ + 2Cl^- \tag{12-15}$$

This method can also be used for quantitative determinations [29].

Redox polymers can be used for impregnating filter paper. Such papers have found various applications, for example, for qualitative tests for the presence of oxidation agents [4].

In all applications the electron exchanger is best chosen in such a way that its standard redox potential is just low enough for accomplishing the desired reduction, or high enough for the desired oxidation. Electron exchangers with unnecessarily low or high standard redox potentials require stronger reducing or oxidizing agents for their regeneration.

12-3. PHYSICOCHEMICAL PROPERTIES

Electron exchangers are characterized by their redox capacity, their standard redox potential, and their reaction rate. The redox capacity indicates the amount (in equivalents) of a substrate which can be oxidized or reduced by a given amount of the resin. The standard redox potential indicates which substrates can be oxidized or reduced. The reaction rate indicates the time required for oxidation or reduction under a given set of conditions.

a. Redox Capacity

The redox capacity is defined as the number of redox equivalents per unit volume or unit weight of the resin and is usually given in milliequivalents per gram of dry resin. The higher the redox capacity, the smaller is the amount of resin required for the oxidation or reduction of a given amount of substrate.

b. Redox Potential

The standard redox potential characterizes the oxidation and reduction strengths of the electron exchanger. The thermodynamic significance of redox potentials is discussed in the following.

Redox potentials of redox couples in solution. The *redox potential* of a redox couple in solution is defined as the electric potential difference between the solution of the couple and the standard hydrogen electrode. This standard electrode is a platinum electrode which is immersed in an acid solution with unit H^+-ion activity and is exposed to hydrogen gas bubbling through under 1 atm pressure. The redox potential of, say, a mixed solution containing Fe^{3+} and Fe^{2+} thus is the potential difference between the half-cells

$$Pt|Fe^{3+}, Fe^{2+} \quad \text{and} \quad \begin{array}{c|c} H^+ & H_2 \\ a_H = 1 & 1 \text{ atm} \end{array}|Pt \tag{12-16}$$

Each oxidation involves, by definition, release of electrons, and each reduction involves uptake of electrons. When two redox couples are in contact with one another (for example, by being in the same solution), electrons can be transferred directly from one species to the other. One species is reduced, the other is oxidized [cf. reaction (12-5)]. In contrast, the two redox couples in a cell such as (12-16) are in contact only via the platinum electrodes. Oxidation or reduction of either couple can only occur when the electrodes are short-circuited, so that electrons can flow from one half-cell to the other. This flow of electrons is an electric current which can do work. The driving force of the current, i.e., the electric potential difference between the two half-cells under reversible conditions (infinitesimal current), is a quantitative measure for the ability of the system to do electric work and thus for the tendency of one couple to reduce or oxidize the other. The potential difference is zero when the two half-cells are in equilibrium with one another. Hence equilibrium between two couples is attained when both have reached the same redox potential.

The oxidation (or reduction) tendency of a couple, say, Fe^{3+}/Fe^{2+} depends on the concentration ratio of the oxidized and the reduced component (Fe^{3+} and Fe^{2+}). The redox potential thus is a function of this ratio. The *standard redox potential* of a redox couple is defined as the redox potential which is attained when the activity ratio of the oxidized and reduced component is unity.

Thermodynamic relations between the standard redox potential, the redox potential, and the equilibrium constant of the oxidation-reduction reaction can be derived in the following way. In the cell (12-16), reaction of one equivalent (without significant concentration changes) according to

$$Fe^{3+} + \tfrac{1}{2}H_2 \to Fe^{2+} + H^+ \tag{12-17}$$

is accompanied by a decrease in free energy

$$-\Delta G = -\sum_i \mu_i n_i = -\sum_i \mu_i^0 n_i - RT \sum_i n_i \ln a_i = RT \left(\ln \mathcal{K} + \ln \frac{[Fe^{3+}][H_2]^{\frac{1}{2}}}{[Fe^{2+}][H^+]} \right) \tag{12-18}$$

where μ_i = chemical potential of species i; μ_i^0 = standard chemical potential of species i; n_i = moles of i appearing or vanishing ($+1$ for Fe^{2+} and H^+, -1 for Fe^{3+}, $-\tfrac{1}{2}$ for H_2); a_i = activity of species i; $\mathcal{K}$ = thermodynamic equilibrium constant of reaction (12-17); square brackets indicate activities.

In a cell such as (12-16) and with reversible current flow the energy is completely recovered as electric work $E\mathfrak{F}$:

$$E \cdot \mathfrak{F} = -\Delta G = RT \left(\ln \mathcal{K} + \ln \frac{[Fe^{3+}][H_2]^{\frac{1}{2}}}{[Fe^{2+}][H^+]} \right) \tag{12-19}$$

where E = electric potential difference between the electrodes; $\mathfrak{F}$ = faraday constant.

When the *standard redox potential* of the couple Fe^{3+}/Fe^{2+} is measured, the activities (or activity ratios) in Eq. (12-19) are all unity by definition. Hence the standard redox potential is

$$E^0 = \frac{RT}{\mathfrak{F}} \ln \mathcal{K} \tag{12-20}$$

When the *redox potential* is measured, the activities of H^+ and H_2 are unity by definition. Hence the redox potential is

$$E_r = E^0 + \frac{RT}{\mathfrak{F}} \ln \frac{[Fe^{3+}]}{[Fe^{2+}]} \tag{12-21}$$

Analogous relations hold for all other redox couples. The quantity $\mathcal{K}$ in these equations is, by definition, the equilibrium constant of the equilibrium between the respective couple and the couple H^+/H_2.

Redox potentials of electron exchangers. Redox potentials of electron exchangers cannot be measured directly since the resin is unable to exchange electrons directly with the platinum electrode. Instead, the redox potential of a dissolved couple which is in equilibrium with the resin can be measured. This potential is given as the redox potential of the electron exchanger. Correspondingly, the standard redox potential of an electron exchanger is the redox potential of a dissolved couple which is in equilibrium with the resin when half of the reactive groups of the latter are oxidized and the other half reduced. This definition is probably not quite unambiguous, but is commonly used.

The electrode reactions of electron exchangers involve protons [cf. Eq. (12-7)]. The redox potential of the resin thus depends on the pH of the solution. For example, the redox potential of a hydroquinone-type resin is approximately given by

$$E_r = E^0 + \frac{RT}{\mathfrak{F}} \ln \frac{[R]^{1/2}[H^+]}{[RH_2]^{1/2}} = E^0 + \frac{RT}{2\mathfrak{F}} \ln \frac{[R]}{[RH_2]} + \frac{RT}{\mathfrak{F}} \ln [H^+] \quad (12\text{-}22)$$

where $[R]$ and $[RH_2]$ are the concentrations of the oxidized and reduced groups, respectively.

The standard redox potential is, by definition, the potential with $[H^+] = 1$, i.e., at pH 0.*

Equation (12-22) shows that the redox potential increases by

$$\left(\frac{RT}{\mathfrak{F}}\right) \ln 10 = 0.059 \text{ volt}$$

when the pH is lowered by one unit. Hence electron exchangers are stronger oxidizing agents and weaker reducing agents when the solution is more acidic. In alkaline solutions, one or both hydroxyl groups of the hydroquinone can dissociate. At high pH, the electrode reaction thus is

$$+ 2e^- \quad (12\text{-}23)$$

instead of Eq. (12-7). The redox potential becomes independent of the pH since Eq. (12-23) does not involve protons or hydroxyl ions.

---

* Occasionally, the redox potential is given as $E_r = E^0 + (RT/2\mathfrak{F}) \ln [R]/[RH_2]$. In this case the standard potential is defined differently by inclusion of the term $(RT/\mathfrak{F}) \ln [H^+]$ and thus is pH dependent.

Experimental measurements of redox potentials show the expected pH dependence [16,17,19] and indicate that, as a rule, the standard redox potential of a couple is little affected by incorporation of the couple into an electron exchanger or redox ion exchanger [17,19,29].

The relation (12-22) is obtained with the assumptions that all functional groups in the resin have the same standard potential, that activity coefficients can be disregarded, and that the reaction proceeds in one single step. Usually, the experimental redox-potential curve is somewhat steeper than Eq. (12-22) indicates (see Fig. 12-1). This deviation has been tentatively explained by differences in the standard potentials of the groups which are, of course, not in an identical environment, and by formation of reaction

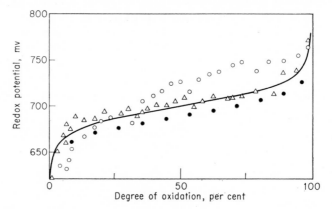

Fig. 12-1. Redox-potential curves of hydroquinone-type electron exchangers ($\bigcirc$, $\triangle$). The redox potential is shown as a function of the degree of oxidation of the resin. *Solid line:* theoretical curve calculated from Eq. (12-22). Values for monomeric hydroquinone ($\bullet$) are shown for comparison. *From G. Manecke* [17].

intermediates such as semiquinones [5,16,17,29]. A rather stable semiquinone is formed, for example, in condensation products of 1,4,5,8-tetrahydroxynaphthalene [31]:

$$\ldots{-}CH_2{-} \quad \rightleftharpoons \quad \ldots{-}CH_2{-} \quad {-}CH_2{-}\ldots \quad + 2H^+ + 2e^-$$

(12-24)

$$\rightleftharpoons \ldots{-}CH_2{-} \quad {-}CH_2{-}\ldots \quad + 4H^+ + 4e^-$$

Here, the semiquinone is stabilized by hydrogen bonding.

Another factor which is not included in the simple picture leading to Eq. (12-22) is mutual interaction between neighboring reactive groups. Recently, an attempt has been made to account for this effect by using a statistical model which closely resembles Katchalsky's model of the ion exchanger (see Secs. 5-1 and 4-4b) [25]. However, this more refined theory has so far not been sufficiently tested.

The standard redox potentials of the most common redox couples are given in Table 12-1. Couples which are suited for incorporation into elec-

Table 12-1. Standard redox potentials of some of the most common redox couples†

Redox couples in acidic solution

Couple	E^0 Volts
$Cr^{2+} = Cr^{3+} + e^-$	-0.41
$Ti^{2+} = Ti^{3+} + e^-$	-0.37
$N_2H_5^+ = N_2 + 5H^+ + 4e^-$	-0.23
$S_2O_6^{2-} + 2H_2O = 2SO_4^{2-} + 4H^+ + 2e^-$	-0.22
$UO_2^+ = UO_2^{2+} + e^-$	$+0.05$
$Ti^{3+} + H_2O = TiO^{2+} + 2H^+ + e^-$	$+0.1$
$Sn^{2+} = Sn^{4+} + 2e^-$	$+0.15$
$Cu^+ = Cu^{2+} + e^-$	$+0.153$
$CH_3OH(aq) = H_2CO(aq) + 2H^+ + 2e^-$	$+0.19$
$Fe(CN)_6^{3+} = Fe(CN)_6^{4+} + e^-$	$+0.36$
*1,4-naphtohydroquinone = 1,4-naphthoquinone $+ 2H^+ + 2e^-$	$+0.480$
*Cu = Cu$^+$ + e$^-$	$+0.521$
*Leukomethylene blue = methylene blue $+ 2H^+ + 2e^-$	$+0.53$
$2I^- = I_2 + 2e^-$	$+0.5355$
$MnO_4^{2-} = MnO_4^- + e^-$	$+0.564$
$PtCl_4^{2-} + 2Cl^- = PtCl_6^{2-} + 2e^-$	$+0.68$
$H_2O_2 = O_2 + 2H^+ + 2e^-$	$+0.682$
*Benzohydroquinone = benzoquinone $+ 2H^+ + 2e^-$	$+0.6994$
*Fe^{2+} = Fe^{3+} + e$^-$	$+0.771$
*Ag = Ag$^+$ + e$^-$	$+0.7991$
$Hg_2^{2+} = 2Hg^{2+} + 2e^-$	$+0.920$
$ClO_3^- + H_2O = ClO_4^- + 2H^+ + 2e^-$	$+1.19$
$\frac{1}{2}I_2 + 3H_2O = IO_3^- + 6H^+ + 5e^-$	$+1.195$
$Ti^+ = Ti^{3+} + 2e^-$	$+1.25$
$2NH_4^+ = N_2H_5^+ + 3H^+ + 2e^-$	$+1.275$
$PdCl_4^{2-} + 2Cl^- = PdCl_6^{2-} + 2e^-$	$+1.288$
$2Cr^{3+} + 7H_2O = Cr_2O_7^{2-} + 14H^+ + 6e^-$	$+1.33$
$NH_4^+ + H_2O = NH_3OH^+ + 2H^+ + 2e^-$	$+1.35$
$2Cl^- = Cl_2 + 2e^-$	$+1.3595$
*Au = Au^{3+} + 3e$^-$	$+1.50$
$Mn^{2+} = Mn^{3+} + e^-$	$+1.51$
$Mn^{2+} + 4H_2O = MnO_4^- + 8H^+ + 5e^-$	$+1.51$
$\frac{1}{2}Br_2 + 3H_2O = BrO_3^- + 6H^+ + 5e^-$	$+1.52$
$Ce^{3+} = Ce^{4+} + e^-$	$+1.61$
$Co^{2+} = Co^{3+} + e^-$	$+1.82$
$2SO_4^{2-} = S_2O_8^{2-} + 2e^-$	$+2.01$

† For sign convention see footnote on p. 555.

Table 12-1. Standard redox potentials of some of the most
common redox couples (*Continued*)

*Redox couples in alkaline solution**

Couple	E_B^0 Volts
$HPO_3^{2-} + 3OH^- = PO_4^{3-} + 2H_2O + 2e^-$	-1.12
$S_2O_4^{2-} + 4OH^- = 2SO_3^{2-} + 2H_2O + 2e^-$	-1.12
$SO_3^{2-} + 2OH^- = SO_4^{2-} + H_2O + 2e^-$	-0.93
$AsO_2^- + 4OH^- = AsO_4^{3-} + 2H_2O + 2e^-$	-0.67
$S_2O_3^{2-} + 6OH^- = 2SO_3^{2-} + 3H_2O + 4e^-$	-0.58
$NO_2^- + 2OH^- = NO_3^- + H_2O + 2e^-$	$+0.01$
$2S_2O_3^{2-} = S_4O_6^{2-} + 2e^-$	$+0.08$
$2NH_3(aq) + 2OH^- = N_2H_4 + 2H_2O + 2e^-$	$+0.1$
$Co(NH_3)_6^{2+} = Co(NH_3)_6^{3+} + e^-$	$+0.1$
$J^- + 6OH^- = JO_3^- + 3H_2O + 6e^-$	$+0.26$
$ClO_2^- + 2OH^- = ClO_3^- + H_2O + 2e^-$	$+0.33$
$ClO_3^- + 2OH^- = ClO_4^- + H_2O + 2e^-$	$+0.36$
$Br^- + 6OH^- = BrO_3^- + 3H_2O + 6e^-$	$+0.61$
$3OH^- = HO_2^- + H_2O + 2e^-$	$+0.88$

* The reference electrode for these couples involving OH^- ions is the hydrogen couple in alkaline solution of unit activity (the potential difference between this couple and the standard hydrogen electrode is 0.828 volt).

From W. M. Latimer [13].

tron exchangers or redox ion exchangers are marked with asterisks. The table can be used for looking up which reactions can be accomplished by a given electron exchanger and which regeneration agents can be used. In its reduced form, the electron exchanger can reduce all couples which have a higher standard potential, and in its oxidized form it can oxidize all couples which have a lower standard potential. Reductive regeneration requires a reducing agent with lower standard potential, oxidative regeneration an oxidizing agent with higher standard potential. Note that the redox potentials are pH dependent if the electrode reactions involve H^+ or OH^- ions.

c. Kinetics

The kinetics of reactions of electron exchangers has so far not been thoroughly investigated. It is safe to assume that the *rate-determining step* is intraparticle diffusion of the substrates and products if the actual chemical reaction is fast and diffusion is slow. This is particularly true with resins of large particle size and low solvent content. On the other hand, the actual chemical reaction of the functional groups may be slower than diffusion and thus be rate-controlling.

The *reaction rate* is usually rather low. The half time of the reaction is often of the order of hours or days [5,19,29]. Not all reactions which are possible according to the standard redox potentials proceed fast enough for practical applications. When diffusion is rate-controlling, the rate can be

increased by reducing the particle size of the resin.   Elevated temperature
enhances the rates of both diffusion and chemical reaction and thus is beneficial.   However, it must be ascertained whether the resin is stable at the
higher temperature under the conditions of the reaction.

12-4. EXPERIMENTAL METHODS

a. Determination of Redox Capacity

The determination is usually made in the following way.   A known amount of the
electron exchanger or redox ion exchanger is placed in a column.   The resin is completely
reduced with a suitable agent and is washed with water from which dissolved oxygen has
been thoroughly removed.   A moderate excess of a sufficiently strong oxidizing agent is
now passed through the column.   The number of equivalents which have been reduced

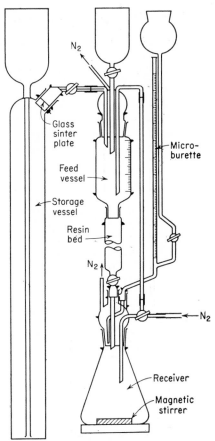

FIG. 12-2. Apparatus for measuring oxidations and reductions with electron exchangers.
The resin is placed in a small glass column which is connected to a feed vessel and a
receiver.   Before and during the measurement, nitrogen is passed through the feed
vessel and the receiver.   A microburette for titrations in the effluent is attached to the
receiver.   The apparatus can be used for determining redox capacities.   *From B.
Sansoni* [29].

by the resin is determined in the effluent by oxidimetric titration. Alternatively, the resin can be completely oxidized and washed, and the oxidation of a reducing agent can then be determined in the same way. The standard redox potential of the oxidizing agent must be higher and that of the reducing agent must be lower than that of the electron exchanger. For most electron exchangers, solutions of Fe^{3+} and dithionite can be used. It is important to exclude air since the presence of dissolved oxygen may cause serious errors. A suitable apparatus is shown in Fig. 12-2.

b. Standard Redox Potential and Potentiometric Titration

The redox potential is defined as the electric potential difference between the couple and the standard hydrogen electrode. Actual measurements, however, are usually made with a calomel electrode as the reference electrode. (The potential difference between the calomel electrode and the standard hydrogen electrode is $+0.2415$ volts.) Redox potentials of dissolved redox couples are usually measured in the cell

$$\text{Pt} \quad | \quad \text{redox couple} \quad \left| \quad \begin{array}{c} \text{KCl} \\ \text{saturated} \end{array} \right| \quad \text{Hg}_2\text{Cl}_2 | \text{Hg} \qquad (12\text{-}25)$$

Redox potentials of electron exchangers and redox ion exchangers are measured with the resin added to the solution of the redox couple.

The redox potential curve (see Fig. 12-1) of an electron exchanger or redox ion exchanger is determined by titrating the completely reduced resin with a sufficiently strong oxidizing agent. The potential difference between a platinum electrode and a calomel

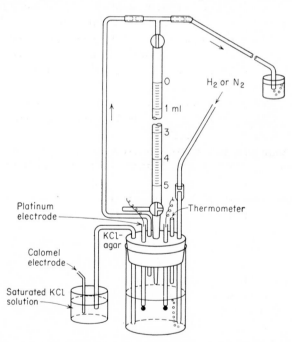

Fig. 12-3. Apparatus for potentiometric titrations of dissolved redox couples and electron exchangers. The titrant is added from the burette to the receiver which contains the resin and a solution of the mediator and is equipped with a calomel and two platinum electrodes (for double determinations). The apparatus is flushed with nitrogen or hydrogen. The electric circuit for potential measurements is shown in Fig. 8-28. *From L. Michaelis* [22].

electrode is measured after each addition of the agent. Sufficient time for attainment of equilibrium after each addition must be allowed [5,16,17,19,32].

The resin is not in direct contact with the electrodes. Hence the measured redox potential is not that of the resin but that of the (practically completely reduced) titrant which is in equilibrium with the resin. The redox potential curve of a couple is very steep when either the oxidized or the reduced component is in great excess (see Fig. 12-1). Under such conditions the potential is very sensitive to even minor disturbances. Therefore electron echangers are usually titrated in the presence of a so-called "mediator," namely, a dissolved redox couple with a standard potential which is similar to that of the resin [16,19]. The mediator is oxidized along with the resin and thus guarantees the presence of a substantial amount of an oxidized component in the solution. In this way the potential is stabilized; however, the amount of the mediator must be kept small since otherwise the potential curve of the mediator rather than that of the resin is obtained. Cassidy, who introduced mediators, recommends the use of one to two equivalents of the mediator per hundred equivalents of the resin [16].

SUMMARY

Electron exchangers are crosslinked polymers which carry built-in reversible redox couples. The reactive groups can be introduced either as constituents of the monomeric units or by substitution after polymerization. Electron exchangers are used for oxidizing or reducing substrates in solutions. In their ability to perform such reactions, electron exchangers closely resemble the respective monomeric redox agents which have been incorporated in the resin matrix. On the other hand, the unique feature of electron exchangers is that they are insoluble and thus are readily separated from the solution with which they have reacted. Also, the electron exchangers can be regenerated after use.

Redox ion exchangers are conventional ion exchangers which carry redox couples either as counter ions or as sorbed solutes. Their behavior closely resembles that of electron exchangers.

Electron exchangers and redox ion exchangers can be characterized by their redox capacity, their standard redox potential, and their reaction rate. The redox capacity (usually given in milliequivalents per gram dry resin) indicates how much resin is required for oxidation or reduction of a given amount of a substrate. The standard redox potential is a quantitative measure for the oxidation and reduction strengths of the resin and indicates which substrates can be oxidized or reduced and which agents can be used for regeneration. The reaction rates are usually considerably lower than those of ion exchange.

The most serious limitations in practical applications of electron exchangers are, as a rule, the low reaction rates and, in many cases, the lack of chemical stability of the resins.

REFERENCES

1. Broser, W., and W. Lautsch, *Naturwissenschaften*, **38**, 208 (1951).
2. Burke, W. J. (E. I. du Pont de Nemours), U.S. Patent 2,418,497, 1947.
3. Cassidy, H. G., *J. Am. Chem. Soc.*, **71**, 402 (1949).

4. Cassidy, H. G., M. Ezrin, and I. H. Updegraff, *J. Am. Chem. Soc.*, **75**, 1615 (1953).
*5. Ezrin, M., and H. G. Cassidy, *Ann. N.Y. Acad. Sci.*, **57**, 79 (1953).
6. Ezrin, M., H. G. Cassidy, and I. H. Updegraff, *J. Am. Chem. Soc.*, **75**, 1610 (1953).
7. Ezrin, M., and H. G. Cassidy, *J. Am. Chem. Soc.*, **78**, 2525 (1956).
8. Gregor, H. P., D. Dolar, and G. K. Hoeschele, *J. Am. Chem. Soc.*, **77**, 3675 (1955).
9. Grubhofer, N., *Naturwissenschaften*, **42**, 557 (1955).
10. I. G. Farbenindustrie, Ger. Patent Appl., I VIb 75,869, 1944.
11. I. G. Farbenindustrie, Ger. Patent Appl., I 77,574, 1944; also listed for Farben-fabriken Bayer, Ger. Patent Appl., F 7,608.
12. Kun, K. A., and H. G. Cassidy, *J. Polymer Sci.*, **44**, 383 (1960).
13. Latimer, W. M., "The Oxidation States of the Elements and Their Potentials in Aqueous Solutions," 2d ed., p. 339, Prentice-Hall, Inc., Englewood Cliffs, N.J., 1952.
14. Lautsch, W., W. Broser, U. Döring, and H. Zoschke, *Naturwissenschaften*, **38**, 210 (1951).
15. Luttinger, L., and H. G. Cassidy, *J. Polymer Sci.*, **20**, 417 (1956).
16. Luttinger, L., and H. G. Cassidy, *J. Polymer Sci.*, **22**, 271 (1956).
17. Manecke, G., *Z. Elektrochem.*, **57**, 189 (1953).
18. Manecke, G., *Z. Elektrochem.*, **58**, 363 (1954).
19. Manecke, G., *Z. Elektrochem.*, **58**, 369 (1954).
20. Manecke, G., *Angew. Chem.*, **67**, 613 (1955).
21. Manecke, G., *Angew. Chem.*, **68**, 582 (1956).
*22. Michaelis, L., in "Physical Methods of Organic Chemistry," A. Weissberger (ed.), vol. II, p. 1096, Interscience Publishers, Inc., New York, 1946.
23. Mills, G. F., and B. N. Dickinson, *Ind. Eng. Chem.*, **41**, 2842 (1949).
24. Overberger, C. G., and A. Lebovits, *J. Am. Chem. Soc.*, **77**, 3675 (1955).
25. Robinson, I. D., M. Fernandez-Rofojo, and H. G. Cassidy, *J. Polymer Sci.*, **39**, 47 (1959).
26. Sansoni, B., *Naturwissenschaften*, **39**, 281 (1952).
27. Sansoni, B., *Naturwissenschaften*, **41**, 212 (1954).
28. Sansoni, B., *Naturwissenschaften*, **41**, 213 (1954).
*29. Sansoni, B., Thesis, Munich, 1956.
30. Sansoni, B., and K. Dorfner, *Angew. Chem.*, **71**, 160 (1959).
31. Soloway, S., and L. Schwartz, *Science*, **121**, 730 (1955).
31a. Trostyanskaya, E. B., and A. S. Tevlina, *Zhur. Anal. Khim.*, **15**, 402 (1960).
32. Updegraff, I. H., and H. G. Cassidy, *J. Am. Chem. Soc.*, **71**, 407 (1949).
33. Verplanck, V., and H. G. Cassidy, *J. Polymer Sci.*, **19**, 307 (1956).

* Review articles are marked with asterisks.

Appendix

SYMBOLS, ABBREVIATIONS, AND UNITS

The most important symbols, abbreviations, and units which are used in the text are listed in the following tables. In cases in which the definition of a quantity is not obvious, reference is made to the page in the text where the definition can be looked up.

Much to the chagrin of all authors and readers there are, in most scientific books, more physical quantities than letters in the Latin and Greek alphabets. This book is no exception. Thus a certain duplication of symbols was unavoidable. A few quantities which appear only rarely have symbols assigned which are used for other quantities in other parts of the book and are not listed in the tables, but are extensively defined where used in the text.

As a general rule, physical quantities and constants are given in italics, and units and chemical symbols (including the symbols A, B, Y, i, etc., for arbitrary species) are given in roman.

Physical Quantities

a_i thermodynamic activity of species i*
$a_{\pm}$ mean thermodynamic activity of an electrolyte*
a^0 Debye-Hückel parameter (distance of closest approach)
C_i concentration of species i in moles per unit volume (molarity)
C total concentration in equivalents per unit volume
$\mathbb{c}$ concentration of cations *plus* anions, page 386
d membrane thickness
D_i diffusion coefficient of species i
D_{AB} interdiffusion coefficient of counter ions A and B
$\bar{D}_0$ mobility parameter of pore liquid, page 406
E electric potential difference
E_0 standard electrode potential
E^0 standard redox potential
E_{diff} diffusion potential
E_{Don} Donnan potential, page 141
E_m membrane potential, page 369

---

* Note that numerical values depend on the choice of the standard and reference states.

E_r redox potential

E_{app} apparent activation energy of over-all process, page 539

E_{diff} activation energy of diffusion

E_r activation energy of chemical reaction

f_i molar activity coefficient of species i

$\mathcal{f}_i$ rational activity coefficient of species i

F Helmholtz free energy

G Gibbs free energy

H enthalpy

H height equivalent of effective plate, pages 453, 463

H_0 plate-height contribution from finite particle size, page 463

H_f plate-height contribution from film diffusion, page 463

H_p plate-height contribution from particle diffusion, page 463

I electric current density (charge transfer through unit cross section per unit time)

J_i flux of species i (moles per unit cross section and unit time)

$(J_i)_{con}$ convective flux of species i, page 329

$(J_i)_{diff}$ diffusion flux of species i, page 268

$(J_i)_{el}$ electric transference of species i, page 268

$\mathcal{g}(x,y)$ $\mathcal{g}$ function of arguments x and y, page 472

k reaction rate constant

k' specific rate constant, page 543

k_{app} apparent rate constant of over-all process, page 539

k_s rate constant of surface reaction, page 536

K_n nth cumulative molal complex-formation constant, page 204

K_{sp} solubility product

K_w dissociation constant of water

$\mathcal{K}$ thermodynamic equilibrium constant of chemical reaction

K_B^A molal selectivity coefficient for exchange of A for B, page 153

$K_B'^A$ molar selectivity coefficient for exchange of A for B, page 154

K_{aB}^A corrected molal selectivity coefficient for exchange of A for B, page 154

$\mathcal{K}_B^A$ thermodynamic equilibrium constant* for exchange of A for B, page 155

$^N\mathcal{K}_B^A$ rational thermodynamic equilibrium constant for exchange of A for B, page 195

m_i concentration of species i in moles per unit weight of solvent (molality)

$\bar{m}_R$ concentration of fixed ionic groups in equivalents per unit weight of solvent in the ion exchanger

M_i over-all molality of species i (including complexes formed by i), page 204

M_i molecular weight of species i

n_i number of moles of species i

N maximum ligand number in (mononuclear) complexes

N number of effective plates in column operations, page 455

$\mathfrak{N}$ number of transfer units (or reaction units) in column operations, page 472

N_i mole fraction of species i

P pressure

q membrane cross section

q internal cross section of columns

$\bar{q}_i$ number of moles of species i in specific amount of ion exchanger

q_I current efficiency, page 398

$\mathfrak{q}$ efficiency of ion-exchanger catalysts, page 543

Q_i amount of species i in moles

Q_{vol} volume capacity, page 75

---

* Note that numerical values depend on the choice of the standard and reference states.

Q_{weight} weight capacity, page 73
r radial space coordinate
r_0 particle radius of spherical ion exchanger beads
$\mathfrak{R}$ electric resistance
S entropy
t time
t_i transference number of species i, page 326
T absolute temperature
$\mathfrak{T}$ throughput ratio in column operations, page 472
u_i electrochemical mobility of species i (negative for anions), page 329
$\bar{u}_0$ mobility parameter of pore liquid, page 330
U fractional attainment of equilibrium, page 260
v linear flow rate in column operations (solution volume per unit cross section of the column and unit time)
$\mathfrak{v}$ convection rate (rate of motion of center of gravity), page 329
v_i partial molar volume of species i
V volume
$\dot{V}$ volume transfer (volume per unit cross section and unit time)
V_b bed volume of columns
$\bar{V}_e$ equivalent volume of ion exchangers
V_i peak retention volume of species i, page 455
$\bar{V}_0$ volume of unstretched matrix, page 89
W solvent content of ion exchangers in weight per cent
x linear space coordinate
x_i equivalent ionic fraction of counter ion i, page 152
X concentration of fixed ionic groups in equivalents per unit volume of the ion exchanger
X_i amount of species i in unit volume of packed bed (including interstitial solution)
$\bar{X}_i$ concentration of species i in the ion exchanger in moles per unit volume of bed
z axial space coordinate in columns
z_i electrochemical valence of ion i (negative for anions)
Z bed length in column operations
α degree of dissociation
α_B^A separation factor for exchange of A for B, page 153
β fractional void volume in ion-exchange beds
γ_i molal activity coefficient of species i
$\gamma_\pm$ mean molal activity coefficient of an electrolyte
$\ddot{o}$ film thickness, page 253
ϵ dielectric constant
ϵ fractional pore volume of ion exchanger
η degree of utilization, pages 424, 466, 533
η_i electrochemical potential of species i, page 141
κ specific electric conductivity
κ Debye-Hückel parameter ($1/\kappa$ = radius of ionic cloud)
κ_b specific electric conductivity of ion-exchange bed
$\bar{\kappa}_0$ convection conductivity, pages 328, 331
λ_i molal distribution coefficient of species i, page 127
λ_i' molar distribution coefficient of species i, page 127
λ_i'' column distribution ratio of species i, page 452
Λ_i over-all molal distribution coefficient of species i (including complexes formed by i), page 207
μ_i chemical potential of species i, page 110
ν number of ions formed by dissociation of an electrolyte

ν_i number of ions of species i formed by dissociation of an electrolyte
Π swelling pressure, page 109
ρ density
ρ_0 specific flow resistance of ion exchanger, page 330
φ electric potential
ϕ osmotic coefficient
ω sign of fixed charges (-1 for cation exchangers, $+1$ for anion exchangers)
ω Thiele modulus, page 533

Subscripts, Superscripts, Etc.

Subscripts Na, Li, A, B, Y, i, etc. refer to the species named.   If not stated otherwise, A, B, C, . . . are counter ions, Y and Z are co-ions, N is a nonelectrolyte, i is an arbitrary species, and w is the solvent.

Subscripts $+$ and $-$ are used for the cation and anion, respectively, in systems with one electrolyte only.

Quantities and symbols with overbars ($\bar{C}_i$, $\overline{Na^+}$, etc.) are used for the interior of the ion exchanger.   Underscored symbols are used for solid phases.

Superscript ^{0} in thermodynamic functions refers to the standard state.

Prime and double prime ($'$ and $''$) are used in membrane systems for denoting the left and right membrane surface, respectively.

Physical Constants

e	elementary charge	$1.602 \cdot 10^{-19}$ coulomb molecule^{-1}
$\mathfrak{F}$	Faraday constant	96,494 coulomb mole^{-1}
g	gravitational constant	981 cm sec^{-2}
k	Boltzmann constant	$1.380 \cdot 10^{-16}$ erg molecule^{-1} deg^{-1}
N_L	Avogadro number	$6.023 \cdot 10^{23}$
R	gas constant	$8.314 \cdot 10^7$ erg mole^{-1} deg^{-1}
		$= 0.0821$ liter atm mole^{-1} deg^{-1}

Units and Conversion Factors

A	angstrom unit	1 A	$= 10^{-8}$ cm
μ	micron	1 μ	$= 10^{-4}$ cm
ml	milliliter	1 ml	$= 10^{-3}$ liter
atm	physical atmosphere	1 atm	$= 1.013 \cdot 10^6$ dyne-cm^{-2}
amp	ampere	1 amp	$= 1$ coulomb sec^{-1}
ma	milliampere	1 ma	$= 10^{-3}$ amp
mv	millivolt	1 mv	$= 10^{-3}$ volt
Ω	ohm	1 Ω	$= 1$ volt amp^{-1}
cal	calorie	1 cal	$= 4.185 \cdot 10^7$ erg
kcal	kilocalorie	1 kcal	$= 1000$ cal
eq	equivalent		
M	molarity	1 M	$= 1$ mole per liter solution
N	normality	1 N	$= 1$ equivalent per liter solution

1 joule $= 1$ volt coulomb $= 10^7$ ergs
$(RT/\mathfrak{F}) \ln x = 59.2 \log x$[mv] at 25°C

Mathematical Symbols

d	complete differential	$$\sum_{n=0}^{N} x_n = x_0 + x_1 + \cdots + x_N$$
∂	partial differential	$$\prod_{n=0}^{N} x_n = x_0 \cdot x_1 \cdot x_2 \cdots x_N$$
Δ	finite difference	$\exp(x) = e^x$
log	decadic logarithm	$\mathrm{erf}(x) = \dfrac{2}{\sqrt{\pi}} \displaystyle\int_{z=0}^{z=x} e^{-z^2}\, \mathrm{d}z$
ln	natural logarithm	$\mathrm{erfc}(x) = 1 - \mathrm{erf}\,(x)$
sin	sine	
cos	cosine	
tan	tangent	$\pi = 3.14159$
cot	cotangent	
sinh	hyperbolic sine	
cosh	hyperbolic cosine	
tanh	hyperbolic tangent	
$|x|$	absolute value of x	
div	divergence	
grad	gradient	

Vectors are given in boldface type.

Conversion Table for U.S. Standard Screen Series*

Mesh	Particle radius, cm	Mesh	Particle radius, cm	Mesh	Particle radius, cm
5	0.20	50	0.015	140	0.0053
10	0.10	60	0.013	170	0.0044
16	0.060	70	0.011	200	0.0037
20	0.042	80	0.0089	230	0.0031
30	0.030	100	0.0075	270	0.0027
40	0.021	120	0.0063	325	0.0022

* Note that most resin manufacturers screen their resins partially air-dried. Thus the beads, when fully water-swollen, are slightly larger than indicated on the container.

Table of the Most Common Commercial Ion Exchangers*

Cation Exchangers

Matrix	Ionic group	Trade name	Manufacturer	Capacity		Moisture content, % wt	Maximum temperature, °C	pH range	Physical form	Remarks
				meq/g dry resin	meq/ml resin bed					
Polystyrene resins	$-SO_3^-$	Amberlite IR-120	Rohm & Haas Co.†	4.3–5	1.9	44–48	120	0–14	Spherical beads	Standard resin, ca. 8% DVB
		Amberlite IR-122	Rohm & Haas Co.†	4.3–5	2.1	40–44	120	0–14	Spherical beads	ca. 10% DVB, higher resistance to oxidizing agents
		Amberlite IR-124	Rohm & Haas Co.†	4.3–5	2.1	37–41	120	0–14	Spherical beads	ca. 12% DVB, higher resistance to oxidizing agents
		Amberlite 200	Rohm & Haas Co.†	4.3	1.75	47–52	120	0–14	Spherical beads	Higher mech. and chem. stability, lower capacity
		Amberlite XE-100	Rohm & Haas Co.†	4.5	1.2	58–65	120	0–14	Spherical beads	ca. 4% DVB
		Amberlyst 15	Rohm & Haas Co.†	4.9	1.2	60–66	120	0–14	Spherical beads	"Macroreticular" resin
		Dowex 50	Dow Chemical Co.‡	4.9–5.2	Depends on crosslinking		150	0–14	Spherical beads	Available with different degrees of crosslinking (Dowex 50-X2 has 2% DVB, etc.); Dowex 50W is improved resin replacing older Dowex 50
		Dowex 50W	Dow Chemical Co.‡	4.9–5.2			150	0–14	Spherical beads	
		Duolite C-20	Chemical Process Co.	5.1	2.2	45–51	150	0–14	Spherical beads	Standard resin, ca. 8% DVB; other degrees of crosslinking on request
		Duolite C-25	Chemical Process Co.	5.1	1.7	55–62	120	0–14	Spherical beads	Porous resin
		Duolite C-27	Chemical Process Co.	5.0	2.1	45–50	150	0–14	Spherical beads	Resin of lighter color
		Imac C-12	"Activit," Holland	4.5	2		120	0–14	Spherical beads	Standard resin, ca. 8% DVB
		Imac C-19	"Activit," Holland	4.5	1.4		120	0–14	Spherical beads	Porous resin
		Ionac C-240	(Permutit Q, marketed by Ionac Co.)							

* Properties given are manufacturers' data and are not strictly comparable since testing procedures differ.
† Amberlite resins (A.R. and C.P. grades) are also marketed by Mallinckrodt.
‡ Dowex resins (analytical grade) are also marketed by Bio-Rad Laboratories.

Table of the Most Common Commercial Ion Exchangers (Continued)

Matrix	Ionic group	Trade name	Manufacturer	Capacity		Moisture content, % wt	Maximum temperature, °C	pH range	Physical form	Remarks
				meq/g dry resin	meq/ml resin bed					
Polystyrene resins (continued)	$-SO_3^-$ (continued)	Lewatit S-100	Farbenfabriken Bayer, Germany (West)	4.75	2.5	40-45	110	0-12	Spherical beads	Standard resin, ca. 8% DVB
		Lewatit S-115	Farbenfabriken Bayer, Germany (West)	4.6	2.4	40-45	110	0-12	Spherical beads	Higher resistance to oxidizing agents
		Nalcite HCR Nalcite HGR Nalcite HDR	(Dowex 50-X8, marketed by Nalco Chemical Co.) (Dowex 50-X10, marketed by Nalco Chemical Co.) (Dowex 50-X12, marketed by Nalco Chemical Co.)							
		Permutit Q	Permutit Co., U.S.A.	4.8	2.0	45-50	120	0-14	Spherical beads	Standard resin; other degrees on crosslinking available
		Permutit RS	Permutit A. G., Berlin, Germany (West)	5.5			150		Spherical beads	
		Resex P	Jos. Crosfield, England						Spherical beads	
		Wofatit KPS	VEB Farbenfabrik Wolfen, Germany (East)	4.5			115		Spherical beads	Standard resin with 10% DVB; resins with 2, 4, 6, and 16% DVB also available
		Zeo-Karb 225	Permutit Co. Ltd., England§	4.8	2.1	45-50	120		Spherical beads	Standard resin with 8% DVB; resins with 1, 2, 4.5, 12, and 20% DVB also available
	$-PO_3^{2-}$	Bio-Rex 63	(Duolite C-63, analytical grade, marketed by Bio-Rad Laboratories)							
		Duolite ES-61	Chemical Process Co.					4-14	Spherical beads	Experimental resin
		Duolite C63	Chemical Process Co.	6.6	3.1-3.3			4-14	Spherical beads	Experimental resin, ca. 6% DVB, more porous than ES-61
		Nalcite X-219	Nalco Chemical Co.					4-14	Spherical beads	Experimental resin
	$-HPO_2^-$	Bio-Rex 62	(Duolite C-62, analytical grade, marketed by Bio-Rad Laboratories)							
		Duolite ES-60	Chemical Process Co.					4-14	Spherical beads	Experimental resin
		Duolite C-62	Chemical Process Co.	6.0	2.6			4-14	Spherical beads	Experimental resin, more porous than ES-60
	$-N(CH_2COOH)_2$	Chelex 100	(Dowex A-1, analytical grade, marketed by Bio-Rad Laboratories)							

§ Zeo-Karb and De-Acidite resins are also marketed under the name Zerolit (with otherwise same designation) by United Water Softeners, London.

Table of the Most Common Commercial Ion Exchangers (Continued)

Matrix	Ionic group	Trade name	Manufacturer	Capacity meq/g dry resin	Capacity meq/ml resin bed	Moisture content, % wt	Maximum temperature, °C	pH range	Physical form	Remarks
Polystyrene resins (continued) Vinyl addition polymers	—N(CH₂COOH)₂ (continued)	Dowex A-1	Dow Chemical Co.	1–1.2	0.33	71–76		4–14	Spherical beads	Chelating resin
	—OSO₃⁻	CFB-P	Chem. Fabrik Budenheim, Germany (West)				100			
	—COOH	Amberlite IRC-50	Rohm & Haas Co.†	9.5	3.5	43–53	120	5–14	Spherical beads	
		Amberlite XE-89	Rohm & Haas Co.†		4.2	52–60	120	5–14	Spherical beads	Special resin for pharmaceutical applications
		(Duolite CS-101, analyt. grade, marketed by Bio-Rad Laboratories)								
		Bio-Rex 70 / Duolite CS-101	Chemical Process Co.	10	3.5		100	6–14	Spherical beads	
		(Permutit H-70, marketed by Ionac Co.)								
		Ionac C-270 / Permutit C	Permutit A. G., Berlin, Germany (West)	10	4		100	6–14	Spherical beads	
		Permutit H-70	Permutit Co., New York	7.9	3.6		95	6–14	Spherical beads	
		Wofatit CP	VEB Farbenfabrik Wolfen, Germany (East)	10			30		Spherical beads	
		Zeo-Karb 226	Permutit Co. Ltd., England§	10	3.5		100		Spherical beads	Available with 2.5 and 4.5% crosslinking
Phenolic resins	—SO₃⁻	(Duolite C-3, analytical grade, marketed by Bio-Rad Laboratories)								
		Bio-Rex 40 / Duolite C-3	Chemical Process Co.	2.9	1.2		60	0–9	Granules	Resins with —CH₂SO₃⁻ groups; C-10 more porous than C-3
		Duolite C-10	Chemical Process Co.	2.9	0.6		40	0–9	Granules	
		Lewatit KSN	Farbenfabriken Bayer, Germany (West)	4.0	1.6	45–50	30	0–8	Granules	
		Wofatit F	VEB Farbenfabrik Wolfen, Germany (West)	2.9			50		Granules	
		Wofatit P		1.9			35		Granules	
	—PO₃²⁻	Zeo-Karb 215	Permutit Co. Ltd., England§	2.6	0.9		40		Granules	—SO₃⁻ groups
		Duolite ES-65	Chemical Process Co.	3.3	1.4				Granules	Experimental resin
	—COOH	Duolite CS-100	Chemical Process Co.	1.9	0.8				Granules	
		(Permutit H, marketed by Ionac Co.)								
		Ionac C-265 / Lewatit CNO	Farbenfabriken Bayer, Germany (West)	4.0	2.5	30–35	40	0–8	Granules	

† Amberlite resins (A.R. and C.P. grades) are also marketed by Mallinckrodt.

§ Zeo-Karb and De-Acidite resins are also marketed under the name Zerolit (with otherwise same designation) by United Water Softeners, London.

Table of the Most Common Commercial Ion Exchangers (Continued)

Matrix	Ionic group	Trade name	Manufacturer	Capacity meq/g dry resin	Capacity meq/ml resin bed	Moisture content, % wt	Maximum temperature, °C	pH range	Physical form	Remarks
Phenolic resins (continued)	—COOH (continued)	Permutit H	Permutit Co., New York	5.0	1.9		65		Granules	
		Permutit HC	Permutit A. G., Berlin, Germany (West)	4.0			40		Granules	
		Resex W	Jos. Crosfield, England	2.5-3					Granules	
		Wofatit CN	VEB Farbenfabrik Wolfen, Germany (East)	2.0			30		Granules	
	—SO$_3^-$ and —COOH	Zeo-Karb 216	Permutit Co. Ltd., England§	2.5	1.1	36-43	30	0-8	Granules	
		Lewatit CNS	Farbenfabriken Bayer, Germany (West)	5.0	2.8		40		Granules	
Coals	—SO$_3^-$	Dusarit S	"Activit," Holland	1.8	0.6		100		Granules	
		Soucol	Jos. Crosfield, England	1.4	0.5		30		Granules	
Alumosilicates		Decalso	Permutit Co., New York	1.2			40		Granules	
		Doucil	Jos. Crosfield, England						Granules	Synthetic zeolites, microcrystals, microcrystals pelletized in clay binder; pore widths: ca. 4, 5, and 12A; for use as specific sorbents
		Molecular Sieve 4A	Linde Co.				400		Pellets	
		Molecular Sieve 5A	Linde Co.				400		Pellets	
		Molecular Sieve 13X	Linde Co.				400		Pellets	
Zirconium-base ion exchangers	—OPO$_3^{2-}$	Bio-Rad ZP-1	Bio-Rad Laboratories	1.0	0.7		300	1-6	Crystals	
	—OWO$_3^-$	Bio-Rad ZT-1	Bio-Rad Laboratories				300	1-6	Crystals	
	—OMoO$_3^-$	Bio-Rad ZM-1	Bio-Rad Laboratories				300	1-6	Crystals	
Ammonium molybdophosphate		Bio-Rad AMP-1	Bio-Rad Laboratories						Microcrystals	
Cellulose	—OC$_2$H$_4$SO$_3^-$	Cellex SE	Bio-Rad Laboratories	0.2					Small rods	
	—OPO$_3^{2-}$	Cellex P	Bio-Rad Laboratories	0.8					Small rods	
	—OCH$_2$COOH	Cell CexM	Bio-Rad Laboratories	0.7					Small rods	

Anion Exchangers

Matrix	Ionic group	Trade name	Manufacturer	meq/g dry resin	meq/ml resin bed	Moisture content, % wt	Maximum temperature, °C	pH range	Physical form	Remarks
Polystyrene resins	—N(alkyl)$_3^+$	Amberlite IRA-400	Rohm & Hass Co.†	2.6	1.2	42-48	60	0-12	Spherical beads	Standard resin, ca. 8% DVB

§ Zeo-Karb and De-Acidite resins are also marketed under the name Zerolit (with otherwise same designation) by United Water Softeners, London.

577

Table of the Most Common Commercial Ion Exchangers (Continued)

Matrix	Ionic group	Trade name	Manufacturer	Capacity		Moisture content, % wt	Maximum temperature, °C	pH range	Physical form	Remarks
				meq/g dry resin	meq/ml resin bed					
Polystyrene resins (continued)	−N(alkyl)$_3^+$ (continued)	Amberlite IRA-401	Rohm & Haas Co.†	3	1.0	54-59	60	0-12	Spherical beads	Porous resin
		Amberlite IRA-401S	Rohm & Haas Co.†		0.8	59-65	60	0-12	Spherical beads	Special resin for sugar treatment
		Amberlite IRA-402	Rohm & Haas Co.†		1.3	53-60	60	0-12	Spherical beads	
		Amberlite IRA-405	Rohm & Haas Co.†		1.6	45-49	60	0-12	Spherical beads	Special resins for uranium recovery
		Amberlite IRA-425	Rohm & Haas Co.†		1.3	50-53	60	0-12	Spherical beads	
		De-Acidite FF	Permutit Co. Ltd., England§	4.0	1.6		60		Spherical beads	Standard resin 7-9% DVB; lower degrees of crosslinking available
		Dowex 1	Dow Chemical Co.‡	3.5	Depends on crosslinking		50		Spherical beads	Standard resin Dowex 1-X8; other crosslinking available
		Dowex 11	Dow Chemical Co.‡				50		Spherical beads	Special resin for uranium recovery
		Dowex 21K	Dow Chemical Co.‡	4.5	1.2	57	50		Spherical beads	Improved mech. stability, easier regeneration
		Duolite A-42	Chemical Process Co.	2.3	0.7		60	0-14	Spherical beads	
		Duolite A-101	Chemical Process Co.	4.0	1.3		60	0-14	Spherical beads	Improved resins, more porous than A-42
		Duolite A-101D	Chemical Process Co.	4.2	1.4		60	0-14	Spherical beads	
		Ionac A-540	(Permutit S-1, marketed by Ionac Co.)							
		Lewatit M-500	Farbenfabriken Bayer, Germany (West)	4.0	1.6	35-45	70	1-14	Spherical beads	Exact nature of fixed ionic groups not disclosed;
		Lewatit MP-500	Farbenfabriken Bayer, Germany (West)	4.0	1.2	55-60	70	1-14	Spherical beads	

† Amberlite resins (A.R. and C.P. grades) are also marketed by Mallinckrodt.
‡ Dowex resins (analytical grade) are also marketed by Bio-Rad Laboratories.
§ Zeo-Karb and De-Acidite resins are also marketed under the name Zerolit (with otherwise same designation) by United Water Softeners, London.

Table of the Most Common Commercial Ion Exchangers (*Continued*)

Matrix	Ionic group	Trade name	Manufacturer	Capacity meq/g dry resin	Capacity meq/ml resin bed	Moisture content, % wt	Maximum temperature, °C	pH range	Physical form	Remarks
Polystyrene resins (*continued*)	$-N(alkyl)_3^+$ (*continued*)	Lewatit M-600	Farbenfabriken Bayer, Germany (West)	3.7	1.6	40–50	40	1–14	Spherical beads	MP resins are porous varieties
		Lewatit MP-600	Farbenfabriken Bayer, Germany (West)	3.7	1.1	60–65	40	1–14	Spherical beads	
		Nalcite SBR Nalcite SBR-P	(Dowex 1, marketed by Nalco Chemical Co.)							Standard resin with 8% DVB
		Permutit ESB	Permutit A. G., Berlin, Germany (West)	3.2	1.2		70		Spherical beads	More porous resin
		Permutit ESB-26	Permutit A. G., Berlin, Germany (West)	3.3	1.3		70		Spherical beads	
		Permutit S-1	Permutit Co., New York	3.1	0.9		50		Spherical beads	
		Resanex HBL	Jos. Crosfield, England	3.5	1.5		60		Spherical beads	
		Resanex HBT	Jos. Crosfield, England	3.5			60		Spherical beads	More porous than HBL
		Wofatit SBW	VEB Farbenfabrik Wolfen, Germany (East)	3.5			60		Spherical beads	
	$-N(alkylol)(alkyl)_2^+$	Amberlite IRA-410	Rohm & Haas Co.†	3.0	1.2	40–45	40	0–12	Spherical beads	Standard resin, ca. 6% DVB
		Amberlite IRA-411	Rohm & Haas Co.†	3.0	0.7		40	0–12	Spherical beads	More porous resin
		Dowex 2	Dow Chemical Co.‡	3.0	Depends on crosslinking		30	0–14	Spherical beads	Standard resin Dowex 2-X8; other degrees of crosslinking available
		Duolite A-40	Chemical Process Co.	3.7	1.1		40	0–14	Spherical beads	
		Duolite A-102	Chemical Process Co.	4.0	1.3		40	0–14	Spherical beads	Improved resins, more porous than A-40
		Duolite A-102D	Chemical Process Co.	4.2	1.4		40	0–14	Spherical beads	

† Amberlite resins (A.R. and C.P. grades) are also marketed by Mallinckrodt.
‡ Dowex resins (analytical grade) are also marketed by Bio-Rad Laboratories.

Table of the Most Common Commercial Ion Exchangers (*Continued*)

Matrix	Ionic group	Trade name	Manufacturer	Capacity		Moisture content, % wt	Maximum temperature, °C	pH range	Physical form	Remarks
				meq/g dry resin	meq/ml resin bed					
Polystyrene resins (*continued*)	$-N(alkylol)(alkyl)_2^+$ (*continued*)	Ionac A-550								
		Nalcite SAR	(Permutit S-2, marketed by Ionac Co.)							
			(Dowex 2, marketed by Nalco Chemical Co.)							
		Permutit ES	Permutit A. G., Berlin, Germany (West)	3.2	1.2		40		Spherical beads	
		Permutit ES-26	Permutit A. G., Berlin, Germany (West)	3.3	1.3		40		Spherical beads	
		Permutit S-2	Permutit Co., New York	3.3	1.2		40		Spherical beads	
	Weak-base amino groups	Amberlite IR-45	Rohm & Haas Co.†	5	2	37-45	100	0-9	Spherical beads	
		De-Acidite G	Permutit Co. Ltd., England§	4.0	1.6		100		Spherical beads	$-N(C_2H_5)_2$ groups only
		De-Acidite M	Permutit Co. Ltd., England§	5.5	2.2		100		Spherical beads	Polyamine groups
		Dowex 3	Dow Chemical Co.	6	3		65		Spherical beads	
		Duolite A-14	Chemical Process Co.	8	2.5				Spherical beads	
		Ionac A-315	(Permutit W, marketed by Ionac Inc.)							
		Lewatit MP-60	Farbenfabriken Bayer, Germany (West)	6.3	2.2	40-50	100		Spherical beads	Tertiary amino groups
		Nalcite WBR	(Dowex 3, marketed by Nalco Chemical Co.)							
		Permutit W	Permutit Co., New York	5.7	2.0		95		Spherical beads	
	Strong- and weak-base groups	De-Acidite H	Permutit Co. Ltd., England	3.8	1.5		100		Spherical beads	
	$-SR_2^+$	Duolite ES-105	Chemical Process Co.		1.2				Spherical beads	Experimental resin
Condensation polymers	$-N(alkyl)_3^+$	Imac S-3	"Activit," Holland		0.6		40		Granules	Highly porous resin
		Lewatit MN	Farbenfabriken Bayer, Germany (West)	2.3	0.9	46-54	30	1-14	Granules	

† Amberlite resins (A.R. and C.P. grades) are also marketed by Mallinckrodt.
§ Zeo-Karb and De-Acidite resins are also marketed under the name Zerolit (with otherwise same designation) by United Water Softeners, London.

Table of the Most Common Commercial Ion Exchangers (Continued)

Matrix	Ionic group	Trade name	Manufacturer	Capacity meq/g dry resin	Capacity meq/ml resin bed	Moisture content, % wt	Maximum temperature, °C	pH range	Physical form	Remarks
Condensation polymers (continued)	Weak-base amino groups	Duolite A-2	Chemical Process Co.	8.4	2.3		40		Granules	Tertiary amino groups only
		Duolite A-2M	Chemical Process Co.	6.5	1.8		50		Granules	Tertiary amino groups only
		Duolite A-4	Chemical Process Co.	7.7	2.0		50	0–5	Granules	
		Duolite A-5	Chemical Process Co.	9.0	2.5				Granules	Tertiary amino groups only
		Duolite A-6	Chemical Process Co.	7.0	2.2		60	0–5	Granules	
		Duolite A-7	Chemical Process Co.	9.1	2.5		40	0–4	Granules	
		Duolite A-30T	Chemical Process Co.	8.9	2.8		80	0–5	Spherical beads	Epoxy-polyamine resin with tertiary amino groups
		Imac A-17	"Activit," Holland				120		Granules	
		Imac A-19	"Activit," Holland	6.0	1.3	40–50			Granules	
		Lewatit MIH-59	Farbenfabriken Bayer, Germany (West)		2.5		30		Granules	
		Permutit E-3	Permutit A. G., Berlin, Germany (West)	6			40		Granules	Tertiary amino groups only
		Permutit E-7P	Permutit A. G., Berlin, Germany (West)	6			40		Granules	Highly porous resin
		Resanex	Jos. Crosfield, England	9	3		60		Granules	
		Wofatit N	VEB Farbenfabrik Wolfen, Germany (East)	4.3			30		Granules	
	Strong- and weak-base groups	Duolite A-30B	Chemical Process Co.	8.7	2.6		80	0–9	Spherical beads	Epoxy-polyamine resin
		Ionac A-300	Permutit Co., New York	8	2		40		Granules	
		Permutit A	(Permutit A, marketed by Ionac Co., New York)							
		Wofatit L-150	VEB Farbenfabrik Wolfen, Germany (East)	10			50		Granules	Polyalkyleneimine resin
Zirconium oxyhydrate		Bio-Rad H20-1	Bio-Rad Laboratories				300		Small rods	
Cellulose	$-OC_2H_5N(C_2H_5)_3^+$	Cellex T	Bio-Rad Laboratories						Small rods	
	$-OC_2H_5N(C_2H_5)_2$	Cellex D	Bio-Rad Laboratories						Small rods	
	Amino groups	Cellex E	Bio-Rad Laboratories						Small rods	
	$-OCH_2-$⬡$-NH_2$	Cellex PAB	Bio-Rad Laboratories						Small rods	

Table of the Most Common Commercial Ion Exchangers (*Continued*)

Matrix	Ionic group	Trade name	Manufacturer	Capacity		Moisture content, % wt	Maximum temperature, °C	pH range	Physical form	Remarks
				meq/g dry resin	meq/ml resin bed					
Redox Ion Exchangers										
Condensation polymer		Duolite S-10	Chemical Process Co.				40	6-10	Granules	Amine resin containing copper; for oxygen removal
Retardion Resins										
Polystyrene resin	$-N(CH_3)_3^+$ $-COO^-$	Retardion 11-A-8	Dow Chemical Co.						Spherical beads	Dowex 1 containing poly-acrylate anion

Table of commercial ion-exchanger membranes*

Matrix	Ionic group	Trade name	Manufacturer	Capacity, meq/g dry membrane	Moisture content, % wt	Thickness, mm	Electric resistance, Ω cm² (ionic form)	Counter-ion transport number (solution used)		Remarks
			Cation-exchanger membranes							
Polyethylene-styrene graft copolymers	$-SO_3^-$	AMF ion C-60	American Machine & Foundry Co.	1.6	35	0.3	5 (K^+)	0.92	(0.2 N KCl)	
		AMF ion C-103C	American Machine & Foundry Co.	1.2	15	0.16	7 (K^+)	0.98	(0.2 N KCl)	
		AMF ion C-313	American Machine & Foundry Co.	0.6	12	0.15	5 (K^+)	0.9	(0.2 N KCl)	
Polystyrene		Asahi membrane	Asahi Chem. Co., Japan			0.16–0.18	1.6 (Na^+)	0.99	(0.5 N NaCl)	
(Undisclosed)		Nalfilm 1†	Nalco Chemical Co.		30	0.1				Porous membrane
		Nalfilm 3†	Nalco Chemical Co.		65	0.1				
Polystyrene		Nepton CR-61	Ionics Inc.	2.8	45–50	0.6		0.9–0.95	(0.6 N NaCl)	Reinforced with Dynel backing
(Undisclosed)		Permaplex C-20	Permutit Co. Ltd., England	3	30–40		20 (Na^+)	0.94	(1 N NaCl)	
Phenolic resin		Zeo-Karb 315	Permutit Co. Ltd., England	1.8	75–83	0.12	1.2 (Na^+)			Experimental membrane
			Anion-exchanger membranes							
Polyethylene-styrene graft copolymer	$-NR^+$	AMF ion A-60	American Machine & Foundry Co.	2.0	22	0.3	7 (Cl^-)	0.93	(0.2 N KCl)	
		AMF ion A-104B	American Machine & Foundry Co.	1.3	13	0.15	9 (Cl^-)	0.98	(0.2 N KCl)	
Polystyrene		Asahi membrane	Asahi Chem. Co., Japan			0.16–0.18	2.5 (Cl^-)	0.99	(0.5 N NaCl)	
(Undisclosed)		Nalfilm 2†	Nalco Chemical Co.		30	0.1				Porous membrane
		Nalfilm 4†	Nalco Chemical Co.		65	0.1				
Polystyrene		Nepton AR-111-A	Ionics Inc.	2.0	40–45	0.6		0.9–0.95	(0.6 N NaCl)	Reinforced with Dynel backing
(Undisclosed)		Permaplex A-20	Permutit Co. Ltd., England	2	30–40		9 (Cl^-)	0.93	(1 N NaCl)	

* Properties given are manufacturers' data and are not strictly comparable since testing procedures differ.

† Manufacturing of Nalfilm membranes has been temporarily discontinued.

Liquid ion exchangers

Designation	Composition	Manufacturer
D2EHPA	Di-2-ethylhexyl phosphoric acid	Union Carbide Chemical Co.
HDPA	Heptadecyl phosphoric acid	Dow Chemical Co.
DDPA	Dodecyl phosphoric acid	Dow Chemical Co.
DBBP	Di-(-n-butyl)-n-butyl-phosphonate	Virginia-Carolina Chemical Corp.
Primene JM-T	Trialkylmethyl amine	Rohm & Haas Co.
Amberlite LA-1	N-Dodecenyl(trialkylmethyl) amine	Rohm & Haas Co.
Amberlite LA-2	N-Lauryl(trialkylmethyl) amine	Rohm & Haas Co.
TIOA	Tri-isooctyl amine	Union Carbide Chemical Co.
Alamine 336	Tricapryl amine	General Mills
Aliquat 336	Tricaprylmethylammonium chloride	General Mills
TLA	Trilauryl amine	Archer-Daniels Midland Co.

TABLES OF MATHEMATICAL FUNCTIONS

Table of the function $U(\tau) = 1 - \dfrac{6}{\pi^2} \sum\limits_{n=1}^{\infty} \exp\left(-n^2\pi^2\tau\right)$ [Eq. (6-9)]*

τ	$U(\tau)$	τ	$U(\tau)$	τ	$U(\tau)$
0.000001	0.0034	0.001	0.1040	0.05	0.6061
0.000003	0.0059	0.002	0.1454	0.07	0.6856
0.00001	0.0107	0.003	0.1764	0.1	0.7705
0.00003	0.0184	0.005	0.2244	0.2	0.9150
0.0001	0.0336	0.007	0.2622	0.3	0.9685
0.0002	0.0473	0.01	0.3085	0.5	0.9956
0.0003	0.0577	0.02	0.4187	0.7	0.9999
0.0005	0.0742	0.03	0.4913	1.0	1.0000

* The values of $\tau < 0.01$ were calculated with a more rapidly converging series given by W. Gautschi:

$$U(\tau) = \frac{6}{\sqrt{\pi}}\tau^{1/2} - 3\tau + \frac{6}{\sqrt{\pi}} \sum_{n=1}^{\infty} \frac{1}{n^2} \exp\left(-n^2/\tau\right)\left(1 - \frac{3\tau}{2n^2} + \frac{15\pi^2}{4n^4} - \cdots\right)$$

(for low values of τ, the first two terms alone give sufficient accuracy).

Table of the function $U(w,\tau) = \dfrac{w+1}{w}\left\{1 - \dfrac{1}{\alpha-\beta}\left[\alpha \exp(\alpha^2\tau)(1 + \operatorname{erf}\alpha\tau^{1/2}) - \beta \exp(\beta^2\tau)(1 + \operatorname{erf}\beta\tau^{1/2})\right]\right\}$ [Eq. (6-15)*]

w	-6.0	-5.5	-5.0	-4.5	-4.0	-3.5	-3.0	-2.5	-2.0	-1.5	-1.0	-0.5
0.05	0.00355	0.00631	0.01120	0.01987	0.03518	0.06207	0.10886	0.18856	0.31994	0.52148	0.78266	0.95803
0.1	0.00372	0.00661	0.01173	0.02080	0.03681	0.06487	0.11351	0.19612	0.33108	0.53522	0.79391	0.96072
0.15	0.00389	0.00691	0.01226	0.02173	0.03843	0.06766	0.11891	0.20358	0.34194	0.54836	0.80430	0.96308
0.2	0.00406	0.00721	0.01279	0.02266	0.04005	0.07044	0.12283	0.21093	0.35252	0.56092	0.81393	0.96515
0.25	0.00422	0.00750	0.01331	0.02359	0.04166	0.07320	0.12743	0.21818	0.36284	0.57295	0.82286	0.96698
0.3	0.00439	0.00780	0.01384	0.02451	0.04372	0.07595	0.13199	0.22532	0.37290	0.58447	0.83116	0.96861
0.35	0.00456	0.00810	0.01437	0.02544	0.04488	0.07869	0.13651	0.23236	0.38271	0.59551	0.83888	0.97006
0.4	0.00473	0.00840	0.01489	0.02636	0.04648	0.08142	0.14099	0.23930	0.39228	0.60610	0.84607	0.97135
0.45	0.00490	0.00864	0.01531	0.02710	0.04776	0.08359	0.14456	0.24478	0.39977	0.61425	0.85147	0.97230
0.5	0.00507	0.00899	0.01595	0.02820	0.04967	0.08683	0.14986	0.25288	0.41073	0.62599	0.85903	0.97358
0.55	0.00523	0.00929	0.01647	0.02912	0.05126	0.08952	0.15423	0.25953	0.41963	0.63534	0.86498	0.97454
0.6	0.00540	0.00959	0.01699	0.03004	0.05284	0.09220	0.15858	0.26608	0.42831	0.64432	0.87038	0.97542
0.65	0.00557	0.00989	0.01752	0.03095	0.05442	0.09486	0.16288	0.27255	0.43678	0.65296	0.87552	0.97622
0.7	0.00574	0.01018	0.01804	0.03187	0.05600	0.09751	0.16716	0.27892	0.44506	0.66126	0.88034	0.97697
0.75	0.00591	0.01048	0.01856	0.03278	0.05757	0.10015	0.17139	0.28520	0.45314	0.66924	0.88488	0.97765
0.8	0.00607	0.01078	0.01909	0.03369	0.05914	0.10278	0.17560	0.29140	0.46104	0.67692	0.88915	0.97829
0.85	0.00624	0.01107	0.01961	0.03460	0.06070	0.10540	0.17977	0.29751	0.46875	0.68432	0.89317	0.97889
0.9	0.00641	0.01137	0.02013	0.03551	0.06226	0.10800	0.18390	0.30354	0.47628	0.69145	0.89696	0.97944
0.95	0.00658	0.01167	0.02065	0.03642	0.06382	0.11059	0.18801	0.30949	0.48365	0.69831	0.90053	0.97996
1.0	0.00675	0.01196	0.02117	0.03732	0.06537	0.11317	0.19208	0.31535	0.49085	0.70493	0.90391	0.98044

$\log \tau$

* Machine calculation on IBM-704 at Oak Ridge National Laboratory.
SOURCE: Dr. G. E. Boyd, Oak Ridge National Laboratory, Oak Ridge, Tenn.

Numerical solutions of Eq. (6-40) for exchange of counter ions of equal valence and different mobilities (infinite solution volume condition, and complete conversion from A form to B form)*

Fractional attainment of equilibrium $U(\tau)$	Dimensionless time, $\tau \equiv \bar{D}_A i/r_0^2$					
	$\bar{D}_A/\bar{D}_B$ = 10	$\bar{D}_A/\bar{D}_B$ = 5	$\bar{D}_A/\bar{D}_B$ = 2	$\bar{D}_A/\bar{D}_B$ = 0.5	$\bar{D}_A/\bar{D}_B$ = 0.2	$\bar{D}_A/\bar{D}_B$ = 0.1
0.1	0.0030	0.0020	0.0013	0.0007	0.0006	0.0005
0.2	0.0122	0.0081	0.0052	0.0031	0.0025	0.0023
0.3	0.0291	0.0194	0.0123	0.0077	0.0062	0.0055
0.4	0.0545	0.0366	0.0235	0.0146	0.0119	0.0108
0.5	0.0910	0.0615	0.0398	0.0249	0.0206	0.0187
0.6	0.141	0.0962	0.0626	0.0398	0.0332	0.0306
0.7	0.212	0.145	0.0952	0.0616	0.0524	0.0487
0.8	0.313	0.215	0.143	0.0958	0.0832	0.0784
0.9	0.470	0.328	0.224	0.159	0.143	0.137

* Interpolated from numerical results calculated by F. Helfferich and M. S. Plesset.

Table of the functions $f(\alpha,x) = \dfrac{1}{2}\left(\dfrac{1}{\alpha-1}\ln\dfrac{1}{x} - \dfrac{\alpha}{\alpha-1}\ln\dfrac{1}{1-x} + 1\right)$ and

$$g(\alpha,y) = -\dfrac{1}{2}\left(\dfrac{\alpha}{\alpha-1}\ln\dfrac{1}{y} - \dfrac{1}{\alpha-1}\ln\dfrac{1}{1-y} - 1\right)^*$$

x	$\alpha =$										y
	1.1	1.2	1.5	2	3	5	10	20	50	100	
0.001	35.0	17.8	7.41	3.95	2.23	1.36	0.88	0.681	0.570	0.534	0.999
0.01	23.5	12.0	5.09	2.79	1.64	1.07	0.75	0.616	0.542	0.518	0.99
0.05	15.2	7.8	3.42	1.90	1.21	0.84	0.64	0.552	0.504	0.489	0.95
0.1	11.4	5.9	2.64	1.55	1.00	0.72	0.57	0.505	0.470	0.455	0.9
0.2	7.3	3.9	1.78	1.08	0.74	0.56	0.47	0.425	0.403	0.395	0.8
0.4	2.3	1.3	0.65	0.45	0.35	0.29	0.27	0.255	0.249	0.247	0.6
0.6	− 2.0	− 1.0	−0.37	−0.16	−0.08	−0.01	0.02	0.031	0.038	0.040	0.4
0.8	− 7.2	− 3.8	−1.69	−1.00	−0.65	−0.48	−0.38	−0.342	−0.319	−0.312	0.2
0.9	−11.6	− 6.1	−2.85	−1.75	−1.20	−0.93	−0.77	−0.709	−0.674	−0.663	0.1
0.95	−15.7	− 8.4	−3.95	−2.47	−1.73	−1.37	−1.16	−1.08	−1.03	−1.01	0.05
0.99	−24.8	−14.7	−6.40	−4.10	−2.95	−2.38	−2.06	−1.93	−1.85	−1.83	0.01
0.999	−37.5	−22.3	−9.87	−6.41	−4.68	−3.82	−3.34	−3.14	−3.03	−2.99	0.001

* For evaluation of Eq. (9-29). To obtain z' (distance from the center of gravity of the boundary) for a given x_B and α_A^B by use of Eq. (9-29), look up the value in the table under $\alpha_A^B = \alpha$ and $x_B = x$ and multiply with $H_p + H_0$, then look up the value for $\alpha_A^B = \alpha$ and $x_B = y$ and multiply with $-(H_f + H_0)$; the sum of the two products is z'.

Table of the function $\mathcal{G}(x,y)$ [Eq. (9-47)]*

x \ y	0	0.2	0.5	1.0	1.5	2.0	2.5	3.0	3.5	4.0	4.5	5.0
0.2	0.81873	0.84870	0.88465	0.92665	0.95333	0.97040	0.98122	0.98819	0.99245	0.99522	0.99697	0.99808
0.5	0.60653	0.66285	0.73288	0.81931	0.87817	0.91811	0.94510	0.96329	0.97551	0.98370	0.98917	0.99282
1.0	0.36788	0.43786	0.53013	0.65425	0.74779	0.81741	0.86870	0.90614	0.93326	0.95277	0.96672	0.97665
1.5	0.22313	0.28835	0.37936	0.51205	0.62150	0.70974	0.77962	0.83412	0.87611	0.90811	0.93227	0.95036
2.0	0.13533	0.18935	0.26901	0.39430	0.50644	0.60350	0.68537	0.75300	0.80795	0.85194	0.88672	0.91393
2.5	0.08208	0.12403	0.18929	0.29955	0.40594	0.50412	0.59177	0.66791	0.73289	0.78717	0.83190	0.86828
3.0	0.04978	0.08105	0.13230	0.22498	0.32086	0.41471	0.50294	0.58333	0.65477	0.71695	0.77013	0.81494
3.5	0.03020	0.05286	0.09193	0.16733	0.25057	0.33662	0.42149	0.50223	0.57687	0.64426	0.70391	0.75582
4.0	0.01832	0.03440	0.06354	0.12338	0.19362	0.27004	0.34885	0.42691	0.50177	0.57172	0.63564	0.69298
4.5	0.01111	0.02235	0.04372	0.09029	0.14822	0.21436	0.28551	0.35869	0.43135	0.50145	0.56748	0.62841
5	0.00674	0.01449	0.02995	0.06563	0.11252	0.16857	0.23131	0.29819	0.36682	0.43507	0.50122	0.56392
6	0.00248	0.00607	0.01390	0.03407	0.06345	0.10169	0.14780	0.20034	0.25765	0.31796	0.37959	0.44101
7	0.00091	0.00253	0.00637	0.01734	0.03490	0.05963	0.09155	0.13024	0.17487	0.22435	0.27744	0.33284
8	0.00033	0.00105	0.00289	0.00867	0.01880	0.03413	0.05524	0.08231	0.11522	0.15351	0.19651	0.24334
9	0.00012	0.00043	0.00130	0.00428	0.00995	0.01914	0.03257	0.05075	0.07397	0.10224	0.13537	0.17293
10	0.00004	0.00018	0.00058	0.00208	0.00518	0.01054	0.01883	0.03063	0.04641	0.06648	0.09096	0.11979
12	0.00001	0.00003	0.00012	0.00048	0.00135	0.00305	0.00598	0.01055	0.01722	0.02641	0.03849	0.05377
14	0.00000	0.00001	0.00002	0.00011	0.00034	0.00084	0.00179	0.00342	0.00598	0.00978	0.01514	0.02236
16		0.00000	0.00000	0.00002	0.00008	0.00022	0.00051	0.00105	0.00197	0.00342	0.00560	0.00873
18				0.00000	0.00002	0.00006	0.00014	0.00031	0.00062	0.00114	0.00197	0.00322
20					0.00000	0.00001	0.00004	0.00009	0.00019	0.00036	0.00076	0.00114

SOURCE: Condensed from S. R. Brinkley's tabulation of the function $\exp(-x-y)\varphi_0(x,y) = 1 - \mathcal{G}(x,y)$, U.S. Bureau of Mines, "Table of the Temperature Distributing Function for Heat Exchange between Fluid and Porous Solid."

Table of the function $g(x,y)$ [Eq. (9-47)] (Continued)

y

x	6	7	8	9	10	12	14	16	18	20	22	25
1	0.98863	0.99453	0.99740	0.99877	0.99943	0.99988	0.99997	0.99999	1.00000			
2	0.95123	0.97295	0.98528	0.99211	0.99583	0.99888	0.99971	0.99993	0.99998	1.00000	1.00000	
3	0.88281	0.92778	0.95652	0.97436	0.98515	0.99524	0.99856	0.99958	0.99988	0.99997	0.99999	1.00000
4	0.78759	0.85748	0.90689	0.94059	0.96288	0.98627	0.99523	0.99842	0.99950	0.99985	0.99995	0.99999
5	0.67555	0.76631	0.83645	0.88843	0.92561	0.96885	0.98782	0.99550	0.99842	0.99947	0.99983	0.99997
6	0.55821	0.66213	0.74915	0.81867	0.87206	0.94025	0.97408	0.98943	0.99592	0.99849	0.99947	0.99989
7	0.44557	0.55381	0.65139	0.73493	0.80340	0.89882	0.95181	0.97852	0.99095	0.99628	0.99861	0.99969
8	0.34456	0.44922	0.55027	0.64253	0.72289	0.84441	0.91935	0.96099	0.98223	0.99232	0.99683	0.99922
9	0.25887	0.35412	0.45222	0.54735	0.63507	0.77841	0.87595	0.93532	0.96832	0.98531	0.99352	0.99825
10	0.18943	0.27186	0.36210	0.45474	0.54489	0.70349	0.82194	0.90053	0.94788	0.97421	0.98787	0.99640
12	0.09460	0.14921	0.21615	0.29258	0.37477	0.54093	0.68841	0.80327	0.88369	0.93520	0.96578	0.98800
14	0.04359	0.07534	0.11854	0.17290	0.23700	0.38449	0.53787	0.67625	0.78746	0.86860	0.92312	0.96866
16	0.01876	0.03543	0.06039	0.09479	0.13898	0.25386	0.39225	0.53540	0.66618	0.77387	0.85504	0.93234
18	0.00762	0.01566	0.02885	0.04865	0.07620	0.15662	0.26784	0.39862	0.53336	0.65766	0.76202	0.87452
20	0.00294	0.00656	0.01303	0.02355	0.03934	0.09085	0.17199	0.27969	0.40399	0.53164	0.65032	0.79432
25	0.00023	0.00061	0.00145	0.00309	0.00603	0.01843	0.04478	0.09094	0.16009	0.25095	0.35772	0.52828
30	0.00001	0.00005	0.00013	0.00032	0.00071	0.00284	0.00874	0.02203	0.04720	0.08854	0.14852	0.27188
35	0.00000	0.00000	0.00001	0.00003	0.00007	0.00035	0.00135	0.00418	0.01084	0.02423	0.04784	0.10928
40			0.00000	0.00000	0.00001	0.00004	0.00017	0.00065	0.00201	0.00533	0.01235	0.03513
45					0.00000	0.00000	0.00002	0.00008	0.00031	0.00097	0.00263	0.00927
50						0.00000	0.00000	0.00001	0.00004	0.00015	0.00047	0.00205

Table of the function $\mathcal{G}(x,y)$ [Eq. (9-47)] (Continued)

x	y 30	40	50	60	70	80
10	0.99961	1.00000	1.00000			
20	0.93227	0.99638	0.99991	1.00000		
25	0.77115	0.97357	0.99860	0.99996	1.00000	
30	0.52581	0.89589	0.98958	0.99945	0.99998	1.00000
35	0.28829	0.73748	0.95430	0.99585	0.99978	0.99999
40	0.12753	0.52234	0.86621	0.98033	0.99834	0.99991
45	0.04623	0.31271	0.71382	0.93533	0.99163	0.99933
50	0.01400	0.15799	0.51997	0.84188	0.97076	0.99646
60	0.00080	0.02501	0.18231	0.51823	0.82165	0.95882
70	0.00003	0.00226	0.03609	0.20221	0.51687	0.80451
80	0.00000	0.00013	0.00460	0.04925	0.21886	0.51578
90		0.00000	0.00037	0.00774	0.06123	0.23304
100			0.00002	0.00082	0.01156	0.07275
110			0.00000	0.00006	0.00153	0.01591
120				0.00000	0.00015	0.00250

x	y 100	150	200	250	300
60	0.99938				
80	0.93704	1.00000			
90	0.77698	0.99996			
100	0.51411	0.99934			
110	0.25601	0.99412			
120	0.09409	0.96849	1.00000		
130	0.02563	0.88988	0.99995		
140	0.00525	0.73127	0.99951		
150	0.00083	0.51152	0.99660		
160	0.00010	0.29473	0.98373	1.00000	
180	0.00000	0.05202	0.85359	0.99968	
200		0.00399	0.50998	0.99144	1.00000
250		0.00000	0.00972	0.50892	0.98444
300			0.00000	0.01731	0.50814
350				0.00002	0.02601

589

Table of the function $\eta(\omega) = \dfrac{3}{\omega}\left(\dfrac{1}{\tanh \omega} - \dfrac{1}{\omega}\right)$ [Eq. (11-33)]

ω	η	ω	η	ω	η
0.1	0.9994	1.5	0.8763	15	0.1867
0.2	0.9973	2	0.8060	20	0.1425
0.3	0.9940	3	0.6716	30	0.09667
0.4	0.9895	4	0.5630	40	0.07313
0.5	0.9837	5	0.4801	50	0.05880
0.7	0.9688	7	0.3674	70	0.04225
1.0	0.9391	10	0.2700	100	0.02970

Table of the function $A(y) = \sqrt{\dfrac{1}{2\pi}} \displaystyle\int_{x=0}^{x=y} \exp(-x^2/2)\, dx$

(Area under the normal curve of error)*

y	$A(y)$	y	$A(y)$	y	$A(y)$	y	$A(y)$	y	$A(y)$
0.01	0.0040	0.12	0.0478	0.50	0.1915	1.1	0.3643	2.2	0.4861
0.02	0.0080	0.14	0.0557	0.55	0.2088	1.2	0.3849	2.4	0.4918
0.03	0.0120	0.16	0.0636	0.60	0.2258	1.3	0.4032	2.6	0.4953
0.04	0.0160	0.18	0.0714	0.65	0.2422	1.4	0.4192	2.8	0.4974
0.05	0.0199	0.20	0.0793	0.70	0.2580	1.5	0.4332	3.0	0.4987
0.06	0.0239	0.25	0.0987	0.75	0.2734	1.6	0.4452	3.2	0.4993
0.07	0.0279	0.30	0.1179	0.80	0.2881	1.7	0.4554	3.4	0.4997
0.08	0.0319	0.35	0.1368	0.85	0.3023	1.8	0.4641	3.6	0.4998
0.09	0.0359	0.40	0.1554	0.90	0.3159	1.9	0.4713	3.8	0.4999
0.10	0.0398	0.45	0.1736	1.00	0.3413	2.0	0.4773	4.0	0.5000

* A more complete table is given in "Handbook of Chemistry and Physics," Chem. Rubber Publ. Co., Cleveland, Ohio.

Table of the functions erf $(x) = \dfrac{2}{\sqrt{\pi}} \displaystyle\int_{x=0}^{x=z} \exp(-z^2)\, dz$, and erfc $(x) = 1 -$ erf (x)*

x	erf (x)	erfc (x)	x	erf (x)	erfc (x)	x	erf (x)	erfc (x)
0	0	1.0	0.65	0.64203	0.35797	1.6	0.97635	0.02365
0.05	0.05637	0.94363	0.70	0.67780	0.32220	1.7	0.98379	0.01621
0.10	0.11246	0.88754	0.75	0.71116	0.28884	1.8	0.98909	0.01901
0.15	0.16800	0.83200	0.80	0.74210	0.25790	1.9	0.99279	0.00721
0.20	0.22270	0.77730	0.85	0.77067	0.22933	2.0	0.99532	0.00468
0.25	0.27633	0.72367	0.90	0.79691	0.20309	2.2	0.99814	0.00186
0.30	0.32862	0.67137	0.95	0.82089	0.17911	2.4	0.99931	0.00069
0.35	0.37938	0.62062	1.0	0.84270	0.15730	2.6	0.99976	0.00024
0.40	0.42839	0.57161	1.1	0.88021	0.11979	2.8	0.99993	0.00007
0.45	0.47548	0.52452	1.2	0.91031	0.08969	3.0	0.99998	0.00002
0.50	0.52050	0.47950	1.3	0.93401	0.06599	3.5	1.00000	0.00000
0.55	0.56332	0.43668	1.4	0.95229	0.04771			
0.60	0.60386	0.39614	1.5	0.96611	0.03389			

* For more complete tables, see "Tables of Probability Functions," Federal Works Agency, Works Project Administration for the City of New York, Report 65-2-97-33, New York, 1941.

Name Index

The index is keyed to the literature references at the end of each chapter and to the page numbers where the respective references are quoted. Reference numbers are in **boldface** type and precede the numbers of the pages on which they are to be found.

Talley, E. A., **225**, 436
Taylor, F. C., Jr., **285**, 149
Taylor, G., **227**, 487; **181, 226,** 488
Taylor, T. I., **228**, 436
Teorell, T., 61; **129**, 340; **125,** 342, 343, 377; **127**, 373, 386, 407, 411; **126, 128**, 407
Tera, F., **22**, 513
Testa, C., **30**, 18
Tetenbaum, M., **119**, 254, 266, 307, 311, 312
Tevlina, A. S., **31a**, 557
Texas Co., **42, 110**, 12; **57**, 13
Thiele, E. W., **46**, 523, 525, 533
Thodos, G., **236**, 479, 483
Thomas, C. L., **286**, 223, 226; **229**, 436, 445; **47**, 520
Thomas, G. G., **62**, 148; **12, 48,** 522, 542–544
Thomas, H. C., **83**, 11; **99**, 96, 195, 196; **88, 213**, 193, 237, 238; **87**, 237, 238; **120**, 254, 286; **96**, 254, 307, 312, 313; **121, 122**, 286; **123**, 312; **230**, 475; 476; 477; **233**, 478; **55, 155, 231, 232**, 479; 484
Thomas, S. L. S., **204**, 33, 39; **98**, 52, 53
Thomas, T. L., **27**, 12
Thompson, H. S., **8**, 2
Thompson, J., **234**, 431
Thompson, S. G., **221, 235,** 436
Tien, C., **236**, 479, 483
Tiger, H. L., **125**, 17; **287**, 166
Tirrell, C. E., **88**, 399
Tolksmith, H., **149**, 52, 54
Toman, M., **130**, 389
Tompkins, E. R., **288**, 214; **239**, 428; **237, 240**, 436, 442; **238**, 442; **152**, 479, 480; 481
Topol, L., **7**, 376
Topp, N. E., **27**, 86, 92, 93
Toy, A. D. F., **208**, 32
Triggs, W. W., **9**, 50
Trombe, F., **241**, 442
Trostyanskaya, E. B., **31a**, 557
Tudge, A. P., **241a**, 482
Tung, H. C., **96a**, 302
Tunitskii, N. N., **32a**, 272
Turse, R., **123a**, 254
Turvolgyi, B. L., **242**, 431
Twigg, G. H., **200**, 488
Tye, F. L., **126**, 38, 39; **127**, 39; **48**, 399; **36**, 404

Ueberreiter, K., **289**, 113
Umezawa, S., **164, 205**, 30
Umland, F., **126**, 18
Union Carbide Chemical Co., 584
Union Carbide Corp., **86**, 12
United Kingdom Atomic Energy Authority, **205a**, 58

U.S. Bureau of Mines, **24a,** 473; 587
United Water Softeners Ltd., **127**, 18; 26; **206**, 48, 49; 575–578; 580
Updegraff, I. H., **6**, 552, 553; **32**, 552, 567; **4**, 559
Urbain, O. M., **207**, 58
Urey, H. C., **228**, 436
Urquhart, D., **23**, 80, 81
Ussing, H. H., **69**, 342, 356, 357, 404, 405

Vageler, P., **290**, 194
Van Deemter, J. J., **243**, 453, 456, 487
Van der Poel, C., **34**, 488
Van Erkelens, P. C., **33b**, 513
Van Heerden, C., **119a**, 476
Van Krevelen, D. W., **119a,** 476
Van Meurs, P., **34**, 488
Vanselow, A. P., **291**, 97, 183, 194
Venanzi, L. M., **31**, 447
Vermaas, D., **53**, 294, 295
Vermeulen, T., **292**, 202; **124,** 261, 286; **55, 125**, 286; **126,** 287; **247**, 428, 449, 453, 456, 464, 472, 474–479; **248**, 429, 449, 471, 477; **101**, 475, 476, 478; **102**, 476; **244**, 476–478; **246**, 476, 478; **100**, 477, 478; **2, 245**, 479; **34**, 516
Verplanck, V., **33**, 552
Vert, Zh. L., **24**, 513
Verwey, E. J. W., **293**, 98
Vielstich, W., **127**, 253
Virginia-Carolina Chemical Corp., 584
Vissers, D. R., **70a**, 14
Voge, H. H., **17**, 521
Voigt, A. F., **210**, 428, 436, 442, 443; **209**, 436, 442, 443

Wabiko, T., **151**, 226, 229; **57,** 295
Wadman, W. H., **49**, 522
Wagner, C., **128**, 269; **50**, 523, 525, 533
Walas, S. M., **50a**, 531
Wall, J. G. L., **251**, 221
Wall, W. F., **240**, 105, 126, 128–130, 132, 148; **28**, 511
Walsh, E. N., **208**, 32
Walter, A. J. R., **173**, 431
Walter, J. E., **129**, 286; **249,** 475, 478
Walton, H. F., **128**, 10; **282,** 129, 132, 163, 222, 223; **294**, 193; **250a**, 436, 444; **34a,** 513, 515
Wantz, J. F., **234**, 431
Ward, D. N., **250**, 436

Wassenegger, H., **210**, 30; **209,** 30, 33; **91**, 49
Wassermann, A., **88**, 18; **216,** 239
Watkins, S. R., **250a**, 436, 444; **34a**, 513, 515
Watson, K. M., **22b**, 531
Waxman, M. H., **284**, 102, 115, 116; **115**, 103, 107, 108, 110, 112, 114–116, 239
Way, J. T., **9**, 2
Wayne Tank & Pump Co., **129**, 12
Wehner, J. F., **50b**, 531
Weiss, D. E., **295**, 148
Weiss, J., **251**, 481; **166**, 481, 482
Weisz, D. B., **296**, 193
Weisz, P. B., **15**, 520; **51**, 523, 525, 540; **52**, 523, 540; **53,** 523, 533, 540; **55**, 522, 524, 540; **54**, 522, 525
Wells, R. A., **66**, 18; **7**, 513; **21**, 515
Wesly, W., **252**, 430
West, D. L., **33**, 184
Westall, R. G., **171**, 436
Westermark, T., **129a**, 295; **35**, 510
Westfall, W. M., **269**, 214
Wetstone, D. M., **89, 90**, 63; **211**, 64; **21**, 384, 411
Wheaton, R. M., **213**, 35, 36, 38; **212, 214**, 52, 53; **148,** 52–54; **297**, 130, 131, 147; **22**, 147; **130**, 294; **253a**, 429; **14**, 431–433; **253**, 431, 432
Wheeler, A., **131**, 302; **56**, 523, 525, 540
Wheelwright, E. J., **214, 217, 254**, 442
Whitcombe, J. A., **298**, 159
White, E. A. D., **8**, 12
White, J. C., **23**, 19
White, R. R., **298**, 159; **118,** 286; **223**, 476; **40**, 522, 523, 527
Whittaker, D., **215**, 49
Wickbold, R., **255a**, 447; **255,** 494, 495
Wicke, E., **256**, 464, 474, 479; **57**, 523, 525, 540
Widen, P. J., **126**, 222
Wibenga, E. H., **131**, 342
Wiegner, G., **10**, 2; **131**, 10, 12; **130**, 11; **299, 300**, 194
Wiesner, W., **132**, 289
Wiklander, L., **210, 301**, 157; **302**, 202
Wiley, R. H., **216, 217, 220, 221**, 40; **218, 219**, 40, 41
Wilhelm, R. H., **50b**, 531
Wilich, M. A., **8**, 510, 511
Wilkins, D. H., **257**, 435, 436; **258**, 435, 444; **36, 36a**, 513, 515

Subject Index